ESSENTIAL
MATHEMATICS

CHAPTERS 1-9 WITH CUSTOM ENHANCEMENTS

MARY KAY BEAVERS

PREPARED EXCLUSIVELY FOR THE MATHEMATICS DEPARTMENT
CITY COLLEGE OF SAN FRANCISCO

Taken from
Essential Mathematics, Second Edition
by Mary Kay Beavers

PEARSON
Custom
Publishing

PEARSON
Prentice
Hall

Taken from:

Essential Mathematics, Second Edition
By Mary Kay Beavers
Copyright ©1995 by HarperCollins College Publishers. Acquired by Addison Wesley Longman, Inc.
A Pearson Education Company
Boston, Massachusetts 02116

This special edition published in cooperation with Pearson Custom Publishing.

Printed in the United States of America

10 9 8 7 6 5 4 3

ISBN 0-536-26147-4

2006360370

RA

Please visit our web site at *www.pearsoncustom.com*

PEARSON CUSTOM PUBLISHING
75 Arlington Street, Suite 300, Boston, MA 02116
A Pearson Education Company

CONTENTS

CHAPTER

Whole Numbers: Place Value, Addition, and Subtraction

OBJECTIVES
- Specify the digit in a numeral that has a certain place value.
- Specify the place value of a certain digit in a numeral.
- Compare whole numbers.
- Write the English name for a whole numeral.
- Write the numeral when given the English name of a whole number.
- Round off a whole number to a given place value.

1 Numbers Less Than 10,000

Betty has 26 dollars and Susan has 206 dollars. You know that Susan has more money than Betty because 206 is more than 26.

$$206 = 2 \text{ hundreds} + 0 \text{ tens} + 6 \text{ ones}$$
$$= \quad 200 \quad + \quad 0 \quad + \quad 6$$

but

$$26 = 2 \text{ tens} + 6 \text{ ones}$$
$$= \quad 20 \quad + \quad 6$$

In the above display, the symbol $=$ (read *equals*) is used to indicate that symbols are representing quantities with the same value. The symbol $+$ (read *plus*) for addition means to combine or total. The numeral 206 is read "two hundred six." The numeral 26 is read "twenty-six." When we write out the numeral in words, we are giving the English name of the numeral.

Each whole number is represented by a symbol called a **whole numeral.** Each numeral consists of one or more of the symbols 0, 1, 2, 3, 4, 5, 6, 7, 8, and 9. Each of these symbols is called a **digit.**

Try These Problems

1. Use the numeral 8034 to answer each question.
   a. What digit is in the hundreds place?
   b. What digit is in the tens place?
   c. What is the place value of the digit 4?
   d. What is the place value of the digit 8?

Write the numeral for each English name.

2. Four hundred thirteen

3. Nine thousand eighty-two

Write the English name for each numeral.

4. 635

5. 3407

Each digit in a whole numeral has a **place value.** For example, in the illustration that follows, the place value for each digit in the numeral 7136 is indicated.

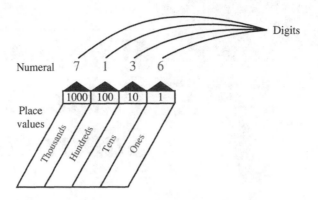

Thus, the numeral 7136 means

$$7 \text{ thousands} + 1 \text{ hundred} + 3 \text{ tens} + 6 \text{ ones}$$
$$= \quad 7000 \quad + \quad 100 \quad + \quad 30 + 6$$
$$= 7136$$

The numeral 7136 is read "seven thousand one hundred thirty-six," which is the English name of the numeral.

The place values one (1), ten (10), a hundred (100), and a thousand (1000) are related in the following way.

$$10 = 10 \text{ ones}$$
$$100 = 10 \text{ tens}$$
$$1000 = 10 \text{ hundreds}$$

 Try Problems 1 through 5.

2 Larger Numbers

The following diagram gives the place values for the numeral 312,036,070,408, which is read "three hundred twelve billion, thirty-six million, seventy thousand, four hundred eight." The commas, placed every third digit starting from the right, serve as an aid in reading the numeral.

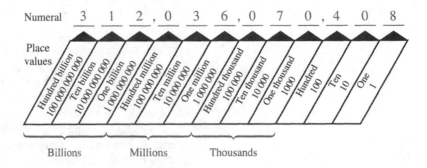

Try These Problems

6. Use the numeral 17,904,083,265 to answer each question.
a. What digit is in the ten millions place?
b. What digit is in the billions place?
c. What is the place value of the digit 9?
d. What is the place value of the digit 8?

Write the numeral for each English name.

7. Seventy-three thousand, nine hundred two

8. Fourteen billion, two hundred four million, eight hundred

In Problems 9 and 10, write the English name for each numeral.

9. 107,034

10. 230,018,276

11. Which is less, 54 or 36?

12. List from smallest to largest: 50; 45; 400; 396; 2100

The place values are related in the following way.

$$10 = 10 \text{ ones}$$
$$100 = 10 \text{ tens}$$
$$1000 = 10 \text{ hundreds}$$
$$10,000 = 10 \text{ thousands}$$
$$100,000 = 10 \text{ ten thousands}$$
$$1,000,000 = 10 \text{ hundred thousands}$$

Observe that as you move to the left from digit to digit in a whole numeral, each place value is 10 of the previous place values. This pattern continues indefinitely.

The following chart gives the English names for several whole numerals.

Whole Numeral	English Name
3200	Three thousand two hundred *or* thirty-two hundred
26,367	Twenty-six thousand, three hundred sixty-seven
704,900	Seven hundred four thousand, nine hundred
85,040,001	Eighty-five million, forty thousand, one
3,052,000,000	Three billion, fifty-two million

Observe that the word *and* should never be used when reading a whole numeral.

Sometimes we use a combination of a numeral and the English language in referring to a whole number. This is especially true for very large whole numbers. For example,

$$3 \text{ million} = 3,000,000$$
$$56 \text{ million} = 56,000,000$$
$$728 \text{ billion} = 728,000,000,000$$

 Try Problems 6 through 10.

3 Comparing Numbers

The first few **whole numbers** are listed here.

0, 1, 2, 3, 4, 5, 6, 7, 8, 9, 10, 11, 12, 13, 14

This list continues indefinitely. In this list, a number to the right is considered more than (or larger than) a number to the left. Also, a number to the left is considered less than (or smaller than) a number to the right. For example,

13 is more than 4

and

16 is less than 25.

 Try Problems 11 and 12.

Try These Problems

13. Is the number 587 closer to 500 or 600?

14. Is the number 12,368 closer to 12,000 or 13,000?

15. Round off the number 5489 to the thousands place.

16. Round off the number 67,683 to the nearest hundred.

Round off the given number to the given place value.

17. 7653; hundreds

18. 385; tens

19. 146,518; thousands

20. 81,932; hundreds

4   Rounding Off Numbers

Suppose you purchase a car for $12,348. In speaking with your friends you might say the car costs $12,000. The price $12,000 is an approximation of the actual cost $12,348. We use the symbol ≈ or ≐ to mean *approximately equal to.* More precisely, the number 12,000 is the result of **rounding off** the number 12,348 to the nearest thousand. Observe that 12,348 is closer to 12,000 than it is to 13,000 because the digit after the thousands place is 3, which is less than 5.

12,348
└────── The digit after the thousands place is less than 5.

≈ 12,000

Here we have rounded to the nearest thousand.

We can round off numbers to any specified place value. Here are more examples.

EXAMPLE 1   Round off 34,792 to the nearest hundred.

SOLUTION   First locate the hundreds place in the number 34,792.

34,792
└──── Hundreds place

We want to know whether this number is closer to 34,700 or 34,800. To see this, look at the digit that is to the right of the hundreds digit. It is a 9. Because it is more than 5, we conclude that the number is closer to 34,800 than 34,700.

34,792
└──── The digit after the hundreds place is more than 5.

≈ 34,800   34,792 is closer to 34,800 than 34,700.   ■

 Try Problems 13 through 16.

EXAMPLE 2   Round off 235 to the tens place.

SOLUTION   First locate the tens place in the number 235.

235
└── Tens place

We want to know whether this number is closer to 230 or 240. The number 235 is exactly halfway between 230 and 240. In this case, we agree to use the higher number for the approximation.

235
└──── The digit after the tens place is equal to 5.

≈ 240   We agree to increase the tens digit from 3 to 4 because the next digit is equal to 5.   ■

Try Problems 17 through 20.

Try These Problems

Round off the given number to the given place value.

21. 392; tens

22. 65,983; hundreds

23. 345,713; thousands

24. 345,713; ten thousands

25. 4,671,324; ten thousands

26. 4,671,324; thousands

27. 108,972; hundreds

28. 8,993,504; hundred thousands

EXAMPLE 3   Round off 129,657 to the nearest thousand.

SOLUTION   First locate the thousands place in the number 129,657.

129,657
 └───── Thousands place

We want to know if this number is closer to 129,000 or 130,000. To see this, look at the digit to the right of the thousands digit 9. Because it is a 6, which is 5 or more, the number 129,657 is closer to 130,000 than 129,000.

129,657
 └─── The digit after the thousands place is more than 5.

≈ 130,000   129,657 is closer to 130,000 than 129,000.

 Try Problems 21 and 22.

Finally we display a chart that gives several numbers rounded off to specified place values.

ROUNDING OFF NUMBERS TO GIVEN PLACE VALUES				
Number	Round Off to the Tens Place	Round Off to the Hundreds Place	Round Off to the Thousands Place	Round Off to the Ten-thousands Place
28	30	0	0	0
569	570	600	1000	0
5325	5330	5300	5000	10,000
13,973	13,970	14,000	14,000	10,000
760,542	760,540	760,500	761,000	760,000
3,800,400	3,800,400	3,800,400	3,800,000	3,800,000

Study the chart carefully enough to make the following observations.

■ The digit in the round-off place is unchanged if the first digit to the right of the round-off place is less than 5.

■ The digit in the round-off place is increased by 1 if the first digit to the right of the round-off place is 5 or more.

■ The digits to the right of the round-off place are replaced by zeros.

■ The digits to the left of the round-off place change only when the digit in the round-off place is a 9 and the first digit to its right is 5 or more.

 Try Problems 23 through 28.

Answers to Try These Problems

1. a. 0 b. 3 c. 1 (one) d. 1000 (thousand)
2. 413   3. 9082   4. Six hundred thirty-five
5. Three thousand four hundred seven
6. a. 0 b. 7 c. 100,000,000 (hundred million)
   d. 10,000 (ten thousand)   7. 73,902   8. 14,204,000,800
9. One hundred seven thousand, thirty-four
10. Two hundred thirty million, eighteen thousand, two
    hundred seventy-six
11. 36   12. 45; 50; 396; 400; 2100   13. 600   14. 12,000
15. 5000   16. 67,700   17. 7700   18. 390   19. 147,000
20. 81,900   21. 390   22. 66,000   23. 346,000   24. 350,000
25. 4,670,000   26. 4,671,000   27. 109,000   28. 9,000,000

EXERCISES   1.1

Use the numeral 78,534 to answer Exercises 1 through 4.

1. What digit is in the hundreds place?
2. What digit is in the ten thousands place?
3. What is the place value of the digit 3?
4. What is the place value of the digit 8?

Use the numeral 52,730,149,869 to answer Exercises 5 through 8.

5. What digit is in the ten billions place?
6. What digit is in the hundred thousands place?
7. What is the place value of the digit 7?
8. What is the place value of the digit 4?
9. Which is larger, 7983 or 10,000?
10. List from smallest to largest: 700; 698; 1000
11. Aron is 63 inches tall. Her sister Ann is 36 inches tall. Who is taller?
12. Last week a head of lettuce was selling for 79 cents. This week a head of lettuce sells for 92 cents. Did the price increase or decrease?
13. Candy has $500 in her checking account. She writes a check for $465. Is there enough money in her account to cover the check?
14. A real estate company purchased an apartment building in Chicago for $1,700,000. A similar building in Houston cost $1,098,000. Which building was more expensive?

Write a whole numeral for each English name.

15. Fourteen
16. Ninety-eight
17. Two hundred eighty
18. Three thousand three hundred eleven
19. Twenty-six hundred
20. One hundred seven thousand, eight
21. Fifteen million, five hundred thousand
22. 75 billion

23. The population of San Francisco one year ago was seven hundred thousand people. Write the population as a whole numeral.
24. The profit last year for an architect's firm was ten thousand dollars. Write the profit as a whole numeral.

Write the English name for each numeral.

25. 47   **26.** 450   **27.** 806   **28.** 3542   **29.** 5500

30. 78,360   **31.** 103,085   **32.** 4,008,701   **33.** 5,070,000,000

34. A car salesperson sold 52 cars last year. Write the English name for the number of cars sold.
35. As an accountant, Sylvia will earn $35,000 this year. Write the English name for Sylvia's yearly salary.

Round off the given number to the given place value.

36. 74; tens   **37.** 863; hundreds

38. 86,317; thousands   **39.** 6829; tens

40. 8654; hundreds   **41.** 4532; thousands

42. 764,938; ten thousands   **43.** 5,087,063; ten thousands

44. 6,357,876; hundred thousands   **45.** 45,490,785; millions

USING THE CALCULATOR #1

TYPES OF CALCULATORS

There are many types of calculators. Four of the commonly used ones are basic, scientific, business, and graphing calculators. In this text, we discuss only the basic and scientific calculators that use an algebraic entry logic. We do not discuss calculators that use reverse Polish notation, nor do we discuss calculators that are programmable. Here we picture an example of the types that will be discussed in this text.

Scientific calculators are not much more expensive than basic calculators and can do a lot more. If you have not already purchased a calculator, and you plan to take more math or science, you should consider buying a scientific calculator. Your mathematics instructor can help you decide which kind of calculator is best for you.

Basic Calculator

Scientific Calculator

1.2	ADDITION AND SUBTRACTION

OBJECTIVES
- ▌ Add two or more whole numbers.
- ▌ Solve an application involving addition of whole numbers.
- ▌ Subtract two whole numbers.
- ▌ Solve an application involving subtraction of whole numbers.
- ▌ Find the missing number in an addition statement.

1 Addition

The Jackson family spent $20 on movie tickets and $8 on popcorn and drinks. To find the total amount spent, we **add** $20 and $8. The symbol + (read *plus*) is used to indicate addition.

$$\$20 + \$8 = \$28$$

The total amount spent was $28.

To add means to combine or total. It does not matter in what order the numbers are written. For example,

$$3 + 8 = 11 \quad \text{and} \quad 8 + 3 = 11$$

When adding more than two numbers, it does not matter which two numbers are added first. For example,

$$4 + 3 + 5 = 7 + 5 = 12$$

and

$$4 + 3 + 5 = 4 + 8 = 12$$

and

$$4 + 3 + 5 = 9 + 3 = 12$$

In an addition problem, the numbers being added are called **terms** and the answer to the addition problem is called the **sum.** For example, in the statement

$$\overset{\text{Terms}}{8 + 7 + 5} = \underset{\text{Sum}}{20}$$

the numbers 8, 7, and 5 are terms and the number 20 is the sum.

When adding larger numbers, care must be taken to add digits with like place values. The procedure is illustrated in the following examples.

EXAMPLE 1   Add: $314 + 2 + 53$

SOLUTION   Arrange the numbers vertically so that digits with like place values form a column.

Try These Problems

Add.

1. 7 + 6 + 4 + 3

2. 13 + 241 + 2105

3. 2564 + 368

4.   7382
           675
        + 3982

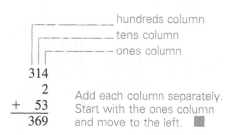

hundreds column
tens column
ones column

314
 2
+ 53
369

Add each column separately.
Start with the ones column
and move to the left.

EXAMPLE 2   Add: 285 + 372

SOLUTION   Arrange the numbers vertically so that digits with like place value form a column.

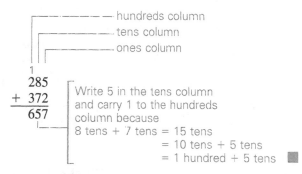

hundreds column
tens column
ones column

1
285
+ 372
657

Write 5 in the tens column
and carry 1 to the hundreds
column because
8 tens + 7 tens = 15 tens
            = 10 tens + 5 tens
            = 1 hundred + 5 tens

Try Problems 1 through 4.

2 Subtraction

If you had \$12 and spent \$7, to find the amount you have left you would **subtract** 7 from 12. The symbol − (read *minus*) is used to indicate subtraction.

$$\$12 - \$7 = \$5$$

The amount you have left is \$5.

To subtract means to take away. Subtraction is the reverse of addition. For example,

$$12 - 7 = 5 \quad \text{because} \quad 5 + 7 = 12$$

It does matter in which order you write down a subtraction problem. For example,

$$12 - 7 = 5$$

but

$$7 - 12 = -5$$

The symbol −5 represents the number "negative five." This number, −5, does not equal 5. We study negative numbers in Chapter 12 of this book.

When subtracting larger numbers, be careful to subtract digits with like place values.

Try These Problems

Subtract.

5. 62 − 19

6. 5837 − 215

7. 865 − 280

8. 13,425 − 7817

EXAMPLE 3   Subtract: 7284 − 31

SOLUTION   Arrange the numbers vertically so that the larger number is on the top and digits with like place values form a column.

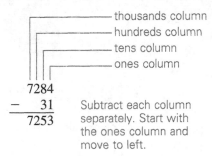

```
  7284
−   31
  7253
```
Subtract each column separately. Start with the ones column and move to left.

CHECK

```
  7253
+   31
  7284
```

In any one column, when the bottom digit is larger than the top digit, **borrowing** must be used. The following examples illustrate how to use borrowing.

EXAMPLE 4   Subtract: 3475 − 752

SOLUTION

```
   2
  3¹4 7 5
−   7 5 2
  2 7 2 3
```
In the hundreds column, 7 is larger than 4, so we must borrow.
Borrow 1 thousand from 3 thousands. Mark out 3 and write 2.
The 1 thousand we borrow is put in the hundreds column to make 14 hundreds because
  1 thousand + 4 hundreds
= 10 hundreds + 4 hundreds
= 14 hundreds

CHECK

```
  ¹752
+ 2723
  3475
```

 Try Problems 5 through 8.

Sometimes there is a 0 digit in the column where you want to borrow. The following examples illustrate how to handle this situation.

EXAMPLE 5   Subtract: 503 − 37

SOLUTION

```
  4 9
  5 0¹3
−   3 7
  4 6 6
```
In the ones column, 7 is larger than 3, so we must borrow. We cannot borrow 1 ten from 0 tens, so we borrow 1 ten from 50 tens. Mark out 50 and write 49. The 1 ten we borrow is put in the ones column to make 13 ones.

Try These Problems

Subtract.

9. 604 − 78

10. 700 − 216

11. 50,302 − 7485

12. 91,000 − 6040

Find the missing number.

13. 7 + ☐ = 15

14. ☐ = 25 + 16

15. 136 = ☐ + 57

16. 807 + ☐ = 2004

CHECK

```
     11
    466
 +   37
    503
```

EXAMPLE 6   Subtract: 600,274 − 3521

SOLUTION

```
  5 9 9
  6̸ 0̸ 0̸¹2 7 4
 −      3 5 2 1
  5 9 6 7 5 3
```

In the hundreds column 5 is larger than 2, so we must borrow. We borrow 1 thousand from 600 thousands. Mark out 600 and write 599. The 1 thousand we borrow is put in the hundreds column to make 12 hundreds.

CHECK

```
      111
     3521
 + 596753
   600274
```

 Try Problems 9 through 12.

3 Finding the Missing Number in an Addition Statement

The statement 6 + 3 = 9 is an addition statement. If any one of the three numbers is omitted, you want to know how to find the missing number. For example, three problems could arise:

1. 6 + 3 = ☐   Here the answer to the addition problem is missing, so we *add* to find the missing number.

The missing number is 6 + 3 = 9.

2. ☐ + 3 = 9   Here one of the terms is missing, so we *subtract* to find the missing number.

The missing number is 9 − 3 = 6.

3. 6 + ☐ = 9   Here one of the terms is missing, so we *subtract* to find the missing number.

The missing number is 9 − 6 = 3.

 Try Problems 13 through 16.

 Answers to Try These Problems

1. 20   2. 2359   3. 2932   4. 12,039   5. 43   6. 5622
7. 585   8. 5608   9. 526   10. 484   11. 42,817   12. 84,960
13. 8   14. 41   15. 79   16. 1197

EXERCISES 1.2

Add.

1. 8 + 36

2. 46 + 5

3. 5 + 7 + 8

4. 3 + 9 + 7

5. 6 + 7 + 5 + 3

6. 6 + 5 + 8 + 9

7.
```
   792
    36
 +  19
```

8.
```
   3099
   8764
 +  278
```

9. 9674 + 20,911 + 450

10. 10,346 + 9807 + 123

11. 8 + 317 + 86

12. 370,816 + 2115 + 92 + 348

13.
```
   124,577
    80,675
   986,501
 +   3,845
```

14.
```
   66,177
    9,323
   50,689
 +  7,135
```

15. Mr. Maguire purchases these items at the supermarket.

Beef $18
Potatoes $ 3
Dog food $ 5
Beer $ 6

What is the total cost?

16. What is the total length of this shaft?

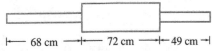

|← 68 cm →|← 72 cm →|← 49 cm →|

17. Ms. Nichols had $915 in her checking account. She deposited $97 in the account. What is her balance now?

18. Ross weighed 176 pounds before going on his vacation. He gained 14 pounds on his trip. What did Ross weigh after his vacation?

Subtract. Check your answers by adding.

19. 43 − 5

20. 759 − 42

21. 638 − 46

22.
```
   2367
 −  124
```

23.
```
   4238
 − 1705
```

24.
```
   72,378
 −  6,084
```

25.
```
   3107
 −  783
```

26.
```
   6324
 −  583
```

27.
```
   64,013
 −  4,208
```

28.
```
   6004
 −   36
```

29.
```
   50,026
 −  1,451
```

30. 700 − 8

31. 300 − 67

32. 5000 − 407

33. 6000 − 1038

34. 8000 − 350

35. 70,000 − 300

36.
```
   200,300
 −   7,502
```

37.
```
   520,036
 −  71,578
```

38.
```
   308,010
 −  73,524
```

39.
```
   400,000
 −  70,293
```

40.
```
   1030
 −  987
```

41.
```
   41,020
 −  9,382
```

42.
```
   310,015
 −  73,046
```

43.
```
   610,003
 −     685
```

44.
```
   100,000
 −  73,600
```

45. Carlos had $50 in his pocket. He spent $12 on lunch for himself and his friend Dorothy. How much money does he have left?

46. Don's goal is to make $3500 during the summer. By the end of July he had earned $2793. How much does he have to earn to reach his goal?

47. At the start of a trip the odometer of a car read 52,037. At the end of the trip the odometer read 54,100. If the odometer measures distance in miles, how far has the car traveled on this trip?

48. Tony weighs 239 pounds. Mike weighs 251 pounds. Who weighs more and by how much?

Find the missing number.

49. $\boxed{} = 9 + 7$

50. $8 + \boxed{} = 11$

51. $\boxed{} + 13 = 32$

52. $47 = 29 + \boxed{}$

53. $135 + \boxed{} = 300$

54. $269 + 87 = \boxed{}$

55. $1305 + \boxed{} = 2002$

56. $30{,}001 = \boxed{} + 7983$

DEVELOPING NUMBER SENSE #1

APPROXIMATING BY ROUNDING

Whether you are computing by using a calculator or paper and pencil, it is always possible to make a careless mistake that causes your answer to be not only wrong, but ridiculously wrong. It is a good idea to approximate the answer to check whether your answer is reasonable. In some cases, an approximation may be all that you are interested in. One method for approximating is to round the numbers being computed to make them easier to work with, then compute the rounded numbers.

For example, suppose that we want to find an approximation for the following addition problem.

$$1280 + 788 + 69$$

We could round off each number to the nearest hundred, then add.

$1280 \approx 1300$
$788 \approx 800$
$69 \approx 100$

Each number is rounded off to the hundreds place.

Adding 1300, 800, and 100, we obtain 2200 for the approximation.

There are no set rules on how to round the numbers to approximate. We could have done the rounding in many ways. Here we show the approximation obtained in another way. This time we round off so that each rounded number has only one nonzero digit. In this way the numbers are extremely easy to work with.

$1280 \approx 1000$
$788 \approx 800$
$69 \approx 70$

Each number is rounded so that the result has only one nonzero digit.

Adding 1000, 800, and 70, we obtain 1870 for the approximation. The actual sum is 2137.

Number Sense Problems

Approximate each answer by rounding off each number to the nearest hundred.

1. 794 + 315   **2.** 643 + 86 + 128   **3.** 2370 − 1496   **4.** 1682 − 379

Approximate each answer by rounding off each number to the nearest thousand.

5. 26,321 − 9718   **6.** 1379 + 899 + 18,956 + 7917

Approximate each answer by rounding off each number so that it contains only one nonzero digit.

7. 534 + 79 + 3598   **8.** 768,000 + 5743 + 52,113   **9.** 214,987 − 5634

USING THE CALCULATOR #2

ADDITION AND SUBTRACTION

Suppose you want to add 24 and 48 on the calculator. Whether you have a basic calculator or scientific calculator, here are the steps you take.

To Compute   24 + 48
Enter   24 + 48 =
Result   72

Suppose you want to add several numbers. For example, you want to compute 20 + 75 + 35 + 20.

To Compute   20 + 75 + 35 + 20
Enter   20 + 75 + 35 + 20 =
Result   150

If you enter + at the end instead of =, the same result is obtained. Also, because addition can be done in any order, it does not matter in what order you enter the terms.

When computing a subtraction problem, you must be careful that the numbers are entered in the correct order. Here is an example.

To Compute   120 − 80
Enter   120 − 80 =
Result   40

Observe that the numbers are entered in the same order as they are written down when using the subtraction symbol −. If you enter the numbers 120 and 80 in the reverse order, you obtain the negative number −40, because −40 is the result of subtracting 120 from 80. Negative numbers are discussed in Chapter 12.

Calculator Problems
Add or subtract as indicated.

1. 7 + 5

2. 28 + 57

3. 479 + 8796

4. 23,986 + 567,982

5. 8 + 2 + 12

6. 17 + 9 + 47 + 185

7. 807 − 469

8. 6003 − 747

9. Subtract 18 from 72.

10. Subtract 537 from 7000.

1.3   LANGUAGE

OBJECTIVES ▌ Translate an English statement to an addition or subtraction statement using math symbols.
▌ Solve problems by translating.

 Translating

The math symbols that we use often have many translations to the English language. Knowing these translations can help in solving application problems. The following chart gives the many English translations for the symbol =.

Math Symbol	English
=	equals
	is equal to
	is the same as
	is
	was
	represents
	gives
	makes
	yields
	will be
	were
	are

The addition statement, $7 + 5 = 12$, is written using math symbols. Some of the ways to read this in English are given in the following chart.

Math Symbols	English
$7 + 5 = 12$	7 plus 5 equals 12.
	The *sum* of 7 and 5 is 12.
	5 more than 7 is equal to 12.
	7 *increased by* 5 yields 12.
	12 represents 7 added to 5.
	7 and 5 is 12.

Because $7 + 5$ equals $5 + 7$, the order that you read the terms 5 and 7 makes no difference; however, when reading the subtraction statement $12 - 5 = 7$, be sure to read 12 and 5 in the correct order, because $12 - 5$ does not equal $5 - 12$.

$$12 - 5 = 7 \quad \text{but} \quad 5 - 12 = -7$$

The number 7 does not equal -7. The number -7 is a negative number. This book covers negative numbers in Chapter 12. The following chart gives several correct ways to read $12 - 5 = 7$.

Math Symbols	English
$12 - 5 = 7$	12 minus 5 equals 7.
	12 take away 5 is 7.
	12 diminished by 5 gives 7.
	12 reduced by 5 yields 7.
	12 subtract 5 is 7.
	5 subtracted from 12 equals 7.
	5 less than 12 is 7.
	The *difference* between 12 and 5 is 7.
	7 represents 12 *decreased by* 5.

Try These Problems

Translate to an addition or subtraction statement using math symbols.

1. The sum of 25 and 17 is 42.
2. The difference between 300 and 112 equals 188.
3. 73 represents 61 increased by 12.
4. 60 minus 18 yields 42.
5. 28 less than 75 is equal to 47.
6. 15 subtracted from 120 gives 105.

Solve.

7. The sum of 79 and 895 yields what number?
8. What number plus 74 equals 3001?
9. 295 represents 81 more than what number?
10. 487 less than 700 is what number?

Note that when using the phrases *subtracted from* or *less than* for the symbol $-$, we read the numbers 12 and 5 in reverse order. That is,

$$5 \text{ subtracted from } 12 \quad \text{means} \quad 12 - 5$$

and

$$5 \text{ less than } 12 \quad \text{means} \quad 12 - 5$$

Try Problems 1 through 6.

2 | Solving Problems by Translating

The following examples illustrate how we can use translating to solve problems.

EXAMPLE 1   What number increased by 18 yields 50?

SOLUTION   Translate the question to math symbols.

What number increased by 18 yields 50?
$$\boxed{} \quad + \quad 18 \quad = \quad 50$$

The missing number is one of the terms in an addition statement, so we subtract the given term 18 from the sum 50 to find the missing term.

$$50 - 18 = 32$$

The answer is 32. ■

EXAMPLE 2   What number represents 205 decreased by 38?

SOLUTION   The question translates to math symbols as follows.

What number represents 205 decreased by 38?
$$\boxed{} \quad = \quad 205 \quad - \quad 38$$

The missing number is the answer to the subtraction problem, $205 - 38$.

$$\begin{array}{r} \overset{1}{}\overset{9}{} \\ 2\ \cancel{0}{}^{1}5 \\ -\ \ 3\ 8 \\ \hline 1\ 6\ 7 \end{array}$$

The answer is 167. ■

Try Problems 7 through 10.

Answers to Try These Problems

1. $25 + 17 = 42$ 2. $300 - 112 = 188$ 3. $73 = 61 + 12$
4. $60 - 18 = 42$ 5. $75 - 28 = 47$ 6. $120 - 15 = 105$
7. 974   8. 2927   9. 214   10. 213

Translate each English statement to an addition or subtraction statement using math symbols.

1. The sum of 18 and 17 is 35.

2. 63 increased by 9 equals 72.

3. 54 represents 63 decreased by 9.

4. The difference between 202 and 78 is 124.

5. 50 more than 360 is equal to 410.

6. 910 take away 14 yields 896.

7. 1023 plus 978 is 2101.

8. 308 subtracted from 4200 equals 3892.

9. 3 is 4 less than 7.

10. 28 represents the sum of 20 and 8.

Solve.

11. 407 minus 82 equals what number?

12. Find the difference between 566 and 463.

13. Find the result when 2000 is increased by 1802.

14. Find the result when 2000 is decreased by 1802.

15. What number increased by 956 yields 3050?

16. 619 subtracted from 1023 gives what number?

17. Find the sum of 5090 and 936.

18. What number is 13,825 plus 86?

19. What number represents 7000 decreased by 64?

20. 30,000 minus 7800 yields what number?

1.4 APPLICATIONS

OBJECTIVES
- Solve applications that involve a total as the sum of parts.
- Find the perimeter of a figure.
- Solve applications that involve increases and decreases.
- Solve applications that involve comparing quantities by addition or subtraction.

There are many situations in your daily life in which addition and subtraction of numbers are needed. In this section we look at some of these situations and give guidelines on how to decide whether to add or subtract.

1   Problems Involving a Total as the Sum of Parts

You know that to add means to combine or total. In the addition statement

$$7 + 9 = 16$$

the sum 16 is the total and the terms 7 and 9 are parts of the total. Recall from Section 1.2 that if any one of the three numbers is missing, you can find the missing number by using the two given numbers. Here we review the procedure.

> *Finding the Missing Number in a Basic Addition Statement*
>
> 1. If the sum (or total) is missing, add the terms (or parts) to find the missing number.
> 2. If one of the terms (or parts) is missing, subtract the given term from the total to find the missing term.

The following examples illustrate how to use this concept to solve some application problems.

EXAMPLE 1   The marked price of a car is $9350. After adding the tax, the total price is $9911. How much is the tax?

SOLUTION   The problem indicates the following.

$$\text{marked price} + \text{tax} = \text{total price}$$
$$\$9350 + \boxed{} = \$9911$$

The tax is a missing term in an addition statement so we subtract.

$$
\begin{array}{r}
9\ \overset{8}{9}{}^{1}1\ 1 \\
-\ 9\ 3\ 5\ 0 \\
\hline
5\ 6\ 1
\end{array}
\begin{array}{l}
\text{— total price} \\
\text{— marked price} \\
\text{— tax}
\end{array}
$$

The tax is $561. ■

EXAMPLE 2   Find the perimeter of this triangle.

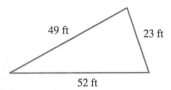

49 ft   23 ft

52 ft

SOLUTION   The **perimeter** of a figure means the total distance around it, so we have the following.

$$\text{Perimeter} = 49 + 23 + 52$$
$$\boxed{} = 49 + 23 + 52$$

▲ **Try These Problems**

1. Barbara bought some chicken breasts and a ham at the supermarket. The total bill was $23. The ham cost $14. What was the cost of the chicken?

2. What is the perimeter of this rectangle?

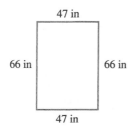

47 in

66 in   66 in

47 in

3. How long is the bottom portion of this pineapple?

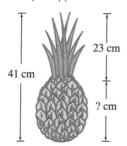

23 cm

41 cm

? cm

4. A swimming pool holds 5000 gallons of water. The swimming pool contains 1870 gallons of water now. How many more gallons are needed to fill the pool?

We add to find the total.

$$
\begin{array}{r}
{}^{1} \\
49 \\
23 \\
+\ 52 \\
\hline
124
\end{array}
$$

The perimeter is 124 feet. ■

EXAMPLE 3   The seat of a chair is 49 centimeters from the floor. The total height of the chair is 108 centimeters. How long is the back of the chair?

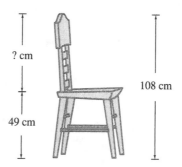

? cm

49 cm

108 cm

SOLUTION   The total height of the chair is found by adding the height of the seat and the length of the back.

$$
\underset{\text{seat}}{\text{Height of}} + \underset{\text{back}}{\text{length of}} = \underset{\text{height}}{\text{total}}
$$

$$
49 \quad + \quad \boxed{} \quad = 108
$$

We are missing a part of the total so we subtract.

$$
\begin{array}{r}
{}^{0}\ {}^{9} \\
\cancel{1}\ \cancel{0}\,{}^{1}8 \\
-\quad 4\ 9 \\
\hline
5\ 9
\end{array}
$$

—— total height
—— parts

The length of the back is 59 centimeters. ■

▲ **Try Problems 1 through 4.**

2   Problems Involving Increases and Decreases

The price of a videocassette recorder decreased from $450 to $300. The amount that the price went down is called the **decrease.** To find the decrease we subtract.

$$
\begin{aligned}
\text{Decrease} &= \underset{\text{price}}{\text{higher}} - \underset{\text{price}}{\text{lower}} \\
&= \$450 - \$300 \\
&= \$150
\end{aligned}
$$

The decrease in price is $150.

Try These Problems

5. The price of apples decreased from 75 cents a pound to 59 cents a pound. What is the decrease in price?

6. An elephant's weight went from 2000 pounds to 1872 pounds. Find the loss in weight.

7. Last year the profit for a small company was $186,000. This year the profit was $200,000. What was the increase in profit?

8. You receive a salary raise. Your original salary was $2460 monthly and now you make $2700 monthly. What was your raise for one month?

Other words can be used to mean decrease. Here we list some situations where a value has gone down and give the corresponding words that can be used to indicate the amount that the value went down.

Situation	Words Indicating the Amount the Value Went Down
There is a sale on sheets. An $80 value is now selling for $60.	The *discount* is $20. The *savings* is $20. The *reduction* in price is $20. The *decrease* in price is $20.
A man lost weight. His weight dropped from 280 pounds to 220 pounds.	The *loss* in weight is 60 pounds. The *reduction* in weight is 60 pounds. The *decrease* is 60 pounds.

 Try Problems 5 and 6.

The population of a town increased from 13,200 to 15,500. The amount that the population went up is called the **increase.** To find the increase we subtract.

$$\text{Increase} = \frac{\text{larger}}{\text{population}} - \frac{\text{smaller}}{\text{population}}$$
$$= 15,500 - 13,200$$
$$= 2300$$

The increase in population is 2300.

Other words can be used to mean increase. Here we list some situations where a value has gone up and give the corresponding words that can be used to indicate the amount that the value went up.

Situation	Words Indicating the Amount the Value Went Up
Your annual salary increased. It went from $40,000 to $42,000.	Your *raise* is $2000. The *gain* in salary is $2000. The *increase* in salary is $2000.
A woman gained weight. Her weight went from 120 pounds to 130 pounds.	Her *gain* in weight is 10 pounds. The *increase* is 10 pounds.

 Try Problems 7 and 8.

3 Problems Involving Comparisons

Two unequal numbers, such as 80 and 95, can be compared using addition and subtraction. Here is a list of several addition and subtraction statements involving 80 and 95 and the corresponding comparison statements in English.

Try These Problems

9. Tom drove 407 miles on Monday and 600 miles on Tuesday. How much farther did he drive on Tuesday?

10. It took Mike 16 hours to paint the exterior of a house. It took him 8 hours more to paint a larger house. How long did it take Mike to paint the larger house?

11. Cathy's annual salary is less than Steve's annual salary by $2900. If Cathy's salary is $38,000, find Steve's salary.

12. The populations of two towns in Florida differ by 38,000 people. If the larger population is 156,000, what is the smaller population?

Comparing Two Numbers	
Math Symbols	**English**
$80 + 15 = 95$	15 more than 80 is 95.
$95 - 15 = 80$	15 less than 95 is 80.
$95 - 80 = 15$	95 and 80 differ by 15. The difference between 95 and 80 is 15. 80 less than 95 is 15.

Now we look at examples of problems involving comparisons.

EXAMPLE 4   The height of a eucalyptus tree is 102 feet and the height of a pine tree is only 75 feet. How much taller is the eucalyptus tree?

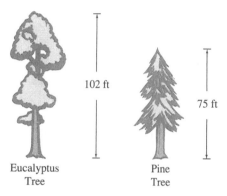

102 ft
75 ft
Eucalyptus Tree
Pine Tree

SOLUTION   To find how much taller the eucalyptus is, we subtract.

$$
\begin{array}{r}
\overset{0\ \ 9}{\cancel{1}}\ \overset{1}{\cancel{0}}2 \\
-\ \ 7\ 5 \\
\hline
2\ 7
\end{array}
$$

height of the eucalyptus
height of the pine
the difference

The eucalyptus tree is 27 feet taller than the pine tree. ■

EXAMPLE 5   Bob jogged 49 miles last week. Susan jogged 13 miles more than Bob. How many miles did Susan jog?

SOLUTION   Because Susan jogged 13 miles more than Bob, we have

$$
\begin{aligned}
\text{Susan's distance} &= \text{Bob's distance} + 13 \\
&= 49 + 13 \\
&= 62
\end{aligned}
$$

Susan jogged 62 miles. ■

 Try Problems 9 through 12.

Now we summarize the material presented in this section by giving guidelines that will help you decide whether to add or subtract.

Situations Requiring Addition or Subtraction

Operation	Situation
+	1. You are looking for the total or whole.
	2. You are looking for the result when a quantity has been increased.
−	1. You are looking for one of the parts in a total or whole.
	2. You are looking for the result when a quantity has been decreased.
	3. You are looking for how much larger one quantity is than another.
	4. You are looking for how much smaller one quantity is than another.

 Answers to Try These Problems

1. $9   2. 226 in   3. 18 cm   4. 3130 gal   5. 16¢   6. 128 lb
7. $14,000   8. $240   9. 193 mi   10. 24 hr   11. $40,900
12. 118,000

EXERCISES 1.4

Solve.

1. Ms. Ridens purchased these items at the department store.

Sweater	$45
Skirt	$76
Shoes	$89

   What was the total cost of the three items?

2. Irene had $792 in a savings account. She withdrew $165. How much is left in the account?

3. The population of a town in Florida increased from 18,003 to 25,000 over a five-year period. What was the increase in population?

4. How far is it from A to B?

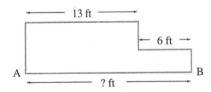

5. Frank operates a printing machine. He printed 40,000 pages on Wednesday. On Thursday he printed 8000 fewer pages. How many pages did he print on Thursday?

6. A certain calculator used to cost $25. Over the past two years the price has decreased by $7. What is the cost of the calculator now?

7. The profit for a company was $1,200,000 last year. This year the profit is $1,098,000. Did the profit increase or decrease, and by how much?

8. An airplane travels 580 miles per hour when the air is still. A 32 mile-per-hour wind is blowing in the direction that the plane is flying. How fast is the plane traveling?

9. Loula is selling her house. Yesterday the Allen family offered her $70,860. Today the Burton family offered her $71,200. Who offered more money and how much more?

10. Judy lost 15 pounds on her vacation in Hawaii. If she weighed 112 pounds after returning, how much did she weigh before the vacation?

11. How tall is the base of this lamp?

12. During the night the temperature dropped from 40°F to 26°F. What was the decrease in temperature?

13. Find the perimeter of this rectangle.

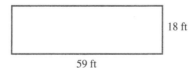

14. Find the perimeter of this floor.

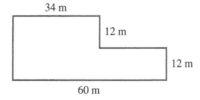

15. Antonio's college tuition for one year was $1400 less than Mohammed's college tuition. If Antonio's tuition was $5100, what was Mohammed's tuition?

16. Rita received a raise. Her salary was $589 a week before the raise. Now she makes $600 a week. What was her raise?

Mr. Yano owns a service station and several apartment buildings. The bar graph gives Mr. Yano's annual salary for each of five years. Use the graph to answer Exercises 17 through 22.

Annual Salary for 5 Years

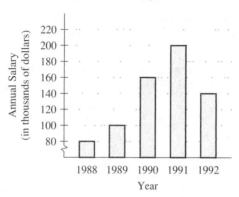

17. What was Mr. Yano's salary in 1991?
18. What was Mr. Yano's salary in 1992?
19. How much more did he earn in 1990 than in 1988?
20. How much more did he earn in 1991 than in 1989?
21. From 1990 to 1991 did his salary increase or decrease, and by how much?
22. From 1991 to 1992 did his salary increase or decrease, and by how much?

CHAPTER 1 SUMMARY

KEY WORDS AND PHRASES

whole numeral [1.1]	term [1.2]	difference [1.3]
digit [1.1]	sum [1.2]	decreased by [1.3]
place value [1.1]	subtraction [1.2]	perimeter [1.4]
whole number [1.1]	borrowing [1.2]	decrease [1.4]
round off [1.1]	translating [1.3]	increase [1.4]
addition [1.2]	increased by [1.3]	

SYMBOLS

= means *is equal to* [1.1]
≈ means *is approximately equal to* [1.1]
≐ means *is approximately equal to* [1.1]
+ means *to add* [1.2]
− means *to subtract* [1.2]

IMPORTANT RULES

The Meaning of Addition [1.2]
To add means to total or combine.

The Meaning of Subtraction [1.2]
To subtract means to take away. Subtraction is the reverse of addition, that is, $9 - 5 = 4$ because $4 + 5 = 9$.

How to Find the Missing Number in an Addition Statement [1.2]
- ▌ If the sum (or total) is missing, then add the terms (or parts) to find the sum.
- ▌ If one of the terms (or parts) is missing, then subtract the known term from the sum (or total) to obtain the missing term.

The Perimeter of a Figure [1.4]
The perimeter of a figure means the total distance around the figure.

CHAPTER 1 REVIEW EXERCISES

Use the numeral 40,356 to answer Exercises 1 through 4.

1. What digit is in the hundreds place?
2. What digit is in the tens place?
3. What is the place value of the digit 6?
4. What is the place value of the digit 4?
5. In the numeral 57,036,894, what digit is in the hundred thousands place?
6. In the numeral 1,238,049,000, what is the place value of the digit 3?
7. List from smallest to largest: 3000; 2099; 2200

In Exercises 8 through 11, round off to the given place value.

8. 723; tens
9. 1086; hundreds
10. 17,982; hundreds
11. 802,541; thousands

In Exercises 12 through 16, write a whole numeral for each English name.

12. Twelve
13. Three hundred eight
14. Fifty-seven thousand, twenty-four
15. Two million, eighty thousand, nine hundred eleven
16. 65 billion

In Exercises 17 through 20, write the English name for each numeral.

17. 18
18. 489
19. 206,801
20. 3,000,800,005

21. The distance between Atlanta, Georgia, and Miami, Florida, is six hundred sixty-five miles. Write the whole numeral for this distance.

Add.

22. 135 + 92
23. 9 + 705 + 36

24.
$$\begin{array}{r} 5604 \\ 738 \\ + \ 2897 \\ \hline \end{array}$$

25.
$$\begin{array}{r} 5,395 \\ 6,027 \\ + \ 98,730 \\ \hline \end{array}$$

26.
$$\begin{array}{r} 72,634 \\ 50,987 \\ + \ 53,668 \\ \hline \end{array}$$

27.
$$\begin{array}{r} 2059 \\ 500 \\ + \ \ \ 18 \\ \hline \end{array}$$

28. 12,938 + 7069 + 258
29. 12,000,813,700 + 20,813,000

Subtract.

30.   915
        $-\ 207$

31.   8231
        $-\ 923$

32.   7034
        $-\ 237$

33.   78,096
        $-\ 8,028$

34.   213,750
        $-\ \ \ 4,387$

35.   402
        $-\ 83$

36.   3004
        $-\ \ 98$

37.   5007
        $-\ \ 72$

38. $6000 - 703$

39. $40,000 - 7036$

40. $200,000 - 51,000$

41. $2,003,005 - 76,324$

42.   9,040,080
        $-\ \ \ 24,567$

43.   211,320
        $-\ \ \ 7,857$

44.   510
        $-\ 82$

45.   32,100
        $-\ 7,986$

46.   1000
        $-\ 317$

47.   611,000
        $-\ \ 17,903$

48.   100,000
        $-\ \ \ 7,200$

49.   210,003,100
        $-\ \ \ \ 7,034,826$

Find the missing number.

50. $218 + \boxed{} = 392$

51. $1046 + 18,739 = \boxed{}$

52. $810 = \boxed{} + 482$

53. $6000 = 910 + \boxed{}$

54. $\boxed{} = 29,038 + 156,400$

55. $\boxed{} + 299 = 10,802$

In Exercises 56 through 59, translate each English statement to an addition or subtraction statement using math symbols.

56. The difference between 1000 and 72 is 928.

57. 4300 increased by 486 is 4786.

58. The sum of 26 and 193 is 219.

59. 800 reduced by 108 is 692.

Solve.

60. How much larger is 51 than 38?

61. Find the sum of 732 and 970.

62. Subtract 34 from 2082.

63. What number is 68 more than 3736?

64. Lisa jogged along the highway for 8 miles, then along the beach for 6 miles. How far did Lisa jog?

65. From 1950 to 1960 the population of Dallas increased from 434,462 to 679,684. What was the increase in population?

66. Chuck has $651 in his checking account. He deposits $1369 in the account. What is the balance after the deposit?

67. The area of Memphis is 141 square miles and the area of San Francisco is 45 square miles. How much larger in area is Memphis than San Francisco?

68. Find the perimeter of this triangle.

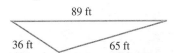

89 ft

36 ft   65 ft

69. Last week Margaret paid the following bills.
Gas and electric $ 36
Mortgage $387
Mastercard $172
Auto insurance $230
What was the total amount paid?

70. During the day the temperature in Phoenix went from 52°F to 91°F. What was the increase in temperature?

71. What is the total height of this sailboat, from the bottom of the keel to the top of the sail?

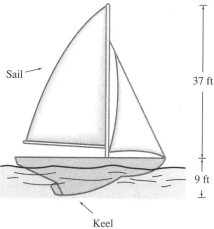

Sail

37 ft

9 ft

Keel

72. The Gateway Arch in St. Louis is 75 feet taller than the Washington Monument. The Gateway Arch is 630 feet tall. What is the height of the Washington Monument?

73. Last year the brake service for Harvey's car cost $175. This year the same service cost $17 more. What did Harvey pay this year?

74. Ashley has a charge account with Sears. His bill this month shows a balance of $223. If he pays $50, what is the new balance?

75. Mr. Wong is driving his car on a business trip. The total distance he must travel is 600 miles. He has already gone 237 miles. How much farther must he go?

76. As a computer programmer, Nancy earns $22,100 annually. As an auto mechanic, Richard earns $17,980. Who earns more money and how much more?

☑ In Your Own Words

Write complete sentences to discuss each of the following. Support your comments with examples or pictures, if appropriate.

77. A student incorrectly writes the numeral 600407 for six hundred forty seven. Discuss how you would help this student to understand the error made.

78. Discuss how the following two problems differ.
  a. ☐ + 82 = 116   **b.** 116 + 82 = ☐

79. Discuss a real-life situation where you need to calculate the perimeter of a figure.

80. Discuss a real-life situation where you need to subtract two numbers.

81. Discuss a real-life situation where you need to add more than two numbers.

CHAPTER 1 PRACTICE TEST

 1. In the numeral 36,178, what digit is in the thousands place?
 2. In the numeral 2,315,406, what digit is in the hundred thousands place?
 3. In the numeral 4863, what is the place value of the digit 8?
 4. In the numeral 715,320,400, what is the place value of the digit 1?
 5. Write the numeral for seven hundred forty-six.
 6. Write the English name for 90,000.
 7. List from smallest to largest: 1002; 799; 801; 98

In Exercises 8 and 9, round off to the given place value.

 8. 674; hundreds
 9. 98,456; thousands

Add.

10. 7346 + 682 + 95
11. 27 + 314 + 82,376

12. $\begin{array}{r} 72,894 \\ 5,843 \\ + \ 96,732 \\ \hline \end{array}$

13. $\begin{array}{r} 536 \\ 4728 \\ 966 \\ + \ 857 \\ \hline \end{array}$

Subtract.

14. $\begin{array}{r} 514 \\ - \ 24 \\ \hline \end{array}$

15. $\begin{array}{r} 703 \\ - \ 288 \\ \hline \end{array}$

16. 2136 − 540

17. 8000 − 2174
18. 50,040 − 386
19. 100,000 − 60,820

Find the missing number.

20. 2103 = ☐ + 932
21. 87 + 95 = ☐

Solve.

22. What number increased by 719 yields 2050?
23. What number is 365 more than 87?
24. Find the difference between 5000 and 92.
25. Ginny has $702 in her checking account. She writes a check for $83. How much is in the account now?
26. What is the total height of this house?

5 ft

16 ft

27. George's annual salary is less than Marilyn's annual salary by $1300. If George's salary is $26,500, find Marilyn's salary.
28. A company needs to hire 1000 new workers. They have already hired 681. How many more workers do they need?

CHAPTER

Whole Numbers: Multiplication and Division

2.1	MULTIPLICATION

OBJECTIVES
- ▌ Multiply two whole numbers.
- ▌ Use a shortcut to multiply whole numbers involving zeros.
- ▌ Multiply more than two numbers.
- ▌ Solve an application using multiplication of whole numbers.

1 Introduction to Multiplication

One shirt costs $7. What is the cost of 4 shirts? To answer this question, we multiply $7 by 4. The symbol $\times$ (read *times*) is used to indicate **multiplication.**

$$4 \times \$7 = \$7 + \$7 + \$7 + \$7$$
$$= \$28$$

The 4 shirts cost $28.

In the multiplication statement

$$4 \times 7 = 28$$

the numbers 4 and 7 are called **factors** or **multipliers,** and the result 28 is called the **product.** Observe that

$$4 \times 7 = 7 + 7 + 7 + 7 = 28$$

and also

$$7 \times 4 = 4 + 4 + 4 + 4 + 4 + 4 + 4 = 28$$

That is, it does not matter in what order the factors are written.

Although the operation of multiplication can be interpreted as repeated addition, you want to be able to compute multiplication without adding repeatedly. That is, you should know that 4 times 7 is 28 without adding.

Here is a completed table of the basic multiplication facts that you must memorize.

X	0	1	2	3	4	5	6	7	8	9
0	0	0	0	0	0	0	0	0	0	0
1	0	1	2	3	4	5	6	7	8	9
2	0	2	4	6	8	10	12	14	16	18
3	0	3	6	9	12	15	18	21	24	27
4	0	4	8	12	16	20	24	28	32	36
5	0	5	10	15	20	25	30	35	40	45
6	0	6	12	18	24	30	36	42	48	54
7	0	7	14	21	28	35	42	49	56	63
8	0	8	16	24	32	40	48	56	64	72
9	0	9	18	27	36	45	54	63	72	81

There are 100 entries in the above table. However, if you make some observations, you see that there are a lot fewer than 100 facts to memorize. Here we list the observations you should make.

▌ Any number multiplied by 0 is 0.
▌ Any number multiplied by 1 is that number.
▌ It does not matter in what order the multipliers are written.

Now you see that you only need to memorize the facts that are outlined in color.

Here are some examples of multiplying numbers with more than one digit by numbers with only one digit.

EXAMPLE 1   Multiply: 3024×2

SOLUTION

$$\begin{array}{r} 3024 \\ \times \quad 2 \\ \hline 6048 \end{array}$$ ▨

EXAMPLE 2   Multiply: 23×4

SOLUTION

$$\begin{array}{r} 1 \\ 23 \\ \times \quad 4 \\ \hline 92 \end{array}$$

Step 1: $4 \times 3 = 12$.
Write 2 in the ones column.
Carry 1 to the tens column, because $12 = 1$ ten $+ 2$ ones
Step 2: $4 \times 2 = 8$, then $8 + 1 = 9$. ▨
Write 9 in the tens column.

Try These Problems

Multiply.

1.   78
      × 6

2.   203
      × 4

3.   2070
     ×   5

4. 5117 × 8

5. 70,846 × 9

EXAMPLE 3   Multiply: 5307 × 8

SOLUTION

    2 5
 5307   Step 1: 8 × 7 = 56.
×   8   Write 6, carry 5.
42456   Step 2: 8 × 0 = 0, then 0 + 5 = 5.
                 Write 5.
                 Step 3: 8 × 3 = 24.
                 Write 4, carry 2.
                 Step 4: 8 × 5 = 40,
                     then 40 + 2 = 42. Write 42.

The answer is 42,456. ■

Try Problems 1 through 5.

Now we look at multiplying two numbers where both numbers have more than one digit.

EXAMPLE 4   Multiply: 412 × 23

SOLUTION   Arrange the numbers vertically so that like place values form a column. It doesn't matter which number is on top, but the work is easier if the numeral with more digits is on top.

    412   Step 1: 3 × 412 = 1236.
×   23   Since 3 is in the ones column,
 1236   write 6 in the ones column.
  824   Step 2: 2 × 412 = 824.
 9476   Since 2 is in the tens column,
                write 4 in the tens column.
                2 tens × 412 = 824 tens.
              Step 3: Add.

The answer is 9476. ■

EXAMPLE 5   Multiply: 513 × 274

SOLUTION

    513
× 274
 2052 ——Write 2 in the ones column.
 3591 ——Write 1 in the tens column.
1026   ——Write 6 in the hundreds column.
140562

The answer is 140,562. ■

Try These Problems

Multiply.

6.   94
   × 23

7.   2135
   × 61

8.   5064
   × 402

9. 5021 × 8316

10. 657 × 30,984

EXAMPLE 6   Multiply: 3108 × 430,165

SOLUTION

```
        430165
      ×   3108
      3441320
      000000
      430165
     1290495
     1336952820
```

Be neat so that the digits line up properly.

The answer is 1,336,952,820. ■

 Try Problems 6 through 10.

2   Shortcuts Involving Zeros

It will be helpful for you to learn a couple of shortcuts for multiplication problems involving many zeros. First we look at a shortcut for multiplying numbers when one or both of them end in zeros.

EXAMPLE 7   Multiply: 5 × 300

SOLUTION
LONG METHOD

```
       300
     ×   5
      1500
```

SHORTCUT

$$5 × 300 = 1500$$

5 × 3 = 15, then attach the 2 zeros

The answer is 1500. ■

EXAMPLE 8   Multiply: 24 × 6000

SOLUTION
LONG METHOD

```
      6000
    ×   24
     24000
     12000
    144000
```

Observe that these three zeros were caused by the three zeros in 6000.

SHORTCUT

```
        24
    ×  6000
     144000
```

Multiply 6 times 24, then attach three zeros.

The answer is 144,000. ■

Try These Problems

Multiply.

11. 7×6000

12. 326×900

13. $70 \times 11{,}200$

14. $8500 \times 365{,}000$

15. $780 \times 15{,}000$

16. $2360 \times 135{,}000$

EXAMPLE 9   Multiply: $40{,}000 \times 700$

SOLUTION

LONG METHOD

$$
\begin{array}{r}
40000 \\
\times\quad 700 \\
\hline
00000 \\
00000 \\
280000 \\
\hline
28000000 \\
\end{array}
$$

Observe that these six zeros were caused by the six zeros in 40000 and 700.

SHORTCUT

$$40000 \times 700 = 28000000$$

six zeros

$4 \times 7 = 28$, then attach six zeros

The answer is 28,000,000. ■

EXAMPLE 10   Multiply: 3250×1800

SOLUTION   Multiply 325×18, then attach three zeros.

$$
\begin{array}{r}
3250 \\
\times\quad 1800 \\
\hline
2600 \\
325 \\
\hline
5850000 \\
\end{array}
$$

three zeros

18×325

Attach three zeros.

The answer is 5,850,000. ■

 Try Problems 11 through 16.

Next we look at a shortcut that can be used when the number placed on bottom has zero digits elsewhere than at the end.

EXAMPLE 11   Multiply: 512×306

SOLUTION

LONG METHOD

$$
\begin{array}{r}
512 \\
\times\quad 306 \\
\hline
3072 \\
000 \\
1536 \\
\hline
156672 \\
\end{array}
$$

This row of zeros contributes nothing to the sum.

SHORTCUT

$$
\begin{array}{r}
512 \\
\times\quad 306 \\
\hline
3072 \\
1536 \\
\hline
156672 \\
\end{array}
$$

Since 3 is in the hundreds column, you must write 6 in the hundreds column.

The answer is 156,672. ■

Try These Problems

Multiply.

17. 732
× 905

18. 4082
× 7008

19. 98,736
× 50,008

20. 500,302 × 710,275

| EXAMPLE 12 | Multiply: 7308 × 6004 |

SOLUTION
LONG METHOD

$$
\begin{array}{r}
7308 \\
\times\ 6004 \\
\hline
29232 \\
0000 \\
0000 \\
43848 \\
\hline
43877232
\end{array}
$$

In the shortcut we omit these zeros.

SHORTCUT

$$
\begin{array}{r}
7308 \\
\times\ 6004 \\
\hline
29232 \\
43848 \\
\hline
43877232
\end{array}
$$

Write 8 in the thousands column, since 6 is in the thousands column.

The answer is 43,877,232. ■

 Try Problems 17 through 20.

3 Multiplying More Than Two Numbers

To multiply more than two numbers, multiply any two of them first, then multiply that result by another one, and continue until all of the numbers have been multiplied. The following examples illustrate the procedure.

| EXAMPLE 13 | Multiply: 5 × 2 × 3 |

SOLUTION
METHOD 1

$$5 \times 2 \times 3 = 10 \times 3 = 30$$

METHOD 2

$$5 \times 2 \times 3 = 5 \times 6 = 30$$

METHOD 3

$$5 \times 2 \times 3 = 15 \times 2 = 30 \quad ■$$

No matter in what order the numbers are multiplied, the result is 30.

| EXAMPLE 14 | Multiply: 7 × 5 × 8 × 4 |

SOLUTION
METHOD 1

$$7 \times 5 \times 8 \times 4 = 40 \times 28 = 1120$$

METHOD 2

$$7 \times 5 \times 8 \times 4 = 56 \times 20 = 1120$$

Try These Problems

Multiply.
21. $4 \times 5 \times 8$
22. $3 \times 3 \times 5 \times 2$
23. $7 \times 6 \times 8 \times 4$
24. $26 \times 5 \times 13$
25. $11 \times 17 \times 5 \times 9$
26. $23 \times 41 \times 3 \times 7$

METHOD 3

$$7 \times 5 \times 8 \times 4 = 35 \times 8 \times 4$$
$$= 280 \times 4$$
$$= 1120 \ \blacksquare$$

No matter in what order the numbers are multiplied, the result is 1120.

 Try Problems 21 through 26.

Answers to Try These Problems

1. 468   2. 812   3. 10,350   4. 40,936   5. 637,614   6. 2162
7. 130,235   8. 2,035,728   9. 41,754,636   10. 20,356,488
11. 42,000   12. 293,400   13. 784,000   14. 3,102,500,000
15. 11,700,000   16. 318,600,000   17. 662,460   18. 28,606,656
19. 4,937,589,888   20. 355,352,003,050   21. 160   22. 90
23. 1344   24. 1690   25. 8415   26. 19,803

EXERCISES 2.1

Multiply.

1. 73×6

2. 84×9

3. 132×7

4. 208×4

5. 900×6

6. 5026×3

7. 7763×5

8. 8184×8

9. 86×32

10. 80×46

11. 341×25

12. 237×74

13. 704×286

14. 800×314

15. 7236×52

16. 5056×304

17. 3046×92 **18.** 75×3379 **19.** 2114×3756 **20.** $824 \times 93{,}406$

Multiply. Use a shortcut.

21. 400×3 **22.** 7000×20 **23.** $90{,}000 \times 800$ **24.** 600×320
25. $8 \times 24{,}000$ **26.** $31{,}200 \times 8000$
27. $2500 \times 68{,}000$ **28.** $126{,}000 \times 18{,}000$

29. 215×108

30. 392×205

31. 3146×4001

32. 5104×6007

33. $2030 \times 91{,}732$ **34.** $50{,}070 \times 2906$
35. $39{,}000 \times 5004$ **36.** $20{,}004 \times 13{,}682$

Multiply.

37. $5 \times 4 \times 3$ **38.** $2 \times 3 \times 3$ **39.** $9 \times 8 \times 6$
40. $7 \times 2 \times 2 \times 5$ **41.** $9 \times 6 \times 3 \times 4$ **42.** $14 \times 6 \times 36 \times 8$
43. $25 \times 30 \times 19$ **44.** $7 \times 16 \times 200 \times 38$

Solve.

45. One window costs $158. What is the cost of 18 windows?

46. A bicyclist goes 17 miles in one hour. How far can she go in 6 hours?

47. Anita's weekly salary is $570. Charles makes 7 times that much. Find Charles' weekly salary.

48. An old machine prints 682 pages in an hour. A new machine prints 15 times that much. How many pages can the new machine print in an hour?

2.2   DIVISION

OBJECTIVES
- Understand how division relates to multiplication.
- Perform long division by using a one, two or three-digit divisor.
- Perform long division when there are zeros in the quotient.
- Solve an application using division of whole numbers.

1   The Meaning of Division

Grandma Hendren has $20 that she wants to distribute equally among her 4 grandchildren. How much money does each child receive? To solve this problem, we divide $20 by 4. The symbols $\overline{)}$ and $\div$ are used to indicate division.

$$4\overline{)20}^{\,5} \quad \text{or} \quad 20 \div 4 = 5$$

Each child receives $5.

Division is the reverse of multiplication. For example,

$$4\overline{)20}^{\,5} \quad \text{because} \quad 4 \times 5 = 20$$

and

$$20 \div 4 = 5 \quad \text{because} \quad 4 \times 5 = 20$$

It does matter in what order you write down a division problem. For example,

$$20 \div 4 = 5$$

but

$$4 \div 20 = \frac{4}{20} = \frac{1}{5} \text{ or } 0.2$$

The number $\frac{1}{5}$ (in fraction form) or 0.2 (in decimal form) is a number less than 1. Fractions are introduced in Chapter 3 and decimals are introduced in Chapter 6.

The division statement $4\overline{)20}^{\,5}$ can be read "4 divided into 20 equals 5" or "20 divided by 4 is 5." Either of these statements can also be used to read the statement $20 \div 4 = 5$. Notice that when we use the symbol

÷ to indicate division, the numbers are written in the reverse order than when using the symbol $\big)\overline{}$. That is,

$$20 \div 4 \quad \text{means} \quad 4\overline{)20}$$

The 4 is written   The 4 is written
second here.   first here.

Each number in a division statement has a special name.

$$\overset{6 \text{ —— quotient}}{8\overline{)48}} \qquad 48 \div 8 = 6 \text{ —— quotient}$$

divisor   dividend   dividend   divisor

In the above example, the **divisor** multiplied by the **quotient** is exactly equal to the **dividend.** When this happens, we say *the division comes out evenly*.

Now we look at a situation where the division does not come out evenly. How many groups of 5 are in 14?

There are 2 groups of 5 with 4 left over. This concept is symbolized using a division statement with **remainder.**

$$\overset{2 \text{ ——quotient}}{5\overline{)14}}$$
$$\underline{10}$$
$$4 \text{ —— remainder}$$

The answer is written 2 R4.

Observe that a division problem with remainder is related to multiplication and addition.

$$\overset{2}{5\overline{)14}} \qquad \overset{2}{\underset{\underline{\times\ 5}}{}}$$ Quotient times divisor.
$$\underline{10} \qquad 10$$
$$4 \qquad \underline{+\ \ 4}$$ —— Add the remainder
$$\qquad\qquad 14$$ —— You get back the dividend.

Use this relationship to check your work when doing division problems.

EXAMPLE 1   Divide: 51 ÷ 6

SOLUTION
$$\overset{?}{6\overline{)51}}$$ How many groups of 6 are in 51?

$$\begin{array}{ccccc} 6 & 6 & 6 & 6 & 6 \\ \underline{\times\ 5} & \underline{\times\ 6} & \underline{\times\ 7} & \underline{\times\ 8} & \underline{\times\ 9} \\ 30 & 36 & 42 & 48 & 54 \end{array}$$

There are 8 groups of 6 in 51.

$$\overset{8}{6\overline{)51}}$$
$$\underline{48} \text{ —— } 6 \times 8 = 48$$
$$3 \text{ —— Subtract to get the remainder.}$$

Try These Problems

Divide.

1. 63 ÷ 7

2. 42 ÷ 6

3. 36 ÷ 6

4. 51 ÷ 8

5. 89 ÷ 9

6. 37 ÷ 5

CHECK

$$
\begin{array}{r}
8 \\
\times\ 6 \\
\hline
48 \\
+\ 3 \\
\hline
51
\end{array}
$$

The answer is 8 R3. ■

Sometimes you will choose the wrong quotient. The following example gives some pointers on how to recognize this so that you can back up and start over.

EXAMPLE 2   Divide: 44 ÷ 9

SOLUTION

UNSUCCESSFUL ATTEMPT

The remainder must be smaller than the divisor. 17 is larger than 9, so the 3 must be changed.

UNSUCCESSFUL ATTEMPT

This number must be smaller than or equal to 44 so we can subtract. 45 is larger than 44, so the 5 must be changed.

SUCCESSFUL ATTEMPT

$$
\begin{array}{r}
4 \\
9\overline{)44} \\
36 \\
\hline
8
\end{array}
$$

36 —— 36 is smaller than 44.

8 —— 8 is smaller than 9.

The answer is 4 R8. ■

 Try Problems 1 through 6.

2 Long Division by A One-Digit Divisor

Now we look at a process called **long division.** This procedure enables you to find the quotient and remainder when the numbers are larger. First we look at examples that involve a one-digit divisor.

EXAMPLE 3   Divide: 159 ÷ 5

SOLUTION

$$
\begin{array}{r}
3\ 1 \\
5\overline{)1\ 5\ 9} \\
1\ 5\ \downarrow \\
\hline
0\ 9 \\
5 \\
\hline
4
\end{array}
$$

Step 1: 5 divided into 1?
It goes 0 times, but we do not have to write the 0 at the beginning.
Step 2: 5 divided into 15? 3
Step 3: 3 times 5? 15
Step 4: 15 subtract 15? 0
Step 5: Bring down 9.
Step 6: 5 divided into 9? 1
Step 7: 1 times 5? 5
Step 8: 9 subtract 5? 4

There are 31 groups of 5 in 159 with 4 left over.
CHECK

$$
\begin{array}{r}
31 \\
\times\ \ 5 \\
\hline
155 \\
+\ \ \ 4 \\
\hline
159
\end{array}
$$

The answer is 31 R4. ■

EXAMPLE 4   Divide: $7\overline{)4256}$

SOLUTION

$$
\begin{array}{r}
6\ 0\ 8 \\
7\overline{)4\ 2\ 5\ 6} \\
4\ 2 \\
\hline
0\ 5 \\
0 \\
\hline
5\ 6 \\
5\ 6 \\
\hline
0
\end{array}
$$

Step 1: 7 divided into 42? 6
Step 2: 6 times 7? 42
Step 3: 42 subtract 42? 0
Step 4: Bring down 5.
Step 5: 7 divided into 5? It goes
0 times. You must write a 0
in the quotient!
Step 6: 0 times 7? 0
Step 7: 5 subtract 0? 5
Step 8: Bring down 6.
Step 9: 7 divided into 56? 8
Step 10: 8 times 7? 56
Step 11: 56 subtract 56? 0

CHECK

$$
\begin{array}{r}
608 \\
\times\ \ \ \ 7 \\
\hline
4256
\end{array}
$$

The answer is 608. ■

EXAMPLE 5   Divide: $20{,}334 \div 4$

SOLUTION

$$
\begin{array}{r}
5\ 0\ 8\ 3 \\
4\overline{)2\ 0\ 3\ 3\ 4} \\
2\ 0 \\
\hline
0\ 3 \\
0 \\
\hline
3\ 3 \\
3\ 2 \\
\hline
1\ 4 \\
1\ 2 \\
\hline
2
\end{array}
$$

Bring down only one digit at a time.
Each time you bring down a digit, you
must divide.

After you subtract, be sure to bring
down the next digit before you divide.

CHECK

$$
\begin{array}{r}
5083 \\
\times\ \ \ \ \ 4 \\
\hline
20332 \\
+\ \ \ \ \ 2 \\
\hline
20334
\end{array}
$$

The answer is 5083 R2. ■

Try These Problems

Divide.

7. 7)616

8. 3)970

9. 8)63,216

10. 1863 ÷ 6

11. 21,049 ÷ 7

12. 75,000 ÷ 5

EXAMPLE 6   Divide: 8)2885

SOLUTION

```
        3 6 0
    8)2 8 8 5
      2 4
      4 8
      4 8
        0 5   — After bringing down the last
          0      digit, you must divide, multiply,
          5      a subtract one more time.
```

CHECK

```
        360
     ×    8
       2880
     +    5
       2885
```

The answer is 360 R5.   ■

Now we summarize the procedure for long division.

Long Division Process

The long division process involves repeating these four steps.

1. Divide.
2. Multiply.
3. Subtract. (This result must be less than the divisor.)
4. Bring down the next digit.

Bring down only one digit at a time. Each time you bring down a digit, you must divide. After you bring down the last digit, you must divide, multiply, and subtract one more time.

 Try Problems 7 through 12.

3   Division by Two- and Three-Digit Numbers

To divide by a two-digit number or a three-digit number, use the same long division process that is used to divide by a one-digit number. The following examples illustrate the procedure.

EXAMPLE 7   Divide: 25)824

SOLUTION

Step 1: 25 into 8? It goes 0 times. We do not have to write a 0 at the beginning.

$$
\begin{array}{r}
3\ 2 \\
25\overline{)8\ 2\ 4} \\
7\ 5 \\
\overline{7\ 4} \\
5\ 0 \\
\overline{2\ 4}
\end{array}
$$

Step 2: 25 into 82?

$$
\begin{array}{ccc}
25 & 25 & 25 \\
\times\ 2 & \times\ 3 & \times\ 4 \\
\overline{50} & \overline{75} & \overline{100}
\end{array}
$$

3 R7
Write 3 above the last digit in 82.

Step 3: Bring down 4.
Step 4: 25 into 74?
2 R24

CHECK

$$
\begin{array}{r}
32 \\
\times\ 25 \\
\overline{160} \\
64 \\
\overline{800} \\
+\ \ 24 \\
\overline{824}
\end{array}
$$

The answer is 32 R24. ◼

The following example illustrates how to recognize when you have chosen the wrong digit in the quotient.

EXAMPLE 8   Divide: $4552 \div 92$

SOLUTION

UNSUCCESSFUL ATTEMPT

$$
\begin{array}{r}
3 \leftarrow ? \\
92\overline{)4552} \\
276 \\
\overline{179}
\end{array}
$$

—— The subtraction result must be smaller than the divisor, 92. 179 is larger than 92, so the 3 must be changed.

UNSUCCESSFUL ATTEMPT

$$
\begin{array}{r}
5 \leftarrow ? \\
92\overline{)4552} \\
460
\end{array}
$$

—— This number must be smaller than 455 so we can subtract. 460 is larger than 455, so the 5 must be changed.

SUCCESSFUL ATTEMPT

$$
\begin{array}{r}
4\ 9 \\
92\overline{)4\ 5\ 5\ 2} \\
3\ 6\ 8 \\
\overline{8\ 7\ 2} \\
8\ 2\ 8 \\
\overline{4\ 4}
\end{array}
$$

The subtraction results, 87 and 44, are each smaller than 92.

The answer is 49 R44. ◼

EXAMPLE 9   Divide: $615\overline{)44{,}286}$

SOLUTION

$$
\begin{array}{r}
72 \\
615\overline{)44286} \\
4305\downarrow \\
\overline{1236} \\
1230 \\
\overline{6}
\end{array}
$$

Step 1: 615 into 442? It goes 0 times. We do not have to write a 0 digit at the beginning.

Step 2: 615 into 4428?

$$
\begin{array}{ccc}
615 & 615 & 615 \\
\times\ 6 & \times\ 7 & \times\ 8 \\
\hline
3690 & 4305 & 4920
\end{array}
$$

7 R123

Write 7 above the last digit in 4428.

Step 3: Bring down 6.

Step 4: 615 into 1236?

$$
\begin{array}{cc}
615 & 615 \\
\times\ 1 & \times\ 2 \\
\hline
615 & 1230
\end{array}
$$

2 R6

CHECK

$$
\begin{array}{r}
615 \\
\times\ \ 72 \\
\hline
1230 \\
4305 \\
\hline
44280 \\
+\ \ \ \ \ 6 \\
\hline
44286
\end{array}
$$

The answer is 72 R6. ■

EXAMPLE 10   Divide: $26\overline{)9626}$

SOLUTION

$$
\begin{array}{r}
370 \\
26\overline{)9626} \\
78\downarrow \\
\overline{182} \\
182 \\
\overline{06} \\
0 \\
\overline{6}
\end{array}
$$

After you bring down the last digit, you must divide, multiply, and subtract one more time.

The answer is 370 R6. ■

Try These Problems

Divide.

13. 750 ÷ 60

14. 9706 ÷ 23

15. 16,281 ÷ 23

16. 40)256,120

17. 15)92,250

18. 36)151,225

19. 9450 ÷ 210

20. 706,854 ÷ 662

EXAMPLE 11   Divide: 930,512 ÷ 186

SOLUTION

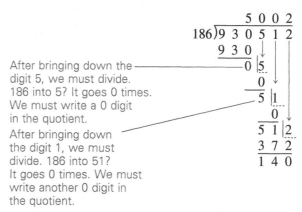

After bringing down the digit 5, we must divide. 186 into 5? It goes 0 times. We must write a 0 digit in the quotient.

After bringing down the digit 1, we must divide. 186 into 51? It goes 0 times. We must write another 0 digit in the quotient.

CHECK

$$
\begin{array}{r}
5002 \\
\times\ \ 186 \\
\hline
30012 \\
40016\ \ \\
5002\ \ \ \ \\
\hline
930372 \\
+\ \ \ \ \ 140 \\
\hline
930512
\end{array}
$$

The answer is 5002 R140. ■

 Try Problems 13 through 20.

4   Paying Special Attention to Zeros in the Quotient

Suppose you are one of the 6 persons who are to share equally an inheritance of $42,540. What is your share? To solve this problem we divide 42,540 by 6.

```
       7 0 9 0 ┐
  6)4 2 5 4 0  │  Your share
    4 2 ↓ ↓ ↓  └  is $7090.
      0 5      
      0        
      5 4      
      5 4      
        0 0    
          0    
          0    
```

The zero digits in the quotient are very important. You want to be careful not to leave them out, since $7090 is a lot more money than $709 or $79. Also be careful that you do not insert extra zeros. The other five persons would not appreciate your claiming a share of $70,090 when there is only $42,540 to begin with.

The following examples give guidelines to help you with division problems involving zeros in the quotient.

EXAMPLE 12 Divide: $45,032 \div 75$

SOLUTION

```
         6 0 0
  75)4 5 0 3 2
     4 5 0↓|
       0:3
         0↓
         3:2
           0
         3 2
```

Slow down! Don't try to take unnecessary shortcuts.

CHECK

```
        75
  ×    600
      45000
  +      32
      45032
```

The answer is 600 R32. ■

EXAMPLE 13 Divide: $840,480 \div 408$

SOLUTION

```
          2 0 6 0
  408)8 4 0 4 8 0
      8 1 6↓
      2 4:4
          0↓
      2 4 4:8
      2 4 4 8↓
            0:0
              0
              0
```

After the division gets started, there is a digit in the quotient to correspond with each of the remaining digits in the dividend.

```
             2 0 6 0
  408)8 4 0 4 8 0
```

The answer is 2060. ■

EXAMPLE 14 Divide: $252,352 \div 63$

SOLUTION

```
          4 0 0 5
  63)2 5 2 3 5 2
     2 5 2↓
       0:3
         0↓
         3:5
           0↓
         3 5:2
         3 1 5
           3 7
```

After you subtract, bring down *only one* digit, then divide. Place the digit in the quotient directly above the digit you brought down.

The answer is 4005 R37. ■

Try These Problems

Divide.

21. 5)35,010

22. 55)15,400

23. 28)560,858

24. 7,645,677 ÷ 152

25. 81,479,320 ÷ 783

 Try Problems 21 through 25.

Answers to Try These Problems

1. 9   2. 7   3. 6   4. 6 R3   5. 9 R8   6. 7 R2   7. 88
8. 323 R1   9. 7902   10. 310 R3   11. 3007   12. 15,000
13. 12 R30   14. 422   15. 707 R20   16. 6403   17. 6150
18. 4200 R25   19. 45   20. 1067 R500   21. 7002   22. 280
23. 20,030 R18   24. 50,300 R77   25. 104,060 R340

EXERCISES 2.2

Divide.

1. 8)75 **2.** 3)97 **3.** 8)526 **4.** 6)624

5. 5)4374 **6.** 7)5322 **7.** 7)7218 **8.** 4)29,296

9. 380 ÷ 40 **10.** 2280 ÷ 76 **11.** 53,020 ÷ 80 **12.** 4680 ÷ 42

13. 7645 ÷ 35 **14.** 16,482 ÷ 15 **15.** 204,555 ÷ 23 **16.** 5,328,200 ÷ 75

17. 800)26,000 **18.** 700)9368 **19.** 280)17,460 **20.** 170)137,360

21. 428)100,580 **22.** 564)4,386,278 **23.** 372)15,713,280 **24.** 685)3,122,230

25. 4804 ÷ 8 **26.** 35,058 ÷ 5 **27.** 456,600 ÷ 76 **28.** 141,363 ÷ 67

29. 1,401,120 ÷ 28 **30.** 56,630 ÷ 700 **31.** 3,424,876 ÷ 428

32. 3,964,590 ÷ 651

Solve.

33. Mr. Yen earned $1512 in a 6-week period. How much did he earn per week?

34. Folding tables are packed 5 to a box. How many boxes are needed to pack 510 tables?

35. A chandelier holds 16 bulbs. How many chandeliers can be outfitted with 650 bulbs? How many bulbs, if any, are left over?

36. A box of candy holds 24 pieces. How many boxes of candy can be filled with 12,125 pieces of candy? How many pieces, if any, are left over?

37. A machine cuts 800 washers from a sheet of metal in one hour. How long does it take the machine to cut out 32,000 washers?

38. Ms. Marcott ordered 7200 ounces of punch for a reception. She expects to have approximately 225 guests at the reception. How much punch does this allow for each guest?

DEVELOPING NUMBER SENSE #2

APPROXIMATING BY ROUNDING

In this feature we look at approximating multiplication and division by rounding. We will round each number so that the resulting multiplication or division is as easy as possible.

For example, suppose you want to approximate 38 × 714. First we round off each number so that the result has only one nonzero digit.

$38 \approx 40$
$714 \approx 700$

Multiplying 40 by 700, we obtain 28,000 for the approximation. The actual product is 27,132.

Next we look at approximating a division problem. Suppose you want an approximation for

Cont. page 46

7704 ÷ 36. First we round off each number so that the result has only one nonzero digit.

$$7704 \approx 8000$$
$$36 \approx 40$$

Next we divide 8000 by 40 to obtain the approximation.

$$
\begin{array}{r}
200 \\
40\overline{)8000} \\
\underline{80}
\end{array}
$$

The approximation is 200. The actual quotient is 214.

When approximating a division problem, do not expect to be able to divide the rounded numbers mentally. However, dividing the rounded numbers will be a lot easier than dividing the original numbers if you are approximating without the help of a calculator.

Number Sense Problems

Approximate each by rounding off each number so the result has only one nonzero digit.

1. 8×71
2. 12×58
3. 6×319
4. 63×782
5. 478×311
6. 7×3289
7. 76×2374
8. $197 \times 67{,}392$
9. $215 \div 5$
10. $644 \div 28$
11. $2958 \div 58$
12. $93{,}294 \div 438$

USING THE CALCULATOR #3

MULTIPLICATION AND DIVISION

Multiplying numbers on a calculator is similar to adding numbers on the calculator. Simply enter $\boxed{\times}$ instead of $\boxed{+}$. Here is an example.

To Compute	25×5
Enter	$25 \boxed{\times} 5 \boxed{=}$
Result	125

Here we show an example of multiplying several numbers.

To Compute	$8 \times 2 \times 5 \times 6$
Enter	$8 \boxed{\times} 2 \boxed{\times} 5 \boxed{\times} 6 \boxed{=}$
Result	480

If you enter another $\boxed{\times}$ instead of $\boxed{=}$, the result is also 480. Also, since multiplication can be done in any order, it does not matter in what order you enter the factors.

When computing a division problem, you must be careful that the numbers are entered in the correct order. Here is an example.

To Compute	$8 \div 2$ or $2\overline{)8}$
Enter	$8 \boxed{\div} 2 \boxed{=}$
Result	4

Observe that the numbers are entered in the order that they are written down when using the division symbol $\div$, but the numbers are entered in the reverse order than they are written down when using the division symbol $\overline{)}$. In either case, remember that the number being divided into is entered first and the divisor is entered second.

If you enter the numbers 8 and 2 in the reverse order, you would obtain the decimal 0.25, since 0.25 is the result of dividing 2 by 8. Decimals are discussed in Chapters 6 and 7.

Cont. page 47

Calculator Problems

Multiply or divide as indicated.

1. 8×9 **2.** 500×7800 **3.** $2 \times 13 \times 7 \times 29$

4. 769×876 **5.** $12 \div 6$ **6.** $32,616 \div 36$

7. $9\overline{)7983}$ **8.** $675\overline{)178,200}$ **9.** Divide 300 by 75.

10. Divide 82 into 498,560.

2.3	THE MISSING NUMBER IN A MULTIPLICATION STATEMENT, MULTIPLES, DIVISIBILITY RULES, AND PRIME FACTORING

OBJECTIVES

▎ Find the missing number in a multiplication statement.
▎ Determine whether a number is divisible by a given number.
▎ Determine whether a number is a multiple of a given number.
▎ Determine whether a number is divisible by 2, 3, 5, 10, 100, or 1000 by using divisibility rules.
▎ Write a number as the product of primes.

1 Finding the Missing Number in a Multiplication Statement

In a multiplication statement such as

$$4 \times 7 = 28 \quad \text{or} \quad 28 = 4 \times 7$$

the numbers 4 and 7 are called **multipliers** (or **factors**) and the answer 28 is called the **product.** We can ask three questions by omitting any one of the three numbers.

1. $4 \times 7 = \boxed{}$

missing number is 28

We are missing the answer to a multiplication problem, so we *multiply* to find the missing number.

2. $4 \times \boxed{} = 28$

$\boxed{}\!\!-\!\!-7$

$4\overline{)28}$

We are missing one of the multipliers, so we *divide* to find the missing number.

Divide the answer 28 by the known multiplier 4. The missing number is 7.

3. $\boxed{} \times 7 = 28$

$\boxed{}\!\!-\!\!-4$

$7\overline{)28}$

We are missing one of the multipliers, so we *divide* to find the missing number.

Divide the answer 28 by the known multiplier 7. The missing number is 4.

Try These Problems

Find the missing number.

1. $5 \times \boxed{} = 500$

2. $448 = \boxed{} \times 16$

3. $\boxed{} = 97 \times 3600$

4. $\boxed{} \times 27 = 21{,}654$

EXAMPLE 1 $\boxed{} \times 7 = 119$

SOLUTION We are missing a multiplier, so we divide to find the missing number.

$$\text{multipliers} \longrightarrow 7\overline{)119} \longleftarrow \begin{array}{l}\text{answer to the multiplication}\\ \text{problem}\end{array}$$

$$\begin{array}{r} 17 \\ 7\overline{)119} \\ 7 \\ \hline 49 \\ 49 \\ \hline \end{array}$$

The answer is 17. ■

EXAMPLE 2 $\boxed{} = 82 \times 794$

SOLUTION We are missing the answer to a multiplication problem, so we multiply to find the missing number.

$$\begin{array}{r} 794 \\ \times 82 \\ \hline 1588 \\ 6352 \\ \hline 65108 \end{array}$$

The answer is 65,108. ■

EXAMPLE 3 $750 = 25 \times \boxed{}$

SOLUTION We are missing a multiplier, so we divide to find the missing number.

$$\text{multipliers} \longrightarrow 25\overline{)750} \longleftarrow \begin{array}{l}\text{answer to the multiplication}\\ \text{problem}\end{array}$$

$$\begin{array}{r} 30 \\ 25\overline{)750} \\ 75 \\ \hline 00 \\ 0 \\ \hline \end{array}$$

The answer is 30. ■

 Try Problems 1 through 4.

2 Multiples and Divisibility Rules

If we multiply 6 by a whole number, we create a **multiple** of 6. Here are some multiples of 6.

$$\begin{array}{ccccc} 6 & 6 & 6 & 6 \\ \times\, 1 & \times\, 2 & \times\, 3 & \times\, 4 \\ \hline 6 & 12 & 18 & 24 \end{array}$$

$$\begin{array}{ccccc} 6 & 6 & 6 & 13 & 28 \\ \times\, 5 & \times\, 6 & \times\, 7 & \times\, 6 & \times\, 6 \\ \hline 30 & 36 & 42 & 78 & 168 \end{array}$$

A multiple of 6 such as 78 is special with relation to 6 because 6 divides evenly into 78. We say, 78 is **divisible by** 6.

$$
\begin{array}{r}
13 \\
6\overline{)78} \\
\underline{6} \\
18 \\
\underline{18}
\end{array}
$$

EXAMPLE 4   Which of these numbers are divisible by 7?

a. 27   **b.** 91   **c.** 406

SOLUTION

a.

$$
\begin{array}{r}
3 \\
7\overline{)27} \\
\underline{21} \\
6
\end{array}
$$

No, 27 is not divisible by 7 because the remainder is 6. The division does not come out evenly.

b.

$$
\begin{array}{r}
13 \\
7\overline{)91} \\
\underline{7} \\
21 \\
\underline{21}
\end{array}
$$

Yes, 91 is divisible by 7 because the remainder is 0. The division comes out evenly.

c.

$$
\begin{array}{r}
58 \\
7\overline{)406} \\
\underline{35} \\
56 \\
\underline{56}
\end{array}
$$

Yes, 406 is divisible by 7 because the remainder is 0. The division comes out evenly.   ■

EXAMPLE 5   Which of these numbers are multiples of 13?

a. 65   **b.** 377   **c.** 397

SOLUTION

a. 65 is a multiple of 13 if 65 is divisible by 13.

$$
\begin{array}{r}
5 \\
13\overline{)65} \\
\underline{65}
\end{array}
$$

Yes, 65 is a multiple of 13.

Try These Problems

5. Which of these numbers are divisible by 3?
 a. 42 **b.** 51 **c.** 117 **d.** 317

6. Which of these numbers are multiples of 11?
 a. 56 **b.** 88 **c.** 187 **d.** 462

Answer yes or no.

7. Indicate whether each number is divisible by 2.
 a. 2461 **b.** 688 **c.** 356
 d. 4003

b. 377 is a multiple of 13 if 377 is divisible by 13.

$$
\begin{array}{r}
29 \\
13\overline{)377} \\
26 \\
\hline
117 \\
117 \\
\hline
\end{array}
$$

Yes, 377 is a multiple of 13.

c. Does 13 divide evenly into 397?

$$
\begin{array}{r}
30 \\
13\overline{)397} \\
39 \\
\hline
7 \\
0 \\
\hline
7 \\
\end{array}
$$

No, 397 is not a multiple of 13. ■

 Try Problems 5 and 6.

The multiples of 2 are 2, 4, 6, 8, 10, 12, 14, 16, 18, . . . , and so on. These numbers are called **even numbers.** Each of them is divisible by 2. It is easy to recognize that a number is divisible by 2 because it always ends in 0, 2, 4, 6, or 8. For example, the number 1336 is divisible by 2 because the last digit is 6 and 6 is an even number.

$$
\begin{array}{r}
668 \\
2\overline{)1336} \\
12 \\
\hline
13 \\
12 \\
\hline
16 \\
16 \\
\hline
\end{array}
$$

Divisibility by 2

Any whole number ending in a 0, 2, 4, 6, or 8 is divisible by 2.

EXAMPLE 6 Which of these numbers is divisible by 2?

a. 572 **b.** 31,580 **c.** 3907 **d.** 90,144

SOLUTION

a. Yes, 572 is divisible by 2 because it ends in a 2.

b. Yes, the number 31,580 is divisible by 2 because it ends in a 0.

c. No, 3907 is not divisible by 2 because it does not end in a 0, 2, 4, 6 or 8. It ends in a 7.

d. Yes, the number 90,144 is divisible by 2 because it ends in a 4. ■

 Try Problem 7.

Try These Problems

Answer yes or no.

8. Indicate whether each number is divisible by 3.

    a. 72 **b.** 813 **c.** 244 **d.** 8052

The multiples of 3 are 3, 6, 9, 12, 15, 18, 21, 24, 27, 30, 33, 36, 39, 42, . . . and so on. Note that in each case the sum of the digits is a multiple of 3. In general, all multiples of 3 have digits whose sum is a multiple of 3. We can use this to help us recognize numbers that are divisible by 3. For example, the number 117 is divisible by 3 because the sum of the digits, $1 + 1 + 7 = 9$, is divisible by 3. Here we check by dividing.

$$
\begin{array}{r}
39 \\
3\overline{)117} \\
9 \\
\overline{27} \\
27 \\
\end{array}
$$

Divisibility by 3

Any whole number is divisible by 3 if the sum of its digits is divisible by 3.

EXAMPLE 7   Which of these numbers are divisible by 3?

a. 51   **b.** 852   **c.** 923

    SOLUTION

a. Yes, 51 is divisible by 3 because $5 + 1 = 6$ and 6 is divisible by 3.

b. Yes, 852 is divisible by 3 because $8 + 5 + 2 = 15$ and 15 is divisible by 3.

c. No, 923 is not divisible by 3 because $9 + 2 + 3 = 14$ and 14 is not divisible by 3. ■

 Try Problem 8.

The multiples of 5 are 5, 10, 15, 20, 25, 30, 35, 40, 45, 50, 55, 60, . . . and so on. Note that each multiple of 5 ends in a 0 or a 5. We can use this to help us recognize when a number is divisible by 5. For example, 3015 is divisible by 5 because it ends in 5. Here we check by dividing.

$$
\begin{array}{r}
603 \\
5\overline{)3015} \\
30 \\
\overline{1} \\
0 \\
\overline{15} \\
15 \\
\end{array}
$$

Divisibility by 5

Any whole number ending in 0 or 5 is divisible by 5.

Try These Problems

Answer yes or no.

9. Indicate whether each number is divisible by 5.
   a. 85 **b.** 3008 **c.** 1045
   d. 70,000

10. Indicate whether each number is divisible by 10.
    a. 955 **b.** 1048 **c.** 830
    d. 8000

EXAMPLE 8   Which of these numbers are divisible by 5?

a. 70   **b.** 135   **c.** 8004

SOLUTION

a. Yes, 70 is divisible by 5 because it ends in a 0.

b. Yes, 135 is divisible by 5 because it ends in 5.

c. No, 8004 is not divisible by 5 because it does not end in a 0 or a 5. It ends in 4. ■

 Try Problem 9.

The multiples of 10 are 10, 20, 30, 40, 50, 60, 70, 80, 90, 100, 110, 120, 130, and so on. Note that multiples of 10 end in a 0. This can help us to recognize when a number is divisible by 10. For example, the number 4130 is divisible by 10 because it ends in a 0. Here we check by dividing.

$$
\begin{array}{r}
413 \\
10\overline{)4130} \\
\underline{40} \\
13 \\
\underline{10} \\
30 \\
\underline{30}
\end{array}
$$

Divisibility by 10

Any whole number ending in a 0 is divisible by 10.

EXAMPLE 9   Which of these numbers are divisible by 10?

a. 156   **b.** 300   **c.** 14,780

SOLUTION

a. No, 156 is not divisible by 10 because it does not end in 0. It ends in 6.

b. Yes, 300 is divisible by 10 because it ends in 0.

c. Yes, 14,780 is divisible by 10 because it ends in 0. ■

 Try Problem 10.

The multiples of 100 are 100, 200, 300, 400, 500, 600, 700, 800, 900, 1000, 1100, 1200, and so on. Observe that each multiple of 100 ends in two 0s. This gives us a way to recognize when a number is divisible by 100. For example, the number 11,600 is divisible by 100 because it ends in two 0s. Here we check by dividing.

$$
\begin{array}{r}
116 \\
100\overline{)11600} \\
\underline{100} \\
160 \\
\underline{100} \\
600 \\
\underline{600}
\end{array}
$$

Try These Problems

Answer yes or no.
11. Indicate whether each number is divisible by 100.
    a. 6002 **b.** 9300 **c.** 88,000
    d. 7050

Divisibility by 100

Any whole number ending in two 0s is divisible by 100.

> **EXAMPLE 10**   Which of these numbers are divisible by 100?

a. 1030 **b.** 3500 **c.** 80,000
    SOLUTION

a. No, 1030 is not divisible by 100 because it does not end in two 0s. It ends in only one 0.

b. Yes, 3500 is divisible by 100 because it ends in two 0s.

c. Yes, the number 80,000 is divisible by 100 because it ends in two 0s.

 Try Problem 11.

We have seen that the multiples of 10 end in one 0, and the multiples of 100 end in two 0s. This pattern continues; that is, the multiples of 1000 end in three 0s, the multiples of 10,000 end in four 0s, and so on.

Now we give a summary of the divisibility rules that you should be familiar with.

Divisibility Rules

1. Any whole number ending in 0, 2, 4, 6, or 8 is divisible by 2.
2. Any whole number is divisible by 3 if the sum of its digits is divisible by 3.
3. Any whole number ending in 0 or 5 is divisible by 5.
4. Any whole number
    is divisible by 10 if it ends in one 0,
    is divisible by 100 if it ends in two 0s,
    is divisible by 1000 if it ends in three 0s,
and so on.

3   Prime Numbers and Prime Factoring

A whole number, other than 1, that is divisible only by itself and 1 is called a **prime number.** For example, the number 13 is a prime number because it is divisible only by 13 and 1. Here is a list of the first ten prime numbers.

First Ten Primes									
2	3	5	7	11	13	17	19	23	29

The number 15 is *not* prime because 15 is divisible by 5 and 3. We can write 15 as the product of primes.

$$15 = 3 \times 5$$

Try These Problems

Write each number as the product of primes.

12. 21

13. 49

14. 10

15. 39

16. 115

In fact, any whole number that is not prime, except for 0 and 1, can be written as the product of primes. The process of writing numbers as the product of primes is called **prime factoring.** The following examples illustrate how to write numbers as the product of primes.

EXAMPLE 11   Write each number as the product of primes.

a. 49   **b.** 35   **c.** 22   **d.** 51

SOLUTION

a. $49 = 7 \times 7$

b. $35 = 5 \times 7$

c. Because 22 ends in 2, it is divisible by 2. Divide 22 by 2 to find the other factor.

$$\begin{array}{r} 11 \\ 2\overline{)22} \\ \underline{22} \end{array}$$

$22 = 2 \times 11$

d. 51 is divisible by 3 because $5 + 1 = 6$ and 6 is divisible by 3. Divide 51 by 3 to find the other factor.

$$\begin{array}{r} 17 \\ 3\overline{)51} \\ \underline{3} \\ 21 \\ \underline{21} \end{array}$$

$51 = 3 \times 17.$ ■

In Example 11, observe that numbers like 49 and 35 are easy to factor because you recognize them as multiplication facts. To factor other numbers, such as 22 and 51, you need to use the divisibility rules and division.

 Try Problems 12 through 16.

Sometimes it takes several steps to get a number written as the product of primes. The following examples illustrate the technique.

EXAMPLE 12   Write each number as the product of primes.

a. 40   **b.** 54   **c.** 2900   **d.** 2205

SOLUTION

a. Because 40 ends in a 0, 40 is divisible by 10.

$$40 = 4 \times 10$$
$$= 2 \times 2 \times 2 \times 5$$

You can get started with any two numbers that multiply together to give 40. Do not stop until all the factors are prime numbers.

▲ **Try These Problems**

Write each number as the product of primes.

17. 60

18. 56

19. 8100

20. 147

21. 425

b. Because 54 ends in 4, 54 is divisible by 2. Divide 54 by 2 to find the other factor.

$$2\overline{)54}$$
$$\underline{27}$$

$$\begin{array}{r} 27 \\ 2\overline{)54} \\ \underline{4} \\ 14 \\ \underline{14} \end{array}$$

$54 = 2 \times 27$ Begin with 2×27.

$ = 2 \times 3 \times 9$ Write 27 as 3×9.

$ = 2 \times 3 \times 3 \times 3$ Finally, $9 = 3 \times 3$.

c. Because 2900 ends in two 0s, it is divisible by 100.

$2900 = 29 \times 100$ Now 29 is prime, but 100 is not prime.

$ = 29 \times 10 \times 10$

$ = 29 \times 2 \times 5 \times 2 \times 5$ Now all the factors are prime.

d. Because 2205 ends in 5, it is divisible by 5. Divide 2205 by 5 to find the other factor.

$$\begin{array}{r} 441 \\ 5\overline{)2205} \\ \underline{20} \\ 20 \\ \underline{20} \\ 5 \\ \underline{5} \end{array}$$

$2205 = 5 \times 441$

$ = 5 \times 3 \times 147$ Since the sum of the digits in 441 is $4 + 4 + 1 = 9$ and 9 is divisible by 3, 441 is divisible by 3.

$$\begin{array}{r} 147 \\ 3\overline{)441} \\ \underline{3} \\ 14 \\ \underline{12} \\ 21 \\ \underline{21} \end{array} \rightarrow 441 = 3 \times 147$$

$ = 5 \times 3 \times 3 \times 49$ 147 is also divisible by 3 because $1 + 4 + 7 = 12$ and 12 is divisible by 3.

$$\begin{array}{r} 49 \\ 3\overline{)147} \\ \underline{12} \\ 27 \\ \underline{27} \end{array} \rightarrow 147 = 3 \times 49$$

$ = 5 \times 3 \times 3 \times 7 \times 7$ Finally, $49 = 7 \times 7$. ■

▲ **Try Problems 17 through 21.**

▲ **Answers to Try These Problems**

1. 100   2. 28   3. 349,200   4. 802
5. a. yes b. yes c. yes d. no
6. a. no b. yes c. yes d. yes
7. a. no b. yes c. yes d. no
8. a. yes b. yes c. no d. yes
9. a. yes b. no c. yes d. yes
10. a. no b. no c. yes d. yes
11. a. no b. yes c. yes d. no
12. 3×7 13. 7×7 14. 2×5 15. 3×13
16. 5×23 17. $2 \times 3 \times 2 \times 5$ 18. $2 \times 2 \times 2 \times 7$
19. $3 \times 3 \times 3 \times 3 \times 2 \times 5 \times 2 \times 5$ 20. $3 \times 7 \times 7$
21. $5 \times 5 \times 17$

EXERCISES 2.3

Find the missing number.

1. $9 \times \boxed{} = 108$ **2.** $8 \times \boxed{} = 136$

3. $572 = 52 \times \boxed{}$ **4.** $\boxed{} = 19 \times 83$

5. $135,000 = \boxed{} \times 450$ **6.** $28,800 = \boxed{} \times 360$

7. $506 \times 8000 = \boxed{}$ **8.** $\boxed{} \times 85 = 25,840$

In Exercises 9 through 12, answer yes or no.

9. Indicate whether each number is divisible by 7.
  a. 42   **b.** 105   **c.** 177   **d.** 322

10. Indicate whether each number is divisible by 11.
  a. 99   **b.** 255   **c.** 666   **d.** 495

11. Indicate whether each number is a multiple of 25.
  a. 75   **b.** 85   **c.** 400   **d.** 3025

12. Indicate whether each number is a multiple of 36.
  a. 110   **b.** 540   **c.** 28,800   **d.** 6120

In Exercises 13 through 22, answer yes or no. Use the divisibility rules for 2, 3, 5, 10, 100, and 1000.

13. Indicate whether each number is divisible by 2.
  a. 30   **b.** 112   **c.** 248   **d.** 35,714

14. Indicate whether each number is divisible by 2.
  a. 81   **b.** 94   **c.** 356   **d.** 1078

15. Indicate whether each number is divisible by 3.
  a. 81   **b.** 93   **c.** 255   **d.** 533

16. Indicate whether each number is divisible by 3.
  a. 73   **b.** 84   **c.** 306   **d.** 1509

17. Indicate whether each number is divisible by 5.
  a. 35   **b.** 570   **c.** 3545   **d.** 5052

18. Indicate whether each number is divisible by 5.
  a. 60   **b.** 315   **c.** 7003   **d.** 9000

19. Indicate whether each number is divisible by 10.
  a. 203   **b.** 200   **c.** 2130   **d.** 7000

20. Indicate whether each number is divisible by 10.
   a. 40   **b.** 3200   **c.** 1905   **d.** 12,460

21. Indicate whether each number is divisible by 100.
   a. 120   **b.** 800   **c.** 13,000   **d.** 40,500

22. Indicate whether each number is divisible by 1000.
   a. 1300   **b.** 2060   **c.** 15,000   **d.** 40,500,000

Write each number as the product of primes.

23. 9	**24.** 14	**25.** 12	**26.** 20	**27.** 45
28. 48	**29.** 55	**30.** 77	**31.** 26	**32.** 85
33. 57	**34.** 92	**35.** 114	**36.** 88	**37.** 245
38. 600	**39.** 150	**40.** 360	**41.** 1200	**42.** 4500
43. 297	**44.** 117	**45.** 87	**46.** 69	**47.** 504
48. 1125				

USING THE CALCULATOR #4

INTRODUCTION TO THE MEMORY KEYS

Most basic and scientific calculators have a memory. This means the calculator has the capability of storing a number that can be recalled later. A number put in the memory remains there while other calculations are done. The memory is usually unaffected by turning off the calculator.

The memory keys on a basic calculator may include all or some of the following.

[M+] Entering a number, then this key, will add the number to the existing memory.

[MR] This is the memory recall key. Enter this key to find out what number is currently in the memory and to ready it for use.

[M−] Entering a number, then this key, will subtract the number from the existing memory. This key can be used to clear the memory on a basic calculator.

[MC] This key clears the memory. Not all basic calculators have this key.

Most scientific calculators have the [M+], [MR], and [M−] keys, but usually do not have the [MC] key. In addition to these memory keys, scientific calculators have a memory-in key that can be used to replace the existing number in the memory with another number.

[Min] or [x→M] This is the memory-in key. Entering a number, then this key, will replace the existing memory with the number. This key can be used to clear the memory on a scientific calculator by putting the number 0 in the memory.

Observe that entering the [C] or [AC] key does not clear the memory. Also, turning off the calculator does not clear the memory.

Calculator Problems

Try each of the following activities on your calculator.

1. Find out what number is currently in the memory of your calculator. If it is not 0, then clear the memory, that is, put a 0 in the memory.

Cont. page 58

2. Put the number 8 in the memory of your calculator. Check to make sure that 8 is really in the memory.

3. Clear the number 8 from the memory, that is, put a 0 in the memory.

4. Put the number 15 in the memory. Now enter 5, then enter the key $\boxed{\text{M+}}$. What number is in the memory now?

Solve the following problems by putting the number 7500 in the memory, then recalling it as needed.

5. $7500 - 657$ **6.** 7500×18 **7.** $7500 \div 12$ **8.** $172{,}500 \div 7500$

Write each of these numbers as the product of primes. Store the number in memory before beginning to check for prime divisors.

9. 221   **10.** 161   **11.** 2109   **12.** 4199

2.4	LANGUAGE

OBJECTIVES   ▌ Translate English statements involving multiplication and division to math symbols.

▌ Translate a division statement written with math symbols to English.

▌ Solve problems by using translations.

1 Translating

The math symbols that we use often have many translations to the English language. Knowing these translations can help in solving application problems. Here we review the many English translations for the symbol = .

English	*Math Symbol*
equals	=
is equal to	
is the same as	
is the result of	
is	
was	
represents	
gives	
makes	
yields	
will be	
are	
were	

Try These Problems

Write a division statement using the symbol $\overline{)}$ *.*

1. 7 divided into 63 equals 9.

2. 100 divided by 25 is 4.

Write a division statement using the symbol $\div$ *.*

3. 5 divided into 35 equals 7.

4. 60 divided by 12 is 5.

Fill in the blank with the appropriate word, by *or* into.

5. $4\overline{)24}^{\,6}$ is read "24 divided
_____ 4 equals 6."

6. $7\overline{)70}^{\,10}$ is read "7 divided
_____ 70 equals 10."

7. 84 ÷ 12 = 7 is read "84 divided _____ 12 is 7."

8. 500 ÷ 25 = 20 is read "25 divided _____ 500 is 20."

The multiplication statement $3 \times 7 = 21$ is written with math symbols. Some of the ways to read this in English are given in the following chart.

English	Math Symbols
Three times seven equals twenty-one.	$3 \times 7 = 21$
The *product* of 3 and 7 is 21.	$21 = 3 \times 7$
21 is 3 times as large as 7.	
3 multiplied by 7 gives 21.	
21 represents 3 multiplied times 7.	

Because 3×7 equals 7×3, the order that you say the factors 3 and 7 makes no difference. However, when reading the division statement $21 \div 3 = 7$, take care to say 21 and 3 in the correct order, because $21 \div 3$ does not equal $3 \div 21$.

$$21 \div 3 = 7, \quad \text{but} \quad 3 \div 21 = \frac{3}{21} = \frac{1}{7}$$

The numbers 7 and $\frac{1}{7}$ are *not* equal. The number $\frac{1}{7}$ is a fraction less than 1. We study fractions in Chapter 3. The following chart gives correct ways to read $21 \div 3 = 7$ or $3\overline{)21}^{\,7}$.

Math Symbols	English
$21 \div 3 = 7$	21 *divided by* 3 is 7.
$3\overline{)21}^{\,7}$	3 *divided into* 21 is 7.

 Try Problems 1 through 8.

Special language is used when the number 2 is a factor in a multiplication statement or 2 is the divisor in a division statement. The following chart illustrates this.

Math Symbols	English
$2 \times 8 = 16$	Two times 8 equals 16.
	Twice 8 equals 16.
	Eight *doubled* is 16.
	16 represents the product of 2 and 8.
$16 \div 2 = 8$	16 divided by 2 equals 8.
	2 divided into 16 equals 8.
$2\overline{)16}^{\,8}$	*Half* of 16 is 8.

2 Solving Problems by Using Translating

The following examples illustrate how we can use translating to solve problems.

Try These Problems

Solve.

9. The product of a number and 17 is 1360. Find the number.

10. What number is twice 268?

11. Find 1659 divided by 7.

12. 408 represents twice what number?

13. Divide 30 into 2070.

14. What number is 450 multiplied by itself?

EXAMPLE 1   Twice a number yields 134. Find the number.

SOLUTION   The sentence, "twice a number yields 134," translates to a multiplication statement.

$$\underbrace{\text{Twice}}_{2 \times} \underbrace{\text{a number}}_{\boxed{}} \underbrace{\text{yields}}_{=} \underbrace{134.}_{134}$$

Because a multiplier is missing, we divide to find the missing multiplier.

$$\begin{array}{r} 67 \\ 2\overline{)134} \\ \underline{12} \\ 14 \\ \underline{14} \end{array}$$

The number is 67. ∎

EXAMPLE 2   Find the product of 50 and 75,000.

SOLUTION   To find the product of two numbers means to multiply.

$$\underbrace{\text{Product of 50 and 75,000}}_{50 \times 75,000} = \boxed{}$$
$$\phantom{\underbrace{\text{Product of 50 and 75,000}}} = \boxed{}$$

$$\begin{array}{r} 75000 \\ \times\ 50 \\ \hline 3750000 \end{array}$$ Multiply 75 by 5 and attach 4 zeros.

The answer is 3,750,000. ∎

EXAMPLE 3   6 divided into 30,048 is what number?

SOLUTION   The question translates to a division statement.

$$\underbrace{\text{6 divided into 30,048}}_{30,048 \div 6} \underbrace{\text{is}}_{=} \underbrace{\text{what number?}}_{\boxed{}}$$

We divide 30,048 by 6 to find the missing number.

$$\begin{array}{r} 5008 \\ 6\overline{)30048} \\ \underline{30} \\ 0 \\ \underline{0} \\ 4 \\ \underline{0} \\ 48 \\ \underline{48} \end{array}$$

The number is 5008. ∎

 Try Problems 9 through 14.

▲ Answers to Try These Problems

1. $7\overline{)63}^{\,9}$ 2. $25\overline{)100}^{\,4}$ 3. $35 \div 5 = 7$ 4. $60 \div 12 = 5$
5. by   6. into   7. by   8. into   9. 80   10. 536   11. 237
12. 204   13. 69   14. 202,500

EXERCISES 2.4

Write a division statement using the symbol $\overline{)}$.

1. 9 divided into 54 equals 6.

2. 4 divided into 52 is 13.

3. 30 divided into 1350 is 45.

4. 15 divided by 3 equals 5.

5. 75 divided by 15 is 5.

6. 400 divided by 40 is 10.

Write a division statement using the symbol ÷.

7. 8 divided into 16 equals 2.

8. 7 divided into 119 equals 17.

9. 50 divided into 600 equals 12.

10. 84 divided by 28 is 3.

11. 621 divided by 3 is 207.

12. 598 divided by 26 equals 23.

Fill in the blank with the appropriate word, by *or* into.

13. $4\overline{)28}^{\,7}$ is read "4 divided _____ 28 equals 7."

14. $4\overline{)28}^{\,7}$ is read "28 divided _____ 4 equals 7."

15. $9\overline{)117}^{\,13}$ is read "117 divided _____ 9 is 13."

16. $9\overline{)117}^{\,13}$ is read "9 divided _____ 117 is 13."

17. $12 \div 4 = 3$ is read "12 divided _____ 4 equals 3."

18. $12 \div 4 = 3$ is read "4 divided _____ 12 equals 3."

19. $144 \div 9 = 16$ is read "9 divided _____ 144 is 16."

20. $144 \div 9 = 16$ is read "144 divided _____ 9 is 16."

Translate each to a multiplication or division statement using math symbols.

21. The product of 17 and 38 is 646.

22. Twenty-five divided into 350 yields 14.

23. Thirty-three represents 3 times 11.

24. 5 equals 490 divided by 98.

25. Twice 230 gives 460.

26. 900 represents twice 450.

Translate to an equation with missing number. Then solve.

27. Eighty-two multiplied by what number is 984?

28. 214 represents twice what number?

29. Divide 810 by 5.

30. Divide 20 into 1040.

31. What number is the product of 1300 and 60?

32. The product of 135 and what number is 8775?

33. What number equals twice 9500?

34. Find half of 712.

Introduction to Unit Analysis

Some numbers have **units** attached to them. Here are three examples.

40 dollars or $40   **12 feet**   **140 days**
\unit   \unit   \unit   \unit

We want to be able to distinguish one type of quantity from another. To do this, pay close attention to the *units*. Here we give some examples.

Rate	Area	Distance	Time	Weight	Volume
24 games per carton	38 square miles	6 feet	3 hours	30 pounds	4 gallons
$250 per month	40 square meters	55 meters	54 minutes	18 ounces	7 cubic feet
2 feet an hour	5 square yards	12 inches	1 second	20 tons	300 liters

Quantities like 34 and 600 are numbers with no units attached.

▶ **Try These Problems**

Identify each of these quantities as a rate, area, distance, time, weight or volume.

1. 45¢ per person   2. 90 feet   3. 64 pounds   4. 60 miles per hour

5. 82 square miles   6. 52 weeks   7. 1 gallon per second   8. 130 minutes

9. 60 tons   10. 16 cubic feet   11. 6 quarts per week   12. 164 square inches

13. Choose all of the **distances** in this list of quantities.
   8 square yards   120 kilometers   500 miles $14 per foot

14. Choose all of the **areas** in this list of quantities.
   25 cents per yard   240 square meters   120 square miles   14 pounds per foot

15. Choose all of the **rates** in this list of quantities.
   8 inches per minute   20 meters   150 square miles $200 per week

Now let's look at operating with quantities that involve units.
Here are some introductory examples.

Introduction

9 tons + 8 tons = 17 tons
13 hours − 7 hours = 6 hours

When adding or subtracting quantities with like units, the result's unit is the same as the other units.

3 x 8 cups = 24 cups
$120 ÷ 4 = $30

When multiplying or dividing a quantity with units by a number with no units, the result's unit is the same as the quantity's unit.

▶ **Try These Problems**

Calculate the following. Give both the number and unit.

16. 9 ounces + 7 ounces   17. 28 days + 8 days   18. 7 x 8 inches

19. 4 cents x 6   20. 30 weeks − 12 weeks   21. 25 cartons − 8 cartons

22. 28 hours ÷ 7   23. 300 years ÷ 15   24. 25 miles + 6 miles

25. 90 pints − 14 pints   26. 205 years x 9   27. 6000 gallons − 415 gallons

28. 204 tons ÷ 6   29. 350 persons ÷ 5   30. $78 x 9

31. 11,000 hours − 48 hours   32. 3000 years − 250 years   33. 250 miles ÷ 5

34. 900 square feet ÷ 18   35. 760 centiliters x 800   36. 5100 tons ÷ 17

Distance & Area

Distance is a measure of how far, how long, how tall, or how wide something or someone is. Examples of distance units are inches, feet, yards, miles, meters, centimeters, and kilometers.

Area is a measure of the extent of a region on a flat surface. We are interested in area to get answers to such questions as,

> How much glass do we need to replace the window?
> How much carpet do we need to cover the floor?
> How much grass sod do we need to cover the yard?

Examples of area units are square feet, square inches, square yards, square miles, square meters, square centimeters, square kilometers and acres. Note that the word "square" placed before a distance unit will create an area unit.

Next we focus on operating with quantities that involve distance and area units.

Distance & Area

1 foot + 9 feet = 10 feet

80 square feet + 50 square feet = 130 square feet

64 miles − 30 miles = 34 miles

When adding or subtracting quantities with like units, the result's unit is the same as the other units.

8 miles x 9 miles = 72 square miles

6 inches x 8 inches = 48 square inches

Distance times distance equals area.

▶ Try These Problems

Calculate the following. Give both the number and unit.

37. 9 feet + 7 feet	38. 8 miles + 5 miles	39. 17 inches − 8 inches
40. 40 yards − 16 yards	41. 8 square miles − 6 square miles	42. 25 miles x 8 miles
43. 20 meters x 7 meters	44. 65 meters + 15 meters	45. 25 miles − 6 miles
46. 7 yards x 80 yards	47. 600 square feet − 1 square foot	48. 6 kilometers x 9 kilometers

Rate Phrases and Rates

The phrase, "*$5 for every 1 lunch* ," is a **rate phrase**. We are comparing the quantity $5 to the quantity 1 lunch. We are saying that for every $5 you can buy 1 lunch or for every 1 lunch you pay $5. When this rate phrase is put in a single quantity form, it is called a **rate.**

Rate Phrase	Rate or Rate Quantity
$5 every 1 lunch	5 dollars per lunch

In rate phrase form we see two quantities. Each quantity has its own unit.

In rate form we see only one quantity consisting of a number and the rate unit.

Here are more examples of rate phrases and a corresponding rate or rate quantity.

Rate Phrase	Rate or Rate Quantity
50 miles every 1 hour	50 miles an hour
3 gallons in 1 minute	3 gallons each minute
1 yard costs $12	$12 per yard
1 person every 8 ounces	8 ounces per person

▶ **Try These Problems**

Write a rate phrase that corresponds to the given rate.

49. $4 per video
50. 12 games per carton
51. 70 miles an hour
52. 130 inches per year
53. 40 students per class
54. 12 gallons per minute

Write a rate that corresponds to the given rate phrase. Be sure to include the number and rate unit.

55. 60¢ for 1 hour
56. 4 bottles in 1 carton
57. 6 feet every 1 second
58. 1 case weighs 20 pounds
59. 5 ounces for every 1 person
60. 1 bottle contains 2 liters

Rate as a Multiplier

If you walk 5 miles per hour and yo do this for 3 hours, you go 15 miles. You go 5 miles the first hour, 5 more miles the second hour, and 5 more miles the third hour. Let's look at how we use multiplication to do this problem, and how the calculation looks with the units attached.

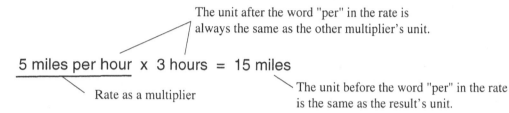

The unit after the word "per" in the rate is always the same as the other multiplier's unit.

5 miles per hour x 3 hours = 15 miles

Rate as a multiplier

The unit before the word "per" in the rate is the same as the result's unit.

The following chart gives more examples.

Rate as a Multiplier	
6 dollars per foot x 8 feet = 48 dollars $45 per hour x 8 hours = $360 60 miles per hour x 4 hours = 240 miles	**Here are three examples with a rate as a multiplier.**
50 pounds x 6 feet per pound = 300 feet 30 days x 2 inches per day = 60 inches	**Observe how the order of the multiplication can switch with the rate second instead of first.**
$56 = $7 per person x 8 persons 70 feet = 5 seconds x 14 feet per second	**Observe that the result of the multiplication can be written first instead of last.**

▶ **Try These Problems**

Calculate the following. Give both the number and unit.

61. 9 dollars per student x 7 students
62. $5 per movie x 6 movies
63. 6 bottles per carton x 30 cartons
64. 10 pints per hour x 4 hours
65. 8 cartons x 13 pounds per carton
66. 8 coats x 70 dollars per coat
67. 30 hours x $9 per hour
68. 80 square feet x $17 per square foot

Each of these unit equations has a rate as a multiplier. Give the missing unit that makes the equation true. Be careful. The missing unit may be a rate unit.

69. inches per minute x minutes = _____
70. $ per carton x cartons = _____
71. square miles x persons per square mile = _____
72. hours x feet per hour = _____
73. ounces per second x _____ = ounces
74. _____ x minutes = envelopes
75. _____ = seconds x feet per second
76. calories = meals x _____

Whole Numbers on the Number Line – Level 1

We like to view numbers on a number line where the numbers are arranged from smallest to largest with uniform distances between adjacent tick marks. A tick mark designates the position of a number. Here we view a number line containing some whole numbers.

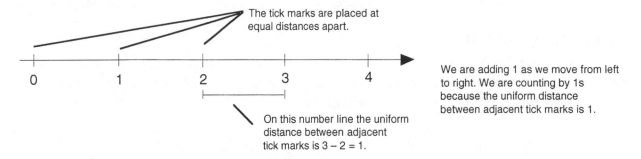

The tick marks are placed at equal distances apart.

We are adding 1 as we move from left to right. We are counting by 1s because the uniform distance between adjacent tick marks is 1.

On this number line the uniform distance between adjacent tick marks is 3 – 2 = 1.

When you view a number line you are seeing numbers associated with **positions** on the number line as well as **distances** between the numbers. Note that you can obtain the distance between two any two numbers by subtracting the smaller number from the larger number. Another way to obtain the distance is to count the number of spaces between the numbers and multiply the number of spaces by the width of each space. Here we look at another example.

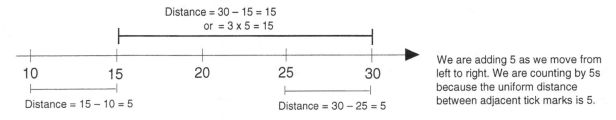

Distance = 30 – 15 = 15
or = 3 x 5 = 15

Distance = 15 – 10 = 5

Distance = 30 – 25 = 5

We are adding 5 as we move from left to right. We are counting by 5s because the uniform distance between adjacent tick marks is 5.

EXAMPLE Label the distance between a pair of adjacent tick marks and then label all the tick marks with the appropriate numbers.

Solution First we subtract 0 from 10 to see that the uniform distance between adjacent tick marks is 10. 10 – 0 = 10. Then we add 10 to each number to obtain the next number: 10 + 10 = 20, 20 + 10 = 30 and 30 + 10 = 40. We show the labeled number line below. Note how we label the distance between adjacent tick marks.

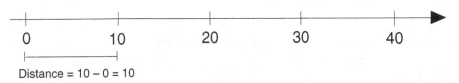

Distance = 10 – 0 = 10

EXERCISES 2-A

For each number line, label the distance between a pair of adjacent tick marks and label all tick marks with the appropriate number.

1.

0   1

2.

0   10

3.

5   25

4.

10   15

5.

75   100

6.

12   16

7.

6   8

8.

14   21

9.

12   15

10.

40   80

Whole Numbers on the Number Line – Level 2

Now you want to learn how to label the remaining tick marks on a number line when you are not given two numbers adjacent to one another. First, you will need to find the uniform distance between adjacent tick marks. This can be done as long as you are given at least two numbers. Follow the steps below to see how this is done for the given number line.

Step 1 – Subtract the two given numbers to find out how far apart they are.

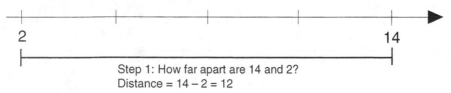

Step 1: How far apart are 14 and 2?
Distance = 14 − 2 = 12

Step 2 – Count the number of spaces between the two numbers.

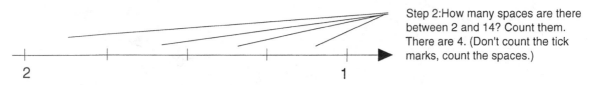

Step 2: How many spaces are there between 2 and 14? Count them. There are 4. (Don't count the tick marks, count the spaces.)

Therefore, a distance of 12 units is being separated into 4 equal parts.

Step 3 – Divide the total distance found in step 1 by the number of equal spaces in step 2.

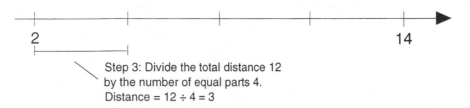

Step 3: Divide the total distance 12 by the number of equal parts 4.
Distance = 12 ÷ 4 = 3

This number 3 is the uniform distance between adjacent tick marks.

Step 4 – Add the uniform distance to each number on the left to obtain the next number on the right.

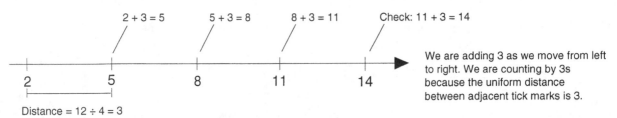

2 + 3 = 5   5 + 3 = 8   8 + 3 = 11   Check: 11 + 3 = 14

We are adding 3 as we move from left to right. We are counting by 3s because the uniform distance between adjacent tick marks is 3.

Distance = 12 ÷ 4 = 3

EXERCISES 2-B

For each number line, label the distance between two given numbers, label the distance between a pair of adjacent tick marks and label all tick marks with the appropriate number.

1.

0   2

2.

6   8

3.

8   14

4.

       12   21

5.

       8   20

6.

0   28

7.

       6   18

8.

              50   100

9.

0   15

10.

       40   80

OBJECTIVES ▌ Solve an application involving equal parts in a total quantity.
▌ Solve an application involving equivalent rates.
▌ Solve an application that involves a rate as a multiplier.
▌ Solve an application that involves the area of a rectangle.
▌ Solve an application by using translations.
▌ Find the average (or mean) of a collection of numbers.
▌ Solve an application involving more than one step.

1   Equal Parts in a Total Quantity

Suppose you have a string that is 20 inches long. If the string is cut into 4 equal pieces, then each piece is 5 inches long. Here we picture the situation.

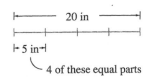

4 of these equal parts

Observe that the numbers are related as follows.

$$\text{Number of equal parts} \times \text{Size of each part} = \text{Total quantity}$$

$$4 \quad\times\quad 5 \quad=\quad 20$$

In general, if a situation involves a number of equal parts making up a total quantity, the following formula always applies.

$$\textbf{Number of equal parts} \times \textbf{Size of each part} = \textbf{Total quantity}$$

A problem can be presented by giving any two of the three quantities and asking for the third quantity. The following examples illustrate this.

EXAMPLE 1 A nurse is to give 15 doses of medicine. Each dose contains 2 milliliters of medicine. How much medicine is needed?

SOLUTION This problem is about 15 doses that are 2 milliliters each, making up a total quantity. We use the formula,

$$\begin{matrix} \text{Number of} \\ \text{equal parts} \end{matrix} \times \begin{matrix} \text{Size of} \\ \text{each part} \\ (m\ell) \end{matrix} = \begin{matrix} \text{Total} \\ \text{quantity} \\ (m\ell) \end{matrix}$$

$$15 \quad \times \quad 2 \quad = \quad \boxed{}$$

The 15 doses is the number of equal parts and 2 milliliters is the size of each part. We are missing the total quantity, so we multiply.

$$15 \times 2 = 30$$

30 milliliters of medicine is needed. ■

EXAMPLE 2 Juan earns $13,000 over a 52-week period. If he earns the same amount each week, what is his weekly salary?

SOLUTION This problem is about 52 equal payments amounting to a total of $13,000. We use the formula,

$$\begin{matrix} \text{Number of} \\ \text{equal parts} \end{matrix} \times \begin{matrix} \text{Size of} \\ \text{each part} \\ (\$) \end{matrix} = \begin{matrix} \text{Total} \\ \text{quantity} \\ (\$) \end{matrix}$$

$$52 \quad \times \quad \boxed{} \quad = \quad 13{,}000$$

The number of equal parts is 52 and $13,000 is the total quantity. We are missing one of the multipliers, so we divide to find the missing number.

$$\begin{array}{r} 250 \\ 52{\overline{\smash{)}13000}} \\ \underline{104} \\ 260 \\ \underline{260} \\ 00 \\ \underline{0} \end{array}$$

The weekly salary is $250. ■

EXAMPLE 3 Stuart sells corn from his garden. He puts 1290 ears of corn in packages with 6 ears in each package. How many packages are made?

SOLUTION This problem is about a total quantity, 1290 ears of corn, being split apart with each part containing 6 ears of corn. We use the formula,

$$\begin{matrix} \text{Number of} \\ \text{equal parts} \end{matrix} \times \begin{matrix} \text{Size of} \\ \text{each part} \\ (\text{ears of corn}) \end{matrix} = \begin{matrix} \text{Total} \\ \text{quantity} \\ (\text{ears of corn}) \end{matrix}$$

$$\boxed{} \quad \times \quad 6 \quad = \quad 1290$$

Try These Problems

Solve.

1. A wire that is 92 inches long is cut into 4 equal pieces. How long is each piece?

2. A truck carries a load of 15 cases. The total load weighs 1230 pounds. What is the weight of each case?

3. One hundred fifty pieces of track that are each 36 feet long are to be laid one right after the other. How far will the track extend?

4. Cindy is transporting 3300 pounds of sand in truckloads of 220 pounds each. How many truckloads will it take to transport all the sand?

5. How many 25-minute speeches fit in a 320-minute time period? How much time, if any, is left over?

6. Kenny and his 5 sisters share equally an inheritance. If each person's share is $2060, what was the total amount of the inheritance?

We are missing a multiplier, the number of equal parts, so we divide.

$$
\begin{array}{r}
215 \\
6\overline{)1290} \\
\underline{12} \\
09 \\
\underline{6} \\
30 \\
\underline{30}
\end{array}
$$

215 packages can be made. ■

EXAMPLE 4   Stephanie has 1260 centimeters of string. She wants to cut it into pieces that are each 16 centimeters long. How many pieces can she cut? How much string, if any, is left over?

SOLUTION   We divide the total quantity, 1260 centimeters, by the size of each piece, 16 centimeters, to find out how many pieces she can cut. The remainder will be the amount of string left over.

$$
\begin{array}{r}
78 \quad\text{—— number of pieces}\\
16\overline{)1260} \\
\underline{112} \\
140 \\
\underline{128} \\
12 \quad\text{—— amount of string left over}
\end{array}
$$

She can cut 78 pieces with 12 centimeters of string left over. ■

 Try Problems 1 through 6.

2   Equivalent Rates

If you drive 50 miles in 1 hour, then the phrase *50 miles in 1 hour,* or *50 miles per hour,* is specifying the **speed** that you are traveling. Speed is one of the many examples of **rate.** A rate is a comparison of two quantities. Here we list some more phrases that indicate rates.

> *Phrases that Indicate Rates*
>
> You type 65 words per minute.
> Chuck paid $30 for each shirt.
> Cynthia jogs 5 miles in 30 minutes.
> Four pounds of coffee cost $20.
> On a map, 1 inch represents 25 miles.

If you drive 50 miles in 1 hour, then you can go 150 miles in 3 hours.

Multiply by 3.   50 miles in 1 hour ⟶ 150 miles in 3 hours   Multiply by 3.

Observe that multiplying both quantities in a rate by the same nonzero number produces an equivalent rate. We can use this to solve problems involving equivalent rates, as shown in the following examples.

EXAMPLE 5   You type 65 words per minute. How many words can you type in 20 minutes?

SOLUTION   The phrase *65 words per minute,* means 65 words every 1 minute.

Multiply   ⌒ 65 words every 1 minute ⌒   Multiply
by 20.   ↳ ? words every 20 minutes ↲   by 20.

If we multiply each quantity in the given rate by 20, we can see how many words can be typed in 20 minutes.

$$65 \times 20 = 1300$$

You can type 1300 words in 20 minutes. ■

EXAMPLE 6   The faucet leaks 1 ounce every 5 hours. How long will it take the faucet to leak 12 ounces?

SOLUTION

Multiply   ⌒ 1 ounce every 5 hours ⌒   Multiply
by 12.   ↳ 12 ounces in ? hours ↲   by 12.

If we multiply each quantity in the given rate by 12, we obtain the number of hours it takes the faucet to leak 12 ounces.

$$5 \times 12 = 60$$

It takes 60 hours for the faucet to leak 12 ounces. ■

In the previous examples, you saw that multiplying both quantities of a rate by the same nonzero number produces an equivalent rate. Now we illustrate that you can also divide both quantities of a rate by the same nonzero number and obtain an equivalent rate.

If 4 pounds of coffee cost $20, then 1 pound of this coffee costs $5.

Divide   ⌒ 4 pounds cost $20 ⌒   Divide
by 4.   ↳ 1 pound costs $5 ↲   by 4.

Observe that dividing both quantities in a rate by the same nonzero number produces an equivalent rate. We can use this to solve problems involving equivalent rates, as shown in the following examples.

EXAMPLE 7   It takes Cynthia 40 minutes to jog 5 miles. How long will it take her to jog 1 mile?

SOLUTION

Divide   ⌒ 40 minutes for 5 miles ⌒   Divide
by 5.   ↳ ? minutes for 1 mile ↲   by 5.

Dividing each quantity in the given rate by 5 gives the number of minutes it takes Cynthia to jog 1 mile.

$$40 \div 5 = 8$$

It takes 8 minutes for Cynthia to jog 1 mile. ■

Try These Problems

7. One ounce of gold is worth $545. What is 3 ounces of gold worth?

8. Steve drives 45 miles in 1 hour. How far can he go in 6 hours?

9. Ellen runs 6 miles in 48 minutes. How long does it take her to run 1 mile?

10. Henry paid $30 for 15 pounds of mushrooms. What is the cost of 1 pound?

11. A cable 17 feet long weighs 68 pounds. What is the weight per foot?

12. On a map, 1 inch represents 200 miles. If two cities are 5 inches apart on the map, what is the actual distance between them?

EXAMPLE 8   Bruce types 2400 words in 30 minutes. How many words can he type in 1 minute?

SOLUTION

Divide by 30.   ⌐ 2400 words in 30 minutes ⌐   Divide by 30.
                    ? words in 1 minute

Dividing both quantities in the given rate by 30 gives the number of words Bruce can type in 1 minute.

$$
\begin{array}{r}
80 \\
30\overline{)2400} \\
\underline{240} \\
00 \\
\underline{0}
\end{array}
$$

Bruce types 80 words per minute. ■

 Try Problems 7 through 12.

3   More About Rates

Because a rate is a comparison of two quantities, the units associated with a rate are like.

    miles per hour
    cost per foot
    ounces for each person
    dollars per pound

If you buy 8 pounds of coffee at $6 per pound, then you pay a total of $48 for this coffee.

$$\text{Dollars per pound} \times \frac{\text{Number of}}{\text{pounds}} = \text{Total dollars}$$

$$6 \qquad \times \qquad 8 \qquad = \qquad 48$$

Note that the rate, $6 per pound, is multiplied by the number of pounds to get the total cost. Notice how the units agree.

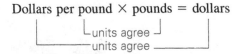

Dollars per pound × pounds = dollars

If you pay close attention to the units associated with a rate, it can help you to solve problems involving rates. Here we show more examples.

$$\text{miles per hour} \quad \times \frac{\text{number of}}{\text{hours}} = \frac{\text{total}}{\text{miles}}$$

$$\text{cost per foot} \quad \times \frac{\text{number of}}{\text{feet}} = \frac{\text{total}}{\text{cost}}$$

$$\text{ounces for each person} \times \frac{\text{number of}}{\text{persons}} = \frac{\text{total}}{\text{ounces}}$$

▲ Try These Problems

13. A rope weighs 28 ounces per foot. How much does 350 feet of this rope weigh?

14. Steve types 65 words per minute. How long will it take him to type 2470 words?

15. The owner of a small business purchases 12 computers that cost $6000 each. What is the total cost?

16. A tank is leaking 8 gallons per minute. How long will it take the tank to leak 472 gallons?

EXAMPLE 9   The Miller family bought 5 opera tickets at $38 each. What was the total cost?

SOLUTION $38 is a rate because it is the cost per ticket.

$$\underset{(\$)}{\text{cost per ticket}} \times \underset{\text{tickets}}{\text{number of}} = \underset{(\$)}{\text{total cost}}$$

$$38 \quad\quad \times \quad 5 \quad = \quad \boxed{}$$

We multiply to find the total cost.

$$38 \times 5 = 190$$

The total cost was $190.   ■

EXAMPLE 10   A car travels 816 miles averaging 48 miles per hour. How long did the trip take?

SOLUTION   The quantity 48 miles per hour is a rate.

$$\text{miles per hour} \times \underset{\text{hours}}{\text{number of}} = \underset{\text{miles}}{\text{total}}$$

$$48 \quad\quad \times \quad \boxed{} \quad = 816$$

A multiplier is missing, so we divide.

$$
\begin{array}{r}
17 \\
48\overline{)816} \\
\underline{48} \\
336 \\
\underline{336} \\
\end{array}
$$

The trip took 17 hours.   ■

 Try Problems 13 through 16.

---

4   Area of a Rectangle

Area is a measure of the extent of a region. A square that measures 1 unit on each side is said to have an area of 1 square unit.

1 unit ▢ 1 unit   Area = 1 square unit

A rectangle that is 3 units wide and 5 units long contains 15 of the 1-square-unit squares. Therefore, the area is 15 square units.

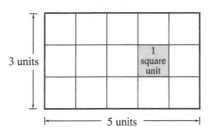

Area = 15 square units

Try These Problems

17. Find the area of this rectangle.

6 cm

23 cm

18. A window is 9 feet wide and 5 feet high. How many square feet of glass are needed for this window?

19. The floor of a room is in the shape of a rectangle with area 360 square feet. If the width is 15 feet, find the length.

20. Anthony bought 910 square inches of glass in the shape of a rectangle. If the glass is 26 inches wide, how long is it?

Observe that the area of this rectangle can be obtained by multiplying the length by the width.

$$Area = length \times width$$
$$= 5 \times 3$$
$$= 15 \text{ square units}$$

In general, the area of any rectangle can be computed by multiplying the length by the width.

Area of a Rectangle

The area of a rectangle is the length times the width.

Area = length × width

EXAMPLE 11   Find the area of a rectangle whose width is 18 feet and length is 25 feet.

SOLUTION

$$\begin{array}{ccc} Area & = length & \times width \\ (sq\ ft) & (ft) & (ft) \\ \boxed{} & = 25 & \times 18 \end{array}$$

Multiply 25 by 18 to find the area.

$$\begin{array}{r} 25 \\ \times\ 18 \\ \hline 200 \\ 25\ \ \\ \hline 450 \end{array}$$

The area is 450 square feet. ■

EXAMPLE 12   The area of a piece of fabric is 3900 square inches. If the fabric is 52 inches wide, how long is it?

SOLUTION   We assume the piece of fabric is in the shape of a rectangle.

$$\begin{array}{ccc} Area & = length & \times width \\ (sq\ in) & (in) & (in) \\ 3900 & = \boxed{} & \times 52 \end{array}$$

The area 3900 square inches is given, and the width 52 inches is given. We are missing the length, one of the multipliers, so we divide.

$$\begin{array}{r} 75 \\ 52\overline{)3900} \\ 364\ \ \\ \hline 260 \\ 260 \\ \hline \end{array}$$

The fabric is 75 inches long. ■

 Try Problems 17 through 20.

Try These Problems

21. There are seven times as many men as women attending the convention. Forty-nine women are at the convention. How many men are there?

22. Ralph bought a condominium for $47,000. The value has doubled in five years. What is the condominium worth after the five years?

23. The cost of a car is 4 times what it was ten years ago. If the car now costs $21,000, what did it cost ten years ago?

24. The length of a rectangle is 9 times as long as the width. If the length is 963 centimeters, what is the width?

5 Problems Involving Translations

In Section 2.4 we saw how translating English phrases to math symbols can be used to solve problems. Now we look at examples involving real-life situations.

EXAMPLE 13 It takes Barbara 3 times as long to paint her deck as it does a professional painter. It took a professional painter 5 hours to do the job. How long would it take Barbara to paint the deck?

SOLUTION The first sentence, "It takes Barbara 3 times as long to paint her deck as it does a professional painter," can be translated to a multiplication statement. The sentence is saying,

Barbara's time (hr)	is	3	times as long as	the professional's time (hr)
☐	=	3	×	5

We are missing Barbara's time which is the answer to the multiplication statement, so we multiply.

$$3 \times 5 = 15$$

It takes Barbara 15 hours to paint the deck. ■

EXAMPLE 14 With a lot of practice, Phil now types 76 words per minute, which is twice his speed a month ago. How fast did he type a month ago?

SOLUTION The sentence, "Phil now types 76 words per minute, which is twice his speed a month ago," translates to a multiplication statement.

Phil's speed now (wpm)	is	twice	his speed a month ago (wpm)
76	=	2 ×	☐

We are missing one of the multipliers, so we divide.

$$\begin{array}{r} 38 \\ 2\overline{)76} \\ \underline{6} \\ 16 \\ \underline{16} \\ \end{array}$$

Phil's typing speed a month ago was 38 words per minute. ■

 Try Problems 21 through 24.

6 Averaging

Fred took three exams. His scores were 75, 88, and 77. He has a total of 240 points.

$$\begin{array}{r} 75 \\ 88 \\ + 77 \\ \hline 240 \end{array}$$

Try These Problems

25. Find the average of 121 and 233.

26. In preparing for her vacation, Teresita bought six dresses at the following prices:

$23 $19 $32 $26 $15 $41

What was the average price of these dresses?

What same score could Fred have made on each of the three exams and still have a total of 240?

$$\begin{array}{r} 80 \\ 3\overline{)240} \end{array} \qquad \left.\begin{array}{r} 80 \\ 80 \\ +\ 80 \\ \hline 240 \end{array}\right\} \begin{array}{l}\text{three scores of} \\ \text{80 give the} \\ \text{same total}\end{array}$$

The score 80 is called the **average** (or **mean**) of the scores 75, 88, and 77. The average of a set of data is a measure of the middle or center of the data. The average of a collection of numbers can be found by adding the numbers, then dividing by how many numbers there are.

To Find the Average of a Collection of Numbers

1. Add all of the numbers in the collection.
2. Divide the sum by how many numbers are in the collection.

EXAMPLE 15   Find the average of 17, 133, 82, and 36.

SOLUTION   First, add the four numbers.

$$17 + 133 + 82 + 36 = 268$$

Second, divide the sum 268 by 4.

$$\begin{array}{r} 67 \\ 4\overline{)268} \\ \underline{24} \\ 28 \\ \underline{28} \end{array}$$

The average of the four numbers is 67. ■

EXAMPLE 16   A salesperson earned the following commissions in the last five weeks:

$168 $194 $216 $186 $136

What is the average weekly commission?

SOLUTION   First, add the five commissions. Second, divide the total 900 by 5.

$$\begin{array}{r} 168 \\ 194 \\ 216 \\ 186 \\ +\ 136 \\ \hline 900 \end{array}\ \text{— total} \qquad \begin{array}{r} 180 \\ 5\overline{)900} \\ \underline{5} \\ 40 \\ \underline{40} \\ 0 \\ \underline{0} \end{array}\ \text{— average}$$

The average weekly commission is $180. ■

Try Problems 25 and 26.

7 Applications Involving More Than One Step

Now we look at examples of applications that require more than one step to solve.

EXAMPLE 17 You plan to put weather stripping around a rectangular window that is 4 feet by 5 feet. If the stripping costs $2 per foot, what is the total cost?

SOLUTION Since the weather stripping costs $2 per foot, the total cost can be found as follows.

Cost per foot $\times$ number of feet = total cost

$$2 \quad \times \quad \boxed{} \quad = \quad \boxed{}$$

Before finding the total cost, we need the number of feet around the rectangular window; that is, we need the *perimeter* of the window.

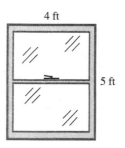

4 ft

5 ft

$$\text{Perimeter} = 5 + 5 + 4 + 4$$
$$= 10 + 8$$
$$= 18 \text{ ft}$$
$$\text{Total Cost} = \text{cost per foot} \times \text{number of feet}$$
$$= 2 \times 18$$
$$= \$36 \quad \blacksquare$$

EXAMPLE 18 If carpeting costs $19 per square yard, what is the total cost of carpeting this floor?

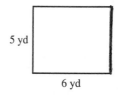

5 yd

6 yd

SOLUTION Since the carpeting costs $19 per square yard, the total cost can be found as follows.

$$\begin{array}{ccc} \text{Cost per} \\ \text{square yard} \end{array} \times \begin{array}{c} \text{number of} \\ \text{square yards} \end{array} = \text{total cost}$$

$$19 \quad \times \quad \boxed{} \quad = \quad \boxed{}$$

Try These Problems

27. A rectangular window is 3 times as wide as it is high. If the height is 6 feet and glass costs $5 per square foot, what is the cost of enough glass for this window?

28. A farmer wishes to fence in a region as shown. If fencing costs $25 per foot, what is the total cost of fencing this region?

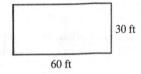

30 ft

60 ft

29. You purchase 8 shirts at $15 each, 5 pairs of socks at $3 each, and 6 pairs of slacks at $34 each. After paying for these items, what will you have left out of $500?

Before finding the total cost, we need the number of square yards that cover the floor space; that is, we need the *area* of the floor. To find the area of the floor, multiply the length by the width.

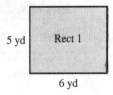

5 yd   Rect 1

6 yd

Area of Rect 1

$= 5 \times 6$

$= 30$ sq yd

$$\text{Total Cost} = \frac{\text{cost per}}{\text{square yard}} \times \frac{\text{number of}}{\text{square yards}}$$

$$= \quad 19 \quad \times \quad 30$$

$$= \$570 \ \blacksquare$$

 Try Problems 27 and 28.

EXAMPLE 19   A tank contained its total capacity of 2000 liters of water, and then began to leak at a rate of 3 liters per hour. How much water was in the tank after 9 hours?

SOLUTION   First we need to find the amount of water that the tank has lost.

$$\frac{\text{Amount}}{\text{lost}} = \frac{\text{amount lost}}{\text{per hour}} \times \frac{\text{number}}{\text{of hours}}$$

$$= \quad 3 \quad \times \quad 9$$

$$= 27 \text{ liters}$$

To find the amount of water remaining in the tank, subtract 27 from 2000.

Amount remaining $= 2000 - 27 = 1973$ liters   ■

 Try Problem 29.

Try These Problems

30. Mr. Harrison, the owner of a small flower market, purchased 3612 flowers. After arranging them in bunches of 18, he took home the left-over flowers and split them equally among four of his neighbors. How many flowers did each neighbor receive?

31. Harriet's annual salary has increased from $37,020 to $50,100 over a 12-year period. On the average, how much did her salary increase each year?

EXAMPLE 20   A machine fills and caps 300 bottles of soda each hour. After 18 hours how many 6-packs of soda have been filled and capped?

SOLUTION   First we find the total number of bottles filled and capped in 18 hours.

$$\begin{aligned} \text{Total number} &= \text{bottles} \times \text{number} \\ \text{of bottles} &\quad\text{each hour}\quad\text{of hours} \\ &= \quad 300 \quad \times \quad 18 \\ &= 5400 \end{aligned}$$

Now we find how many 6-packs can be made from 5400 bottles. Divide 5400 by 6.

$$6\overline{)5400}^{\,900}$$

After 18 hours, 900 6-packs have been filled and capped. ■

 Try Problem 30.

EXAMPLE 21   After having a massive heart attack, a patient's weight dropped from 270 pounds to 218 pounds in 4 weeks. On the average, how much weight did the patient lose per week?

SOLUTION   First find the total weight lost by subtracting 218 from 270.

$$\begin{aligned} \text{Weight lost} &= 270 - 218 \\ &= 52 \text{ pounds} \end{aligned}$$

The weight lost per week is a rate. We know that

$$\begin{aligned} \text{weight lost} &\times \text{number} = \text{total weight} \\ \text{per week} &\quad\text{of weeks}\quad\quad\text{lost} \\ \boxed{} &\times \quad 4 \quad = \quad 52 \end{aligned}$$

We are missing a multiplier, so we divide 52 by 4 to find the missing multiplier.

$$\begin{array}{r} 13 \\ 4\overline{)52} \\ \underline{4} \\ 12 \\ \underline{12} \end{array}$$

The patient lost 13 pounds per week. ■

 Try Problem 31.

Now we summarize the material in this section by giving guidelines that will help you to decide whether to multiply or divide.

Situations that Require Multiplication

$\times$

1. You are looking for a total quantity.

$$\text{Total} \atop \text{quantity} = {\text{size of} \atop \text{each part}} \times {\text{number of} \atop \text{equal parts}}$$

2. You are looking for a total, as in the following examples.

$$\text{Total miles} = \text{miles per hour} \times {\text{number} \atop \text{of hours}}$$

$$\text{Total cost} = \text{cost per pound} \times {\text{number} \atop \text{of pounds}}$$

3. You are looking for a number that is a certain amount times as large as another number.
4. You are looking for the area of a rectangle.

$$\text{Area} = \text{length} \times \text{width}$$

Situations that Require Division

$\div$

1. A total quantity is being separated into a number of equal parts.

$${\text{Size of} \atop \text{each part}} = \text{total quantity} \div {\text{number of} \atop \text{equal parts}}$$

$${\text{Number of} \atop \text{equal parts}} = \text{total quantity} \div {\text{size of} \atop \text{each part}}$$

2. You are looking for a missing multiplier in a multiplication statement.

$${\text{Missing} \atop \text{multiplier}} = {\text{answer to the} \atop \text{multiplication problem}} \div {\text{given} \atop \text{multiplier}}$$

3. You are looking for an average.

$${\text{Average of a} \atop \text{collection of numbers}} = {\text{sum of} \atop \text{the numbers}} \div {\text{how many} \atop \text{numbers}}$$

$${\text{Average cost} \atop \text{per item}} = \text{total cost} \div {\text{number of} \atop \text{items}}$$

$${\text{Average miles} \atop \text{per hour}} = \text{total miles} \div {\text{number of} \atop \text{hours}}$$

Answers to Try These Problems

1. 23 in   2. 82 lb   3. 5400 ft   4. 15 truckloads
5. 12 speeches, 20 min left over   6. $12,360   7. $1635
8. 270 mi   9. 8 min   10. $2   11. 4 lb   12. 1200 mi
13. 9800 oz   14. 38 min   15. $72,000   16. 59 min
17. 138 sq cm   18. 45 sq ft   19. 24 ft   20. 35 in
21. 343 men   22. $94,000   23. $5250   24. 107 cm
25. 177   26. $26   27. $540   28. $4500   29. $161   30. 3
31. $1090

EXERCISES 2.5

Solve.

1. A program consists of 8 speeches that are each 15 minutes long. If the speeches are given one right after the other, how long is the program?

2. A cord that is 2232 centimeters long is cut into 36 equal pieces. How long is each piece?

3. Carlos has 3145 pounds of fertilizer dust that he wants to spray equally over 185 acres of land. How much should he spray over each acre?

4. Mr. Benitez purchased 18,300 square yards of land in Texas. He wants to divide it into lots of 500 square yards each. How many lots will he have? How much land, if any, is left over?

5. A chandelier holds 18 bulbs. How many chandeliers can be outfitted with 3700 bulbs? How many bulbs, if any, are left over?

6. Twelve partners in a company share equally a profit. If each person's share is $39,000, what is the total profit?

7. Susan walks 4 miles in 1 hour. How far can she walk in 8 hours?

8. One share of a utility stock costs $98. What is the cost of 50 shares of this stock?

9. Five ounces of gold is worth $2650. What is 1 ounce of gold worth?

10. Smoked salmon costs $36 for 3 pounds. What is the cost of 1 pound?

11. On an architect's drawing, 5 centimeters represents an actual distance of 200 yards. What distance is represented by 1 centimeter?

12. A cable weighs 38 ounces every foot. What is the weight of 760 feet of this cable?

13. An Illinois farmer sold 8400 bushels of corn at $6 per bushel. What was the total income?

14. A machine seals potato-chip sacks at the rate of 360 sacks per hour. How many sacks are sealed at the end of 48 hours?

15. A car traveled 715 miles in 13 hours. What is the average number of miles traveled in 1 hour?

16. During the 21 school days last March, the total attendance in a school was 8526. What was the average daily attendance?

17. A car is traveling at an average speed of 50 miles per hour. How long does it take to go 1600 miles?

18. A 15-ounce can of tomatoes costs 75 cents. What is the cost per ounce?

19. A tank leaks 3 ounces per hour. How long will it take the tank to leak 315 ounces?

20. Carpeting costs $15 per square yard. How many square yards of carpeting can you buy for $840?

21. Find the area of this rectangle.

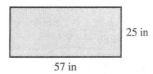

57 in
25 in

22. A rectangular floor is 15 feet wide and 26 feet long. How many square feet of carpeting are needed to cover this floor?

23. A rectangular piece of fabric has an area of 1620 square inches. If it is 36 inches wide, how long is it?

24. A piece of paper has an area of 88 square inches. If the paper is 11 inches long, how wide is it?

25. The width of a rectangle is 18 inches. The length is 5 times the width. Find the area of the rectangle.

26. The width of a rectangle is 52 inches. The length is 9 inches more than the width. Find the perimeter of the rectangle.

27. A carpet measures 5 yards by 8 yards. It costs $19 per square yard. What is the total cost of the carpet?

28. Mr. Bergeron bought a plot of land that is 300 feet wide and 350 feet long. After keeping 35,000 square feet for himself, he wants to divide the remaining land into lots of equal size for his 14 grandchildren. How much land will each grandchild receive?

29. Find the total area of this floor.

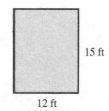

15 ft

12 ft

30. Find the total area of this region.

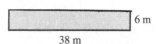

6 m

38 m

31. Carpeting costs $16 per square yard. What is the cost of carpeting this room?

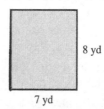

8 yd

7 yd

32. Warren's annual salary is six times what it was ten years ago. Ten years ago his salary was $9200. What is his salary now?

33. One nail is twice as long as another nail. If the shorter nail is 55 millimeters long, what is the length of the longer nail?

34. The current value of a house is 3 times what it was fifteen years ago. If the value now is $240,000, what was the value fifteen years ago?

35. Brenda earns twice as much as Ricor. If Brenda's salary is $75,000, how much does Ricor earn?

36. Curtis used to have an automobile that went only 9 miles per gallon of gasoline. His new compact car goes 4 times farther on a gallon of gas. How far does his new car go on a gallon of gasoline?

37. Janet is a receptionist and bookkeeper in an office. She makes $850 per month. Her friend Ann is an engineer making three times as much as Janet. What is Ann's monthly salary?

38. Kathy's bowling scores for 3 games were the following:
120   141   135
What was her average score?

39. The rainfall for a city during a 4-year period was as follows:

1989	37 inches
1990	24 inches
1991	28 inches
1992	35 inches

What was the average yearly rainfall?

40. A car traveled a total of 315 miles in 5 days. What was the average number of miles traveled each day?

41. A student's quiz scores are five 80s, three 70s, and two 60s. What is the average score?

42. Tony has a piece of string that is 850 centimeters long. After cutting off 200 centimeters, he wants to divide the remaining string into 26 equal pieces. How long will each piece be?

43. Elaine walks 4 miles each hour. She jogs 6 miles each hour. If Elaine walks for 3 hours and jogs for 2 hours, how far does she go?

44. George types 62 words per minute and Gertrude types 55 words per minute. How many words can they type if they both type for 25 minutes?

45. Steven and his two sisters inherited $153,000. After paying taxes of $15,600, they divided the remaining money equally. How much did each person receive?

46. A rectangular plot of land is twice as long as it is wide. If the width is 80 feet, and you plan to put fencing around the plot that costs $19 per foot, what is the cost of the fencing?

47. Dede purchases 17 refrigerators at $715 each and 29 stoves at $568 each. How much did she spend?

48. You purchase 6 pounds of coffee at $7 per pound and 15 coffee cups at $4 each. How much money do you have left out of $150?

49. A man weighed 300 pounds. He then began to lose 5 pounds per week. After 8 weeks, how much does he weigh?

50. Over a 12-hour period, the temperature dropped from 110° Fahrenheit to 62° Fahrenheit. On the average, how much did the temperature drop each hour?

The bar graph gives the weight of 6 persons. Use the graph to answer Exercises 51 through 54.

51. How much does Edna weigh?

52. How much does Art weigh?

53. What is the average weight of the 6 persons?

54. What is the average weight of the 3 women: Edna, Linda, and Sue?

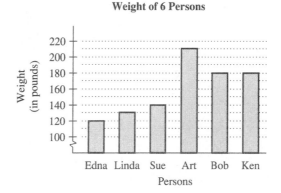

Weight of 6 Persons

CHAPTER 2 SUMMARY

KEY WORDS AND PHRASES

multiplication [2.1]
factor [2.1, 2.3]
multiplier [2.1, 2.3]
product [2.1, 2.3, 2.4]
division [2.2]
divisor [2.2]
dividend [2.2]

quotient [2.2]
remainder [2.2]
long division [2.2]
multiple [2.3]
divisible by [2.3]
even number [2.3]
prime number [2.3]

prime factoring [2.3]
divided by [2.4]
divided into [2.4]
speed [2.5]
rate [2.5]
area [2.5]
average (mean) [2.5]

SYMBOLS

$\times$ means   to multiply [2.1]
$)$ means   to divide [2.2]
$\div$ means   to divide [2.2]

IMPORTANT RULES

The Meaning of Multiplication [2.1]

Multiplication indicates repeated addition, for example, 3×5 means $5 + 5 + 5$.

The Meaning of Division [2.2]

Division is the reverse of multiplication, that is, $30 \div 5 = 6$ because $5 \times 6 = 30$.

The Long Division Process [2.2]

The long division process involves repeating these four steps

■ Divide
■ Multiply
■ Subtract (This result must be less than the divisor.)
■ Bring down the next digit.

Bring down only one digit at a time. Each time you bring down a digit, you must divide. After you bring down the last digit, you must divide, multiply, and subtract one more time.

How to Find the Missing Number in a Multiplication Statement [2.3]

■ If the product is missing, multiply to find the missing product.
■ If a multiplier (or factor) is missing, divide the product by the given multiplier to find the missing multiplier.

Divisibility Rules [2.3]

■ Any whole number ending in 0, 2, 4, 6, or 8 is divisible by 2.
■ Any whole number is divisible by 3 if the sum of its digits is divisible by 3.
■ Any whole number ending in a 0 or 5 is divisible by 5.
■ Any whole number
       is divisible by 10 if it ends in one 0,
       is divisible by 100 if it ends in two 0s,
       is divisible by 1000 if it ends in three 0s,
    and so on.

The Meaning of a Prime Number [2.3]

A prime number is a whole number, other than 1, that is divisible only by itself and 1. Examples of prime numbers are 2, 3, 5, 7, and 11.

The Area of a Rectangle [2.5]

Area measures the extent of the surface of a region. The area of a rectangle is found by multiplying the length by the width.

$$\text{Area of a rectangle} = \text{length} \times \text{width}$$

How to Find the Average (or Mean) of a Collection of Numbers [2.5]

▐ Add all of the numbers in the collection.

▐ Divide the sum by how many numbers are in the collection.

CHAPTER 2 REVIEW EXERCISES

Multiply.

1.	28	**2.**	971	**3.**	207	**4.**	8062
	× 41		× 13		× 54		× 27
5.	16307	**6.**	3056	**7.**	535	**8.**	9382
	× 458		× 859		× 288		× 716

9. 250 × 1700   **10.** 192 × 30,000

11. 208 × 307   **12.** 5138 × 3009

13. 4 × 6 × 2   **14.** 9 × 2 × 7

15. 2 × 2 × 3 × 5   **16.** 7 × 7 × 4 × 5

Divide.

17. 5$\overline{)38}$ **18.** 4$\overline{)120}$ **19.** 8$\overline{)6712}$ **20.** 6$\overline{)32,494}$

21. 70$\overline{)160}$ **22.** 30$\overline{)18,022}$ **23.** 15$\overline{)8325}$ **24.** 96,160 ÷ 48

25. 98,216 ÷ 93   **26.** 500$\overline{)8346}$ **27.** 800$\overline{)65,820}$ **28.** 910$\overline{)783,000}$

29. 403$\overline{)706,000}$ **30.** 615$\overline{)3,111,900}$

Find the missing number.

31. 9 × ☐ = 225   **32.** ☐ × 18 = 126

33. 8 × 48 = ☐   **34.** 975 = ☐ × 65

35. 4796 = 11 × ☐   **36.** ☐ = 40 × 900

Answer yes or no.

37. Indicate whether each number is divisible by 12.
    a. 86   **b.** 336   **c.** 1308   **d.** 11,650

38. Indicate whether each number is divisible by 35.
    a. 320   **b.** 565   **c.** 2100   **d.** 10,710

39. Indicate whether each number is a multiple of 25.
    a. 675   **b.** 1050   **c.** 2300   **d.** 6085

40. Indicate whether each number is a multiple of 19.
    a. 57   **b.** 171   **c.** 199   **d.** 5738

41. Indicate whether each number is divisible by 5.
    a. 300   **b.** 715   **c.** 8326   **d.** 2010

42. Indicate whether each number is divisible by 3.
    a. 51   **b.** 1212   **c.** 792   **d.** 3456

43. Indicate whether each number is divisible by 100.
    a. 9090   **b.** 5005   **c.** 3000   **d.** 21,500

44. Indicate whether each number is divisible by 1000.
    a. 4008   **b.** 30,500   **c.** 9000   **d.** 70,000

Write each number as the product of primes.

45. 18   **46.** 54   **47.** 168   **48.** 441   **49.** 750

50. 140   **51.** 2700   **52.** 24,000   **53.** 351   **54.** 255

Write a division statement using the symbol $\overline{)}$.

55. 4 divided into 12 equals 3.

56. 100 divided by 5 is 20.

Write a division statement using the symbol $\div$.

57. 8 divided into 72 is 9.

58. 325 divided by 25 equals 13.

Fill in the blank with the appropriate word, by *or* into.

59. $5\overline{)35}$ is read "5 divided _____ 35 is 7."

60. $5\overline{)35}$ is read "35 divided _____ 5 is 7."

61. $130 \div 10 = 13$ is read "130 divided _____ 10 equals 13."

62. $130 \div 10 = 10$ is read "10 divided _____ 130 equals 13."

Translate each English statement to a multiplication or division statement using math symbols.

63. The product of 3 and 16 is 48.

64. 800 is a number twice as large as 400.

65. 29 equals 174 divided by 6.

66. 13 divided into 585 is 45.

67. 68 equals 4 times 17.

68. 60 multiplied times 400 yields 24,000.

69. Eighty-one is nine multiplied times itself.

70. Sixteen divided into eight thousand eighty yields five hundred five.

Solve.

71. What number multiplied by 15 equals 3015?

72. Find the product of 750 and 8000.

73. Find the difference between 51 and 17.

74. What number is 57 divided by 19?

75. Find twice 950.

76. Find the average of 36, 42, and 54.

77. List the first five multiples of 8.

78. Is 68 a multiple of 17? If so, write 68 as the product of 17 and another whole number.

79. Eight partners share equally a profit of $18,000. How much money does each partner receive?

80. Crabmeat sells for $7 a pound. What is the cost of 15 pounds of crabmeat?

81. Pam's bowling scores were as follows: 119   127   125   117
    What was her average score?

82. A city allocates $810,000 for salaries for park recreation assistants during the summer. How many assistants can be hired with a salary of $750 for each?

83. A machine cuts the threads in a screw at the rate of 75 screws per hour. How long does it take the machine to cut the threads in 3150 screws?

84. A bookstore purchased 900 textbooks from a publisher at $15 a book. What was the total cost to the bookstore?

85. What is the total area of this floor?

14 ft

8 ft

86. The length of a rectangle is 3 times its width. If the width measures 49 feet, find the area of the rectangle.

87. If Virna can walk 5 miles in 75 minutes, how long will it take her to walk 1 mile?

88. The area of a rectangle is 1360 square meters. If the width is 17 meters, find the perimeter.

89. Last year Chris earned $65,000. This year he earned 3 times that much. What is the increase in his earnings?

90. A parking garage charges $3 for the first hour, then $2 per hour for each additional hour. You enter the garage at 9 AM and leave at 2 PM. How much do you pay?

✎ **In Your Own Words**

Write complete sentences to discuss each of the following. Support your comments with examples or pictures, if appropriate.

91. Discuss two ways of deciding whether a number is divisible by 5.

92. Discuss two ways of deciding whether a number is divisible by 3.

93. Discuss how the following two problems differ.
    a. ☐ × 28 = 420   **b.** 28 × 420 = ☐

94. Discuss the difference between finding the perimeter of a rectangle and finding the area of a rectangle.

95. Give examples of at least three different rates that you experience in your life.

CHAPTER 2 PRACTICE TEST

Multiply.

1.   9237
    ×   8

2.   8037
    ×   67

3.   532
    × 417

4. 600 × 8000

5. 73,000 × 13

6.   208
    × 307

7.   5482
    × 3009

8. 7 × 2 × 3

9. 3 × 5 × 5 × 7

Divide.

10. $8\overline{)6712}$ **11.** $6\overline{)36,494}$ **12.** $15\overline{)8325}$

13. $96,160 \div 48$ **14.** $783,000 \div 910$ **15.** $615\overline{)3,111,900}$

Find the missing number.

16. $25 \times \boxed{} = 30,750$ **17.** $\boxed{} = 450 \times 900$

Answer yes or no.

18. Is 184 a multiple of 23? **19.** Is 351 divisible by 3?

Write each number as the product of primes.

20. 42 **21.** 850

Fill in the blank with the appropriate word by *or* into.

22. $8\overline{)40}^{\,5}$ is read "40 divided _____ 8 equals 5."

23. $666 \div 6 = 111$ is read "6 divided _____ 666 is 111."

Solve.

24. Twice what number yields 908?

25. Find the average of 682, 1016, and 801.

26. Seven friends share equally the cost of renting a ski cabin for the winter season. The total rent is $2275. What is each person's share?

27. Karin sells corn from her garden. She puts 2000 ears of corn in packages with 8 ears in each package. How many packages can she make? How many, if any, ears of corn are left over?

28. The area of a desk top is 1050 square inches. The desk is 25 inches wide. How long is it?

29. Mr. Martinez works in the food and beverage department at a hotel. He ordered 4350 ounces of punch for a reception. He is expecting approximately 150 guests. How much punch does this allow for each guest?

30. George has a piece of string that is 850 centimeters long. After cutting off 200 centimeters, he wants to divide the remaining string into 26 equal pieces. How long will each of these pieces be?

31. What is the cost of carpeting this floor space if the carpeting costs $28 per square yard?

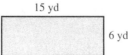

15 yd

6 yd

32. A jet travels for 8 hours at 450 miles per hour, then travels for 4 hours at 580 miles per hour. How much farther did the jet travel during the 8-hour period than during the 4-hour period?

33. A tank leaks 20 ounces of water every 300 minutes. How long does it take for the tank to leak 1 ounce?

CUMULATIVE REVIEW EXERCISES: CHAPTERS 1–2

1. Write the English name for 64,098.

2. Write the numeral for two million, thirteen thousand, five hundred.

3. Round off 148,106 to the nearest ten thousand.

Perform the indicated operations.

4. $8796 + 652 + 376,552$

5. $8000 - 752$

6. $70,000 \times 3400$

7. $253,680 \div 28$

Find the quotient and remainder.

8. $8986 \div 35$

9. $600,700 \div 150$

10. $50,796 \div 516$

Write each number as the product of primes.

11. 36

12. 275

13. 9000

14. 637

Find the missing number.

15. $\boxed{} \times 75 = 450$

16. $701 = \boxed{} + 189$

Solve.

17. Find the difference between 5010 and 349.

18. Find the product of 4580 and 308.

19. Find the sum of 240, 673, and 548.

20. Find the average of 68, 74, and 98.

21. What number increased by 65 is 200?

22. What number times 65 is 1170?

23. A shopping center has a rectangular parking lot that is 350 feet by 280 feet.
    a. Find the area of the lot.   b. Find the perimeter of the lot.

24. Ms. Sanchez has saved $850 to buy a sofa. The sofa she wants costs only $685. How much money will she have left after buying the sofa?

25. Frank's checking account balance is $405. He writes checks for $82, $78, and $136. What is his balance now?

26. Melissa bought a car for $9900. She plans to pay for it by making 36 equal monthly payments. How much is her monthly payment?

27. A race car travels 450 miles in 3 hours. At this rate, how far does the car go in 1 hour?

28. Joshua's watch loses 1 minute every 15 hours. At this rate, how long does it take his watch to lose 5 minutes?

29. Irene had grades of 92, 86, 75, 88, and 94 on five exams.
    a. What is the total number of points on all five exams?
    b. What is the average of the five scores?
    c. How much larger is the highest score than the lowest score?

30. A restaurant contains 8 booths that each seat 6 persons, 5 booths that seat 2 persons, 12 tables that seat 4 persons, and 6 tables that seat 6 persons. How many customers can eat in the restaurant at one time?

31. The Hamilton family budgeted $1300 for the month of November. Their expenses for that month amounted to $287 for food, $435 for rent, $138 for clothing, $68 for utilities, $65 for entertainment, $148 for medical bills, and $125 for other miscellaneous items. Are their expenses over or under their budget, and by how much?

An Introduction to Fractions

Counting by Fractions - Wholes & Halves

If 1 pizza is separated into 2 equal parts, each part is $\frac{1}{2}$ pizza.
We say, "one half" pizza.

    Each part is $\frac{1}{2}$ pizza, "one half" pizza

1 pizza $\frac{2}{2}$ pizza, "two halves" pizza

In the fraction, $\frac{1}{2}$, the denominator, 2, specifies how many equal parts the 1 whole is separated into.

EXERCISES 3-A

How many pizzas are in each group? Give both a numeral and the corresponding English name. Give both in at least two ways.

1. **2.** **3.**

4. **5.** **6.**

7. **8.**

9. **10.**

11. **12.**

Count as specified. List the numbers. Do it in two ways.

A) using improper fractions like $\frac{2}{2}, \frac{3}{2}, \frac{4}{2}, \frac{5}{2}$

B) using whole & mixed numbers like $1, 1\frac{1}{2}, 2, 2\frac{1}{2}$

13. Count from $\frac{1}{2}$ to 4 by $\frac{1}{2}$s.

14. Count from $\frac{1}{2}$ to $\frac{13}{2}$ by $\frac{1}{2}$s.

15. Count from $\frac{1}{2}$ to $\frac{10}{2}$ by $\frac{1}{2}$s.

16. Count from $\frac{1}{2}$ to $4\frac{1}{2}$ by $\frac{1}{2}$s.

17. Count from $\frac{3}{2}$ to $\frac{15}{2}$ by $\frac{1}{2}$s.

18. Count from $\frac{5}{2}$ to $\frac{17}{2}$ by $\frac{1}{2}$s.

19. Count from $\frac{7}{2}$ to 7 by $\frac{1}{2}$s.

20. Count from $5\frac{1}{2}$ to $9\frac{1}{2}$ by $\frac{1}{2}$s.

Counting by Fractions - Wholes, Halves & Fourths

If 1 pizza is separated into 4 equal parts, each part is $\frac{1}{4}$ pizza.
We say, "one fourth" pizza.

    Each piece is $\frac{1}{4}$ pizza, "one fourth" pizza

1 pizza $1 = \frac{4}{4}$ pizza, "four fourths" pizza

In the fraction, $\frac{1}{4}$, the denominator, 4, specifies the number of equal parts the 1 whole is separated into.

EXERCISES 3-B

How many pizzas are in each group? Give both a numeral and the English name.

1.

2.

3.

4.

5.

6.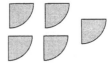

How many pizzas are in each group? Give both a numeral and the English name.
Do it in at least two ways.

7.

8.

9.

10.

11.

12.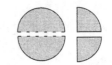

13.

14.

15.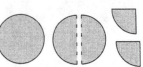

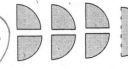 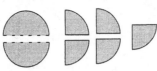

Count as specified. List the numbers. Do it in two ways.
A) using improper fractions like $\frac{4}{4}$, $\frac{5}{4}$, $\frac{6}{4}$, $\frac{7}{4}$, $\frac{8}{4}$
B) using whole & mixed numbers like 1, $1\frac{1}{4}$, $1\frac{2}{4}$, $1\frac{3}{4}$, 2

16. Count from $\frac{1}{4}$ to 2 by $\frac{1}{4}$s.

17. Count from $\frac{1}{4}$ to 4 by $\frac{1}{4}$s.

18. Count from $\frac{1}{4}$ to $\frac{9}{4}$ by $\frac{1}{4}$s.

19. Count from $\frac{1}{4}$ to $\frac{13}{4}$ by $\frac{1}{4}$s.

20. Count from $\frac{1}{4}$ to $3\frac{3}{4}$ by $\frac{1}{4}$s.

21. Count from $\frac{1}{4}$ to $4\frac{2}{4}$ by $\frac{1}{4}$s.

22. Count from $\frac{5}{4}$ to $\frac{19}{4}$ by $\frac{1}{4}$s.

23. Count from $\frac{9}{4}$ to $6\frac{1}{4}$ by $\frac{1}{4}$s.

Counting by Fractions

In a fraction like $\frac{3}{4}$, the denominator, 4, can indicate how many equal parts a quantity of one whole has been separated into. In this case, the numerator, 3, is counting how many 1/4s we have. Because we separated 1 into 4 equal parts, it takes 4 of the 1/4s to make 1. So, we have 4/4 = 1. Likewise, 2/2 = 1, 3/3 =1, 5/5 = 1, 6/6 = 1, 7/7 = 1, 8/8 = 1 and so on.

It can be helpful to count by fractions to discover that a quantity can be expressed in fractional form in more than one way.

Here we count from 1/3 to 3 in two ways.

Using improper fractions: $\quad \frac{1}{3}, \ \frac{2}{3}, \ \frac{3}{3}, \ \frac{4}{3}, \ \frac{5}{3}, \ \frac{6}{3}, \ \frac{7}{3}, \ \frac{8}{3}, \ \frac{9}{3}$

Using whole and mixed numbers: $\quad \frac{1}{3}, \ \frac{2}{3}, \ 1 , \ 1\frac{1}{3}, 1\frac{2}{3}, \ 2, \ 2\frac{1}{3}, 2\frac{2}{3}, \ 3$

As soon as you reach the value of 1 there is more than one way to continue the counting. When counting in two ways it is helpful to align the equal values underneath each other to make certain you do not leave out a value. Note the following equalities in the above lists.

$$\frac{3}{3}=1 , \quad \frac{4}{3}=1\frac{1}{3}, \quad \frac{5}{3}=1\frac{2}{3}, \quad \frac{6}{3}=2, \quad \frac{7}{3}=2\frac{1}{3}, \quad \frac{8}{3}=2\frac{2}{3} \quad \text{and} \quad \frac{9}{3}=3$$

EXERCISES 3-C
Count as specified. List the numbers. Do it in two ways.
A) using improper fractions and B) using whole and mixed numerals.

1. Count from $\frac{1}{2}$ to 4 by $\frac{1}{2}$s.

2. Count from $\frac{1}{2}$ to $5\frac{1}{2}$ by $\frac{1}{2}$s.

3. Count from $\frac{1}{4}$ to $\frac{9}{4}$ by $\frac{1}{4}$s.

4. Count from $\frac{1}{4}$ to $\frac{14}{4}$ by $\frac{1}{4}$s.

5. Count from $\frac{1}{3}$ to 4 by $\frac{1}{3}$s.

6. Count from $\frac{1}{3}$ to $5\frac{1}{3}$ by $\frac{1}{3}$s.

7. Count from $\frac{1}{5}$ to 2 by $\frac{1}{5}$s.

8. Count from $\frac{1}{5}$ to $\frac{16}{5}$ by $\frac{1}{5}$s.

9. Count from $\frac{1}{6}$ to $\frac{20}{6}$ by $\frac{1}{6}$s.

10. Count from $\frac{1}{6}$ to 2 by $\frac{1}{6}$s.

11. Count from $\frac{1}{7}$ to $2\frac{3}{7}$ by $\frac{1}{7}$s.

12. Count from $\frac{1}{8}$ to 2 by $\frac{1}{8}$s.

Picture Statements & Addition Equations -Wholes, Halves & Fourths

To add means to total or to combine. We can use the pictures of wholes, halves and fourths of circles to look at some addtion situations and write corresponding equations.

Study this picture statement to see that you agree with what it is saying. Then observe how the statement is written using numbers instead of pictures.

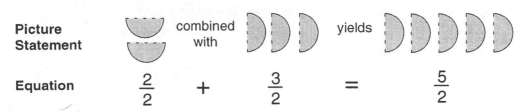

Picture Statement

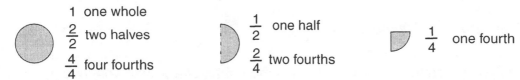

Equation

$$\frac{2}{2} \quad + \quad \frac{3}{2} \quad = \quad \frac{5}{2}$$

EXERCISES 3-D

Complete the picture statement by filling in the box with an appropriate picture.
For your picture, use any appropriate combination of wholes, halves and fourths.

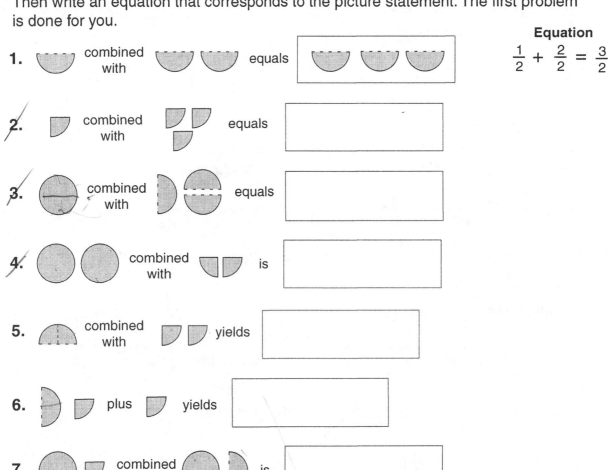

Then write an equation that corresponds to the picture statement. The first problem is done for you.

Picture Statements & Subtraction Equations -Wholes, Halves & Fourths

To subtract means to take away. We can use pictures of wholes, halves and fourths of circles to look at some subtraction situations and write corresponding equations.

Study this picture statement to see that you agree with what it is saying. Then observe how the statement is written using symbols instead of pictures and words.

Picture Statement take away yields

Equation $\quad 1\frac{1}{4} \quad - \quad \frac{3}{4} \quad = \quad \frac{1}{2}$

EXERCISES 3-E

Complete the picture statement by filling in the box with an appropriate picture. For your picture, use any appropriate combination of wholes, halves and fourths.

 1 one whole $\qquad$ $\frac{1}{2}$ one half $\qquad$ $\frac{1}{4}$ one fourth

Then write an equation that corresponds to the picture statement. The first problem is done for you. Any fractional forms of the numbers are okay.

Equation

1. take away equals $\qquad$ $\frac{3}{2} - \frac{1}{2} = \frac{2}{2}$ or 1

2. 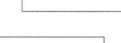 take away  equals [ ]

3. take away equals [ ]

4. take away is [ ]

5. take away leaves

6. minus yields

7. 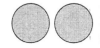 minus makes

Fractions Representing Shaded & Unshaded Regions

Now we associate fractions with shaded regions and unshaded regions. Pay close attention to the amount that is one whole and observe how many equal parts the one whole is divided into so that you know the denominator that will be needed.

In the picture below, each one whole is separated into 3 equal parts so we are counting 1/3s or thirds. Therefore, we use the denominator 3.

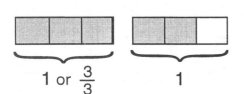

Shaded Amount = $\frac{5}{3}$ or $1\frac{2}{3}$

Unshaded Amount = $\frac{1}{3}$

Total Amount = $\frac{6}{3}$ or 2 or $1\frac{3}{3}$

1 or $\frac{3}{3}$ 　　 1

EXERCISES 3-F

For each picture, give the shaded amount, the unshaded amount and the total.
When possible, give the amounts in more than one way. Label your results as above.

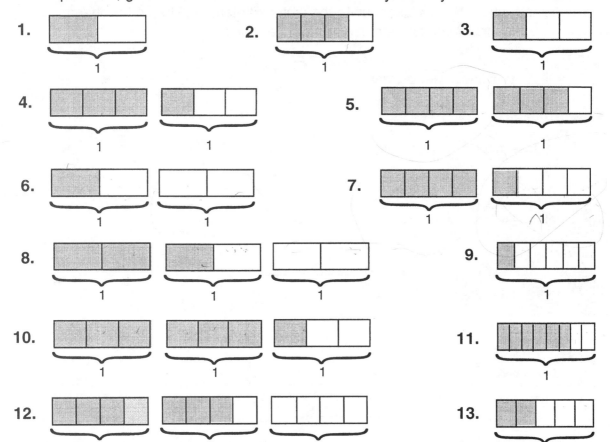

Fractions on the Number Line – Level 1

We like to view fractions on a number line where the numbers are arranged from smallest to largest with uniform distances between adjacent tick marks. A tick mark designates the position of a number. Here we view a number line containing some fractions with denominator 2.

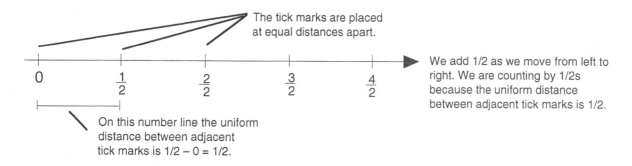

The tick marks are placed at equal distances apart.

We add 1/2 as we move from left to right. We are counting by 1/2s because the uniform distance between adjacent tick marks is 1/2.

On this number line the uniform distance between adjacent tick marks is 1/2 – 0 = 1/2.

Because 2/2 = 1 and 4/2 = 2, these positions could have been labeled with these whole numbers.

When you view a number line you are seeing numbers associated with **positions** on the number line as well as **distances** between the numbers. Note that you can obtain the distance between two any two numbers by subtracting the smaller number from the larger number. Here we look at another example.

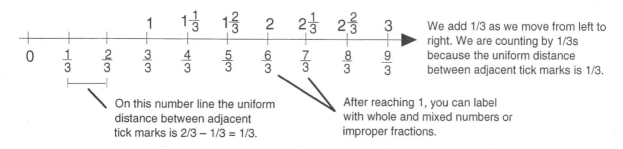

We add 1/3 as we move from left to right. We are counting by 1/3s because the uniform distance between adjacent tick marks is 1/3.

On this number line the uniform distance between adjacent tick marks is 2/3 – 1/3 = 1/3.

After reaching 1, you can label with whole and mixed numbers or improper fractions.

EXAMPLE Label the distance between a pair of adjacent tick marks and then label all the tick marks with the appropriate numbers.

Solution First we subtract 2/4 from 3/4 to see that the uniform distance between adjacent tick marks is 1/4. Then we add 1/4 to each number to obtain the next number.

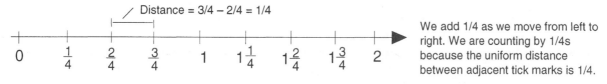

Distance = 3/4 – 2/4 = 1/4

We add 1/4 as we move from left to right. We are counting by 1/4s because the uniform distance between adjacent tick marks is 1/4.

EXERCISES 3-G

For each number line, label the distance between a pair of adjacent tick marks and label all unlabeled tick marks with the appropriate number. Any fractional form is okay.

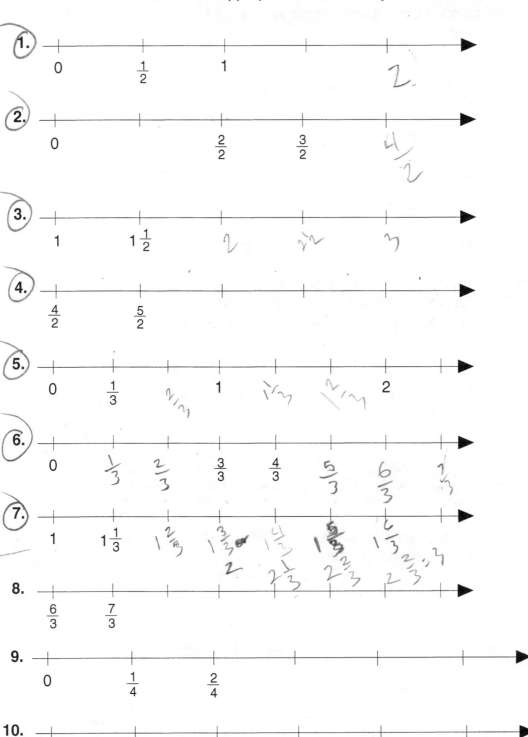

1.

0     $\frac{1}{2}$ 1   2.

2.

0       $\frac{2}{2}$ $\frac{3}{2}$ $\frac{4}{2}$

3.

1     $1\frac{1}{2}$ 2   2½   3

4.

$\frac{4}{2}$ $\frac{5}{2}$

5.

0    $\frac{1}{3}$ $\frac{2}{3}$ 1 $1\frac{1}{3}$ $1\frac{2}{3}$ 2

6.

0    $\frac{1}{3}$ $\frac{2}{3}$ $\frac{3}{3}$ $\frac{4}{3}$ $\frac{5}{3}$ $\frac{6}{3}$ $\frac{7}{3}$

7.

1    $1\frac{1}{3}$ $1\frac{2}{3}$ $1\frac{3}{3}$ or 2 $1\frac{4}{3}$ $2\frac{1}{3}$ $1\frac{5}{3}$ $2\frac{2}{3}$ $1\frac{6}{3}=2\frac{2}{3}=3$

8.

$\frac{6}{3}$ $\frac{7}{3}$

9.

0     $\frac{1}{4}$ $\frac{2}{4}$

10.

1       $1\frac{3}{4}$ 2

Fractions on the Number Line – Level 2

Now you want to learn how to label the remaining tick marks on a number line when you are not given two numbers adjacent to one another. First, you will need to find the uniform distance between adjacent tick marks. This can be done as long as you are given at least two numbers. Follow the steps below to see how this is done for the given number line.

Step 1 – Subtract any two given numbers to find out how far apart they are.

Step 1: How far apart are 0 and 1?
Distance = 1 – 0 = 1

Step 2 – Count the number of spaces between the two numbers.

Step 2: How many spaces are there between 0 and 1? Count them. There are 3. (Don't count the tick marks, count the spaces.)

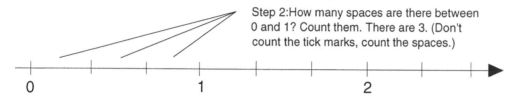

Therefore, a distance of 1 unit is separated into 3 equal parts.

Step 3 – Divide the total distance found in step 1 by the number of equal spaces in step 2.

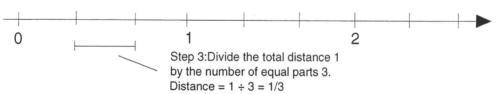

Step 3: Divide the total distance 1 by the number of equal parts 3.
Distance = 1 ÷ 3 = 1/3

This number 1/3 is the uniform distance between adjacent tick marks.

Step 4 – Add the uniform distance to each number on the left to obtain the next number on the right.

0 + 1/3 = 1/3   1/3 + 1/3 = 2/3   2/3 + 1/3 = 3/3 or 1

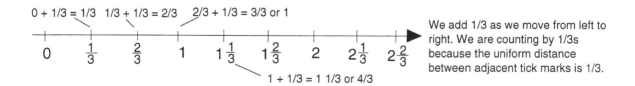

We add 1/3 as we move from left to right. We are counting by 1/3s because the uniform distance between adjacent tick marks is 1/3.

1 + 1/3 = 1 1/3 or 4/3

EXERCISES 3-H
For each number line, label the distance between a pair of given numbers, label the distance between a pair of adjacent tick marks and label all unlabeled tick marks with the appropriate number. Any fractional forms are okay.

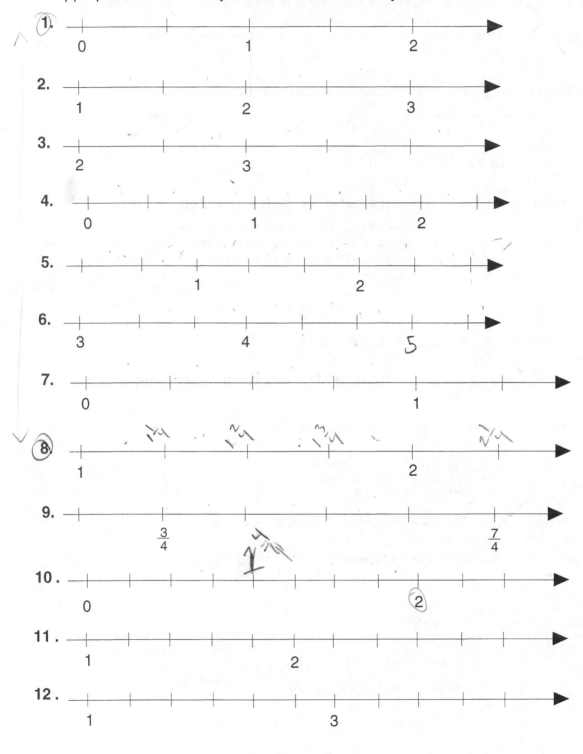

OBJECTIVES   ▌   Write a fraction or a mixed numeral represented by a shaded region.
              ▌   Recognize whether a fraction is less than, equal to, or more than the number 1.

1   Fractions Less Than or Equal to One Whole

Ian bought a pizza and cut it into 6 *equal* parts as shown in the figure. Each slice is $\frac{1}{6}$ (one-sixth) of the pizza.

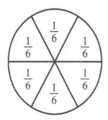

If he eats 2 slices, then he eats $\frac{2}{6}$ (two-sixths) of the pizza.

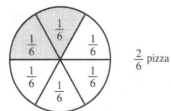

$\frac{2}{6}$ pizza

Try These Problems

Write a fraction represented by the shaded region. Assume each figure represents one whole.

1.

2.

3.

4.

If he eats 5 slices, then he eats $\frac{5}{6}$ (five-sixths) of the pizza.

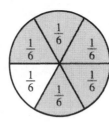

$\frac{5}{6}$ pizza

If he eats 6 slices, then he eats $\frac{6}{6}$ (six-sixths) of the pizza or one whole pizza.

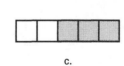

$\frac{6}{6} = 1$ pizza

The numbers $\frac{1}{6}, \frac{2}{6}, \frac{5}{6}$, and $\frac{6}{6}$ are called **fractions.** Fractions help us to talk about part or all of a whole. The horizontal bar is called the **fraction bar,** and the numbers above and below the fraction bar are called the **numerator** and **denominator,** respectively.

Fraction—— $\frac{5}{6}$ ——Numerator
bar   ——Denominator

Here are some more examples where fractions represent part of one whole.

EXAMPLE 1   Write a fraction represented by the shaded region. Assume each figure represents one whole.

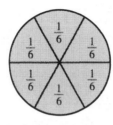

a.   b.   c.

SOLUTION

a. Because 1 out of 4 equal parts is shaded, the fraction is $\frac{1}{4}$ (one-fourth).

b. Because 1 out of 3 equal parts is shaded, the fraction is $\frac{1}{3}$ (one-third).

c. Because 3 out of 5 equal parts are shaded, the fraction is $\frac{3}{5}$ (three-fifths).

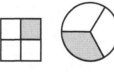 **Try Problems 1 through 4.**

2 | Fractions More Than or Equal to One Whole

Antoinette bought 3 pizzas and cut each one into 8 *equal* parts as shown in the figure. Each slice is $\frac{1}{8}$ (one-eighth) of a pizza.

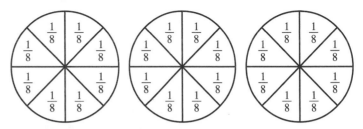

If she and her friends eat 8 slices, then they eat $\frac{8}{8}$ (eight-eighths) pizza or 1 pizza.

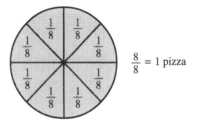

$\frac{8}{8}$ = 1 pizza

If she and her friends eat 11 slices, then they eat $\frac{11}{8}$ (eleven-eighths) pizzas or $1\frac{3}{8}$ (one and three-eighths) pizzas.

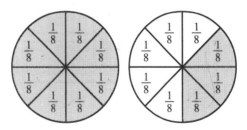

$\frac{11}{8}$ or $1\frac{3}{8}$ pizzas

If she and her friends eat 21 slices, then they eat $\frac{21}{8}$ (twenty-one eighths) pizzas or $2\frac{5}{8}$ (two and five-eighths) pizzas.

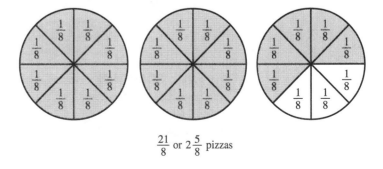

$\frac{21}{8}$ or $2\frac{5}{8}$ pizzas

Fractions like $\frac{11}{8}$ and $\frac{21}{8}$, that have a numerator more than the denominator, are numbers more than 1 whole. These numbers can be written in two ways.

$$\frac{11}{8} = \frac{8}{8} + \frac{3}{8} = 1 + \frac{3}{8} = 1\frac{3}{8} \rightarrow \text{Therefore, } \frac{11}{8} = 1\frac{3}{8}$$

$$\frac{21}{8} = \frac{8}{8} + \frac{8}{8} + \frac{5}{8} = 1 + 1 + \frac{5}{8} = 2\frac{5}{8} \rightarrow$$

$$\text{Therefore, } \frac{21}{8} = 2\frac{5}{8}$$

The fraction $\frac{11}{8}$ is called an **improper fraction,** and when it is written in the form $1\frac{3}{8}$, it is called a **mixed numeral.** In general, an improper fraction is a fraction with the numerator more than the denominator, and its value is more than 1.

EXAMPLE 2   Write an improper fraction and a mixed numeral or whole numeral that represent the shaded regions. Assume each separate figure represents 1 whole.

SOLUTION   Because each separate figure is divided into 3 equal parts, each part is $\frac{1}{3}$.

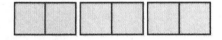

$$\frac{3}{3} \qquad + \qquad \frac{2}{3} \qquad = \qquad \frac{5}{3} \qquad \text{five-thirds}$$

$$1 \qquad + \qquad \frac{2}{3} \qquad = \qquad 1\frac{2}{3} \qquad \text{one and two-thirds}$$

The improper fraction is $\frac{5}{3}$ and the mixed numeral is $1\frac{2}{3}$. ■

EXAMPLE 3   Write an improper fraction and a mixed numeral or whole numeral that represent the shaded regions. Assume each separate figure represents 1 whole.

SOLUTION   Because each separate figure is divided into 2 equal parts, each part is $\frac{1}{2}$.

Try These Problems

Write an improper fraction and a mixed numeral or a whole numeral that represent the shaded regions. Assume each separate figure represents one whole.

5.

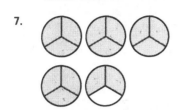

6.

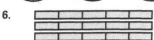

7.

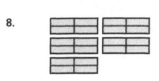

8.

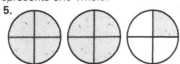

9. Which of these fractions are equal to one whole?
$\frac{12}{12}, \frac{7}{12}, \frac{19}{12}, \frac{8}{4}, \frac{8}{8}, \frac{4}{4}$

10. Which of these fractions are more than one whole?
$\frac{7}{30}, \frac{30}{7}, \frac{75}{25}, \frac{25}{75}, \frac{2}{3}, \frac{3}{2}$

11. Which of these fractions are less than one whole?
$\frac{9}{10}, \frac{10}{9}, \frac{4}{12}, \frac{12}{4}, \frac{33}{80}, \frac{80}{33}$

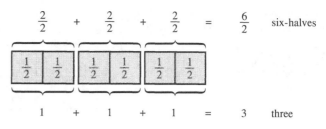

$$\frac{2}{2} + \frac{2}{2} + \frac{2}{2} = \frac{6}{2} \quad \text{six-halves}$$

$$1 + 1 + 1 = 3 \quad \text{three}$$

The improper fraction is $\frac{6}{2}$ and the whole numeral is 3. ■

 Try Problems 5 through 8.

After picturing fractions represented by shaded regions, you should have discovered the following basic properties of fractions.

Some Basic Properties of Fractions

1. A fraction with a numerator less than the denominator is a number less than 1 whole. (For example, the fractions $\frac{1}{4}$, $\frac{2}{7}$, and $\frac{19}{20}$ are each less than 1.)

2. A fraction with a numerator more than the denominator is a number more than 1 whole. (For example, the fractions $\frac{5}{4}$, $\frac{12}{7}$, and $\frac{41}{20}$ are each more than 1.)

3. A fraction with a numerator that equals the denominator is equal to 1 whole. (For example, the fractions $\frac{4}{4}$, $\frac{7}{7}$, and $\frac{20}{20}$ are each equal to 1.)

 Try Problems 9 through 11.

Answers to Try These Problems

1. $\frac{1}{5}$ 2. $\frac{1}{6}$ 3. $\frac{2}{3}$ 4. $\frac{7}{7} = 1$ 5. $\frac{9}{4}, 2\frac{1}{4}$ 6. $\frac{15}{5}, 3$ 7. $\frac{14}{3}, 4\frac{2}{3}$

8. $\frac{20}{4}, 5$ 9. $\frac{12}{12}, \frac{8}{8}, \frac{4}{4}$ 10. $\frac{30}{7}, \frac{75}{25}, \frac{3}{2}$ 11. $\frac{9}{10}, \frac{4}{12}, \frac{33}{80}$

EXERCISES 3.1

Write a fraction represented by the shaded region. Assume each figure represents one whole.

1.

2.

3.

4.

5.

6.

7.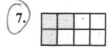

8.

9.

10.

Write an improper fraction and a mixed numeral or a whole numeral that represent the shaded regions. Assume each separate figure represents one whole.

11.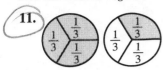

12.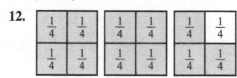

13.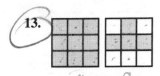

14.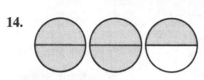

15.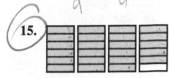

16.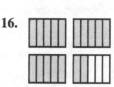

17.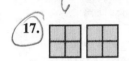

18.

Choose the fractions in each group that are more than one whole.

19. $\frac{5}{7}, \frac{7}{5}, \frac{8}{3}, \frac{3}{8}, \frac{30}{13}, \frac{13}{30}$ **20.** $\frac{4}{4}, \frac{7}{7}, \frac{9}{8}, \frac{8}{9}, \frac{23}{50}, \frac{50}{23}$

Choose the fractions in each group that equal one whole.

21. $\frac{4}{8}, \frac{8}{4}, \frac{8}{8}, \frac{4}{4}, \frac{12}{13}, \frac{13}{13}$ **22.** $\frac{2}{2}, \frac{6}{2}, \frac{2}{6}, \frac{9}{9}, \frac{17}{17}, \frac{18}{17}$

Choose the fractions in each group that are less than one whole.

23. $\frac{2}{5}, \frac{5}{2}, \frac{5}{5}, \frac{7}{12}, \frac{12}{7}, \frac{12}{12}$ **24.** $\frac{1}{8}, \frac{9}{8}, \frac{8}{8}, \frac{21}{25}, \frac{28}{25}, \frac{3}{4}$

3.2   READING AND WRITING FRACTIONS

OBJECTIVES   ▌ Write a fraction for the English name of a fraction.
               ▌ Write the English name of a fraction.
               ▌ Write a mixed numeral for the English name of a mixed numeral.
               ▌ Write the English name of a mixed numeral.

1   The English Name of a Fraction

You need to become familiar with the English names for fractions. Some examples follow.

Try These Problems

Write a fraction for each English name.

1. Two-halves

2. Two-thirds

3. Three-fifths

4. Eleven-ninths

Write the English name for each fraction.

5. $\frac{1}{6}$

6. $\frac{5}{2}$

Write a fraction for each English name.

7. Nine-tenths

8. Ten-seventeenths

9. Eighteen forty-seconds

10. Sixty-five sixty-thirds

Write the English name for each fraction.

11. $\frac{12}{13}$

12. $\frac{8}{50}$

Fraction	English Name
$\frac{1}{2}$	one-half
$\frac{3}{2}$	three-halves
$\frac{1}{3}$	one-third
$\frac{12}{4}$	twelve-fourths
$\frac{4}{5}$	four-fifths
$\frac{7}{6}$	seven-sixths
$\frac{5}{7}$	five-sevenths
$\frac{33}{8}$	thirty-three eighths

Observe that when the denominator is 4, 5, 6, 7, . . . , the English name ends in *-ths*.

 Try Problems 1 through 6.

Now let's look at fractions with larger denominators. Study the following examples.

Fraction	English Name
$\frac{7}{10}$	seven-tenths
$\frac{11}{18}$	eleven-eighteenths
$\frac{1}{20}$	one-twentieth
$\frac{3}{72}$	three seventy-seconds
$\frac{77}{83}$	seventy-seven eighty-thirds
$\frac{9}{95}$	nine ninety-fifths

 Try Problems 7 through 12.

Later, when you study decimals, it will be especially important for you to be familiar with the English names for fractions with denomina-

Try These Problems

Write a fraction for each English name.

13. Eight-tenths

14. Thirty hundredths

15. Seven hundredths

16. Sixty-two tenths

17. Thirteen thousandths

18. Three hundred-thousandths

19. Fifty ten-thousandths

20. Ninety-six thousandths

Write the English name for each fraction.

21. $\frac{18}{100}$

22. $\frac{33}{10}$

23. $\frac{4}{1000}$

24. $\frac{27}{10,000}$

Write a mixed numeral for each English name.

25. Ten and three-fourths

26. Eight and nine-thirteenths

27. Twelve and seventeen-fortieths

28. Sixty-seven and twenty-three hundredths

Write the English name for each mixed numeral.

29. $4\frac{5}{8}$

30. $13\frac{2}{11}$

31. $50\frac{17}{100}$

tors like 10, 100, 1000, 10,000 and so on. At this time let's take a closer look at some of these.

Fraction	English Name
$\frac{23}{10}$	twenty-three tenths
$\frac{1}{100}$	one hundredth
$\frac{15}{100}$	fifteen hundredths
$\frac{3}{1000}$	three thousandths
$\frac{90}{10,000}$	ninety ten-thousandths
$\frac{82}{100,000}$	eighty-two hundred-thousandths

 Try Problems 13 through 24.

2 The English Name of a Mixed Numeral

A mixed numeral like $4\frac{2}{3}$ has a whole part and a fraction part. The word *and* is used in the English name to separate the two parts clearly.

$$4\frac{2}{3} \text{ is read "four and two-thirds."}$$

Here are some additional examples.

Mixed Numeral	English Name
$5\frac{2}{7}$	five and two-sevenths
$13\frac{9}{10}$	thirteen and nine-tenths
$25\frac{12}{25}$	twenty-five and twelve twenty-fifths
$9\frac{3}{100}$	nine and three hundredths

 Try Problems 25 through 31.

 Answers to Try These Problems

1. $\frac{2}{2}$ 2. $\frac{2}{3}$ 3. $\frac{3}{5}$ 4. $1\frac{1}{9}$ 5. one-sixth   6. five-halves   7. $\frac{9}{10}$

8. $\frac{10}{17}$ 9. $\frac{18}{42}$ 10. $\frac{65}{63}$ 11. twelve-thirteenths   12. eight-fiftieths

13. $\frac{8}{10}$ 14. $\frac{30}{100}$ 15. $\frac{7}{100}$ 16. $\frac{62}{10}$ 17. $\frac{13}{1000}$ 18. $\frac{3}{100,000}$ 19. $\frac{50}{10,000}$

20. $\frac{96}{1000}$ 21. eighteen hundredths   22. thirty-three tenths

23. four thousandths   24. twenty-seven ten-thousandths

EXERCISES 3.2

Write a fraction for each.

1. One-half 2. Nine-fourths 3. Twelve-fifths
4. Eighty-five thirds 5. Two-thirteenths
6. Ninety-three two-hundredths 7. Eleven-thirtieths
8. One thousand twenty-thirds 9. Five-tenths
10. Forty-five hundredths 11. Thirty-six thousandths
12. Eighteen hundred-thousandths

Write the English name for each.

13. $\frac{7}{2}$ 14. $\frac{3}{7}$ 15. $\frac{6}{11}$ 16. $\frac{86}{90}$ 17. $\frac{1}{100}$ 18. $\frac{5}{10,000}$

Write a mixed numeral for each.

19. Six and two-fifths 20. Fifteen and seven-tenths
21. Sixty and three hundredths 22. Five and thirteen thousandths

Write the English name for each.

23. $9\frac{3}{10}$ 24. $80\frac{1}{2}$ 25. $14\frac{17}{100}$ 26. $27\frac{8}{13}$

3.3	RAISING FRACTIONS TO HIGHER TERMS AND CONVERTING WHOLE NUMERALS TO FRACTIONS

OBJECTIVES ▮ Write two equal fractions represented by a shaded region.
▮ Find a missing numerator so that two fractions are equal.
▮ Find a missing numerator so that a whole numeral is equal to a fraction.
▮ Raise a fraction to higher terms to have a specified denominator.
▮ Convert a whole numeral to a fraction having a specified denominator.

1 Raising Fractions to Higher Terms

If you bought a pizza, there are many ways you could eat $\frac{1}{2}$ of the pizza. If you cut the pizza into 2 equal parts and ate 1 part, you would eat $\frac{1}{2}$ of the pizza.

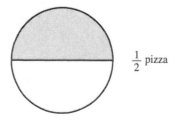

$\frac{1}{2}$ pizza

If you cut the pizza into 4 equal parts and ate 2 parts, you would eat $\frac{2}{4}$ of the pizza, which is the same as $\frac{1}{2}$ of the pizza.

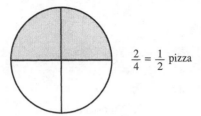

$$\frac{2}{4} = \frac{1}{2} \text{ pizza}$$

If you cut the pizza into 6 equal parts and ate 3 parts, you would eat $\frac{3}{6}$ of the pizza, which is the same as $\frac{1}{2}$ of the pizza.

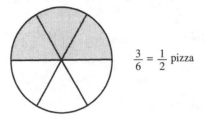

$$\frac{3}{6} = \frac{1}{2} \text{ pizza}$$

If you cut the pizza into 8 equal parts and ate 4 parts, you would eat $\frac{4}{8}$ of the pizza, which is the same as $\frac{1}{2}$ of the pizza.

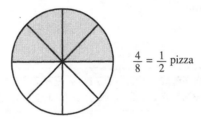

$$\frac{4}{8} = \frac{1}{2} \text{ pizza}$$

The fractions $\frac{1}{2}$, $\frac{2}{4}$, $\frac{3}{6}$, and $\frac{4}{8}$ are equal numbers.

$$\frac{1}{2} = \frac{2}{4} = \frac{3}{6} = \frac{4}{8}$$

Observe that the fraction $\frac{2}{4}$ can be obtained from $\frac{1}{2}$ by multiplying the numerator and denominator by 2.

$$\frac{1}{2} = \frac{1 \times 2}{2 \times 2} = \frac{2}{4}$$

The fraction $\frac{3}{6}$ can be obtained from $\frac{1}{2}$ by multiplying the numerator and denominator by 3.

$$\frac{1}{2} = \frac{1 \times 3}{2 \times 3} = \frac{3}{6}$$

The fraction $\frac{4}{8}$ can be obtained from $\frac{1}{2}$ by multiplying the numerator and denominator by 4.

$$\frac{1}{2} = \frac{1 \times 4}{2 \times 4} = \frac{4}{8}$$

Try These Problems

Write two equal fractions represented by the shaded region. Assume each figure represents one whole.

1.

2.

3.

Find the missing numerator so that the two numbers are equal.

4. $\frac{3}{5} = \frac{?}{10}$

5. $\frac{5}{6} = \frac{?}{24}$

6. $\frac{1}{12} = \frac{?}{60}$

7. $\frac{5}{9} = \frac{?}{153}$

In general, we can multiply the numerator and denominator of a fraction by the *same* nonzero number without changing the value of the fraction. The process of multiplying the numerator and denominator by the same number is called **raising the fraction to higher terms.**

Raising a Fraction to Higher Terms

Multiplying the numerator and denominator of a fraction by the same nonzero number does not change the value of the fraction.

EXAMPLE 1   Write two equal fractions represented by the shaded region. Assume the figure represents one whole.

SOLUTION   First, view the figure as divided into 12 equal parts. Nine of these parts are shaded, so the fraction is $\frac{9}{12}$.

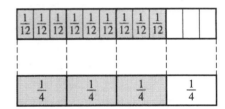

Second, view the figure as divided into 4 equal parts. Three of these parts are shaded, so the fraction is $\frac{3}{4}$. The fractions are $\frac{9}{12}$ and $\frac{3}{4}$. ■

Try Problems 1 through 3.

EXAMPLE 2   Find the missing numerator so that the two fractions are equal.

a. $\frac{2}{5} = \frac{?}{45}$ **b.** $\frac{3}{7} = \frac{?}{161}$

SOLUTION

a.
$$\frac{2}{5} = \frac{2 \times 9}{5 \times 9}$$
$$= \frac{18}{45}$$

Divide 45 by 5 to obtain 9. $5\overline{)45}^{\,9}$
Multiply numerator and denominator of $\frac{2}{5}$ by 9 to obtain an equal fraction with denominator 45.

The missing number is 18.

b.
$$\frac{3}{7} = \frac{3 \times 23}{7 \times 23}$$
$$= \frac{69}{161}$$

Divide 161 by 7 to obtain 23. $7\overline{)161}^{\,23}$
Multiply numerator and denominator of $\frac{3}{7}$ by 23 to obtain an equal fraction with denominator 161.

The missing numerator is 69. ■

   **Try Problems 4 through 7.**

Try These Problems

Find the missing numerator so that the two numbers are equal.

8. $1 = \frac{?}{9}$

9. $1 = \frac{?}{12}$

2 Writing Whole Numerals as Fractions

Recall from Section 3.1 that the number 1 can be written as a fraction in many ways. The pictures that follow illustrate this.

$1 = \frac{1}{1}$ □ **one**

$1 = \frac{2}{2}$ $\boxed{\frac{1}{2}}\boxed{\frac{1}{2}}$ **one** equals **two-halves**

$1 = \frac{3}{3}$ $\boxed{\frac{1}{3}}\boxed{\frac{1}{3}}\boxed{\frac{1}{3}}$ **one** equals **three-thirds**

$1 = \frac{4}{4}$ $\boxed{\frac{1}{4}}\boxed{\frac{1}{4}}\boxed{\frac{1}{4}}\boxed{\frac{1}{4}}$ **one** equals **four-fourths**

We can write 1 in fractional form simply by making the numerator equal the denominator.

 Try Problems 8 and 9.

The number 2 can also be written as a fraction in many ways. The pictures that follow illustrate this.

$2 = \frac{2}{1}$ □ □ **two**

$2 = \frac{4}{2}$ $\boxed{\frac{1}{2}}\boxed{\frac{1}{2}}$ $\boxed{\frac{1}{2}}\boxed{\frac{1}{2}}$ **two** equals **four-halves**

$2 = \frac{6}{3}$ $\boxed{\frac{1}{3}}\boxed{\frac{1}{3}}\boxed{\frac{1}{3}}$ $\boxed{\frac{1}{3}}\boxed{\frac{1}{3}}\boxed{\frac{1}{3}}$ **two** equals **six-thirds**

$2 = \frac{8}{4}$ $\boxed{\frac{1}{4}}\boxed{\frac{1}{4}}\boxed{\frac{1}{4}}\boxed{\frac{1}{4}}$ $\boxed{\frac{1}{4}}\boxed{\frac{1}{4}}\boxed{\frac{1}{4}}\boxed{\frac{1}{4}}$ **two** equals **eight-fourths**

We can write 2 as a fraction with any nonzero denominator. The following example illustrates how to do this.

EXAMPLE 3   Find the missing numerator so that the two numbers are equal.

a. $2 = \frac{?}{5}$ **b.** $2 = \frac{?}{12}$

 **Try These Problems**

Find the missing numerator so that the two numbers are equal.

10. $2 = \frac{?}{8}$

11. $2 = \frac{?}{15}$

12. $4 = \frac{?}{3}$

13. $6 = \frac{?}{2}$

14. $7 = \frac{?}{40}$

15. $18 = \frac{?}{6}$

SOLUTION

a. $2 = \dfrac{2}{1}$ Write 2 as $\frac{2}{1}$.

$= \dfrac{2 \times 5}{1 \times 5}$ Multiply numerator and denominator by 5 to obtain an equal fraction with denominator 5.

$= \dfrac{10}{5}$

The missing numerator is 10.

b. $2 = \dfrac{2}{1}$ Write 2 as $\frac{2}{1}$.

$= \dfrac{2 \times 12}{1 \times 12}$ Multiply numerator and denominator by 12 to obtain an equal fraction with denominator 12.

$= \dfrac{24}{12}$

The missing numerator is 24. ■

 Try Problems 10 and 11.

Any whole numeral can be written as a fraction with any nonzero denominator. The following example illustrates how to do this.

EXAMPLE 4   Find the missing numerator so that the two numbers are equal.

a. $3 = \frac{?}{9}$ **b.** $12 = \frac{?}{4}$

SOLUTION

a. $3 = \dfrac{3}{1}$ Write 3 as $\frac{3}{1}$.

$= \dfrac{3 \times 9}{1 \times 9}$ Multiply numerator and denominator by 9 to obtain an equal fraction with denominator 9.

$= \dfrac{27}{9}$

The missing numerator is 27.

b. $12 = \dfrac{12}{1}$ Write 12 as $\frac{12}{1}$.

$= \dfrac{12 \times 4}{1 \times 4}$ Multiply numerator and denominator by 4 to obtain an equal fraction with denominator 4.

$= \dfrac{48}{4}$

The missing numerator is 48. ■

 Try Problems 12 through 15.

EXERCISES 3.3

Write two equal fractions represented by the shaded region. Assume each figure represents one whole.

1.   **2.**  **3.**

4.   **5.**   **6.**

7. 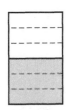 **8.**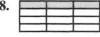

Find the missing numerator so that the two numbers are equal.

9. $\frac{3}{4} = \frac{?}{20}$ **10.** $\frac{5}{9} = \frac{?}{18}$ **11.** $\frac{10}{3} = \frac{?}{12}$ **12.** $\frac{7}{6} = \frac{?}{54}$

13. $\frac{11}{5} = \frac{?}{65}$ **14.** $\frac{7}{4} = \frac{?}{96}$ **15.** $\frac{2}{25} = \frac{?}{350}$ **16.** $\frac{5}{36} = \frac{?}{288}$

17. $1 = \frac{?}{8}$ **18.** $1 = \frac{?}{37}$ **19.** $3 = \frac{?}{2}$ **20.** $3 = \frac{?}{5}$

21. $5 = \frac{?}{7}$ **22.** $8 = \frac{?}{9}$ **23.** $6 = \frac{?}{21}$ **24.** $25 = \frac{?}{5}$

25. Convert $\frac{1}{3}$ to a fraction with denominator 24.

26. Write a fraction with denominator 30 that has the same value as $\frac{7}{6}$.

27. Write a fraction with denominator 42 that has the same value as $\frac{5}{7}$.

28. Write a fraction with denominator 8 that is equal to the whole number 3.

29. Write a fraction with denominator 15 that is equal to the whole number 4.

30. Convert 16 to a fraction with denominator 6.

| **3.4** | CONVERTING IMPROPER FRACTIONS TO MIXED NUMERALS AND VICE VERSA |

OBJECTIVES
▌ Convert an improper fraction to a mixed or whole numeral.
▌ Convert a mixed numeral to an improper fraction.
▌ Recognize whether or not a fraction can be converted to a mixed numeral.

1 Converting Improper Fractions to Mixed Numerals or Whole Numerals

In Section 3.1 you learned that an improper fraction (a fraction more than one whole) can be written as a whole numeral or mixed numeral. The picture that follows illustrates that $\frac{12}{3}$ is equal to 4.

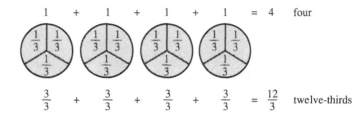

$$1 \quad + \quad 1 \quad + \quad 1 \quad + \quad 1 \quad = \quad 4 \quad \text{four}$$

$$\frac{3}{3} \quad + \quad \frac{3}{3} \quad + \quad \frac{3}{3} \quad + \quad \frac{3}{3} \quad = \quad \frac{12}{3} \quad \text{twelve-thirds}$$

Observe that we can obtain the whole numeral 4 from the improper fraction $\frac{12}{3}$ without viewing the picture. The numerator 12 divided by the denominator 3 yields 4.

$$\frac{12}{3} = 12 \div 3 = 4$$

or

$$\frac{12}{3} \rightarrow 3\overline{)12}^{\;4} \rightarrow \frac{12}{3} = 4$$

In some cases an improper fraction does not equal a whole numeral but can be written as a mixed numeral. The following picture illustrates that $\frac{11}{4}$ is equal to $2\frac{3}{4}$.

$$1 \quad + \quad 1 \quad + \quad \frac{3}{4} \quad = \quad 2 + \frac{3}{4} = 2\frac{3}{4} \quad \text{two and three-fourths}$$

$$\frac{4}{4} \quad + \quad \frac{4}{4} \quad + \quad \frac{3}{4} \quad = \quad \frac{11}{4} \quad \text{eleven-fourths}$$

Observe that we can obtain the mixed numeral $2\frac{3}{4}$ from the improper fraction $\frac{11}{4}$ without viewing the picture. Divide the numerator 11 by the denominator 4.

$$\frac{11}{4} \rightarrow 4\overline{)11}^{\;2} \rightarrow \frac{11}{4} = 2\frac{3}{4}$$
$$\underline{8}$$
$$3$$

After performing the division, the quotient 2 tells you how many wholes are in $\frac{11}{4}$ and the remainder 3 tells you how many $\frac{1}{4}$s are left over. Note that the denominator 4 in the mixed numeral is the same as the original denominator in the improper fraction. Now we look at more examples.

Try These Problems

Convert each of these improper fractions to a mixed or whole numeral.

1. $\frac{42}{7}$

2. $\frac{75}{25}$

3. $\frac{38}{5}$

4. $\frac{74}{9}$

5. $\frac{3240}{30}$

6. $\frac{252}{25}$

EXAMPLE 1   Convert each improper fraction to a mixed or whole numeral.

a. $\frac{91}{13}$ b. $\frac{565}{8}$

SOLUTION

a. $\frac{91}{13}$ means 91 divided by 13.

$$13\overline{)91} \atop \underline{91} \atop {}^{7}$$

$$\frac{91}{13} = 7$$

b. $\frac{565}{8}$ means 565 divided by 8.

$$8\overline{)565} \atop \underline{56} \atop 5 \atop \underline{0} \atop 5 \atop {}^{70}$$

$$\frac{565}{8} = 70\frac{5}{8} \quad \blacksquare$$

 Try Problems 1 through 6.

2 | Converting Mixed Numerals to Improper Fractions

You have learned to convert improper fractions to mixed numerals by dividing the numerator by the denominator. For example,

$$\frac{22}{5} \rightarrow 5\overline{)22} \atop \underline{20} \atop 2 \atop {}^{4} \rightarrow \frac{22}{5} = 4\frac{2}{5}$$

We can reverse this process and convert a mixed numeral to an improper fraction. Let's begin here with $4\frac{2}{5}$ and show how to obtain the improper fraction $\frac{22}{5}$.

$$4\frac{2}{5} = 4 + \frac{2}{5}$$

The mixed numeral $4\frac{2}{5}$ is a shortcut notation for $4 + \frac{2}{5}$.

$$= \frac{4 \times 5}{1 \times 5} + \frac{2}{5}$$

Write 4 as $\frac{4}{1}$, then multiply numerator and denominator by 5 so that 4 is written as a fraction with the same denominator as $\frac{2}{5}$.

$$= \frac{20}{5} + \frac{2}{5}$$

Observe that $\frac{20}{5}$ is the same as 4.

$$= \frac{22}{5}$$

Add the numerators and place this over the common denominator.

By using the above procedure, we convert the whole numeral 4 to a fraction with denominator 5, then add this fraction to the fraction $\frac{2}{5}$. The result is $\frac{22}{5}$. There is a shortcut for obtaining the result $\frac{22}{5}$. Observe that

Try These Problems

Convert each of these mixed numerals to an improper fraction.

7. $2\frac{1}{3}$

8. $7\frac{3}{4}$

9. $1\frac{7}{20}$

10. $24\frac{9}{13}$

the denominator 5 is the same denominator that was in the mixed numeral $4\frac{2}{5}$. Also the numerator 22 can be obtained by multiplying the whole numeral 4 by the denominator 5, then adding the original numerator 2. For example,

$$4\frac{2}{5} = \frac{22}{5}$$

To obtain 22, multiply 4 by 5, then add 2.
Keep the same denominator 5.

EXAMPLE 2   Convert $6\frac{7}{12}$ to an improper fraction.

SOLUTION

LONG METHOD

$$6\frac{7}{12} = 6 + \frac{7}{12}$$

$$= \frac{6 \times 12}{1 \times 12} + \frac{7}{12}$$

$$= \frac{72}{12} + \frac{7}{12} \qquad \text{Convert 6 to } \frac{72}{12}.$$

$$= \frac{79}{12} \qquad \text{Add the fractions.}$$

SHORTCUT

$$6\frac{7}{12} = \frac{79}{12}$$

To obtain 79, multiply 6 by 12, then add 7.
Keep the same denominator 12.

CHECK

$$\frac{79}{12} \rightarrow 12\overline{)79} \begin{array}{c} 6 \\ \underline{72} \\ 7 \end{array} \rightarrow \frac{79}{12} = 6\frac{7}{12} \quad \blacksquare$$

Now we state a general rule for converting a mixed numeral to an improper fraction. In this rule we state both the long method and the shortcut.

Converting a Mixed Numeral to an Improper Fraction

Long Method

1. Write the whole numeral part as an improper fraction with a denominator that is the same as the denominator in the fractional part.
2. Add the two fractions by adding the numerators and placing this over the common denominator.

Shortcut

Multiply the whole numeral by the denominator, then add the numerator to obtain the numerator of the improper fraction. Keep the same denominator.

 Try Problems 7 through 10.

▲ Answers to Try These Problems

1. 6   2. 3   3. $7\frac{3}{5}$ 4. $8\frac{2}{9}$ 5. 108   6. $10\frac{2}{25}$ 7. $\frac{7}{3}$ 8. $\frac{31}{4}$
9. $\frac{27}{20}$ 10. $\frac{321}{13}$

EXERCISES 3.4

Convert each of these improper fractions to a mixed or whole numeral.

1. $\frac{20}{4}$ 2. $\frac{54}{6}$ 3. $\frac{36}{5}$ 4. $\frac{63}{8}$ 5. $\frac{245}{6}$

6. $\frac{191}{9}$ 7. $\frac{200}{8}$ 8. $\frac{480}{15}$ 9. $\frac{211}{20}$ 10. $\frac{5115}{17}$

11. $\frac{6622}{22}$ 12. $\frac{5200}{13}$

Convert each of these mixed numerals to an improper fraction.

13. $3\frac{1}{4}$ 14. $2\frac{8}{9}$ 15. $7\frac{2}{5}$ 16. $1\frac{12}{17}$ 17. $13\frac{3}{4}$

18. $25\frac{1}{6}$ 19. $34\frac{4}{5}$ 20. $18\frac{5}{7}$ 21. $3\frac{8}{11}$ 22. $8\frac{1}{20}$

23. $15\frac{9}{10}$ 24. $36\frac{3}{41}$

A fraction less than one whole cannot *be written as a whole or mixed numeral.*
Write each of these numbers as a whole or mixed numeral if possible. If not possi-
ble, say not possible.

25. $\frac{1}{3}$ 26. $\frac{3}{3}$ 27. $\frac{3}{1}$ 28. $\frac{5}{3}$ 29. $\frac{4}{2}$

30. $\frac{3}{4}$ 31. $\frac{4}{4}$ 32. $\frac{13}{4}$ 33. $\frac{13}{27}$ 34. $\frac{13}{13}$

35. $\frac{27}{13}$ 36. $\frac{49}{7}$

3.5   REDUCING FRACTIONS TO LOWEST TERMS

OBJECTIVES   ▮ Reduce a fraction to lowest terms (or simplify a fraction).
             ▮ Decide whether or not a fraction can be reduced to lowest terms.

1   Numerators and Denominators that Factor Easily

Recall from Section 3.3 that you can multiply the numerator and denominator of a fraction by the *same* nonzero number without changing
the value of the fraction. For example,

$$\frac{3}{4} = \frac{3 \times 5}{4 \times 5} = \frac{15}{20}$$

This process is called **raising the fraction to higher terms.** We can
reverse this process and divide the numerator and denominator by the
same nonzero number without changing the value of the fraction. For
example,

$$\frac{15}{20} = \frac{15 \div 5}{20 \div 5} = \frac{3}{4}$$

Try These Problems

Reduce to lowest terms.

1. $\frac{10}{25}$
2. $\frac{9}{15}$
3. $\frac{18}{24}$
4. $\frac{14}{49}$
5. $\frac{56}{72}$

This process is called reducing the fraction to lower terms. In fact, we say that $\frac{3}{4}$ is **reduced to lowest terms** (or **simplified**) because the only common divisor of 3 and 4 is 1. The fraction $\frac{15}{20}$ is *not* reduced to lowest terms (or *not* simplified) because a common divisor of 15 and 20 is 5, a number other than 1.

To reduce a fraction to lowest terms you must be able to find common divisors of the numerator and denominator. Viewing the numerator and denominator in factored form can be helpful. For example,

$$\frac{15}{21} = \frac{\cancel{3} \times 5}{\cancel{3} \times 7} = \frac{5}{7} \qquad \text{Write 15 in factored form.}$$
Write 21 in factored form.

Cancelling the common factor 3 from the numerator and denominator is equivalent to dividing the numerator and denominator by 3.

EXAMPLE 1   Reduce to lowest terms: $\frac{42}{63}$

SOLUTION   There is more than one way to write the steps when simplifying fractions. We show this problem done in two different ways.

METHOD 1

$$\frac{42}{63} = \frac{6 \times \cancel{7}}{\cancel{7} \times 9}$$
Cancel the common factor 7. This is equivalent to dividing the numerator and denominator by 7.

$$= \frac{6}{9}$$
Do not stop until all common factors have been cancelled.

$$= \frac{2 \times \cancel{3}}{3 \times \cancel{3}}$$
Cancel the common factor 3. This is equivalent to dividing the numerator and denominator by 3.

$$= \frac{2}{3}$$

METHOD 2

$$\frac{42}{63} = \frac{42 \div 3}{63 \div 3}$$
Divide numerator and denominator by 3.

$$= \frac{14}{21}$$

$$= \frac{14 \div 7}{21 \div 7}$$
Divide numerator and denominator by 7.

$$= \frac{2}{3} \ \blacksquare$$

Try Problems 1 through 5.

If you factor the numerator and denominator as the product of primes, and there are no common prime factors, then the fraction is reduced to lowest terms. For example, consider the fraction $\frac{25}{36}$.

$$\frac{25}{36} = \frac{5 \times 5}{6 \times 6} = \frac{5 \times 5}{2 \times 3 \times 2 \times 3}$$

Try These Problems

Reduce to lowest terms, if possible. If not possible, say not possible.

6. $\frac{64}{72}$

7. $\frac{12}{25}$

8. $\frac{21}{81}$

9. $\frac{49}{54}$

Because there are no common prime factors in the numerator and denominator, the fraction is reduced to lowest terms. Recall that the first few prime numbers are as follows.

Primes Less Than 20							
2	3	5	7	11	13	17	19

A prime number has no divisors, other than itself and one.

EXAMPLE 2   Reduce to lowest terms, if possible. If not possible, say *not possible.*

a. $\frac{28}{48}$ **b.** $\frac{35}{54}$

SOLUTION

a.
$$\frac{28}{48} = \frac{4 \times 7}{6 \times 8}$$

$$= \frac{\cancel{2} \times \cancel{2} \times 7}{\cancel{2} \times 3 \times \cancel{2} \times 2 \times 2}$$

Cancel two factors of 2. This is equivalent to dividing numerator and denominator by 4.

$$= \frac{7}{12}$$

b.
$$\frac{35}{54} = \frac{5 \times 7}{6 \times 9}$$

$$= \frac{5 \times 7}{2 \times 3 \times 3 \times 3}$$

There are no common prime factors to cancel.

$$= \frac{35}{54}$$

It is not possible to reduce $\frac{35}{54}$.

 Try Problems 6 through 9.

In case the fraction can be written as a mixed numeral, then either the improper fraction form or the mixed numeral form is considered simplified (reduced to lowest terms) as long as the fraction that appears has no common factors in the numerator and denominator, other than 1, and the fractional part of the mixed numeral is less than 1 whole.

EXAMPLE 3   Simplify: $\frac{30}{18}$.

SOLUTION

$$\frac{30}{18} = \frac{6 \times 5}{2 \times 9}$$

$$= \frac{\cancel{2} \times \cancel{3} \times 5}{\cancel{2} \times \cancel{3} \times 3}$$

Cancel the common factors 2 and 3. This is equivalent to dividing the numerator and denominator by 6.

$$= \frac{5}{3} \text{ or } 1\frac{2}{3}$$

Try These Problems

Simplify.

10. $\frac{16}{12}$

11. $\frac{36}{12}$

12. $\frac{63}{42}$

13. $\frac{63}{45}$

In Example 3, both $\frac{5}{3}$ and $1\frac{2}{3}$ are considered simplified.

In case the fraction can be written as a whole numeral, then only the whole numeral form is considered simplified. For example, the fractions $\frac{12}{3}$ and $\frac{8}{1}$ are *not* simplified. The simplified forms are 4 and 8, respectively.

$$\frac{12}{3} = \frac{\cancel{3} \times 4}{\underset{1}{\cancel{3}}} = 4 \qquad \frac{8}{1} = 8$$

 Try Problems 10 through 13.

We summarize the previous discussion by writing a rule for reducing fractions to lowest terms.

> ### *Reducing Fractions to Lowest Terms (Simplifying Fractions)*
>
> 1. Write the numerator and denominator as the product of primes.
> 2. Cancel all common factors from the numerator and denominator. (This is equivalent to dividing the numerator and denominator by the same nonzero number.)
> 3. If the fraction can be written as a mixed numeral, either the improper fraction form or the mixed numeral form is accepted as simplified.
> 4. If the fraction can be written as a whole numeral, then only the whole numeral form is considered simplified.

2 Larger Numerators and Denominators

Now we look at strategies for reducing more difficult fractions to lowest terms. You want to be able to recognize more prime numbers. Here we list the first 16 primes.

First Sixteen Primes							
2	3	5	7	11	13	17	19
23	29	31	37	41	43	47	53

Also, you want to recall the divisibility rules that were covered in Chapter 2. Here we list them for review.

Divisibility Rules

1. Any whole number ending in 0, 2, 4, 6, or 8 is divisible by 2. (For example, 20, 32, 74, 126, and 708 are all divisible by 2.)
2. Any whole number with digits that add up to a number divisible by 3 is itself divisible by 3. (For example, 42, 51, 72 and 462 are all divisible by 3.)
3. Any whole number ending in 5 or 0 is divisible by 5. (For example, 785 and 810 are both divisible by 5.)
4. Any whole number ending in
   one 0 is divisible by 10
   two 0s is divisible by 100
   three 0s is divisible by 1000
   and so on. (For example, 3050 is divisible by 10, and 17,000 is divisible by 1000.)

The following examples illustrate how to simplify more difficult fractions.

EXAMPLE 4 Simplify: $\frac{28}{91}$

SOLUTION Because the numerator 28 is easy to factor, we write 28 as the product of primes, then check to see if any of these prime factors are divisors of 91.

$$28 = 4 \times 7$$
$$= 2 \times 2 \times 7$$

The prime factors of 28 are 2 and 7. Is 91 divisible by 2? No, because 91 does not end in 0, 2, 4, 6, or 8. (91 is not even.) Is 91 divisible by 7? Divide 91 by 7 to find out.

$$\begin{array}{r} 13 \\ 7\overline{)91} \\ \underline{7} \\ 21 \\ \underline{21} \end{array}$$

Yes, $91 = 7 \times 13$. Now we can reduce the fraction to lowest terms.

$$\frac{28}{91} = \frac{4 \times \cancel{7}}{\cancel{7} \times 13} \qquad \text{Cancel the common factor 7.}$$
$$= \frac{4}{13}$$

The fraction $\frac{4}{13}$ is reduced to lowest terms because there are no common prime factors in the numerator and denominator.

$$\frac{4}{13} = \frac{2 \times 2}{13} \qquad \text{This fraction cannot be reduced to lowest terms.}$$

Therefore, $\frac{28}{91} = \frac{4}{13}$. ■

EXAMPLE 5   Simplify: $\frac{117}{360}$

SOLUTION   Write either the numerator or denominator as the product of primes, whichever is easier.

$$360 = \quad 36 \quad \times \quad 10$$
$$= \quad 6 \quad \times \quad 6 \quad \times 5 \times 2$$
$$= 2 \times 3 \times 2 \times 3 \times 5 \times 2$$

The prime factors of 360 are 2, 3, and 5. Check to see if 2, 3, or 5 are divisors of 117. Is 117 divisible by 2? No, because 117 does not end in 0, 2, 4, 6, or 8. Is 117 divisible by 3? Yes, because the sum of the digits is 9 and 9 is divisible by 3. Divide 117 by 3 to find the other factor.

$$\begin{array}{r} 39 \\ 3\overline{)117} \\ \underline{9} \\ 27 \\ \underline{27} \end{array}$$

Therefore, $117 = 3 \times 39$. Note that 3 is also a divisor of 39.

$$117 = 3 \times 39$$
$$= 3 \times 3 \times 13$$

Now we can see how to reduce the original fraction to lowest terms.

$$\frac{117}{360} = \frac{\cancel{3} \times \cancel{3} \times 13}{2 \times \cancel{3} \times 2 \times \cancel{3} \times 5 \times 2}$$

Cancel two factors of 3.

$$= \frac{13}{2 \times 2 \times 5 \times 2}$$

There are no more common prime factors in the numerator and denominator.

$$= \frac{13}{40} \quad \blacksquare$$

EXAMPLE 6   Simplify: $\frac{204}{85}$

SOLUTION   Begin by factoring either the numerator or the denominator as the product of primes. We choose 85 because it seems easier. Because 85 ends in 5, it is divisible by 5.

$$\begin{array}{r} 17 \\ 5\overline{)85} \\ \underline{5} \\ 35 \\ \underline{35} \end{array}$$

Therefore,

$$85 = 5 \times 17$$

and the only prime factors of 85 are 5 and 17. Now check to see if the numerator 204 is divisible by 5 or 17. Is 204 divisible by 5? No, because it does not end in 5 or 0. Is 204 divisible by 17?

Try These Problems

Simplify.

14. $\frac{36}{150}$

15. $\frac{24}{68}$

16. $\frac{147}{180}$

17. $\frac{133}{76}$

18. $\frac{104}{195}$

19. $\frac{253}{207}$

20. $\frac{40}{120}$

21. $\frac{130}{2500}$

22. $\frac{25,000}{1500}$

23. $\frac{1200}{90}$

$$
\begin{array}{r}
12 \\
17\overline{)204} \\
\underline{17} \\
34 \\
\underline{34}
\end{array}
$$

Yes, $204 = 12 \times 17$. Now we can reduce the fraction to lowest terms.

$$\frac{204}{85} = \frac{12 \times \cancel{17}}{5 \times \cancel{17}}$$ Cancel the common factor 17.

$$= \frac{2 \times 2 \times 3}{5}$$ Make sure there are no common prime factors left to cancel.

$$= \frac{12}{5} \text{ or } 2\frac{2}{5} \blacksquare$$

 Try Problems 14 through 19.

EXAMPLE 7   Simplify: $\frac{3600}{42,000}$

SOLUTION

$$\frac{3600}{42,000} = \frac{36 \times 100}{42 \times 1000}$$

$$= \frac{36 \times \cancel{10} \times \cancel{10}}{42 \times \cancel{10} \times \cancel{10} \times 10}$$ Cancel the two factors of 10.

$$= \frac{\cancel{6} \times 6}{\cancel{6} \times 7 \times 10}$$ Cancel the common factor 6.

$$= \frac{\cancel{2} \times 3}{7 \times \cancel{2} \times 5}$$ Cancel the common factor 2.

$$= \frac{3}{35}$$

 Try Problems 20 through 23.

 Answers to Try These Problems

1. $\frac{2}{5}$ **2.** $\frac{3}{5}$ **3.** $\frac{3}{4}$ **4.** $\frac{2}{7}$ **5.** $\frac{7}{9}$ **6.** $\frac{8}{9}$ **7.** not possible   **8.** $\frac{7}{27}$
9. not possible   **10.** $\frac{4}{3}$ or $1\frac{1}{3}$ **11.** 3   **12.** $\frac{3}{2}$ or $1\frac{1}{2}$ **13.** $1\frac{2}{5}$
14. $\frac{6}{25}$ **15.** $\frac{6}{17}$ **16.** $\frac{49}{60}$ **17.** $\frac{7}{4}$ or $1\frac{3}{4}$ **18.** $\frac{8}{15}$ **19.** $\frac{11}{9}$ or $1\frac{2}{9}$ **20.** $\frac{1}{3}$
21. $\frac{13}{250}$ **22.** $\frac{50}{3}$ or $16\frac{2}{3}$ **23.** $\frac{40}{3}$ or $13\frac{1}{3}$

EXERCISES 3.5

Reduce to lowest terms, if possible. If not possible, say not possible.

1. $\frac{6}{9}$ **2.** $\frac{10}{15}$ **3.** $\frac{12}{8}$ **4.** $\frac{30}{18}$ **5.** $\frac{24}{40}$

6. $\frac{27}{54}$ **7.** $\frac{54}{72}$ **8.** $\frac{45}{56}$ **9.** $\frac{64}{81}$ **10.** $\frac{60}{48}$

11. $\frac{21}{70}$ **12.** $\frac{35}{20}$ **13.** $\frac{36}{8}$ **14.** $\frac{28}{49}$ **15.** $\frac{48}{42}$

16. $\frac{13}{20}$ **17.** $\frac{17}{21}$ **18.** $\frac{72}{80}$ **19.** $\frac{54}{90}$ **20.** $\frac{120}{75}$

Simplify.

21. $\frac{42}{66}$　　**22.** $\frac{72}{117}$　　**23.** $\frac{15}{85}$　　**24.** $\frac{16}{84}$　　**25.** $\frac{91}{14}$

26. $\frac{80}{15}$　　**27.** $\frac{77}{140}$　　**28.** $\frac{60}{204}$　　**29.** $\frac{165}{45}$　　**30.** $\frac{126}{147}$

31. $\frac{90}{315}$　　**32.** $\frac{147}{196}$　　**33.** $\frac{55}{132}$　　**34.** $\frac{77}{143}$　　**35.** $\frac{39}{104}$

36. $\frac{26}{65}$　　**37.** $\frac{78}{52}$　　**38.** $\frac{156}{117}$　　**39.** $\frac{85}{68}$　　**40.** $\frac{153}{34}$

41. $\frac{68}{136}$　　**42.** $\frac{102}{255}$　　**43.** $\frac{133}{171}$　　**44.** $\frac{152}{57}$　　**45.** $\frac{228}{285}$

46. $\frac{380}{570}$　　**47.** $\frac{525}{390}$　　**48.** $\frac{380}{360}$　　**49.** $\frac{117}{135}$　　**50.** $\frac{288}{135}$

51. $\frac{441}{504}$　　**52.** $\frac{560}{693}$　　**53.** $\frac{120}{42}$　　**54.** $\frac{63}{1800}$　　**55.** $\frac{810}{4500}$

56. $\frac{70}{3600}$　　**57.** $\frac{2100}{14,000}$　　**58.** $\frac{11,200}{8400}$　　**59.** $\frac{25,300}{781,000}$　　**60.** $\frac{5200}{31,200}$

Adding Fractions with Like Denominators

EXAMPLE $\dfrac{1}{3} + \dfrac{1}{3} = \dfrac{1+1}{3} = \dfrac{2}{3}$

Add the numerators, 1 + 1 = 2, and put this over the common denominator 3.

EXAMPLE $\dfrac{1}{4} + \dfrac{1}{4} + \dfrac{2}{4} = \dfrac{1+1+2}{4} = \dfrac{4}{4}$ or 1

EXAMPLE $2\dfrac{2}{5} + 1\dfrac{4}{5} = 3\dfrac{6}{5} = 3 + 1\dfrac{1}{5} = 4\dfrac{1}{5}$ or $\dfrac{21}{5}$

When adding mixed numbers, you can add the wholes separately from the fractions. If answering with a mixed number, write the fraction part less than one whole. Here we converted $3\dfrac{6}{5}$ to the mixed number $4\dfrac{1}{5}$. Observe that $4\dfrac{1}{5}$ has the fractional part, $\dfrac{1}{5}$, less than 1. It takes $\dfrac{5}{5}$ to make 1.

The result $4\dfrac{1}{5}$ can also be written as the improper fraction $\dfrac{21}{5}$. Both forms are considered simplified.

EXERCISES 3-I

Add & simplify. When possible, express the result in more than one way.

1. $\dfrac{1}{2} + \dfrac{1}{2} + \dfrac{1}{2}$

2. $\dfrac{3}{2} + \dfrac{1}{2} + \dfrac{2}{2}$

3. $\dfrac{4}{2} + \dfrac{3}{2} + \dfrac{1}{2} + \dfrac{1}{2}$

4. $\dfrac{1}{4} + \dfrac{1}{4} + \dfrac{1}{4}$

5. $\dfrac{1}{4} + \dfrac{1}{4} + \dfrac{3}{4}$

6. $\dfrac{3}{4} + \dfrac{1}{4} + \dfrac{1}{4} + \dfrac{2}{4}$

7. $\dfrac{1}{3} + \dfrac{4}{3}$

8. $\dfrac{1}{3} + \dfrac{3}{3} + \dfrac{2}{3}$

9. $\dfrac{5}{3} + \dfrac{1}{3} + \dfrac{1}{3} + \dfrac{4}{3} + \dfrac{1}{3}$

10. $\dfrac{2}{5} + \dfrac{1}{5}$

11. $\dfrac{3}{5} + \dfrac{4}{5} + \dfrac{1}{5}$

12. $\dfrac{3}{5} + \dfrac{2}{5} + \dfrac{1}{5} + \dfrac{6}{5}$

13. $1 + \dfrac{1}{2}$

14. $1 + \dfrac{2}{3} + \dfrac{1}{3}$

15. $\dfrac{2}{4} + \dfrac{1}{4} + 1 + 3$

16. $1\dfrac{1}{3} + \dfrac{1}{3}$

17. $\dfrac{1}{4} + 2\dfrac{3}{4} + \dfrac{1}{4}$

18. $\dfrac{2}{5} + \dfrac{1}{5} + 1\dfrac{3}{5} + 3$

19. $\dfrac{1}{6} + 1\dfrac{1}{6} + 1\dfrac{3}{6}$

20. $2\dfrac{1}{5} + \dfrac{2}{5} + 1\dfrac{1}{5}$

21. $2\dfrac{1}{8} + \dfrac{3}{8} + 3\dfrac{2}{8} + 1\dfrac{3}{8}$

Introduction to Subtracting Fractions with Like Denominators

EXAMPLE $\dfrac{6}{8} - \dfrac{2}{8} = \dfrac{6-2}{8} = \dfrac{4}{8} = \dfrac{4 \times 1}{2 \times 4} = \dfrac{1}{2}$

Subtract the numerators, $6 - 2 = 4$, and put this over the common denominator 8. Simplify the answer.

EXAMPLE $8\dfrac{3}{5} - 2\dfrac{1}{5} = 6\dfrac{2}{5}$

When subtracting mixed numbers, you can subtract the wholes separately from the fractions. Before doing this, make sure the fraction you are subtracting is smaller than the fraction you are subtracting from. Observe here that 1/5 is smaller than 3/5.

EXAMPLE $9\dfrac{5}{6} - 2 = 7\dfrac{5}{6}$

When subtracting a whole number from a mixed number, subtract the whole numbers and keep the fraction.

EXERCISES 3-J
Subtract & simplify. If possible, write the result in more than one way.

1. $\dfrac{4}{8} - \dfrac{1}{8}$
2. $\dfrac{7}{6} - \dfrac{2}{6}$
3. $\dfrac{6}{2} - \dfrac{4}{2}$

4. $\dfrac{7}{4} - \dfrac{3}{4}$
5. $\dfrac{7}{2} - \dfrac{3}{2}$
6. $\dfrac{7}{2} - \dfrac{1}{2}$

7. $\dfrac{8}{3} - \dfrac{4}{3}$
8. $\dfrac{11}{3} - \dfrac{9}{3}$
9. $\dfrac{13}{4} - \dfrac{8}{4}$

10. $\dfrac{2}{5} - \dfrac{1}{5}$
11. $\dfrac{9}{5} - \dfrac{2}{5}$
12. $\dfrac{12}{5} - \dfrac{2}{5}$

13. $\dfrac{5}{8} - \dfrac{3}{8}$
14. $\dfrac{9}{10} - \dfrac{7}{10}$
15. $\dfrac{9}{4} - \dfrac{7}{4}$

16. $\dfrac{12}{9} - \dfrac{6}{9}$
17. $9\dfrac{3}{4} - 2\dfrac{1}{4}$
18. $3\dfrac{2}{5} - 1\dfrac{1}{5}$

19. $8\dfrac{3}{6} - \dfrac{1}{6}$
20. $2\dfrac{4}{5} - \dfrac{1}{5}$
21. $12\dfrac{1}{8} - 3$

22. $8\dfrac{4}{9} - 6$
23. $7\dfrac{4}{8} - 2\dfrac{2}{8}$
24. $11\dfrac{7}{9} - 4\dfrac{4}{9}$

25. $7\dfrac{4}{4} - \dfrac{1}{4}$
26. $8\dfrac{1}{2} - 2\dfrac{1}{2}$
27. $10\dfrac{2}{9} - \dfrac{2}{9}$

Subtracting Fractions Involving Renaming

EXAMPLE $\quad 1 - \dfrac{2}{5} = \dfrac{5}{5} - \dfrac{2}{5} = \dfrac{3}{5}$

Write 1 as 5/5 so that you can do the subtraction.

EXAMPLE $\quad 8 - 2\dfrac{1}{3} = 7\dfrac{3}{3} - 2\dfrac{1}{3} = 5\dfrac{2}{3}$

Write 8 as $7\dfrac{3}{3}$ so that you can do the subtraction.

EXAMPLE $\quad 7\dfrac{1}{4} - 3\dfrac{3}{4}$

$\qquad = 6\dfrac{4}{4} + \dfrac{1}{4} - 3\dfrac{3}{4} \qquad$ Replace 7 with $6\dfrac{4}{4}$

$\qquad = 6\dfrac{5}{4} - 3\dfrac{3}{4} = 3\dfrac{2}{4} = 3\dfrac{1}{2} \qquad$ Add $\dfrac{4}{4}$ and $\dfrac{1}{4}$ to get $\dfrac{5}{4}$

EXERCISES 3-K

Subtract & simplify. If possible, write the result in more than one way.

1. $\quad 1 - \dfrac{3}{8}$

2. $\quad 1 - \dfrac{5}{6}$

3. $\quad 1 - \dfrac{1}{3}$

4. $\quad 1 - \dfrac{3}{4}$

5. $\quad 2 - \dfrac{1}{2}$

6. $\quad 2 - \dfrac{3}{5}$

7. $\quad 3 - \dfrac{2}{3}$

8. $\quad 6 - \dfrac{5}{8}$

9. $\quad 5 - \dfrac{2}{7}$

10. $\quad 6 - \dfrac{3}{7}$

11. $\quad 7 - 1\dfrac{2}{5}$

12. $\quad 8 - 2\dfrac{3}{5}$

13. $\quad 3 - 1\dfrac{1}{8}$

14. $\quad 4 - 2\dfrac{7}{8}$

15. $\quad 6 - 4\dfrac{3}{4}$

16. $\quad 5 - 4\dfrac{6}{9}$

17. $\quad 9\dfrac{3}{8} - \dfrac{5}{8}$

18. $\quad 4\dfrac{2}{7} - \dfrac{4}{7}$

19. $\quad 8\dfrac{1}{6} - \dfrac{5}{6}$

20. $\quad 7\dfrac{2}{5} - \dfrac{4}{5}$

21. $\quad 8\dfrac{1}{8} - 3\dfrac{7}{8}$

22. $\quad 9\dfrac{2}{6} - 6\dfrac{5}{6}$

23. $\quad 7\dfrac{2}{11} - 3\dfrac{9}{11}$

24. $\quad 11\dfrac{2}{9} - 3\dfrac{5}{9}$

25. $\quad 7\dfrac{1}{4} - \dfrac{3}{4}$

26. $\quad 8\dfrac{1}{3} - 2\dfrac{2}{3}$

27. $\quad 8\dfrac{1}{9} - 7\dfrac{4}{9}$

Fractional Forms Review

It is important that you become fluent with changing numbers from one form to another. Here we give a review of the conversion strategies discussed in Chapter 3.

- **Writing 1 as a fraction**

$$1 = \frac{1}{1} = \frac{2}{2} = \frac{3}{3} = \frac{4}{4} = \cdots$$

- **Writing whole numbers as fractions or mixed numbers**

$$1 = \frac{1}{1} \qquad 2 = \frac{2}{1} \qquad 3 = \frac{3}{1} \qquad 4 = \frac{4}{1} \qquad 8 = \frac{8}{1}$$

$$2 = 1\frac{3}{3} \qquad 3 = 2\frac{5}{5} \qquad 4 = 3\frac{2}{2} \qquad 8 = 7\frac{4}{4}$$

- **Raising fractions to higher terms**

$$\frac{2}{5} = \frac{2 \times 3}{5 \times 3} = \frac{6}{15} \qquad \frac{3}{4} = \frac{3 \times 5}{4 \times 5} = \frac{15}{20} \qquad \frac{7}{1} = \frac{7 \times 6}{1 \times 6} = \frac{42}{6}$$

- **Reducing fractions to lower terms**

$$\frac{2}{6} = \frac{\cancel{2} \times 1}{\cancel{2} \times 3} = \frac{1}{3} \qquad \frac{30}{45} = \frac{6 \times \cancel{5}}{\cancel{5} \times 9} = \frac{2 \times \cancel{3}}{3 \times \cancel{3}} = \frac{2}{3} \qquad \frac{600}{150} = \frac{6 \times 10 \times \cancel{10}}{\cancel{10} \times 15} = \frac{2 \times \cancel{3} \times 2 \times \cancel{5}}{\cancel{3} \times \cancel{5} \times 1} = \frac{4}{1} = 4$$

- **Converting fractions to whole or mixed numbers**

$$\frac{6}{2} = 6 \div 2 = 3 \qquad \frac{24}{4} = 24 \div 4 = 6 \qquad \frac{72}{6} = 72 \div 6 = 12$$

$$\frac{17}{3} = 17 \div 3 \quad \longrightarrow \quad 3\overline{)\begin{array}{l} 5 \\ 17 \\ 15 \\ \hline 2 \end{array}} \quad \longrightarrow \quad \frac{17}{3} = 5\frac{2}{3}$$

- **Converting mixed numbers to improper fractions**

Here we show three ways to see that $2\frac{1}{3} = \frac{7}{3}$.

$$2\frac{1}{3} = 2 + \frac{1}{3}$$
$$= 1 + 1 + \frac{1}{3}$$
$$= \frac{3}{3} + \frac{3}{3} + \frac{1}{3} = \frac{7}{3}$$

$$2\frac{1}{3} = 2 + \frac{1}{3}$$
$$= \frac{2}{1} + \frac{1}{3}$$
$$= \frac{2 \times 3}{1 \times 3} + \frac{1}{3}$$
$$= \frac{6}{3} + \frac{1}{3} = \frac{7}{3}$$

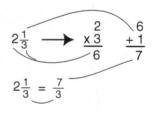

$$2\frac{1}{3} = \frac{7}{3}$$

- **Renaming mixed numbers**

$$5\frac{4}{4} = 5 + \frac{4}{4} = 5 + 1 = 6 \qquad\qquad 6\frac{5}{4} = 6 + \frac{5}{4} = 6 + 1\frac{1}{4} = 7\frac{1}{4}$$

$$3\frac{1}{8} = 3 + \frac{1}{8} = 2\frac{8}{8} + \frac{1}{8} = 2\frac{9}{8} \qquad\qquad 9\frac{2}{5} = 9 + \frac{2}{5} = 8\frac{5}{5} + \frac{2}{5} = 8\frac{7}{5}$$

Here we are shifting 1 whole from the whole part to the fractional part. You'll need this when subtracting mixed numbers.

EXERCISES 3-L

Choose all the fractions in each list that are **equal** to 1.

1. $\dfrac{2}{2}$, $\dfrac{1}{2}$, $\dfrac{3}{2}$, $\dfrac{5}{5}$, $\dfrac{4}{1}$, $\dfrac{1}{1}$

2. $\dfrac{1}{5}$, $\dfrac{5}{5}$, $\dfrac{5}{1}$, $\dfrac{7}{7}$, $\dfrac{9}{9}$, $\dfrac{2}{3}$

Choose all the fractions in each list that are **equal** to 2.

3. $\dfrac{9}{4}$, $\dfrac{12}{5}$, $\dfrac{8}{4}$, $1\dfrac{2}{2}$, $\dfrac{2}{1}$, $\dfrac{14}{7}$

4. $2\dfrac{4}{4}$, $1\dfrac{5}{5}$, $\dfrac{2}{4}$, $\dfrac{1}{2}$, $\dfrac{6}{3}$, $\dfrac{5}{3}$

Choose all the fractions in each list that are **equal** to 6.

5. $\dfrac{6}{6}$, $\dfrac{6}{1}$, $\dfrac{18}{3}$, $5\dfrac{4}{4}$, $\dfrac{2}{12}$, $\dfrac{1}{6}$

6. $4\dfrac{12}{6}$, $\dfrac{30}{5}$, $\dfrac{5}{30}$, $6\dfrac{7}{7}$, $\dfrac{6}{36}$, $\dfrac{12}{2}$

Choose all the fractions in each list that are **equal** to $\dfrac{1}{3}$.

7. $\dfrac{3}{9}$, $\dfrac{2}{6}$, $\dfrac{3}{1}$, $1\dfrac{1}{3}$, $\dfrac{10}{300}$, $\dfrac{7}{28}$

8. $\dfrac{12}{4}$, $\dfrac{5}{15}$, $\dfrac{1}{30}$, $1\dfrac{3}{3}$, $\dfrac{3}{3}$, $\dfrac{8}{24}$

Choose all the fractions in each list that are **equal** to $5\dfrac{3}{4}$.

9. $\dfrac{15}{4}$, $\dfrac{20}{3}$, $\dfrac{15}{3}$, $4\dfrac{7}{4}$, $\dfrac{23}{4}$, $5\dfrac{6}{8}$

10. $\dfrac{12}{5}$, $3\dfrac{1}{3}$, $3\dfrac{11}{4}$, $\dfrac{69}{12}$, $\dfrac{46}{8}$, $5\dfrac{9}{15}$

Write each of these whole numbers in the specified form.

11. $7 = 6\dfrac{?}{5}$

12. $8 = 7\dfrac{?}{4}$

13. $5 = 3\dfrac{?}{6}$

14. $3 = 1\dfrac{?}{2}$

Write each of these mixed numbers in the specified form.

15. $5\dfrac{2}{3} = 4\dfrac{?}{3}$

16. $7\dfrac{4}{5} = 6\dfrac{?}{5}$

17. $4\dfrac{3}{4} = 2\dfrac{?}{4}$

18. $6\dfrac{7}{8} = 4\dfrac{?}{8}$

Write each of these numbers in three other ways. Try to show a variety of forms.

19. 3

20. 7

21. $\dfrac{3}{5}$

22. $\dfrac{6}{7}$

23. $\dfrac{16}{20}$

24. $\dfrac{56}{63}$

25. $\dfrac{27}{8}$

26. $\dfrac{58}{13}$

27. $3\dfrac{1}{7}$

28. $6\dfrac{3}{8}$

29. $2\dfrac{8}{3}$

30. $5\dfrac{9}{6}$

3.6	A FRACTION AS DIVISION, RATIO, AND WHAT FRACTION OF ONE QUANTITY IS ANOTHER QUANTITY

OBJECTIVES
- Solve an application involving a total quantity split into a number of equal parts.
- Write a fraction that represents a division problem.
- Write the division problem represented by a fraction.
- Find the ratio of one quantity to another quantity.
- Find what fraction of one quantity is another quantity.
- Solve an application involving ratio.
- Solve an application involving finding what fraction of one quantity is another quantity.

1 A Fraction as Division

In Section 3.4 you learned that an improper fraction can be converted to a whole or mixed numeral by dividing the numerator by the denominator. For example,

$$\frac{12}{3} = 12 \div 3 = 4$$

and

$$\frac{14}{3} \rightarrow 3\overline{)14} \begin{array}{c} 4 \\ \underline{12} \\ 2 \end{array} \rightarrow \frac{14}{3} = 4\frac{2}{3}$$

Here we see that the fraction bar indicates division. That is,

$$\frac{\text{Numerator}}{\text{Denominator}} = \text{Numerator} \div \text{Denominator}$$

In this section, we look at several ways to interpret a fraction as division.

Suppose you have 6 gallons of paint to be divided equally among 3 workers. How much paint does each worker receive? To solve this problem, we divide 6 by 3.

$$3\overset{2}{\overline{)6}} \quad \text{or} \quad 6 \div 3 = 2 \quad \text{or} \quad \frac{6}{3} = 2$$

In this problem a total quantity is being split into a number of equal parts and the following general relationship applies.

$$\begin{array}{ccc} \text{Size of} \\ \text{each part} \end{array} = \begin{array}{c} \text{total} \\ \text{quantity} \end{array} \div \begin{array}{c} \text{number of} \\ \text{equal parts} \end{array}$$
$$= \quad 6 \quad \div \quad 3$$
$$= \quad 2$$

or

$$\begin{array}{c} \text{Size of} \\ \text{each part} \end{array} = \frac{\text{total quantity}}{\text{number of equal parts}}$$
$$= \frac{6}{3}$$
$$= 2$$

Each worker receives 2 gallons of paint.

Now suppose that you have only 2 gallons of paint to split equally among 3 workers. How much paint does each worker receive? Here the total amount of paint to be split apart is 2 gallons, and the number of equal parts is 3. If we use the above relationship, we have

$$\begin{array}{c} \text{Size of} \\ \text{each part} \end{array} = \frac{\text{total quantity}}{\text{number of equal parts}}$$
$$= \frac{2 \text{ gallons}}{3}$$
$$= \frac{2}{3} \text{ gallon}$$

Therefore, each worker receives $\frac{2}{3}$ gallon paint. We can check the answer. If 3 workers each have $\frac{2}{3}$ gallon paint, is the total 2 gallons?

$$\frac{2}{3} + \frac{2}{3} + \frac{2}{3} = \frac{6}{3} = 2$$

Yes, the total is 2 gallons. Therefore, $\frac{2}{3}$ gallon is the correct amount for each worker.

Separating a Quantity Into a Number of Equal Parts

$$\text{Size of each part} = \text{total quantity} \div \text{number of equal parts}$$

$$= \frac{\text{total quantity}}{\text{number of equal parts}}$$

EXAMPLE 1   Seven persons share equally a pizza. How much pizza does each person receive?

SOLUTION   We want to separate 1 pizza into 7 equal parts.

$$\text{Size of each part} = \frac{\text{total quantity}}{\text{number of equal parts}}$$

$$= \frac{1 \text{ pizza}}{7}$$

$$= \frac{1}{7} \text{ pizza}$$

Each person receives $\frac{1}{7}$ pizza. ■

EXAMPLE 2   A rope that is 3 meters long is cut into 5 equal pieces. How long is each piece?

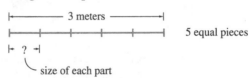

SOLUTION   We want to separate 3 meters of rope into 5 equal pieces.

$$\text{Size of each part} = \frac{\text{total quantity}}{\text{number of equal parts}}$$

$$= \frac{3 \text{ meters}}{5}$$

$$= \frac{3}{5} \text{ meter}$$

CHECK $\frac{3}{5} + \frac{3}{5} + \frac{3}{5} + \frac{3}{5} + \frac{3}{5} = \frac{15}{5} = 3$

Each piece measures $\frac{3}{5}$ meter. ■

EXAMPLE 3   Twelve persons share equally 20 pounds of cheese. How much cheese does each person receive? Simplify the answer.

SOLUTION   We want to separate 20 pounds of cheese into 12 equal parts.

Try These Problems

Solve.

1. Four families share equally 12 quarts of milk. How much milk does each family receive? Simplify the answer.

2. Twelve families share equally 4 quarts of milk. How much milk does each family receive? Simplify the answer.

3. Mary Thomas split a pecan pie equally among 8 persons. How much pie did each person receive?

4. A board that is 7 feet long is cut into 10 equal pieces. How long is each piece?

5. A board that is 10 feet long is cut into 7 equal pieces. How long is each piece?

6. Write as a fraction.
   a. $4 \div 5$
   b. $17 \div 5$
   c. $7\overline{)20}$
   d. $9\overline{)4}$

7. Write as a division problem using the symbol $\div$.
   a. $\frac{1}{8}$
   b. $\frac{3}{5}$
   c. $\frac{8}{3}$
   d. $\frac{10}{7}$

8. Write as a division problem using the symbol $\overline{)}$.
   a. $\frac{1}{9}$
   b. $\frac{2}{3}$
   c. $\frac{9}{4}$
   d. $\frac{11}{5}$

Write a fraction for each.

9. Nine-halves

10. Thirty-sevenths

11. Eight divided by three

12. Eight divided into three

$$\frac{\text{Size of}}{\text{each part}} = \frac{\text{total quantity}}{\text{number of equal parts}}$$

$$= \frac{20 \text{ pounds}}{12}$$

$$= \frac{20}{12} \text{ pounds}$$

$$= \frac{5 \times 4}{3 \times 4} \text{ pounds}$$

$$= \frac{5}{3} \quad \text{or} \quad 1\frac{2}{3} \text{ pounds}$$

Each person receives $\frac{5}{3}$ or $1\frac{2}{3}$ pounds of cheese. ■

 Try Problems 1 through 5.

The fraction bar indicates division as shown here.

$$\frac{\text{Numerator}}{\text{Denominator}} = \text{Numerator} \div \text{Denominator}$$

The denominator is *always* the divisor. This gives us three ways to write a division problem as illustrated by the following chart.

Fraction	*Division Using* $\div$	*Division Using* $\overline{)}$	*English*
$\frac{1}{8}$	$1 \div 8$	$8\overline{)1}$	One-eighth One divided by eight Eight divided into one
$\frac{2}{5}$	$2 \div 5$	$5\overline{)2}$	Two-fifths Two divided by five Five divided into two
$\frac{5}{2}$	$5 \div 2$	$2\overline{)5}$	Five-halves Five divided by two Two divided into five
$\frac{14}{3}$	$14 \div 3$	$3\overline{)14}$	Fourteen-thirds Fourteen divided by three Three divided into fourteen

It is important that you know how to write the two numbers in the correct order and that you use the correct language to read the fraction or division problem.

 Try Problems 6 through 12.

2 Ratio—A Comparison By Division

Suppose a committee consists of 5 persons: 2 women and 3 men. We can compare the number of women to the number of men by division.

Try These Problems

Write a fraction for each. Simplify, if possible.
13. The ratio of 2 to 11.
14. The ratio of 11 to 2.
15. The ratio of 36 to 27.
16. The ratio of 27 to 36.

We say, "the **ratio** of women to men is 2 to 3." We write,

$$\text{Ratio of women to men} = \frac{2}{3} \begin{array}{l} \text{—— number of women} \\ \text{—— number of men} \end{array}$$

We can compare the quantities in the reverse order.

$$\text{Ratio of men to women} = \frac{3}{2} \begin{array}{l} \text{—— number of men} \\ \text{—— number of women} \end{array}$$

We can also compare either one of the quantities to the total number of persons on the committee.

$$\text{Ratio of men to the total} = \frac{3}{5} \begin{array}{l} \text{—— number of men} \\ \text{—— total} \end{array}$$

To recognize a comparison by division pay close attention to the language. The word *ratio* indicates to form a fraction, and the quantity that follows the word *to* is put in the denominator.

EXAMPLE 4   Write a fraction for each. Simplify.

a. The ratio of 18 to 30.   **b.** The ratio of 49 to 35.

SOLUTION

a. The ratio of 18 to 30 $= \dfrac{18}{30}$ The quantity following the word *to* is put in the denominator.

$$= \frac{\cancel{3} \times 6}{\cancel{3} \times 10}$$

$$= \frac{\cancel{2} \times 3}{\cancel{2} \times 5}$$

$$= \frac{3}{5}$$

b. The ratio of 49 to 35 $= \dfrac{49}{35}$ The quantity following the word *to* is put in the denominator.

$$= \frac{7 \times \cancel{7}}{5 \times \cancel{7}}$$

$$= \frac{7}{5}$$

Because a ratio compares two quantities by division, we prefer to leave the answer $\frac{7}{5}$ as an improper fraction rather than a mixed numeral. ■

 **Try Problems 13 through 16.**

EXAMPLE 5   Ed, a mechanic, earned $28,000 last year while Alice, his girlfriend, earned $70,000 as a financial planner.

a. Find the ratio of Ed's earnings to Alice's earnings.

b. Find the ratio of Alice's earnings to their total earnings.

Simplify both results.

◣ Try These Problems

17. A board 15 feet long is cut into two pieces. One piece is 9 feet long, the other is 6 feet long.
a. What is the ratio of the shorter piece to the longer piece?
b. What is the ratio of the longer piece to the shorter piece?
c. What is the ratio of the longer piece to the total?

18. A football team played a total of 52 games. They won 13 of them and lost the rest.
a. What is the ratio of wins to losses?
b. What is the ratio of wins to total games?

SOLUTION

a.
$$\frac{\text{Ratio of Ed's earnings}}{\text{to Alice's earnings}} = \frac{\text{Ed's earnings}}{\text{Alice's earnings}}$$

$$= \frac{28{,}000}{70{,}000}$$

$$= \frac{28 \times \cancel{1000}}{70 \times \cancel{1000}}$$

$$= \frac{4 \times \cancel{7}}{\cancel{7} \times 10}$$

$$= \frac{\cancel{2} \times 2}{\cancel{2} \times 5}$$

$$= \frac{2}{5}$$

b.
$$\frac{\text{Ratio of Alice's earnings}}{\text{to their total earnings}} = \frac{\text{Alice's earnings}}{\text{Total earnings}}$$

$$= \frac{70{,}000}{28{,}000 + 70{,}000}$$

$$= \frac{70{,}000}{98{,}000}$$

$$= \frac{70 \times \cancel{1000}}{98 \times \cancel{1000}}$$

$$= \frac{7 \times 10}{2 \times 49}$$

$$= \frac{\cancel{7} \times \cancel{2} \times 5}{\cancel{2} \times \cancel{7} \times 7}$$

$$= \frac{5}{7} \quad ■$$

◣ Try Problems 17 and 18.

3 What Fraction of One Quantity Is Another Quantity?

There is another way to verbalize a comparison by division other than using the word *ratio*. If there are 5 committee members including 2 women and 3 men, we say

$$\frac{\text{The fraction of the}}{\text{committee that is women}} = \frac{2}{5} \begin{array}{l} \text{—— number of women} \\ \text{—— total} \end{array}$$

Here we are comparing the number of women to the total number of persons on the committee by division. Note that the phrase *fraction of* indicates to form a fraction. The quantity that follows the phrase *fraction of* is put in the denominator and the other quantity mentioned is put in the numerator. Here are some examples.

Try These Problems

19. What fraction of 54 is 49?

20. 132 is what fraction of 88?

What fraction of 10 is 3? $\dfrac{3}{10}$

What fraction of 3 is 10? $\dfrac{10}{3}$ or $3\dfrac{1}{3}$

140 is what fraction of 210? $\dfrac{140}{210} = \dfrac{2 \times \cancel{7} \times \cancel{10}}{3 \times \cancel{7} \times \cancel{10}} = \dfrac{2}{3}$

210 is what fraction of 140? $\dfrac{210}{140} = \dfrac{3 \times \cancel{7} \times \cancel{10}}{2 \times \cancel{7} \times \cancel{10}} = \dfrac{3}{2} = 1\dfrac{1}{2}$

Try Problems 19 and 20.

EXAMPLE 6   What fraction of these figures are circles?

SOLUTION   What fraction of these figures are circles? $\frac{3}{5}$

The quantity mentioned after the phrase *fraction of* is put in the denominator. The other quantity is put in the numerator. $\frac{3}{5}$ of these figures are circles. ∎

EXAMPLE 7   The legs of this bar stool are what fraction of the total height?

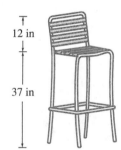

12 in

37 in

SOLUTION   The legs of this bar stool are what fraction of the total height?

$$\dfrac{37}{12 + 37} \quad \begin{array}{l}\text{—— height of the legs} \\ \text{—— total height}\end{array}$$

$$= \dfrac{37}{49}$$

The legs are $\frac{37}{49}$ of the total height. ∎

EXAMPLE 8   Dorothy owed a friend $30. She paid the friend $14. What fraction of the debt does she still owe? Simplify.

Try These Problems

21. What fraction of the figures are triangles?

22. What fraction of these circles is *not* shaded?

23. The Miami Dolphins won 12 of the 15 games they played and lost the rest. What fraction of the games did they lose? Simplify.

24. Susanne purchased these items at the grocery store.

Ground beef $5
Chicken breasts $8
Apples $2
Bananas $3
Lettuce $1
Bread $1

The amount spent on fruit is what fraction of the total bill? Simplify.

SOLUTION   What fraction of the debt does she still owe?

$$\frac{\mathbf{30} - 14}{30}$$ —— amount she still owes
—— original debt

$$= \frac{16}{30}$$

$$= \frac{\cancel{2} \times 8}{\cancel{2} \times 15}$$

$$= \frac{8}{15}$$

Dorothy still owes $\frac{8}{15}$ of the debt. ■

 Try Problems 21 through 24.

Now we summarize three ways that a fraction can represent division.

A Fraction as Division

1. A total quantity is separated into a number of equal parts and you are looking for the size of each part.

$$\begin{matrix} \text{Size of} \\ \text{each part} \end{matrix} = \text{total quantity} \div \begin{matrix} \text{number of} \\ \text{equal parts} \end{matrix}$$

$$= \frac{\text{total quantity}}{\text{number of equal parts}}$$

2. You want to know the ratio of one quantity to another quantity.

$$\text{Ratio of 4 to 7} = \frac{4}{7}$$

The quantity following the word *to* is put in the denominator.

3. You want to know what fraction of one quantity is another quantity.

$$\text{What fraction of 7 is 4?} \quad \frac{4}{7}$$

The quantity following the phrase *fraction of* is put in the denominator.

 Answers to Try These Problems

1. 3 qt   2. $\frac{1}{3}$ qt   3. $\frac{1}{8}$ pie   4. $\frac{7}{10}$ ft   5. $\frac{10}{7}$ or $1\frac{3}{7}$ ft
6. a. $\frac{4}{5}$ b. $\frac{17}{5}$ c. $\frac{20}{7}$ d. $\frac{4}{3}$ 7. a. 1 : 6
7. b. 3 ÷ 5 c. 8 ÷ 3 d. 10 : 7   8. a. 9)1 b. 3)2
8. c. 4)9 d. 5)11   9. $\frac{9}{2}$ 10. $\frac{30}{7}$ 11. $\frac{8}{3}$
12. $\frac{3}{8}$ 13. $\frac{2}{11}$ 14. $\frac{11}{2}$ 15. $\frac{4}{3}$ 16. $\frac{3}{4}$
17. a. $\frac{2}{3}$ b. $\frac{3}{2}$ c. $\frac{3}{5}$ 18. a. $\frac{1}{3}$ b. $\frac{1}{4}$
19. $\frac{49}{54}$ 20. $\frac{3}{2}$ 21. $\frac{4}{7}$ 22. $\frac{8}{15}$ 23. $\frac{1}{5}$ 24. $\frac{1}{4}$

EXERCISES 3.6

Answer with a fraction. Simplify, if possible.

1. Twenty gallons of paint are distributed equally among 5 workers. How much paint does each worker receive?

2. Five gallons of paint are distributed equally among 20 workers. How much paint does each worker receive?

3. Six persons share equally 9 pounds of cheese. How much cheese does each person receive?

4. Nine persons share equally 6 pounds of cheese. How much cheese does each person receive?

5. A string that is 1 foot long is cut into 5 equal pieces. How long is each piece?

6. Six children share equally 1 gallon of ice cream. How much ice cream does each child receive?

7. Bob, Steve, and Marge share equally a quart of milk. How much milk does each person receive?

8. A pound of butter is distributed equally among Carol, Sue, Jedd, and John. How much butter does each person receive?

9. Ed and Dick go trekking in the Himalayan mountains. The total distance of the trip is 100 kilometers. They want to spread this equally over a 3-day period. How far will they trek each day?

10. A wire is cut into 150 equal pieces. If the wire is 45 inches long, how long is each piece?

Write as a fraction. Simplify, if possible.

11. $2 \div 7$	**12.** $7 \div 2$	**13.** $20\overline{)8}$	**14.** $8\overline{)20}$
15. $35 \div 15$	**16.** $15 \div 35$	**17.** $5\overline{)3}$	**18.** $3\overline{)5}$

Write as a division problem using the symbol $\div$

19. $\frac{1}{8}$	**20.** $\frac{4}{9}$	**21.** $\frac{19}{5}$	**22.** $\frac{23}{8}$
23. $4\overline{)3}$	**24.** $2\overline{)17}$	**25.** 4 divided by 15	

26. 3 divided into 5

Write as a division problem using the symbol $\overline{)}$.

27. $\frac{1}{12}$	**28.** $\frac{5}{8}$	**29.** $\frac{12}{5}$	**30.** $\frac{32}{9}$
31. $8 \div 13$	**32.** $26 \div 3$	**33.** 6 divided into 1	

34. 25 divided by 4

Write a fraction for each. Simplify, if possible.

35. Two-thirds	**36.** Eleven-halves
37. Eight-tenths	**38.** Twenty-four ninths
39. One divided by five	**40.** Twelve divided by eight
41. Thirty-six divided into nine	**42.** hree divided into seven
43. The ratio of 3 to 11.	**44.** The ratio of 15 to 18.
45. The ratio of 17 to 5.	**46.** The ratio of 48 to 90.
47. What fraction of 50 is 35?	**48.** What fraction of 12 is 52?
49. 2 is what fraction of 400?	**50.** 28 is what fraction of 21?

51. What fraction of these figures are arrows?

52. What fraction of these figures are *not* circles?

53. What is the ratio of the number of triangles to the number of circles? Simplify.

54. What is the ratio of the number of circles to the total number of figures? Simplify.

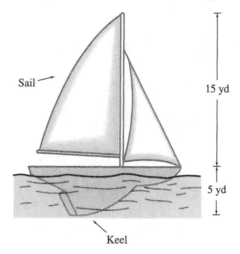

55. Find the ratio of the height of the sail to the total height of the sailboat. Simplify.

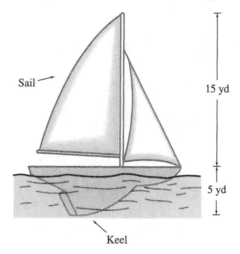

56. What is the ratio of the length of the cab to the total length of the truck? Simplify.

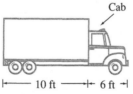

57. The woman's torso is what fraction of her total height?

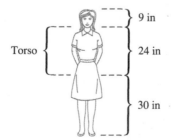

58. The thread portion of the screw is what fraction of its total length?

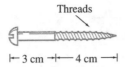

Threads

|← 3 cm →|← 4 cm →|

59. If you had $50 and you spent $23, what fraction of your money did you spend?

60. There are 7 students absent in a class of 32. What fraction of the class is present?

61. A shipment contains 350 pink grapefruit and 400 white grapefruit. What fraction of the shipment is pink grapefruit?

62. A grocery bill is as follows:

Bananas	$1
Apples	$2
Ham	$8
Chicken	$5
Frozen vegetables	$3
Tax	$1

What fraction of the bill is spent on fruit?

63. A baseball player got 35 hits out of 100 times at bat. Find the ratio of the number of hits to the number of times at bat? Simplify.

64. Out of 2000 workers, 1600 are nonsmokers. Find the ratio of smokers to nonsmokers. Simplify.

65. A rectangle has length 68 feet and width 17 feet. What is the ratio of the area to the perimeter? Simplify.

66. The height of a rectangular window is 42 inches. The width is 3 times the height. What is the ratio of the height to the perimeter?

67. The price of a microwave oven decreased from $450 to $400. The decrease in price is what fraction of the original price?

68. The price of a stock increased from $50 to $65. The increase in price is what fraction of the original price?

The total population of a town in southern California is 60,000 persons. The bar graph gives the distribution of the population by race. Use the graph to answer Exercises 69 through 72.

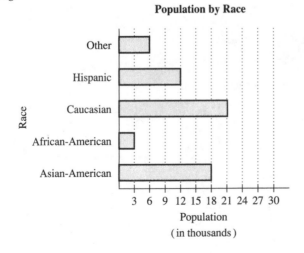

Population by Race

69. Find the ratio of the number of African-Americans to the number of Asian-Americans.

70. Find the ratio of the number of Caucasians to the number of Asian-Americans.

71. What fraction of the total population is Hispanic?

72. What fraction of the total population is African-American?

Lisa, Liz, and Kent bought an apartment building together for $325,000. The circle graph gives the portion of the building that each person owns. Use the graph to answer Exercises 73 through 76.

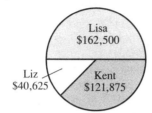

Portion of Building Owned

73. What fraction of the building does Kent own?

74. What fraction of the building does Liz own?

75. What is the ratio of Liz's share to Lisa's share?

76. What is the ratio of Lisa's share to Kent's share?

CHAPTER 3 SUMMARY

KEY WORDS AND PHRASES

fraction [3.1]

fraction bar [3.1]

numerator [3.1]

denominator [3.1]

improper fraction [3.1, 3.4]

mixed numeral [3.1, 3.4]

raising a fraction to higher terms [3.3]

reduce to lowest terms [3.5]

simplify [3.5]

ratio [3.6]

SYMBOLS

The fraction bar indicates division. For example, $\frac{3}{4}$ means $3 \div 4$

IMPORTANT RULES

When a Fraction Is Less Than, Equal to, or More Than the Number 1 [3.1]

■ A fraction that has a numerator less than the denominator is less than the number 1. For example, the fractions $\frac{7}{8}$ and $\frac{12}{25}$ are each less than 1.

■ A fraction that has a numerator more than the denominator is more than the number 1. For example, the fractions $\frac{7}{4}$ and $\frac{30}{9}$ are each more than 1.

■ A fraction that has a numerator equal to the denominator is equal to the number 1. For example, the fractions $\frac{6}{6}$ and $\frac{50}{50}$ are each equal to 1.

Raising a Fraction to Higher Terms [3.3]

Multiplying the numerator and denominator by the same nonzero number does not change the value of a fraction.

Converting an Improper Fraction to a Mixed or Whole Numeral [3.4]

Divide the numerator by the denominator. The quotient is the whole part. If there is a remainder, other than 0, the remainder over the divisor (the original denominator) is the fraction part.

Converting a Mixed Numeral to an Improper Fraction [3.4]
LONG METHOD
▌ Write the whole numeral part as an improper fraction with a denominator that is the same as the denominator in the fractional part.
▌ Add the two fractions by adding the numerators and placing this over the common denominator.

SHORTCUT
Multiply the whole numeral by the denominator, then add the numerator to obtain the numerator of the improper fraction. Keep the same denominator.

Reducing a Fraction to Lowest Terms (Simplifying Fractions) [3.5]
▌ Dividing the numerator and denominator of a fraction by the same nonzero number does not change the value of the fraction. This is equivalent to canceling common factors from the numerator and denominator.
▌ A fraction is reduced to lowest terms (or simplified) when there are no common divisors of the numerator and denominator, other than 1.
▌ When a fraction is more than 1, and does not equal a whole numeral, either the improper fraction form or the mixed numeral form is considered simplified.
▌ When a fraction equals a whole numeral, only the whole numeral form is considered simplified.

Divisibility Rules [3.5]
These rules are listed on page 106.

A Fraction as Division [3.6]
A summary of how a fraction represents division is on page 117.

CHAPTER 3 REVIEW EXERCISES

Write the English name for each.

1. $\frac{1}{2}$ **2.** $\frac{2}{3}$ **3.** $\frac{6}{13}$

4. $3\frac{1}{4}$ **5.** $14\frac{2}{5}$ **6.** $20\frac{13}{100}$

Write a fraction represented by the shaded region. Assume each figure represents one whole.

7.    **8.**

Write an improper fraction and a mixed numeral or a whole numeral that represents the shaded regions. Assume each separate figure represents one whole.

9. 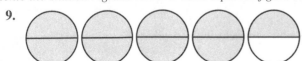   **10.**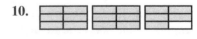

11. 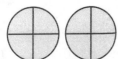   **12.**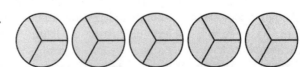

Choose the fractions in each group that are more than one whole.

13. $\frac{7}{9}, \frac{21}{5}, \frac{13}{17}, \frac{13}{13}, \frac{11}{2}$

14. $\frac{130}{21}, \frac{19}{4}, \frac{3}{4}, \frac{15}{43}, \frac{9}{9}$

Choose the fractions in each group that are equal to one whole.

15. $\frac{1}{3}, \frac{4}{1}, \frac{4}{4}, \frac{6}{2}, \frac{30}{30}$

16. $\frac{15}{15}, \frac{8}{1}, \frac{1}{1}, \frac{7}{7}, \frac{1}{12}$

Name two equal fractions represented by the shaded region. Assume each figure represents one whole.

17.  **18.** **19.** **20.**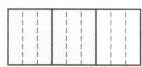

Find the missing numerator so that the two numbers are equal.

21. $\frac{4}{5} = \frac{?}{35}$ **22.** $\frac{13}{9} = \frac{?}{108}$ **23.** $1 = \frac{?}{12}$ **24.** $6 = \frac{?}{30}$

25. Convert $\frac{2}{7}$ to a fraction with denominator 56.

26. Write a fraction with denominator 4 that is equal to the whole number 8.

Convert each of these improper fractions to a mixed or whole numeral.

27. $\frac{47}{8}$ **28.** $\frac{300}{15}$ **29.** $\frac{475}{25}$ **30.** $\frac{83}{4}$

Convert each of these mixed numerals to an improper fraction.

31. $5\frac{2}{7}$ **32.** $35\frac{1}{4}$ **33.** $12\frac{5}{6}$ **34.** $7\frac{6}{23}$

A fraction less than one whole cannot *be written as a whole or mixed numeral. Write each of these numbers as a whole or mixed numeral, if possible. If not possible, say* not possible.

35. $\frac{16}{3}$ **36.** $\frac{3}{16}$ **37.** $\frac{16}{16}$ **38.** $\frac{1}{4}$ **39.** $\frac{4}{1}$ **40.** $\frac{125}{6}$

Reduce to lowest terms, if possible. If not possible, say not possible.

41. $\frac{15}{50}$ **42.** $\frac{42}{28}$ **43.** $\frac{36}{49}$ **44.** $\frac{32}{56}$ **45.** $\frac{54}{42}$ **46.** $\frac{27}{70}$

Simplify.

47. $\frac{24}{45}$ **48.** $\frac{50}{135}$ **49.** $\frac{126}{140}$ **50.** $\frac{294}{36}$ **51.** $\frac{165}{75}$

52. $\frac{198}{385}$ **53.** $\frac{132}{65}$ **54.** $\frac{68}{102}$ **55.** $\frac{7000}{1400}$ **56.** $\frac{36,000}{240,000}$

Write a fraction for each. Simplify, if possible.

57. $13 \div 3$ **58.** $3 \div 13$ **59.** $54\overline{)45}$ **60.** $45\overline{)54}$

61. 12 divided by 20 **62.** 12 divided into 20

63. Five-thirds **64.** Thirteen-halves **65.** Seven-fifths

66. Twenty-one sixty-thirds

67. The ratio of 4 to 12.

68. The ratio of 180 to 3600.

69. What fraction of 800 is 160?

70. 620 is what fraction of 155?

71. What fraction of these triangles is shaded?

72. What fraction of these figures are circles?

73. What is the ratio of the number of shaded squares to the number of unshaded squares?

74. A wine glass has measurements as shown in the diagram. What is the ratio of the height of the stem to the total height.

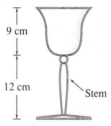

75. Courtney and her two sisters share equally 5 pounds of nuts. How many pounds of nuts does each person receive?

76. A string is 3 meters long. Mr. Lau cuts the string into 12 equal pieces. How long is each piece?

77. A church is giving away food to the homeless. They started with 50 gallons of milk. On Tuesday, they gave away 15 gallons. On Wednesday, the remaining milk was distributed equally to 60 persons. How much milk did each person receive on Wednesday?

78. Josette has 18 gallons of white paint and 7 gallons of blue paint. If she mixes it all together and then distributes it equally among 8 workers, how much paint does each worker receive?

79. Mr. Wilson borrowed $18,000 to buy a car. After the first year, he had paid $3600 on his loan. What fraction of the loan does he still owe?

80. The length of a rectangle is 6 feet more than its width. If the width is 72 feet, find the ratio of the length to the perimeter.

81. The population of a city increased from 175,000 to 250,000 in 15 years. What is the ratio of the increase in population to the original population?

82. The price of a software program decreased from $650 to $520. The decrease in price is what fraction of the original price?

✐ In Your Own Words

Write complete sentences to discuss each of the following. Support your comments with examples or pictures, if appropriate.

83. Discuss how you can decide whether a fraction is less than, more than or equal to the number 1.

84. Add the same number to the numerator and denominator of a fraction and discuss whether this procedure generates fractions equal to the original fraction.

85. Discuss what can be done to a fraction without changing its value.

86. Multiples of 10 (numbers like 10, 100, 1000, etc.) have only two different types of prime factors. What are the two primes? Discuss how you can use this fact to quickly conclude that a fraction like $\frac{321}{1000}$ is reduced to lowest terms.

87. Discuss the three ways to indicate division using math symbols; in each case, give three ways to read the statement using English.

CHAPTER 3 PRACTICE TEST

1. What fraction of the figure is shaded? Assume the figure represents one whole.

2. What fraction of these figures are squares?

$\frac{3}{8}$

3. Write an improper fraction and a mixed numeral represented by the shaded region. Assume each separate figure represents one whole.

$3\frac{1}{4} = \frac{13}{4}$

4. Write *two* equal fractions represented by the shaded region. Assume the figure represents one whole.

5. Choose the fractions that are less than one whole.
$\frac{5}{8}$ $\frac{7}{6}$ $\frac{6}{7}$ $\frac{8}{8}$ $\frac{1}{8}$ $\frac{8}{1}$

Find the missing numerator so that the two numbers are equal.

6. $\frac{5}{8} = \frac{?}{48}$ **7.** $\frac{3}{14} = \frac{?}{84}$ **8.** $6 = \frac{?}{4}$

Reduce to lowest terms, if possible. If not possible, say not possible.

9. $\frac{16}{56}$ **10.** $\frac{45}{36}$ **11.** $\frac{200}{250}$ **12.** $\frac{78}{117}$

13. Write $\frac{2}{5}$ as a division problem using the symbol $\overline{)}$.

14. Write the English name for $\frac{7}{11}$.

15. Write the English name for $4\frac{3}{5}$.

Convert each to a whole or mixed numeral.

16. $\frac{13}{5}$ **17.** $\frac{449}{18}$ **18.** $\frac{5740}{82}$

Convert each to an improper fraction.

19. $12\frac{3}{8}$ **20.** $9\frac{17}{20}$

Write a fraction for each. Simplify, if possible.

21. $5 \div 7$

22. 49 divided into 140

23. The ratio of 150 to 725.

24. What fraction of 42 is 12?

25. A basket contains 150 pieces of fruit, consisting of apples and pears. If there are 67 apples, what fraction of the total pieces of fruit are pears?

26. The lower trunk of the tree is what fraction of the total height of the tree?

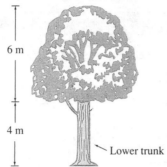

27. A calculus class consists of 24 men and 6 women. What is the ratio of the number of women to the total number of persons in the class?

28. Allan wants to cut his 27-centimeter piece of wire into 20 equal pieces. How long will each piece be?

29. A nurse takes care of 40 patients. If he has 15 centiliters of medicine to distribute among them equally, how much medicine does each patient receive?

30. Mr. Pakey received a $12,000 bonus. He bought 4 suits at $350 each, a computer for $4200, and new ski boots for $250. What is the ratio of the money spent to the total bonus?

Fractions: Multiplication and Division

OBJECTIVES

▌ Multiply two fractions.
▌ Cancel correctly when multiplying fractions.
▌ Multiply more than two fractions.
▌ Solve an application involving multiplication of fractions.

1   Multiplying Fractions

The recipe for a lemon cheesecake calls for $\frac{2}{3}$ cup of evaporated milk. The chef of a small cafe wants to make 4 of these cheesecakes. How much evaporated milk will the chef need? To solve this problem we need to multiply $\frac{2}{3}$ by 4.

$$4 \times \frac{2}{3} = ?$$

Because one of the factors, 4, is a whole number, we can interpret this multiplication problem as repeated addition.

$$4 \times \frac{2}{3} = \frac{2}{3} + \frac{2}{3} + \frac{2}{3} + \frac{2}{3}$$

$$= \frac{2 + 2 + 2 + 2}{3}$$

$$= \frac{8}{3} \quad \text{or} \quad 2\frac{2}{3}$$

Observe that we can obtain the correct answer without using repeated addition.

Try These Problems

Multiply and simplify.

1. $3 \times \frac{2}{5}$
2. $16 \times \frac{9}{7}$
3. $\frac{1}{8} \times \frac{13}{2}$
4. $2\frac{1}{2} \times \frac{3}{4}$
5. $8 \times 4\frac{2}{3}$
6. $7\frac{3}{5} \times 2\frac{1}{3}$

$$4 \times \frac{2}{3} = \frac{4}{1} \times \frac{2}{3}$$

Convert 4 to a fraction. $4 = \frac{4}{1}$

$$= \frac{4 \times 2}{1 \times 3}$$

Multiply the numerators to obtain the numerator of the product. Multiply the denominators to obtain the denominator of the product.

$$= \frac{8}{3} \quad \text{or} \quad 2\frac{2}{3}$$

The answer may be left as an improper fraction or as a mixed numeral.

This illustrates that the procedure for multiplying fractions is to multiply the numerators to obtain the numerator of the answer, and multiply the denominators to obtain the denominator of the answer. Here are more examples.

EXAMPLE 1   Multiply: $\frac{4}{5} \times \frac{9}{11}$

SOLUTION

$$\frac{4}{5} \times \frac{9}{11} = \frac{4 \times 9}{5 \times 11}$$

Multiply the numerators.
Multiply the denominators.

$$= \frac{36}{55} \quad \blacksquare$$

EXAMPLE 2   Multiply: $5\frac{3}{8} \times 7$

SOLUTION

$$5\frac{3}{8} \times 7 = \frac{43}{8} \times \frac{7}{1}$$

Convert $5\frac{3}{8}$ to a fraction.

$$5\frac{3}{8} = \frac{43}{8}$$

Convert 7 to a fraction.

$$7 = \frac{7}{1}$$

$$= \frac{43 \times 7}{8 \times 1}$$

Multiply the numerators.
Multiply the denominators.

$$= \frac{301}{8} \quad \text{or} \quad 37\frac{5}{8}$$

The answer may be left as an improper fraction or as a mixed numeral. $\blacksquare$

 Try Problems 1 through 6.

2 Multiplication Involving Canceling

Consider the multiplication problem

$$\frac{10}{9} \times \frac{4}{15}$$

If we multiply the numerators and the denominators, we obtain an answer that is not reduced to lowest terms.

$$\frac{10}{9} \times \frac{4}{15} = \frac{10 \times 4}{9 \times 15}$$

$$= \frac{40}{135}$$

The numbers 40 and 135 are both divisible by 5.

$$= \frac{\cancel{5} \times 8}{\cancel{5} \times 27}$$

$$= \frac{8}{27}$$

There is an easier way to do this problem. Observe that one of the numerators, 10, and one of the denominators, 15, have a common factor 5. The common factor 5 can be canceled *before* multiplying. Here we show the problem done in this way.

$$\frac{10}{9} \times \frac{4}{15} = \frac{2 \times \cancel{5}}{9} \times \frac{4}{3 \times \cancel{5}}$$

Cancel the common factor 5 from the numerator and denominator before multiplying.

$$= \frac{2 \times 4}{9 \times 3}$$

$$= \frac{8}{27}$$

Here are more examples.

EXAMPLE 3 Multiply: $12\frac{1}{2} \times \frac{8}{15}$

SOLUTION

$$12\frac{1}{2} \times \frac{8}{15}$$

$$= \frac{25}{2} \times \frac{8}{15}$$

Convert $12\frac{1}{2}$ to $\frac{25}{2}$ before canceling common factors.

$$= \frac{5 \times \cancel{5}}{\underset{1}{\cancel{2}}} \times \frac{4 \times \cancel{2}}{3 \times \cancel{5}}$$

$$= \frac{20}{3} \quad \text{or} \quad 6\frac{2}{3} \quad \blacksquare$$

EXAMPLE 4 Multiply: $\frac{3}{800} \times \frac{5200}{27}$

SOLUTION

$$\frac{3}{800} \times \frac{5200}{27}$$

$$= \frac{\overset{1}{\cancel{3}}}{8 \times \cancel{100}} \times \frac{52 \times \cancel{100}}{\cancel{3} \times 9}$$

Both 800 and 5200 are divisible by 100. Both 3 and 27 are divisible by 3.

$$= \frac{1}{8} \times \frac{52}{9}$$

Cancel common factors from 8 and 52 before multiplying.

$$8 = 2 \times 4 = 2 \times 2 \times 2$$
$$52 = 2 \times 26$$
$$ = 2 \times 2 \times 13$$

Try These Problems

Multiply and simplify.

7. $\frac{11}{5} \times \frac{15}{16}$

8. $\frac{21}{23} \times \frac{3}{14}$

9. $\frac{25}{8} \times \frac{18}{65}$

10. $3\frac{1}{3} \times \frac{9}{400}$

11. $4\frac{2}{3} \times \frac{27}{35}$

12. $180 \times 2\frac{5}{6}$

$$= \frac{1}{2 \times \cancel{4}} \times \frac{\cancel{4} \times 13}{9}$$

$$= \frac{1 \times 13}{2 \times 9}$$

$$= \frac{13}{18} \quad \blacksquare$$

Therefore, 8 and 52 have a common factor 4.

 Try Problems 7 through 12.

Now consider the problem

$$\frac{36}{42} \times \frac{25}{7}$$

Observe that the numerator and denominator of the first fraction have a common factor 6.

$$\frac{36}{42} \times \frac{25}{7} = \frac{6 \times 6}{6 \times 7} \times \frac{25}{7}$$

It is easier to cancel this common factor 6 from the numerator and denominator before multiplying. This is all right because dividing the numerator and denominator of a fraction by the same nonzero number does not change the value of the fraction.

$$\frac{36}{42} \times \frac{25}{7} = \frac{\cancel{6} \times 6}{\cancel{6} \times 7} \times \frac{25}{7}$$

$$= \frac{6}{7} \times \frac{25}{7}$$

No more canceling can be done.

$$= \frac{6 \times 25}{7 \times 7}$$

$$= \frac{150}{49} \quad \text{or} \quad 3\frac{3}{49}$$

Here are more examples.

EXAMPLE 5   Multiply: $\frac{33}{55} \times \frac{39}{52}$

SOLUTION

$$\frac{33}{55} \times \frac{39}{52}$$

$$= \frac{3 \times 11}{5 \times 11} \times \frac{3 \times 13}{2 \times 2 \times 13}$$

Write each numerator and denominator as the product of primes.
$33 = 3 \times 11$
$55 = 5 \times 11$
$39 = 3 \times 13$
$52 = 4 \times 13$
$ = 2 \times 2 \times 13$

$$= \frac{3 \times \cancel{11}}{5 \times \cancel{11}} \times \frac{3 \times \cancel{13}}{2 \times 2 \times \cancel{13}}$$

$$= \frac{3 \times 3}{5 \times 2 \times 2}$$

$$= \frac{9}{20} \quad \blacksquare$$

Cancel the common factor 11 from the numerator and denominator of the first fraction. Cancel the common factor 13 from the numerator and denominator of the second fraction.

Try These Problems

Multiply and simplify.

13. $\frac{36}{45} \times \frac{8}{25}$

14. $\frac{3}{7} \times \frac{12}{16}$

15. $\frac{30}{150} \times \frac{26}{65}$

16. $\frac{21}{63} \times \frac{60}{25}$

17. $9000 \times \frac{50}{75}$

18. $\frac{55}{77} \times 4\frac{3}{8}$

EXAMPLE 6   Multiply: $\frac{40}{100} \times 235$

SOLUTION

$$\frac{40}{100} \times 235$$

$$= \frac{4 \times \cancel{10}}{10 \times \cancel{10}} \times \frac{235}{1}$$ Both 40 and 100 are divisible by 10.

$$= \frac{4}{10} \times \frac{235}{1}$$

$$= \frac{\cancel{2} \times 2}{\cancel{2} \times 5} \times \frac{\cancel{5} \times 47}{1}$$ More canceling can be done before multiplying.

$$= \frac{2 \times 47}{1 \times 1}$$

$$= \frac{94}{1} = 94 \quad \blacksquare$$

EXAMPLE 7   Multiply: $33\frac{1}{3} \times \frac{63}{7000}$

SOLUTION

$$33\frac{1}{3} \times \frac{63}{7000}$$

$$= \frac{100}{3} \times \frac{63}{7000}$$ Convert $33\frac{1}{3}$ to $\frac{100}{3}$ before beginning the canceling process.

$$= \frac{\overset{1}{\cancel{100}}}{3} \times \frac{63}{\cancel{100} \times 70}$$ Both 100 and 7000 are divisible by 100.

$$= \frac{1}{3} \times \frac{63}{70}$$

$$= \frac{1}{\underset{1}{\cancel{3}}} \times \frac{\cancel{3} \times 3 \times \cancel{7}}{\cancel{7} \times 10}$$ Remember to cancel the common factor 7 in the numerator and denominator of the second fraction.

$$= \frac{1 \times 3}{1 \times 10}$$

$$= \frac{3}{10} \quad \blacksquare$$

Try Problems 13 through 18.

Now we summarize the procedure for multiplying fractions.

Multiplying Fractions

1. Convert the mixed numerals to improper fractions and convert the whole numerals to fractions.
2. Cancel as much as possible. Each time you cancel a factor from a numerator, you must cancel the same factor from a denominator.
3. Multiply the numerators to obtain the numerator of the answer. Multiply the denominators to obtain the denominator of the answer.
4. Check to make sure the answer is simplified. When the answer is an improper fraction, you may leave it as an improper fraction or you may convert it to a mixed numeral.

---

3 Multiplying More Than Two Fractions

Recall from Chapter 2 that to multiply more than two numbers, we must first multiply any two of them, then multiply that result by another one, and continue until all of the numbers have been multiplied. Here we show a problem done in several ways.

$$6 \times 5 \times 2 \times 8 = 30 \times 2 \times 8$$
$$= 60 \times 8$$
$$= 480$$

$$6 \times 5 \times 2 \times 8 = 6 \times 5 \times 16$$
$$= 6 \times 80$$
$$= 480$$

$$6 \times 5 \times 2 \times 8 = 48 \times 10$$
$$= 480$$

Now we look at a problem involving fractions done in several ways.

$$\frac{1}{2} \times \frac{3}{5} \times 8 = \frac{3}{\overset{}{\underset{5}{10}}} \times \frac{\overset{4}{8}}{1} = \frac{12}{5}$$ Here we multiply $\frac{1}{2}$ by $\frac{3}{5}$ first.

$$\frac{1}{2} \times \frac{3}{5} \times 8 = \frac{1}{\underset{1}{2}} \times \frac{\overset{12}{24}}{5} = \frac{12}{5}$$ Here we multiply $\frac{3}{5}$ by 8 first.

$$\frac{1}{2} \times \frac{3}{5} \times 8 = \frac{1}{\underset{1}{2}} \times \frac{3}{5} \times \frac{\overset{4}{8}}{1}$$ Observe that it is all right to cancel the common factor 2 before multiplying.

$$= \frac{1 \times 3 \times 4}{1 \times 5 \times 1}$$

$$= \frac{12}{5}$$

▲ **Try These Problems**

Multiply and simplify.

19. $\frac{15}{16} \times \frac{3}{5} \times \frac{24}{7}$

20. $\frac{11}{36} \times \frac{5}{3} \times \frac{2}{22}$

21. $\frac{12}{15} \times \frac{3}{27} \times 15 \times \frac{3}{4}$

22. $20 \times \frac{4}{35} \times \frac{3}{10} \times \frac{7}{8}$

EXAMPLE 8 Multiply: $1\frac{1}{2} \times 15 \times \frac{5}{9}$

SOLUTION

$$1\frac{1}{2} \times 15 \times \frac{5}{9}$$

$$= \frac{\overset{1}{\cancel{3}}}{2} \times \frac{15}{1} \times \frac{5}{\underset{3}{\cancel{9}}}$$ Cancel the common factor 3 from the numerator and denominator.

$$= \frac{1 \times \overset{5}{\cancel{15}} \times 5}{2 \times 1 \times \cancel{3}}$$ Cancel another factor of 3.

$$= \frac{25}{2} \quad \text{or} \quad 12\frac{1}{2} \quad ■$$

EXAMPLE 9 Multiply: $\frac{49}{14} \times \frac{5}{9} \times 50 \times \frac{3}{11}$

SOLUTION

$$\frac{49}{14} \times \frac{5}{9} \times \frac{50}{1} \times \frac{3}{11}$$

$$= \frac{7 \times \cancel{7}}{\cancel{2} \times \cancel{7}} \times \frac{5}{\cancel{3} \times 3} \times \frac{\cancel{2} \times 25}{1} \times \frac{\overset{1}{\cancel{3}}}{11}$$ Cancel common factors 7, 2, and 3.

$$= \frac{7 \times 5 \times 25}{3 \times 11}$$

$$= \frac{875}{33} \quad \text{or} \quad 26\frac{17}{33} \quad ■$$

▲ **Try Problems 19 through 22.**

▲ **Answers to Try These Problems**

1. $\frac{6}{5}$ or $1\frac{1}{5}$ 2. $\frac{144}{7}$ or $20\frac{4}{7}$ 3. $\frac{13}{16}$ 4. $\frac{15}{8}$ or $1\frac{7}{8}$ 5. $\frac{112}{3}$ or $37\frac{1}{3}$
6. $\frac{266}{15}$ or $17\frac{11}{15}$ 7. $\frac{33}{16}$ or $2\frac{1}{16}$ 8. $\frac{9}{46}$ 9. $\frac{45}{52}$ 10. $\frac{3}{40}$
11. $\frac{18}{5}$ or $3\frac{3}{5}$ 12. 510 13. $\frac{32}{125}$ 14. $\frac{9}{28}$ 15. $\frac{2}{25}$ 16. $\frac{4}{5}$
17. 6000 18. $\frac{25}{8}$ or $3\frac{1}{8}$ 19. $\frac{27}{14}$ or $1\frac{13}{14}$ 20. $\frac{5}{108}$ 21. 1 22. $\frac{3}{5}$

EXERCISES 4.1

Multiply and simplify.

1. $5 \times \frac{2}{3}$ **2.** $9 \times \frac{3}{14}$ **3.** $\frac{2}{11} \times \frac{3}{7}$ **4.** $\frac{5}{8} \times \frac{13}{9}$

5. $6\frac{8}{9} \times \frac{5}{27}$ **6.** $12\frac{1}{8} \times \frac{9}{8}$ **7.** $130 \times \frac{1}{9}$ **8.** $2000 \times \frac{2}{7}$

9. $\frac{7}{8} \times \frac{8}{19}$ **10.** $\frac{6}{7} \times \frac{5}{9}$ **11.** $44 \times \frac{8}{11}$ **12.** $48 \times \frac{7}{30}$

13. $5\frac{2}{5} \times \frac{20}{63}$ **14.** $250 \times 66\frac{2}{3}$ **15.** $\frac{26}{35} \times \frac{28}{39}$ **16.** $\frac{48}{135} \times 2\frac{13}{36}$

17. $\frac{15}{20} \times 1\frac{1}{2}$ **18.** $12 \times \frac{5000}{700}$ **19.** $\frac{60}{100} \times 153$ **20.** $\frac{11}{3} \times \frac{32}{56}$

21. $\frac{24}{40} \times \frac{15}{27}$ **22.** $\frac{18}{27} \times \frac{22}{550}$ **23.** $6\frac{1}{4} \times \frac{27}{75}$ **24.** $\frac{6}{100} \times 3500$

25. $\frac{40}{340} \times 1700$ **26.** $12\frac{3}{4} \times \frac{28}{21}$ **27.** $\frac{30}{36} \times \frac{91}{35}$ **28.** $\frac{98}{27} \times \frac{36}{105}$

29. $6\frac{7}{8} \times \frac{40}{900}$ **30.** $\frac{75}{77} \times 13\frac{1}{5}$ **31.** $\frac{57}{24} \times \frac{21}{38}$ **32.** $\frac{68}{85} \times \frac{65}{22}$

33. $\frac{33}{91} \times \frac{104}{42}$ **34.** $\frac{13}{2000} \times \frac{8}{3900}$ **35.** $\frac{360}{500} \times 3\frac{1}{6}$ **36.** $16\frac{2}{7} \times 11\frac{2}{3}$

37. $\frac{2}{3} \times \frac{6}{7} \times \frac{15}{4}$ **38.** $\frac{1}{10} \times \frac{5}{8} \times \frac{25}{3}$ **39.** $2\frac{1}{2} \times \frac{3}{5} \times 3\frac{1}{4}$ **40.** $6\frac{2}{3} \times \frac{15}{24} \times 1\frac{1}{2}$

41. $\frac{3}{2} \times \frac{6}{7} \times \frac{5}{9} \times \frac{14}{25}$ **42.** $\frac{2}{5} \times \frac{3}{4} \times 8\frac{1}{2} \times 5\frac{1}{3}$

Solve.

43. Jeffrey bought $3\frac{3}{4}$ pounds of round steak at \$4 a pound. How much did he pay for the steak?

44. Suppose you buy 60 shares of a stock selling for $16\frac{3}{4}$ dollars per share. What is the total cost?

45. Susann bought $4\frac{2}{3}$ yards of fabric that sells for \$9 a yard. How much did she pay for the fabric?

46. A desk top measures $4\frac{1}{2}$ meters long and $2\frac{1}{4}$ meters wide. Find the area of the desk top.

DEVELOPING NUMBER SENSE #3

MULTIPLYING BY A NUMBER LESS THAN, EQUAL TO, OR MORE THAN 1

Here we show 200 multiplied by 3, 2, and $1\frac{1}{2}$. How do the products compare with 200 and why?

$$3 \times 200 = 600 \qquad 2 \times 200 = 400$$
$$1\frac{1}{2} \times 200 = 300$$

Observe that the results—600, 400, and 300—are each more than 200 because the numbers 3, 2, and $1\frac{1}{2}$ are each more than 1.

If we multiply 200 by 1, we obtain 200.

$$1 \times 200 = 200$$

In general, any number multiplied by 1 is that number.

What happens if we multiply 200 by a fraction that is less than 1? Let's look at a few examples.

$$\frac{3}{4} \times 200 = 150 \qquad \frac{1}{2} \times 200 = 100$$
$$\frac{1}{4} \times 200 = 50$$

Observe that the results 150, 100, and 50 are each less than 200 because the numbers $\frac{3}{4}$, $\frac{1}{2}$, and $\frac{1}{4}$ are each less than 1.

Number Sense Problems

Without computing, decide whether the result is less than, equal to, or more than 84.

1. 5×84 **2.** $2\frac{1}{4} \times 84$ **3.** $\frac{2}{3} \times 84$ **4.** 1×84 **5.** $\frac{4}{10} \times 84$ **6.** $\frac{3}{2} \times 84$

Without computing, decide whether the result is less than, equal to, or more than 682.

7. $\frac{1}{6} \times 682$ **8.** $\frac{7}{5} \times 682$ **9.** 12×682 **10.** $13\frac{3}{4} \times 682$

11. $\frac{8}{8} \times 682$ **12.** $\frac{12}{13} \times 682$

Without computing, decide whether the result is less than, equal to, or more than $25\frac{1}{2}$.

13. $\frac{1}{2} \times 25\frac{1}{2}$ **14.** $5\frac{3}{4} \times 25\frac{1}{2}$ **15.** $\frac{5}{2} \times 25\frac{1}{2}$ **16.** $1 \times 25\frac{1}{2}$

4.2	DIVISION

OBJECTIVES ▌ Divide two fractions.
▌ Perform division of fractions indicated by a fraction bar.
▌ Solve an application problem involving division.

1 Dividing Fractions

A piece of wire $4\frac{1}{2}$ feet long is to be cut into pieces that are each $\frac{3}{4}$ foot. How many pieces can be cut? We want to know how many lengths of $\frac{3}{4}$ foot there are in a total length of $4\frac{1}{2}$ feet. In Section 2.5, we learned that in a situation like this we must divide the total quantity by the size of each part to obtain the number of equal parts. The only difference here is that fractions are involved. Here we picture the situation.

How many $\frac{3}{4}$s are in $4\frac{1}{2}$?

$$\begin{array}{ccc}
\text{Number of equal} \\ \text{parts} & \times & \text{size of each} \\ \text{part} & = & \text{total quantity} \\
? & \times & \dfrac{3}{4} & = & 4\dfrac{1}{2}
\end{array}$$

To solve this problem we need to divide $4\frac{1}{2}$ by $\frac{3}{4}$. From the picture, we see that 6 of the $\frac{3}{4}$-foot pieces make up the total length of $4\frac{1}{2}$ feet. We can check this by multiplying $\frac{3}{4}$ by 6.

$$\begin{aligned}
6 \times \frac{3}{4} &= \frac{6}{1} \times \frac{3}{4} \\
&= \frac{\cancel{2} \times 3}{1} \times \frac{3}{\cancel{2} \times 2} \\
&= \frac{3 \times 3}{1 \times 2} \\
&= \frac{9}{2} \quad \text{or} \quad 4\frac{1}{2}
\end{aligned}$$

We have shown that $4\frac{1}{2} \div \frac{3}{4} = 6$, but we want to be able to divide fractions without viewing a picture. Observe that the following procedure gives the correct answer 6 for the problem $4\frac{1}{2} \div \frac{3}{4}$.

$$4\frac{1}{2} \div \frac{3}{4} = \frac{9}{2} \div \frac{3}{4}$$

Convert $4\frac{1}{2}$ to $\frac{9}{2}$.

$$= \frac{9}{2} \times \frac{4}{3}$$

Change the division to multiplication and invert the second fraction.

$$= \frac{\cancel{3} \times 3}{\underset{1}{\cancel{2}}} \times \frac{\cancel{2} \times 2}{\underset{1}{\cancel{3}}}$$

Cancel the common factor 2. Cancel the common factor 3.

$$= \frac{3 \times 2}{1 \times 1}$$

Multiply the fractions.

$$= 6$$

Observe that dividing by $\frac{3}{4}$ is the same as multiplying by $\frac{4}{3}$. The fraction $\frac{4}{3}$ is called the **reciprocal** of $\frac{3}{4}$. Therefore, *dividing by a fraction is the same as multiplying by its reciprocal.* Here are more examples.

EXAMPLE 1   Divide: $\frac{5}{2} \div \frac{1}{4}$

SOLUTION

$$\frac{5}{2} \div \frac{1}{4}$$

$$= \frac{5}{2} \times \frac{4}{1}$$

Change $\div$ to $\times$ and invert the second fraction.

$$= \frac{5}{\underset{1}{\cancel{2}}} \times \frac{\cancel{2} \times 2}{1}$$

Cancel the common factor 2.

$$= \frac{10}{1}$$

$$= 10 \quad \blacksquare$$

EXAMPLE 2   Divide: $\frac{15}{19} \div 3$

SOLUTION

$$\frac{15}{19} \div 3$$

$$= \frac{15}{19} \div \frac{3}{1}$$

Convert 3 to a fraction. $3 = \frac{3}{1}$

$$= \frac{15}{19} \times \frac{1}{3}$$

Change $\div$ to $\times$ and invert the second fraction.

$$= \frac{5 \times \cancel{3}}{19} \times \frac{1}{\underset{1}{\cancel{3}}}$$

Cancel the common factor 3.

$$= \frac{5 \times 1}{19 \times 1}$$

Multiply the fractions.

$$= \frac{5}{19} \quad \blacksquare$$

Try These Problems

Divide and simplify.

1. $\frac{7}{3} \div \frac{1}{9}$

2. $\frac{2}{3} \div \frac{12}{5}$

3. $8 \div 10\frac{2}{3}$

4. $\frac{25}{125} \div 20$

5. $3\frac{2}{3} \div \frac{2}{27}$

6. $12\frac{3}{5} \div 1\frac{4}{5}$

7. $140 \div 42$

8. $48 \div 200$

EXAMPLE 3 Divide: $5 \div 12\frac{3}{5}$

SOLUTION

$$5 \div 12\frac{3}{5}$$

$$= \frac{5}{1} \div \frac{63}{5} \qquad \begin{array}{l}\text{Convert 5 to a fraction. } 5 = \frac{5}{1} \\ \text{Convert } 12\frac{3}{5} \text{ to an improper fraction.} \\ 12\frac{3}{5} = \frac{63}{5}\end{array}$$

$$= \frac{5}{1} \times \frac{5}{63} \qquad \begin{array}{l}\text{Change } \div \text{ to } \times \text{ and invert the} \\ \text{second fraction.}\end{array}$$

$$= \frac{5 \times 5}{1 \times 63} \qquad \text{Multiply the fractions.}$$

$$= \frac{25}{63} \quad \blacksquare$$

Here is a summary of the procedure for dividing fractions.

Dividing Fractions

1. Convert each mixed numeral to an improper fraction. Convert the whole numerals to fractions.
2. Change division ($\div$) to multiplication ($\times$) and invert the divisor. The divisor is the second number.
3. Cancel as much as possible, then multiply the fractions.
4. Check to make sure the answer is simplified. When the answer is an improper fraction, you may leave it as an improper fraction or you may write it as a mixed numeral.

Try Problems 1 through 8.

2 Indicating Division with the Fraction Bar

Recall from Chapter 3 that the fraction bar used to name fractions indicates division. For example,

$$\frac{12}{3} \quad \text{means} \quad 12 \div 3$$

$$\frac{3}{12} \quad \text{means} \quad 3 \div 12$$

$$\frac{1\frac{1}{2}}{\frac{1}{3}} \quad \text{means} \quad 1\frac{1}{2} \div \frac{1}{3}$$

$$\frac{\frac{1}{3}}{1\frac{1}{2}} \quad \text{means} \quad \frac{1}{3} \div 1\frac{1}{2}$$

Try These Problems

Divide and simplify.

9. $\dfrac{\frac{5}{3}}{4}$

10. $\dfrac{\frac{3}{7}}{1\frac{1}{9}}$

11. $\dfrac{8}{2\frac{1}{2}}$

12. $\dfrac{4\frac{3}{5}}{\frac{4}{5}}$

13. $\dfrac{\frac{7}{21}}{\frac{8}{27}}$

14. $\dfrac{\frac{54}{12}}{8\frac{1}{4}}$

EXAMPLE 4 Divide: $\dfrac{\frac{8}{9}}{5}$

SOLUTION

$$\frac{\frac{8}{9}}{5} = \frac{8}{9} \div 5$$

The numerator $\frac{8}{9}$ is written first.
The denominator 5 is written second.

$$= \frac{8}{9} \times \frac{1}{5}$$

$$= \frac{8}{45} \ \blacksquare$$

EXAMPLE 5 Divide: $\dfrac{2\frac{1}{2}}{5\frac{3}{4}}$

SOLUTION

$$\frac{2\frac{1}{2}}{5\frac{3}{4}} = 2\frac{1}{2} \div 5\frac{3}{4}$$

The numerator $2\frac{1}{2}$ is written first. The denominator $5\frac{3}{4}$ is written second.

$$= \frac{5}{2} \div \frac{23}{4}$$

$$= \frac{5}{2} \times \frac{4}{23}$$

$$= \frac{5}{\underset{1}{\cancel{2}}} \times \frac{\cancel{2} \times 2}{23}$$

$$= \frac{10}{23} \ \blacksquare$$

Try Problems 9 through 14.

Answers to Try These Problems

1. 21 2. $\frac{5}{18}$ 3. $\frac{3}{4}$ 4. $\frac{1}{100}$ 5. $\frac{99}{2}$ or $49\frac{1}{2}$ 6. 7 7. $\frac{10}{3}$ or $3\frac{1}{3}$

8. $\frac{6}{25}$ 9. $\frac{5}{12}$ 10. $\frac{27}{7}$ or $3\frac{6}{7}$ 11. $\frac{16}{5}$ or $3\frac{1}{5}$ 12. $\frac{23}{4}$ or $5\frac{3}{4}$

13. $\frac{9}{8}$ or $1\frac{1}{8}$ 14. $\frac{6}{11}$

EXERCISES 4.2

Divide and simplify.

1. $\frac{3}{5} \div \frac{1}{2}$ 2. $\frac{5}{9} \div \frac{1}{5}$ 3. $\frac{9}{10} \div \frac{2}{3}$ 4. $\frac{3}{4} \div \frac{7}{8}$

5. $\frac{7}{29} \div 1\frac{5}{9}$ 6. $\frac{3}{200} \div 2\frac{7}{16}$ 7. $5 \div \frac{1}{3}$ 8. $27 \div \frac{3}{5}$

9. $1050 \div \frac{2}{5}$ 10. $5400 \div 1\frac{1}{5}$ 11. $1\frac{2}{3} \div 40$ 12. $\frac{27}{81} \div 3$

13. $13\frac{1}{2} \div 15$ 14. $8\frac{3}{4} \div 10$ 15. $3 \div 7$ 16. $7 \div 3$

17. $6 \div 10$ 18. $10 \div 6$ 19. $560 \div 40$ 20. $40 \div 560$

21. $2\frac{1}{3} \div \frac{2}{15}$ 22. $3\frac{4}{7} \div \frac{30}{28}$ 23. $9\frac{3}{8} \div \frac{45}{24}$ 24. $1\frac{1}{5} \div 12\frac{1}{3}$

25. $16\frac{2}{3} \div 5\frac{1}{5}$ 26. $4\frac{4}{11} \div 1\frac{23}{33}$ 27. $9\frac{3}{4} \div 9\frac{3}{4}$ 28. $\frac{8}{19} \div \frac{8}{19}$

29. $\dfrac{\frac{3}{10}}{4}$ 30. $\dfrac{\frac{14}{21}}{8}$ 31. $\dfrac{36}{2\frac{2}{3}}$ 32. $\dfrac{150}{4\frac{1}{6}}$

33. $\dfrac{7\frac{1}{2}}{3\frac{4}{5}}$ **34.** $\dfrac{3\frac{9}{10}}{6\frac{1}{2}}$ **35.** $\dfrac{\frac{15}{250}}{\frac{12}{8}}$ **36.** $\dfrac{6\frac{3}{4}}{\frac{14}{63}}$

37. $\dfrac{2800}{\frac{49}{50}}$ **38.** $\dfrac{15\frac{3}{5}}{\frac{35}{91}}$

Solve and simplify.

39. A board 5 feet long is separated into 3 equal pieces. How long is each piece?

40. A board 3 feet long is separated into 5 equal pieces. How long is each piece?

41. The contents of a can is to be divided into 5 equal parts. If the can holds $\frac{7}{8}$ of a liter, how much will be in each part?

42. A wire is to be cut into 20 equal pieces. If the wire has a total length of $2\frac{1}{2}$ meters, how long is each piece?

43. Warren wants to make bows for his Christmas tree. Each bow requires $1\frac{1}{2}$ feet of ribbon. He has purchased 75 feet of ribbon. How many bows can he make?

44. A wire that is $49\frac{1}{2}$ centimeters long is to be cut into $2\frac{1}{4}$-centimeter pieces. How many of the smaller pieces can be cut?

4.3   THE MISSING NUMBER IN A MULTIPLICATION STATEMENT

OBJECTIVE   ▌   Find the missing number in a multiplication statement.

In the multiplication statement

$$4 \times 6 = 24 \quad \text{or} \quad 24 = 4 \times 6$$

the numbers 4 and 6 are called the **factors** or **multipliers.** The answer to the multiplication problem, 24, is called the **product** of 4 and 6. Note that the statement can be written with the product located after the equality symbol or before the equality symbol.

Three questions can be asked by omitting any one of the three numbers.

1. $4 \times 6 = \boxed{}$ The answer to the multiplication problem is missing, so multiply.
   24 is the missing number.

2. $\boxed{} \times 6 = 24$ A multiplier is missing, so divide. The answer to the multiplication problem is divided by the given multiplier.
   $24 \div 6 = \boxed{}$
   4 is the missing number.

3. $4 \times \boxed{} = 24$ A multiplier is missing, so divide. The answer to the multiplication problem is divided by the given multiplier.

   $24 \div 4 \quad = \boxed{}$
   6 is the missing number.

When both multipliers are *more* than 1, the product is the largest of the three numbers. However, do not expect this to be true when one of the multipliers is *less* than 1. Study these examples:

Try These Problems

Find the missing number.

1. $\frac{1}{4} \times 120 = \boxed{}$

2. $\frac{3}{5} \times 63 = \boxed{}$

3. $\boxed{} = 2\frac{5}{6} \times 27$

4. $\boxed{} = 3\frac{1}{5} \times \frac{15}{24}$

1. $8 \times 9 = 72$
2. $2 \times 3\frac{1}{2} = 7$

Here both multipliers are more than 1, so the product is the largest of the three numbers.

3. $\frac{3}{4} \times 200 = 150$ Because $\frac{3}{4}$ is less than 1, the product 150 is less than 200.

You can use this observation to help you decide if your answer is reasonable. Now we look at some examples of finding the missing number in a multiplication statement.

EXAMPLE 1 $\boxed{} = \frac{4}{5} \times 200$

SOLUTION   The answer to the multiplication problem is missing, so multiply $\frac{4}{5}$ by 200.

$$\frac{4}{5} \times 200 = \frac{4}{5} \times \frac{200}{1} = \frac{4}{\underset{1}{\cancel{5}}} \times \frac{\cancel{5} \times 40}{1} = \frac{160}{1} = 160 \quad \blacksquare$$

In Example 1 we expect to get an answer less than 200 because $\frac{4}{5}$ is less than 1.

 Try Problems 1 through 4.

EXAMPLE 2 $5 \times \boxed{} = \frac{3}{4}$

SOLUTION   The number $\frac{3}{4}$ is the answer to the multiplication problem, and the number 5 is the known multiplier. The other multiplier is missing, so divide $\frac{3}{4}$ by 5.

$$\begin{aligned}
\begin{matrix}\text{Missing} \\ \text{multiplier}\end{matrix} &= \begin{matrix}\text{answer to the} \\ \text{multiplication} \\ \text{problem}\end{matrix} \div \begin{matrix}\text{known} \\ \text{multiplier}\end{matrix} \\[6pt]
&= \quad\quad \frac{3}{4} \quad\quad \div \quad\quad 5 \\[6pt]
&= \frac{3}{4} \div \frac{5}{1} \\[6pt]
&= \frac{3}{4} \times \frac{1}{5} \\[6pt]
&= \frac{3}{20}
\end{aligned}$$

CHECK

$$5 \times \frac{3}{20} \overset{?}{=} \frac{3}{4}$$

$$\frac{\overset{1}{\cancel{5}}}{1} \times \frac{3}{\underset{4}{\cancel{20}}} \overset{?}{=} \frac{3}{4}$$

$$\frac{3}{4} = \frac{3}{4}$$

The missing multiplier is $\frac{3}{20}$. $\blacksquare$

Try These Problems

Find the missing number.

5. $4 = \frac{1}{4} \times \boxed{}$

6. $\frac{9}{200} \times \boxed{} = 45$

7. $3\frac{1}{2} = \boxed{} \times 1\frac{1}{2}$

8. $\frac{2}{3} = 9 \times \boxed{}$

EXAMPLE 3 $8\frac{1}{3} = 2\frac{1}{2} \times \boxed{}$

SOLUTION   The number $8\frac{1}{3}$ is the answer to the multiplication problem, and the number $2\frac{1}{2}$ is the known multiplier. The other multiplier is missing, so divide $8\frac{1}{3}$ by $2\frac{1}{2}$.

$$\text{Missing multiplier} = \frac{\text{answer to the multiplication problem}}{} \div \text{known multiplier}$$

$$= 8\frac{1}{3} \div 2\frac{1}{2}$$

$$= \frac{25}{3} \div \frac{5}{2}$$

$$= \frac{\overset{5}{\cancel{25}}}{3} \times \frac{2}{\underset{1}{\cancel{5}}}$$

$$= \frac{10}{3} \quad \text{or} \quad 3\frac{1}{3} \quad \blacksquare$$

 Try Problems 5 through 8.

Now we summarize the procedure for finding the missing number in a multiplication statement.

> *Finding the Missing Number in a Multiplication Statement*
>
> **1.** If you are missing the answer to the multiplication problem, then multiply.
>
> **2.** If you are missing one of the multipliers, then divide. Be careful not to divide backward. Here is how it works.
>
> $$\text{Missing multiplier} = \frac{\text{answer to the multiplication problem}}{} \div \text{known multiplier}$$

 Answers to Try These Problems

1. 30   **2.** $\frac{189}{5}$ or $37\frac{4}{5}$ **3.** $\frac{153}{2}$ or $76\frac{1}{2}$ **4.** 2   **5.** 16   **6.** 1000

7. $\frac{7}{3}$ or $2\frac{1}{3}$ **8.** $\frac{2}{27}$

EXERCISES 4.3

Find the missing number and simplify.

1. $\frac{1}{6} \times 18 = \boxed{}$ **2.** $\frac{1}{8} \times 32 = \boxed{}$

3. $\frac{1}{5} \times 42 = \boxed{}$ **4.** $16 \times \boxed{} = 2$

5. $12 \times \boxed{} = 3$ **6.** $35 \times \boxed{} = 7$

7. $\boxed{} \times 63 = 9$ **8.** $\boxed{} \times 48 = 24$

9. $\boxed{} \times 30 = 5$ **10.** $90 = \frac{1}{4} \times \boxed{}$

11. $8 = \frac{1}{9} \times \boxed{}$ **12.** $17 = \frac{1}{3} \times \boxed{}$

13. $\boxed{} = \frac{3}{5} \times 20$ **14.** $\boxed{} = \frac{2}{3} \times 36$

15. $\boxed{} = \frac{4}{7} \times 200$ **16.** $45 = \boxed{} \times 54$

17. $14 = \boxed{} \times 49$ **18.** $21 = \boxed{} \times 56$

19. $40 = 50 \times \boxed{}$ **20.** $28 = 40 \times \boxed{}$

21. $18 = 120 \times \boxed{}$ **22.** $\frac{3}{400} \times \boxed{} = 24$

23. $\frac{5}{120} \times \boxed{} = 30$ **24.** $\frac{5}{80} \times \boxed{} = 150$

25. $50{,}000 = 4\frac{3}{10} \times \boxed{}$ **26.** $\boxed{} \times 5\frac{1}{5} = 1300$

4.4   LANGUAGE

OBJECTIVES
- Find a fraction of a number.
- Translate an English statement to a multiplication or division statement using math symbols.
- Solve problems using translations.

1 Finding a Fraction of a Number

The picture shows 12 small squares.

To shade $\frac{1}{3}$ of the 12 squares means to shade 1 out of 3 equal parts.

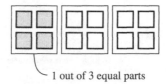

1 out of 3 equal parts

From the picture you see that $\frac{1}{3}$ of the 12 squares is 4 squares. Observe that we can find $\frac{1}{3}$ of 12 without viewing the picture because the correct result 4 can be obtained by multiplying 12 by $\frac{1}{3}$.

$$\frac{1}{3} \text{ of } 12$$

$$= \frac{1}{3} \times 12 \qquad \text{The word } of \text{ used in this way translates to multiplication.}$$

$$= \frac{1}{3} \times \frac{12}{1}$$

$$= \frac{12}{3}$$

$$= 4$$

Try These Problems

Translate to an equation. Solve.

1. $\frac{1}{4}$ of 60
2. $\frac{3}{4}$ of 60
3. $\frac{2}{7}$ of $5\frac{3}{5}$
4. What number is $\frac{5}{12}$ of $\frac{2}{25}$?
5. Find $7\frac{1}{2}$ of $9\frac{3}{5}$.
6. $\frac{36}{240}$ of 900 is what number?

To shade $\frac{2}{3}$ of the 12 squares means to shade 2 out of 3 equal parts.

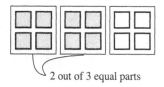

2 out of 3 equal parts

From the picture you see that $\frac{2}{3}$ of the 12 squares is 8 squares. Observe that we can find $\frac{2}{3}$ of 12 without viewing the picture because the correct result 8 can be obtained by multiplying 12 by $\frac{2}{3}$.

$$\frac{2}{3} \text{ of } 12$$

$$= \frac{2}{3} \times 12 \qquad \text{The word } of \text{ used in this way translates to multiplication.}$$

$$= \frac{2}{3} \times \frac{12}{1}$$

$$= \frac{2}{\underset{1}{\cancel{3}}} \times \frac{4 \times \cancel{3}}{1}$$

$$= 8$$

In general, to find a fraction of a number, translate the word *of* to multiplication. Here are some more examples.

1. $\dfrac{1}{4}$ of $20 = \dfrac{1}{4} \times \dfrac{20}{1} = \dfrac{20}{4} = 5$

2. $\dfrac{3}{4}$ of $20 = \dfrac{3}{4} \times \dfrac{20}{1} = \dfrac{3}{\underset{1}{\cancel{4}}} \times \dfrac{\cancel{4} \times 5}{1} = 15$

3. $3\dfrac{1}{2}$ of $12 = 3\dfrac{1}{2} \times 12 = \dfrac{7}{2} \times \dfrac{12}{1} = \dfrac{7}{\underset{1}{\cancel{2}}} \times \dfrac{\cancel{2} \times 6}{1} = 42$

4. $\dfrac{3}{10}$ of $2\dfrac{1}{2} = \dfrac{3}{10} \times \dfrac{5}{2} = \dfrac{3}{2 \times \cancel{5}} \times \dfrac{\overset{1}{\cancel{5}}}{2} = \dfrac{3}{4}$

Finding a Fraction of a Number

To find a fraction of a number, multiply the fraction by the number, that is, the word *of* used in this way translates to multiplication.

 Try Problems 1 through 6.

2 Language That Translates to Multiplication

Here is a review of the many English translations for the symbol =.

English	Math Symbols
equals	=
is equal to	
is the same as	
is the result of	
is	
was	
represents	
gives	
makes	
yields	
will be	
are	
were	

The multiplication statement $\frac{2}{3} \times 12 = 8$ or $8 = \frac{2}{3} \times 12$ is written with math symbols. Some of the ways to read this statement in English are given in the following chart.

English	Math Symbols
Two-thirds times twelve equals eight.	$\frac{2}{3} \times 12 = 8$
$\frac{2}{3}$ of 12 is 8.	$8 = \frac{2}{3} \times 12$
8 is $\frac{2}{3}$ times as large as 12.	
8 is $\frac{2}{3}$ as large as 12.	
8 is the *product* of $\frac{2}{3}$ and 12.	
$\frac{2}{3}$ multiplied by 12 yields 8.	

Because $\frac{2}{3} \times 12$ equals $12 \times \frac{2}{3}$, the order in which we say the multipliers makes no difference.

The following examples illustrate how to use translating to solve problems.

EXAMPLE 1   20 equals $\frac{3}{4}$ multiplied by what number?

SOLUTION

$$20 \text{ equals } \underbrace{\frac{3}{4} \text{ multiplied by}} \underbrace{\text{what number}}$$

$$20 \quad = \quad \frac{3}{4} \quad \times \quad \boxed{}$$

A multiplier is missing, so divide the answer 20 by the given multiplier $\frac{3}{4}$.

$$\begin{matrix}\text{Missing} \\ \text{multiplier}\end{matrix} = \begin{matrix}\text{answer to the} \\ \text{multiplication} \\ \text{problem}\end{matrix} \div \begin{matrix}\text{known} \\ \text{multiplier}\end{matrix}$$

$$= \quad 20 \quad \div \quad \frac{3}{4}$$

$$= \frac{20}{1} \times \frac{4}{3}$$

$$= \frac{80}{3} \quad \text{or} \quad 26\frac{2}{3} \quad \blacksquare$$

EXAMPLE 2   What number is $\frac{2}{3}$ of 600?

SOLUTION

$$\text{What number} \quad \text{is} \quad \frac{2}{3} \quad \text{of} \quad 600?$$
$$\downarrow \qquad \downarrow$$
$$\boxed{} \quad = \quad \frac{2}{3} \quad \times \quad 600$$

The answer to the multiplication statement is missing, so multiply $\frac{2}{3}$ by 600.

$$\frac{2}{3} \times 600 = \frac{2}{3} \times \frac{600}{1}$$

$$= \frac{2}{\underset{1}{\cancel{3}}} \times \frac{\cancel{3} \times 200}{1}$$

$$= 400 \quad \blacksquare$$

EXAMPLE 3   What fraction of 48 is 36?

SOLUTION

$$\text{What fraction} \quad \text{of} \quad 48 \quad \text{is} \quad 36?$$
$$\downarrow \qquad\qquad \downarrow$$
$$\boxed{} \quad \times \quad 48 \quad = \quad 36$$

A multiplier is missing, so divide the answer 36 by the multiplier 48 to find the missing multiplier.

$$\begin{matrix}\text{Missing} \\ \text{multiplier}\end{matrix} = \begin{matrix}\text{answer to the} \\ \text{multiplication} \\ \text{problem}\end{matrix} \div \begin{matrix}\text{known} \\ \text{multiplier}\end{matrix}$$

$$= \quad 36 \quad \div \quad 48$$

$$= \frac{36}{48}$$

$$= \frac{3 \times \cancel{12}}{4 \times \cancel{12}}$$

$$= \frac{3}{4} \quad \blacksquare$$

Try These Problems

Translate to an equation. Solve

7. $12\frac{1}{2}$ is what fraction of 100?

8. $5\frac{2}{5}$ times what number yields 135?

9. $\frac{5}{8}$ equals $\frac{2}{400}$ of what number?

10. $\frac{1}{6}$ of $30\frac{3}{4}$ is what number?

11. The product of $\frac{2}{10}$ and $\frac{15}{17}$ is what number?

12. 900 represents the product of $\frac{7}{4}$ and what number?

13. What fraction of $\frac{1}{4}$ is $\frac{3}{8}$?

14. Find $2\frac{1}{2}$ of 425.

EXAMPLE 4 $16\frac{2}{3}$ represents $\frac{4}{5}$ of what number?

SOLUTION

$$16\frac{2}{3} \quad \text{represents} \quad \frac{4}{5} \quad \text{of} \quad \text{what number?}$$
$$\downarrow \qquad\qquad\qquad \downarrow$$
$$16\frac{2}{3} \quad = \quad \frac{4}{5} \quad \times \quad \boxed{}$$

A multiplier is missing, so divide the answer $16\frac{2}{3}$ by the multiplier $\frac{4}{5}$ to find the missing multiplier.

$$\begin{array}{ccc} \text{Missing} \\ \text{multiplier} \end{array} = \begin{array}{c} \text{answer to the} \\ \text{multiplication} \\ \text{problem} \end{array} \div \begin{array}{c} \text{known} \\ \text{multiplier} \end{array}$$

$$= \quad 16\frac{2}{3} \quad \div \quad \frac{4}{5}$$

$$= \frac{50}{3} \times \frac{5}{4}$$

$$= \frac{\cancel{2} \times 25}{3} \times \frac{5}{\cancel{2} \times 2}$$

$$= \frac{125}{6} \quad \text{or} \quad 20\frac{5}{6} \quad \blacksquare$$

 Try Problems 7 through 14.

Special language is used when the number 2 or the number $\frac{1}{2}$ is a multiplier.

Math Symbols	English
2×7	*Twice* 7.
	Double 7.
	Two times seven.
$\frac{1}{2} \times 7$	*Half of* 7.
	Half 7.
	One-half times seven.
	Divide 7 in half.

Now we look at more examples of solving problems by translating.

EXAMPLE 5   Find twice $\frac{3}{5}$.

SOLUTION

$$\underline{\text{twice } \frac{3}{5}}$$

$$= 2 \times \frac{3}{5} \qquad \textit{Twice} \text{ means to multiply by 2.}$$

$$= \frac{2}{1} \times \frac{3}{5}$$

$$= \frac{6}{5} \quad \text{or} \quad 1\frac{1}{5} \quad \blacksquare$$

Try These Problems

Translate to an equation. Solve.

15. Find twice $\frac{6}{7}$.

16. Double $19\frac{1}{4}$.

17. Take half of $\frac{9}{10}$.

18. Divide $6\frac{1}{3}$ in half.

19. Twice what number yields $8\frac{1}{4}$?

20. Half what number yields $\frac{1}{40}$?

EXAMPLE 6   What number is half of $7\frac{1}{3}$?

SOLUTION

$$\underset{\downarrow}{\text{What number}} \quad \underset{\downarrow}{\text{is}} \quad \underbrace{\text{half of}} \quad 7\frac{1}{3}$$

$$\boxed{} = \frac{1}{2} \times 7\frac{1}{3} \qquad \textit{Half of } \text{means to multiply by } \frac{1}{2}.$$

$$= \frac{1}{\underset{1}{2}} \times \frac{\overset{11}{22}}{3}$$

$$= \frac{11}{3} \quad \text{or} \quad 3\frac{2}{3} \quad \blacksquare$$

EXAMPLE 7   Doubling what number yields $3\frac{1}{4}$?

SOLUTION

$$\underbrace{\text{Doubling}} \text{ what number yields } 3\overset{\downarrow}{\frac{1}{4}}$$

$$2 \times \quad \boxed{} \quad = \quad 3\frac{1}{4}$$

A multiplier is missing, so we divide $3\frac{1}{4}$ by 2 to find the missing multiplier.

$$\underset{\text{multiplier}}{\text{Missing}} = \underset{\text{problem}}{\overset{\text{answer to the}}{\text{multiplication}}} \div \underset{\text{multiplier}}{\text{known}}$$

$$= \quad 3\frac{1}{4} \quad \div \quad 2$$

$$= \frac{13}{4} \times \frac{1}{2}$$

$$= \frac{13}{8} \text{ or } 1\frac{5}{8} \quad \blacksquare$$

Try Problems 15 through 20.

3   Language That Translates to Division

When reading the division statement $8 \div \frac{2}{3} = 12$, take care to say 8 and $\frac{2}{3}$ in the correct order because $8 \div \frac{2}{3}$ does not equal $\frac{2}{3} \div 8$.

$$8 \div \frac{2}{3} = \frac{\overset{4}{8}}{1} \times \frac{3}{\underset{1}{2}} = 12$$

$$\frac{2}{3} \div 8 = \frac{2}{3} \div \frac{8}{1} = \frac{\overset{1}{2}}{3} \times \frac{1}{\underset{4}{8}}$$

$$= \frac{1}{12}$$

Try These Problems

Solve.

21. Divide $8\frac{1}{2}$ by 3.

22. Divide $8\frac{1}{2}$ into 3.

23. Divide $\frac{1}{3}$ by $20\frac{2}{3}$.

24. Divide $\frac{1}{3}$ into $20\frac{2}{3}$.

25. What number equals $9\frac{3}{4}$ divided into 52?

The number 12 does not equal the number $\frac{1}{12}$. The number 12 is more than 1, but the number $\frac{1}{12}$ is less than 1. The following chart gives correct ways to read the division statement $8 \div \frac{2}{3} = 12$.

Math Symbols	*English*
$8 \div \dfrac{2}{3} = 12$	8 *divided by* $\dfrac{2}{3}$ equals 12.
	$\dfrac{2}{3}$ *divided into* 8 equals 12.

Note that the word *by* is used when the statement is read from left to right as we read words in a book; however, the word *into* is used if we read the divisor first. The divisor is the number that comes after the division symbol.

Recall that the fraction bar is also used to indicate division. For example,

$$\frac{8}{\frac{2}{3}} = 8 \div \frac{2}{3}$$

The following chart gives correct ways to read the division statement $\frac{8}{\frac{2}{3}} = 12$.

Math Symbols	*English*
$\dfrac{8}{\frac{2}{3}} = 12$	8 *divided by* $\dfrac{2}{3}$ is 12.
	$\dfrac{2}{3}$ *divided into* 8 is 12.

Note that the word *by* is used when we read the numerator first, but the word *into* is used when we read the denominator first.

 Try Problems 21 through 25.

Suppose a basket contains 5 apples and 8 oranges. Recall from Section 3.6 that we can compare the number of apples to the number of oranges by division. We say, "the **ratio** of apples to oranges is 5 to 8." We write,

$$\text{Ratio of apples to oranges} = \frac{\text{number of apples}}{\text{number of oranges}} = \frac{5}{8}$$

We can also compare the quantities in the reverse order.

$$\text{Ratio of oranges to apples} = \frac{\text{number of oranges}}{\text{number of apples}} = \frac{8}{5}$$

We can also compare either one of the quantities to the total amount of fruit in the basket.

$$\text{Ratio of oranges to the total} = \frac{\text{number of oranges}}{\text{total}}$$

$$= \frac{8}{13}$$

Try These Problems

Solve.

26. Find the ratio of $2\frac{1}{2}$ to 30.

27. Find the ratio of 45 to $3\frac{1}{3}$.

To recognize a comparison by division pay close attention to the language. The word *ratio* indicates to form a fraction, and the quantity that follows the word *to* is placed in the denominator.

EXAMPLE 8   Find the ratio of $9\frac{1}{3}$ to 14. Simplify.

SOLUTION

$$\text{Ratio of } 9\frac{1}{3} \text{ to } 14 = \frac{9\frac{1}{3}}{14}$$

The quantity following the word *to* is placed in the denominator.

$$= 9\frac{1}{3} \div 14$$

Perform the indicated division and simplify.

$$= \frac{28}{3} \times \frac{1}{14}$$

$$= \frac{2 \times 2 \times 7}{3} \times \frac{1}{2 \times 7}$$

$$= \frac{2}{3} \ \blacksquare$$

 Try Problems 26 and 27.

 Answers to Try These Problems

1. 15 2. 45 3. $\frac{8}{5}$ or $1\frac{3}{5}$ 4. $\frac{1}{30}$ 5. 72 6. 135 7. $\frac{1}{8}$

8. 25 9. 125 10. $\frac{41}{8}$ or $5\frac{1}{8}$ 11. $\frac{3}{17}$ 12. $\frac{3600}{7}$ or $514\frac{2}{7}$

13. $\frac{3}{2}$ or $1\frac{1}{2}$ 14. $\frac{2125}{2}$ or $1062\frac{1}{2}$ 15. $\frac{12}{7}$ or $1\frac{5}{7}$ 16. $\frac{77}{2}$ or $38\frac{1}{2}$

17. $\frac{9}{20}$ 18. $\frac{19}{6}$ or $3\frac{1}{6}$ 19. $\frac{33}{8}$ or $4\frac{1}{8}$ 20. $\frac{1}{20}$ 21. $\frac{17}{6}$ or $2\frac{5}{6}$

22. $\frac{6}{17}$ 23. $\frac{1}{62}$ 24. 62 25. $\frac{16}{3}$ or $5\frac{1}{3}$ 26. $\frac{1}{12}$

27. $\frac{27}{2}$ or $13\frac{1}{2}$

EXERCISES 4.4

Translate each English statement to a multiplication or division statement using math symbols.

1. $\frac{2}{5}$ of 25 is 10.

2. 75 is $\frac{3}{4}$ of 100.

3. The product of $\frac{3}{5}$ and $\frac{5}{6}$ equals $\frac{1}{2}$.

4. $13\frac{1}{2}$ is the product of $4\frac{1}{2}$ and 3.

5. The ratio of 3 to $\frac{1}{4}$ is 12.

6. The ratio of $\frac{1}{4}$ to 3 is $\frac{1}{12}$.

7. Forty-hundredths times 200 gives 80.

8. Fourteen is the result of multiplying $\frac{2}{7}$ by 49.

9. $2\frac{2}{3}$ divided into 4 equals $1\frac{1}{2}$.

10. $2\frac{2}{3}$ divided by 4 equals $\frac{2}{3}$.

11. $4\frac{1}{2}$ is half of 9.

12. Half $\frac{3}{4}$ is $\frac{3}{8}$.

13. $\frac{7}{8}$ is twice as large as $\frac{7}{16}$.

14. 25 is the result of doubling $12\frac{1}{2}$.

Translate to an equation. Then solve.

15. $\frac{2}{5}$ of 900.

16. $\frac{3}{8}$ of $8\frac{4}{5}$.

17. $1\frac{1}{2}$ of 70.

18. 5 of $3\frac{3}{4}$.

19. Find $\frac{8}{9}$ of 81.

20. Three-fifths of 30,100 is what number?

21. Find the product of $5\frac{1}{3}$ and $\frac{3}{4}$.

22. Find the ratio of $5\frac{1}{3}$ to $\frac{3}{4}$.

23. Divide $18\frac{1}{2}$ by 5.

24. Divide 5 by $18\frac{1}{2}$.

25. Divide $\frac{2}{5}$ into 60.

26. Divide 60 into $\frac{2}{5}$.

27. Double $4\frac{1}{4}$.

28. What number is twice $\frac{10}{23}$?

29. Find half of $50\frac{3}{4}$.

30. Half of what number yields $\frac{3}{4}$?

31. $13\frac{1}{2}$ is what number times $\frac{3}{20}$?

32. $\frac{80}{3}$ represents twice what number?

33. One-third of what number is represented by 80?

34. $52\frac{1}{3}$ equals $\frac{5}{7}$ of what number?

35. What number is the ratio of $6\frac{1}{4}$ to 200?

36. What number is the ratio of 200 to $6\frac{1}{4}$?

37. Fifty represents $\frac{7}{20}$ of what number?

38. $\frac{9}{10}$ equals $4\frac{1}{4}$ of what number?

39. 6 is what fraction of 200?

40. $18\frac{2}{3}$ is what fraction of 7?

41. $\frac{3}{5}$ of 9000 is what number?

42. What number times $16\frac{1}{4}$ equals 5?

43. $\frac{9}{40}$ of what number is 180?

44. $\frac{20}{7}$ of $16\frac{1}{3}$ is what number?

45. What fraction of 80 is 200?

46. $\frac{7}{200}$ of what number is 4?

4.5   APPLICATIONS

OBJECTIVES
- Solve an application involving equal parts in a total quantity.
- Solve an application involving equivalent rates.
- Convert a rate to its equivalent rate.
- Solve an application by interpreting a rate as a ratio.
- Solve an application by using a rate as a multiplier.
- Solve an application involving the area of a rectangle.
- Solve an application by using translations.

1   Equal Parts in a Total Quantity

Suppose we have a wire that is 36 inches long. If the wire is cut into 4 equal pieces, then each piece is 9 inches long. Here we picture the situation.

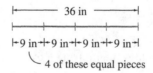

4 of these equal pieces

Observe that the numbers are related as follows:

$$
\begin{array}{ccc}
\text{Number of} & \text{Size of} & \text{total} \\
\text{equal parts} \times & \text{each part} = & \text{quantity} \\
& \text{(in)} & \text{(in)} \\
4 \times & 9 = & 36
\end{array}
$$

In general, if a situation involves a total quantity that is being split up into a number of equal parts, the following always applies.

$$\begin{array}{c}\text{Number of} \\ \text{equal parts}\end{array} \times \begin{array}{c}\text{Size of} \\ \text{each part}\end{array} = \begin{array}{c}\text{total} \\ \text{quantity}\end{array}$$

A problem can be presented by giving any two of the three quantities and asking for the third quantity. The following examples illustrate this.

EXAMPLE 1   A rope that is 4 feet long is cut into 12 equal pieces. How long is each piece?

SOLUTION   We use the formula,

$$\begin{array}{c}\text{Number of} \\ \text{equal parts}\end{array} \times \begin{array}{c}\text{Size of} \\ \text{each part} \\ \text{(ft)}\end{array} = \begin{array}{c}\text{total} \\ \text{quantity} \\ \text{(ft)}\end{array}$$

$$12 \quad \times \quad \boxed{} \quad = \quad 4$$

A multiplier is missing, so we divide 4 by 12 to find the missing multiplier.

$$\begin{array}{c}\text{Size of} \\ \text{each part}\end{array} = \frac{\text{total quantity}}{\text{number of equal parts}}$$

$$= \frac{4}{12}$$

$$= \frac{\overset{1}{\cancel{4}}}{3 \times \cancel{4}}$$

$$= \frac{1}{3}\text{ft}$$

Each piece is $\frac{1}{3}$ foot long. ■

In Example 1 it is important to note that the total quantity is not always the largest of the three numbers.

EXAMPLE 2   A 14-foot log is cut into pieces that are each $1\frac{3}{4}$ feet long. How many of the smaller pieces can be cut?

SOLUTION   We want to know how many of the $1\frac{3}{4}$-foot pieces make up the total 14 feet.

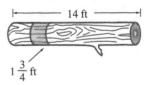

We use the formula,

$$\begin{array}{c}\text{Number of} \\ \text{equal parts}\end{array} \times \begin{array}{c}\text{Size of} \\ \text{each part} \\ \text{(ft)}\end{array} = \begin{array}{c}\text{total} \\ \text{quantity} \\ \text{(ft)}\end{array}$$

$$\boxed{} \quad \times \quad 1\frac{3}{4} \quad = \quad 14$$

A multiplier is missing, so we divide 14 by $1\frac{3}{4}$ to find the missing multiplier.

$$\begin{aligned} \text{Number of} \atop \text{equal parts} &= {\text{total} \atop \text{quantity}} \div {\text{size of} \atop \text{each part}} \\[2mm] &= \quad 14 \quad \div \quad 1\frac{3}{4} \\[2mm] &= \frac{14}{1} \div \frac{7}{4} \\[2mm] &= \frac{\overset{2}{\cancel{14}}}{1} \times \frac{4}{\underset{1}{\cancel{7}}} \\[2mm] &= 8 \end{aligned}$$

8 pieces can be cut.   ■

EXAMPLE 3   Ten children share $1\frac{1}{2}$ gallons of milk equally. How much milk will each child get?

SOLUTION   The $1\frac{1}{2}$ gallons of milk is the quantity that is being separated into 10 equal parts. We use the formula,

$$\begin{aligned} {\text{Number of} \atop \text{equal parts}} \times {\text{Size of} \atop \text{each part} \atop \text{(gal)}} &= {\text{total} \atop \text{quantity} \atop \text{(gal)}} \\[2mm] 10 \quad \times \quad \boxed{} &= 1\frac{1}{2} \end{aligned}$$

The total quantity is the quantity that is being split apart, *not* necessarily the larger number.

A multiplier is missing, so we divide $1\frac{1}{2}$ by 10 to find the missing multiplier.

$$\begin{aligned} {\text{Size of} \atop \text{each part}} &= {\text{total} \atop \text{quantity}} \div {\text{number of} \atop \text{equal parts}} \\[2mm] &= \quad 1\frac{1}{2} \quad \div \quad 10 \\[2mm] &= \frac{3}{2} \times \frac{1}{10} \\[2mm] &= \frac{3}{20} \text{ gal} \end{aligned}$$

Each child receives $\frac{3}{20}$ gallon of milk.   ■

EXAMPLE 4   A nurse needs to give out 32 doses of medicine. Each dose contains $1\frac{1}{8}$ milliliters. How much medicine does she need?

SOLUTION   The 32 doses is the number of equal parts and $1\frac{1}{8}$ milliliters is the size of each part. We are missing the total quantity.

Try These Problems

1. Three people share equally 2 pizzas. How much pizza does each person receive?

2. Two people share equally 3 pizzas. How much pizza does each person receive?

3. Thirty milliliters of medicine is to be given out in doses of $1\frac{1}{5}$ milliliters each. How many doses can be given?

4. A board that is $6\frac{3}{10}$ meters long is cut into 6 equal pieces. How long is each piece?

5. Fifteen persons share equally $4\frac{4}{5}$ pounds of cheese. How much cheese does each person receive?

6. A chef needs 50 servings of soup that each contain $14\frac{1}{2}$ ounces. How much soup does the chef need?

$$\begin{array}{ccc} \text{Total} \\ \text{quantity} \\ (\text{m}\ell) \end{array} = \begin{array}{c} \text{number of} \\ \text{equal parts} \end{array} \times \begin{array}{c} \text{size of} \\ \text{each part} \\ (\text{m}\ell) \end{array}$$

$$= \quad 32 \quad \times \quad 1\frac{1}{8}$$

$$= \frac{32}{1} \times \frac{9}{8}$$

$$= \frac{\overset{4}{\cancel{8} \times 4}}{1} \times \frac{9}{\underset{1}{\cancel{8}}}$$

$$= 36 \text{ m}\ell$$

The nurse needs 36 milliliters of medicine. ■

 Try Problems 1 through 6.

Unit Analysis

Some numbers have **units** attached to them. Here are three examples.

$$\underset{\searrow\text{unit}}{\textbf{5 dollars}} \quad \textbf{or} \quad \underset{\searrow\text{unit}}{\textbf{\$5}} \qquad \underset{\searrow\text{unit}}{\tfrac{2}{3}\textbf{ mile}} \qquad \underset{\searrow\text{unit}}{15\tfrac{1}{4}\textbf{ hours}}$$

We want to be able to distinguish one type of quantity from another. To do this, pay close attention to the *units*. Here we give some examples.

Rate	Area	Distance	Time	Weight	Volume
6 bottles per carton	25 square miles	6 miles	4 hours	3 pounds	4 gallons
$5000 per year	4 square meters	16 meters	50 minutes	8 ounces	7 cubic feet
$4\frac{2}{3}$ miles an hour	$6\frac{1}{4}$ acres	$5\frac{1}{3}$ yards	$\frac{3}{4}$ second	$2\frac{1}{2}$ tons	$\frac{3}{10}$ centiliter

Quantities like $8\frac{2}{3}$, 25 and $\frac{1}{4}$ are numbers with no units attached.

▶ Try These Problems

Identify each of these quantities as a rate, area, distance, time, weight or volume.

1. 5¢ per person
2. 9 yards
3. 60 gallons
4. 55 miles per hour
5. $8\frac{5}{6}$ square feet
6. $15\frac{2}{3}$ days
7. $\frac{3}{4}$ gallon per minute
8. 900 seconds
9. $60\frac{1}{10}$ meters
10. $\frac{1}{8}$ mile
11. $4\frac{5}{8}$ quarts
12. $16\frac{1}{4}$ square inches

13. Choose all of the **rates** in this list of quantities.

    9 feet per second   15 kilometers $2\frac{2}{3}$ gallons per week   100 square miles

14. Choose all of the **areas** in this list of quantities.

    25 yards $2\frac{1}{4}$ ounces per minute   85 square meters $14 per square foot

---

Introduction

$9 \text{ tons} + 6 \text{ tons} = 15 \text{ tons}$
$12\frac{1}{2} \text{ hours} - 7 \text{ hours} = 5\frac{1}{2} \text{ hours}$

When adding or subtracting quantities with like units, the result's unit is the same as the other units.

$3 \times \frac{2}{3} \text{ cup} = 2 \text{ cups}$
$\$1 \div 4 = \$\frac{1}{4}$

When multiplying or dividing a quantity with units by a number with no units, the result's unit is the same as the quantity's unit.

▶ Try These Problems

Calculate the following. Give both the number and unit. Simplify the fractions.

15. 9 ounces + 7 ounces
16. 18 days – 6 days
17. 9 x 8 feet
18. 24 cents ÷ 6
19. 3 ounces ÷ 5
20. 5 cartons x 8
21. $19\frac{1}{4}$ hours + 8 hours
22. 3 years – $\frac{1}{2}$ year
23. 2 miles ÷ 6
24. 9 pints ÷ 18
25. 200 years x $2\frac{1}{4}$
26. 60 gallons x $\frac{3}{4}$

Distance & Area

$1 \text{ foot} + 6 \text{ feet} = 7 \text{ feet}$

$50 \text{ square inches} + 30 \text{ square inches} = 80 \text{ square inches}$

$6\frac{1}{2} \text{ miles} - 4\frac{1}{2} \text{ miles} = 2 \text{ miles}$

When adding or subtracting quantities with like units, the result's unit is the same as the other units.

$6 \text{ miles} \times 9 \text{ miles} = 54 \text{ square miles}$

$\frac{3}{4} \text{ inch} \times 8 \text{ inches} = 6 \text{ square inches}$

Distance times distance equals area.

► **Try These Problems**

Calculate the following. Give both the number and unit. Simplify the fractions.

27. 8 miles + 7 miles
28. 9 meters x 8 meters
29. 21 miles − 8 miles
30. 204 feet − 26 feet
31. 36 feet x 8 feet
32. 15 meters + 6 meters
33. $9\frac{1}{4}$ yards + $\frac{3}{4}$ yard
34. 3 square inches − $1\frac{1}{3}$ square inches
35. $3\frac{3}{8}$ inches x $6\frac{2}{3}$ inches
36. 6 miles x $\frac{4}{5}$ mile
37. $2\frac{5}{8}$ square miles + $5\frac{1}{8}$ square miles
38. 6 inches − $\frac{3}{4}$ inch

Dividing Quantities and Rates

5 ounces ÷ 6 ounces = $\dfrac{5 \text{ ounces}}{6 \text{ ounces}} = \dfrac{5}{6}$ **When dividing two quantities with like units, the result is a number with no units.**

150 miles ÷ 5 hours = $\dfrac{150 \text{ miles}}{5 \text{ hours}}$ = 30 miles per hour   **Dividing two quantities with unlike units gives a rate. The divisor's unit is the same as the unit after the word "per" in the resulting rate.**

6 feet per second x 4 seconds = 24 feet

$\dfrac{6 \text{ feet}}{1 \text{ second}}$ x 4 seconds = 24 feet   **Here is an example of a rate as a multiplier. The unit before the word "per" in the rate is the same as the result's unit. The second equation has the rate written in a ratio form.**

► **Try These Problems**

Calculate the following. Give both the number and unit. Simplify the fractions.

39. 36 miles ÷ 6 miles
40. 3 hours ÷ 9 hours
41. 20 gallons ÷ 8 gallons
42. 40 tons ÷ 5 hours
43. 6 feet ÷ 12 seconds
44. 21 cartons ÷ 40 days
45. 5 trees per mile x 9 miles
46. 8 feet a second x 14 seconds
47. 2 tons x 4 loads per ton
48. $2\frac{2}{3}$ inches ÷ $\frac{1}{6}$ inch
49. 5 feet ÷ $17\frac{1}{2}$ feet
50. $10\frac{2}{3}$ minutes ÷ 18 cents
51. $4 per foot x $\frac{7}{8}$ foot
52. $6\frac{1}{2}$ inches a week x 30 weeks
53. 130 barrels ÷ $8\frac{2}{3}$ pounds

Fill in the blank with the appropriate unit that makes the statement true.

54. meters + meters = _____
55. meters x meters = _____
56. miles − miles = _____
57. gallons per mile x miles = _____
58. inches ÷ seconds = _____
59. $ ÷ persons = _____
60. miles per hour x hours = _____
61. feet x feet = _____
62. _____ = pounds per month x months
63. _____ = $ per square foot x square feet
64. square yards = _____ x yards
65. feet x _____ = square feet
66. days x gallons per day = _____
67. miles ÷ gallons = _____

Rate Phrases and Rates

The phrase, "*$20 for every 1 shirt*," is a **rate phrase**. We are comparing the quantity $20 to the quantity 1 shirt. We are saying that for every $20 you can buy 1 shirt or for every 1 shirt you pay $20. When this rate phrase is put in a single quantity form, it is called a **rate**.

Rate Phrase

$20 every 1 shirt

In rate phrase form we see two quantities. Each quantity has its own units.

Rate or Rate Quantity

20 dollars per shirt

In rate form we see only one quantity consisting of a number and the rate unit.

Here are more examples of rate phrases and a corresponding rate or rate quantity.

Rate Phrase	Rate or Rate Quantity
50 miles every 1 hour	50 miles an hour
$2\frac{3}{4}$ gallons in 1 minute	$2\frac{3}{4}$ gallons each minute
1 yard costs $12	$12 per yard
1 person every $\frac{2}{3}$ ounce	$\frac{2}{3}$ ounce per person

▶ **Try These Problems**

Write a rate phrase that corresponds to the given rate.

68. $6 per ticket

69. 24 items per carton

70. 45 miles an hour

71. $\frac{1}{2}$ inch per mile

72. $12\frac{1}{2}$ miles a day

73. $\frac{2}{3}$ gallon per minute

Write a rate that corresponds to the given rate phrase. Be sure to include the number and rate units.

74. 50¢ for 1 hour

75. 4 bottles per 1 carton

76. 60 feet in 1 second

77. 1 nail weighs $\frac{1}{20}$ pound

78. $\frac{1}{4}$ ounce for every 1 person

79. 1 foot weighs $2\frac{2}{3}$ pounds

Introduction to Generating Equivalent Rate Phrases

Here are some examples of rate phrases.

- 8 dollars for 1 hour
- $\frac{1}{5}$ ounce every 1 foot
- 50 nails weigh $1\frac{1}{4}$ pounds

We can generate equivalent rate phrases by **multiplying both quantities in a rate phrase by the same nonzero number.** Here we look at generating some rate phrases that are equivalent to, "*8 dollars for 1 hour.*"

8 dollars for 1 hour	8 dollars for 1 hour	8 dollars for 1 hour
x 4 x 4	x 6 x 6	x $\frac{1}{2}$ x $\frac{1}{2}$
32 dollars for 4 hours	48 dollars for 6 hours	4 dollars for $\frac{1}{2}$ hour

▶ **Try These Problems**

Multiply the two quantities in the given rate phrase by 8 to generate an equivalent rate phrase. Write your steps as shown above.

80. 9¢ for 1 minute

81. $4 for every 1 hot dog

82. 16 miles per 1 hour

83. $\frac{2}{3}$ ounce in 1 minute

84. $2\frac{1}{4}$ inches per 100 miles

85. $15 for every $\frac{3}{4}$ yard

We can also generate equivalent rate phrases by **dividing both quantities in a rate phrase by the same nonzero number.** Here we look at some examples.

8 dollars for 1 hour	$\frac{1}{5}$ ounce every 1 foot
÷ 8 ÷ 8	÷ $\frac{1}{5}$ ÷ $\frac{1}{5}$
1 dollar for $\frac{1}{8}$ hour	1 ounce every 5 feet

50 nails weigh $1\frac{1}{4}$ pounds $\quad\longrightarrow\quad 1\frac{1}{4} \div 50 = \frac{5}{4} \div \frac{50}{1}\quad\longleftarrow$ Show the calculation steps when the
÷ 50 $\qquad$ ÷ 50 $\qquad\qquad\qquad = \frac{5}{4} \times \frac{1}{50}$ $\qquad$ work cannot be done mentally.
1 nail weighs $\frac{1}{40}$ pound $\qquad\qquad\qquad = \frac{\cancel{5} \times 1}{4} \times \frac{1}{\cancel{5} \times 10} = \frac{1}{40}$

▶ **Try These Problems**

Divide the two quantities in the given rate phrase by 5 to generate an equivalent rate phrase.
Write your steps as shown in the previous examples.

86. 20¢ for 1 minute   87. $15 for every 1 pound   88. $12\frac{1}{2}$ miles in 4 hours

Divide the two quantities in the given rate phrase by $\frac{5}{3}$ to generate an equivalent rate phrase.
Write your steps as shown in the previous examples.

89. $\frac{2}{3}$ ounce in 1 minute   90. $3\frac{1}{8}$ inches in 1 day   91. $10 for every $1\frac{2}{3}$ yards

---

> **Rule for Generating Equivalent Rate Phrases**
> Multiply or divide both quantities in a rate phrase by the same nonzero number to generate an equivalent rate phrase.

Three Important Number Properties

We have learned that multiplying or dividing both quantities in a rate phrase by the same nonzero number generates an equivalent rate phrase. This can be very useful in solving problems that involve rates or rate phrases. We need to learn how to choose the appropriate number to multiply or divide by. Before doing this it will be helpful to observe some special number properties.

Three Important Number Properties

$1 \times 4 = 4$ $1 \times 6 = 6$ $1 \times \frac{1}{2} = \frac{1}{2}$ $1 \times 2\frac{3}{4} = 2\frac{3}{4}$

Any number multiplied by 1 equals that number.

$4 \div 4 = 1$ $6 \div 6 = 1$ $\frac{1}{2} \div \frac{1}{2} = 1$ $2\frac{3}{4} \div 2\frac{3}{4} = 1$

Any nonzero number divided by itself equals 1.

$3 \div 4 = \frac{3}{4}$ $1 \div 20 = \frac{1}{20}$ $11 \div 2 = \frac{11}{2}$ or $5\frac{1}{2}$

A whole number divided by a whole number equals a fraction. The first number is the numerator and the second number is the denominator.

▶ **Try These Problems**

Find the value of each.

92. 12×1 93. 1×5 94. $2\frac{1}{3} \times 1$ 95. $\frac{5}{4} \times 1$ 96. $20 \div 20$ 97. $15 \div 15$

98. $12\frac{1}{2} \div 12\frac{1}{2}$ 99. $\frac{5}{6} \div \frac{5}{6}$ 100. $1 \div 4$ 101. $5 \div 3$ 102. $12 \div 16$ 103. $24 \div 18$

Calculate each. Give both the number and unit.

104. 4 hours ÷ 4   105. 18 miles ÷ 20   106. 1 gallon × 7   107. 4 square miles ÷ 3

108. 1 pound × $\frac{3}{4}$ 109. $\frac{1}{20}$ day ÷ $\frac{1}{20}$ 110. 1 liter × $3\frac{1}{10}$ 111. 1 foot ÷ 8

Finding the Missing Quantity in a Rate Phrase

Now we look at finding a missing quantity in a rate phrase. We will use our knowledge of how to generate equivalent rate phrases and also the three number properties discussed previously.

EXAMPLE Find the missing quantity that makes the second rate phrase equivalent to the first one.

$4 for every 1 binder

__?__ for   6 binders

Solution Write down the given rate phrase. Write the rate phrase with missing quantity under the given one so that like units align.

$4 for every 1 binder

__?__ for   6 binders

Look on the side where two known quantities are under each other. Then you see where you want to go. Think, what do we multiply or divide 1 by to get a result of 6? We multiply by 6. 1 x 6 = 6.

$4 for every 1 binder
x 6   x 6

__?__ for   6 binders

Therefore, we multiply both quantities in the given rate phrase by 6 to generate an equivalent rate phrase. $4 x 6 = $24 and 1 binder x 6 = 6 binders.

Answer $24 for   6 binders

EXAMPLE Find the missing quantity that makes the two rate phrases equivalent.

8 ounces in 2 seconds

1 ounce in   __?__

Solution Write down the given rate phrase. Write the rate phrase with missing quantity under the given one so that like units align.

8 ounces in 2 seconds

1 ounce in   __?__

Look on the side where you have two known quantities under each other. They should have the same units. Then you see where you want to go. Think, what do we multiply or divide 8 by to get a result of 1? We divide 8 by 8. 8 ÷ 8 = 1.

8 ounces in 2 seconds
÷ 8   ÷ 8

1 ounce in   __?__

Therefore, we divide both quantities in the given rate phrase by 8 to generate the equivalent rate phrase.

$$2 \div 8 = \frac{2}{8} = \frac{\cancel{2} \times 1}{\cancel{2} \times 4} = \frac{1}{4}$$

Answer 1 ounce in $\frac{1}{4}$ second

▶ **Try These Problems**

Find the missing quantity that makes the two rate phrases equivalent. Give the number and units. Write your steps as shown above. Show clearly the number you choose to multiply or divide by.

112. $40 for 1 hour
 __?__ for 3 hours

113. 1 gallon every 3 minutes
 7 gallons in __?__

114. 160 miles every 4 hours
 __?__ every 1 hour

115. 9 feet weigh 72 pounds
 1 foot weighs __?__

116. 1 inch for 45 miles
 $\frac{3}{5}$ inch for __?__

117. 3 ounces every 8 minutes
 __?__ each 1 minute

118. 12 ounces in 15 minutes
 1 ounce in __?__

119. 6 dollars for 1 hour
 __?__ for $8\frac{1}{4}$ hours

120. 1 adult per 6 children
 __?__ per 1 child

EXAMPLE Find the missing quantity that makes the two rate phrases equivalent.

$\frac{1}{2}$ gallon every $3\frac{1}{3}$ miles

_____?_____ in 1 mile

Solution $\frac{1}{2}$ gallon every $3\frac{1}{3}$ miles

_____?_____ every 1 mile

Look here because you see where you want to go. Using multiplication or division, what would we do to $3\frac{1}{3}$ to get a result of 1? We divide $3\frac{1}{3}$ by $3\frac{1}{3}$. $3\frac{1}{3} \div 3\frac{1}{3} = 1$.

$\frac{1}{2}$ gallon every $3\frac{1}{3}$ miles
$\div 3\frac{1}{3}$ $\div 3\frac{1}{3}$
_____?_____ every 1 mile

We divide both quantities in the given rate phrase by $3\frac{1}{3}$ to generate the equivalent rate phrase.

$\frac{1}{2} \div 3\frac{1}{3} = \frac{1}{2} \div \frac{10}{3}$

$= \frac{1}{2} \times \frac{3}{10} = \frac{3}{20}$

Answer $\frac{3}{20}$ gallon every 1 mile

EXAMPLE Find the missing quantity that makes the two rate phrases equivalent.

1 ounce every 6 minutes

$2\frac{3}{4}$ ounces in ___?___

Solution 1 ounce every 6 minutes

$2\frac{3}{4}$ ounces every ___?___

Look on the side with "ounces" because you see where you want to go. Using multiplication or division, what would we do to 1 to get a result of $2\frac{3}{4}$? We multiply 1 by $2\frac{3}{4}$. $1 \times 2\frac{3}{4} = 2\frac{3}{4}$.

1 ounce every 6 minutes
$\times 2\frac{3}{4}$ $\times 2\frac{3}{4}$
$2\frac{3}{4}$ ounces every ___?___

We multiply both quantities in the given rate phrase by $2\frac{3}{4}$ to generate the equivalent rate phrase.

$6 \times 2\frac{3}{4} = \frac{6}{1} \times \frac{11}{4}$

$= \frac{2 \times 3}{1} \times \frac{11}{2 \times 2} = \frac{33}{2}$ or $16\frac{1}{2}$

Answer $2\frac{3}{4}$ ounces every $16\frac{1}{2}$ minutes

▶ **Try These Problems**

Find the missing quantity that makes the two rate phrases equivalent. Give both the number and unit. Show clearly the number you choose to multiply or divide by.

121. \$30 for $1\frac{1}{4}$ hours

_____? for 1 hour

122. $3\frac{1}{5}$ gallons every 1 minute

____?____ every $\frac{3}{4}$ minute

123. 1 mile per $\frac{2}{3}$ hour

$6\frac{3}{4}$ miles per ___?___

124. $\frac{5}{6}$ foot weighs 1 pound

1 foot weighs ___?___

125. 1 inch for 9 miles

$\frac{2}{3}$ inch for ___?___

126. $3\frac{1}{3}$ ounces every $7\frac{1}{2}$ minutes

___?___ each 1 minute

Solving Applications using Equivalent Rate Phrases

EXAMPLE Stephanie can jog 1 mile in 8 minutes. How long will it take her to jog $4\frac{1}{2}$ miles?

Solution Write down the given rate phrase. ⟶ 1 mile in 8 minutes

Write the question as a rate phrase with missing quantity. Be sure to arrange like units under each other. → $4\frac{1}{2}$ miles in ___?___

Look on the side with "miles." Think. What can we do to 1, using × or ÷, to get a result of $4\frac{1}{2}$? Multiply 1 by $4\frac{1}{2}$.

Multiply both quantities in the given rate phrase by $4\frac{1}{2}$ to generate an equivalent rate phrase.

1 mile in 8 minutes
$\times 4\frac{1}{2}$ $\times 4\frac{1}{2}$
$4\frac{1}{2}$ miles in ___?___

$8 \times 4\frac{1}{2} = \frac{8}{1} \times \frac{9}{2}$

$= \frac{2 \times 4}{1} \times \frac{9}{2 \times 1}$

$= \frac{36}{1} = 36$

Show the calculation steps when the work cannot be done mentally.

Answer $4\frac{1}{2}$ miles in 36 minutes

EXAMPLE   Betsy can jog $1\frac{1}{4}$ miles in $12\frac{1}{2}$ minutes. How far can she go in 1 minute?

Solution   Write down the given rate phrase.

$1\frac{1}{4}$ miles in $12\frac{1}{2}$ minutes

Write the question as a rate phrase with missing quantity. Be sure to arrange like units under each other.

_____?_____ in 1 minute

What can we do to $12\frac{1}{2}$, using x or ÷, to get a result of 1? Divide by $12\frac{1}{2}$.

Divide both quantities in the given rate phrase by $12\frac{1}{2}$ to generate an equivalent rate phrase.

$$
\begin{array}{c}
1\frac{1}{4}\ \text{mile}\quad \text{in}\quad 12\frac{1}{2}\ \text{minutes}\\
\div 12\frac{1}{2}\qquad\quad \div 12\frac{1}{2}\\
\hline
\_\_?\_\_\ \text{in}\quad 1\ \text{minute}
\end{array}
$$

$1\frac{1}{4} \div 12\frac{1}{2} = \frac{5}{4} \div \frac{25}{2}$

$= \frac{5}{4} \times \frac{2}{25}$

$= \frac{5 \times 1}{2 \times 2} \times \frac{2 \times 1}{5 \times 5} = \frac{1}{10}$

Show the calculation steps when the work cannot be done mentally.

Answer $\frac{1}{10}$ mile in 1 minute

EXAMPLE   A faucet leaks $3\frac{3}{4}$ ounces per minute. At this rate, how many ounces have leaked in 12 minutes?

Solution   First, we write the given rate in a rate phrase form.

$3\frac{3}{4}$ ounces per minute   ⟶ $3\frac{3}{4}$ ounces per 1 minute

Write the question as a rate phrase with missing quantity so that like units align.   ⟶   _____?_____ per 12 minutes

We want to go from 1 to 12, so we multiply by 12.

$$
\begin{array}{c}
3\frac{3}{4}\ \text{ounces per 1 minute}\\
\text{x } 12\qquad\qquad \text{x } 12\\
\hline
\_\_?\_\_\quad \text{per 12 minutes}
\end{array}
$$

$3\frac{3}{4} \times 12 = \frac{15}{4} \times \frac{12}{1}$

$= \frac{5 \times 3}{4 \times 1} \times \frac{3 \times 4}{1} = \frac{45}{1} = 45$

Show the calculation steps when the work cannot be done mentally.

Answer   45 ounces every 12 minutes

▶ **Try These Problems**

Use equivalent rate phrases to solve each of these application problems. Show steps clearly.

127.   One pound of bananas costs 56 cents. How much do $1\frac{3}{8}$ pounds cost?

128.   A utility stock costs $50\frac{3}{4}$ dollars per 1 share. What is the total cost of 12 shares?

129.   Ed can run 4 miles in 27 minutes. How long will it take him to run 1 mile?

130.   Dick bought Stephanie some fabric while he was in Paris. He paid $27 for $4\frac{1}{2}$ yards. How much did the fabric cost for 1 yard?

131.   Seventy nails weigh $1\frac{3}{4}$ pounds. What does 1 nail weigh?

132.   Water leaks from a faucet at the rate of $2\frac{2}{3}$ ounces per hour. How much water has leaked after $5\frac{1}{2}$ hours?

Focus on Rate as a Multiplier

Suppose you walk 5 miles per hour and you do this for 3 hours. You go 5 miles the first hour, then 5 more miles the second hour, and then 5 more miles the third hour. So you go 15 miles in 3 hours. Let's look at how to view the problem using multiplication and how the calculation looks with the units attached.

The unit after the word "per" in the rate is always the same as the other multiplier's unit.

5 miles per hour x 3 hours = 15 miles

Rate as a multiplier

The unit before the word "per" in the rate is the same as the result's unit.

When the rate, 5 miles per hour, is multiplied by 3 hours, the "hour" units cancel and we end up with "miles." Here are more examples. Study carefully how the units work. It can help you with problem solving.

$20 per shirt x 6 shirts = $120

15 feet per minute x 10 minutes = 150 feet

$6\frac{1}{2}$ weeks x 2 pounds per week = 13 pounds

2 pounds = 60 nails x $\frac{1}{30}$ pound per nail

In each equation note the following:
1) The rate is one of the multipliers.
2) The unit after the word "per" in the rate is the same as the other muliplier's unit.
3) The unit before the word "per" in the rate is the same as the result's unit.

To focus on the units more carefully, here we look at the above equations without the numbers.

$ per shirt x shirts = $

feet per minute x minutes = feet

weeks x pounds per week = pounds

pounds = nails x pound per nail

One multiplier has a rate unit. The other multiplier's unit is the same as the unit after the word "per" in the rate.

▶ **Try These Problems**

Find the missing quantity that makes the statement true. Include both the number and unit.

133. $15 per cake x 7 cakes = _____

134. 4 items per carton x 8 cartons = _____

135. $5\frac{1}{2}$ miles per hour x 6 hours = _____

136. $4\frac{3}{4}$ minutes x 16 feet per minute = _____

137. 100 nails x $\frac{1}{24}$ pound per nail = _____

138. _____ = $4\frac{1}{5}$ ounces per day x 10 days

139. _____ = $\frac{1}{4}$ inch per week x $3\frac{1}{2}$ weeks

140. _____ = $6\frac{2}{3}$ hours x $\frac{1}{10}$ gallon per hour

More on Rate as a Multiplier

EXAMPLE   Find the missing quantity that makes the equation true. Give both the number and unit.

$3\frac{1}{2}$ inches per day x _____ = 14 inches

Solution   First, we know the following structure for the units.

inches per day x days = inches

Therefore, the unit of the missing multiplier is "days."

Because we are missing the multiplier, we divide the result 14 by the given multiplier $3\frac{1}{2}$ to obtain the missing multiplier.

$14 \div 3\frac{1}{2} = \frac{14}{1} \div \frac{7}{2}$
$= \frac{14}{1} \times \frac{2}{7}$
$= \frac{2 \times 7}{1} \times \frac{2}{7 \times 1}$
$= \frac{4}{1} = 4$

Answer   The missing quantity is 4 days.

EXAMPLE   Find the missing quantity that makes the equation true. Give both the number and units.

8 yards = $1\frac{1}{5}$ minutes x _____

Solution   First, we can see the following unit structure.

yards = minutes x yards per minute

Therefore, the missing multiplier is a rate. The unit is "yards per minute."
Because we are missing the multiplier, we divide the result 8 by the given multiplier $1\frac{1}{5}$ to obtain the missing multiplier.

$8 \div 1\frac{1}{5} = \frac{8}{1} \div \frac{6}{5}$
$= \frac{8}{1} \times \frac{5}{6}$
$= \frac{2 \times 4}{1} \times \frac{5}{2 \times 3}$
$= \frac{20}{3}$ or $6\frac{2}{3}$

Answer   The missing quantity is $6\frac{2}{3}$ yards per minute.

EXAMPLE   Find the missing quantity that makes the equation true. Give both the number and unit.

$$\underline{\hspace{2cm}} = 6\tfrac{3}{4} \text{ pounds per person} \times 24 \text{ persons}$$

Solution   First, we can see the following unit structure. ➡ **pounds = pounds per person × persons**

Note the missing quantity is the result of multiplication and the unit is "pounds." We multiply $6\tfrac{3}{4}$ by 24 to find the missing number.

$$6\tfrac{3}{4} \times 24 = \tfrac{27}{4} \times \tfrac{24}{1}$$
$$= \tfrac{27}{\cancel{4} \times 1} \times \tfrac{\cancel{4} \times 6}{1}$$
$$= \tfrac{162}{1} = 162$$

Answer   The missing quantity is 162 pounds.

▶ Try These Problems

Each of these unit equations involves a rate as a multiplier. Give the missing unit.

141. $ per person × _____ = $

142.   _____ × days = inches

143.   feet per second × _____ = feet

144.   persons = persons per square mile × _____

145.   cartons × pounds per carton = _____

146.   liters = liters per bottle × _____

147.   inches = _____ × weeks

148.   _____ = hours × $ per hour

Find the missing quantity that makes the statement true. Give both the number and units.

149. $8 per calculator × _____ = $32

150.   _____ × 6 days = 30 persons

151. $7\tfrac{1}{2}$ miles per hour × _____ = 60 miles

152.   4 ounces = $\tfrac{3}{4}$ minute × _____

153.   2 hours × $1\tfrac{2}{3}$ seconds per hour = _____

154. $2\tfrac{2}{5}$ ounces = $3\tfrac{1}{5}$ ounces per day × _____

155.   52 inches = _____ × 6 weeks

156.   _____ = $\tfrac{5}{6}$ hour × $\tfrac{3}{5}$ gallon per hour

Solving Applications by using a Rate as a Multiplier

There are some cases where you may want to set up a multiplication statement, using the rate as a multiplier, to solve an application problem. This is particularly helpful when the rate is given or when you are looking for the rate. Here we look at three examples.

EXAMPLE   Fatima can swim $\tfrac{3}{4}$ lap each minute. How many laps can she swim in $1\tfrac{1}{2}$ minutes?

Solution   We are given the rate, "$\tfrac{3}{4}$ lap each minute."
We are looking for the number of laps in $1\tfrac{1}{2}$ minutes.

Write a unit equation with ➡ **laps each minute × minutes = laps**
the rate as a multiplier.

Put the known quantities ➡ $\tfrac{3}{4}$ × $1\tfrac{1}{2}$ = _____?_____
in the appropriate positions.

Because we are missing the result of the multiplication, we multiply the two factors.

$$\tfrac{3}{4} \times 1\tfrac{1}{2} = \tfrac{3}{4} \times \tfrac{3}{2}$$
$$= \tfrac{9}{8} \text{ or } 1\tfrac{1}{8}$$

Answer   Fatima can swim $1\tfrac{1}{8}$ laps in $1\tfrac{1}{2}$ minutes.

EXAMPLE   A car averages 48 miles per hour. How many hours will it take the car to travel 204 miles?

Solution   We are given the rate, 48 miles per hour.

Set up the structure. ➡ **miles per hour × hours = miles**

Put the known quantities in the appropriate positions. ➡   48   × ___?___ = 204

Because we are missing the multiplier, we divide the result 204 by the given multiplier 48 to obtain the missing multiplier.

$$204 \div 48 = \tfrac{204}{48}$$
$$= \tfrac{51 \times \cancel{4}}{\cancel{4} \times 12}$$
$$= \tfrac{\cancel{3} \times 17}{\cancel{3} \times 4} = \tfrac{17}{4} \text{ or } 4\tfrac{1}{4}$$

Answer   It takes $4\tfrac{1}{4}$ hours to go 204 miles.

EXAMPLE   A rope weighs $2\frac{1}{2}$ pounds for every 5 feet. How many pounds per foot is this?

Solution   We are looking for the number of "pounds per foot."
Therefore, we are looking for the rate.

Set up the structure. $\longrightarrow$ **pounds per foot x feet = pounds**

Put the known quantities
in the appropriate positions. $\longrightarrow$ _____?_____   x   5   = $2\frac{1}{2}$

Because we are missing the multiplier, we divide the
result $2\frac{1}{2}$ by the given multiplier 5 to obtain the
missing multiplier.

$$2\frac{1}{2} \div 5 \;=\; \frac{5}{2} \div \frac{5}{1}$$
$$=\; \frac{5}{2} \times \frac{1}{5}$$
$$=\; \frac{1 \times \cancel{5}}{2} \times \frac{1}{\cancel{5} \times 1} = \frac{1}{2}$$

Answer   The rope weighs $\frac{1}{2}$ pound per foot.

▶ **Try These Problems**

Solve each of these applications by setting up a multiplication equation with the rate as a multiplier.

157. An entertainment stock sells for $20\frac{5}{8}$ per share. What is the cost of 160 shares of this stock?

158. A watch gains $2\frac{1}{2}$ minutes each day. How many days will it take the watch to gain 30 minutes?

159. Carlos can swim 1 lap in $1\frac{1}{2}$ minutes. How many laps per minute is this?

160. A fabric sells for $30 per yard. How many yards can you buy for $620?

161. A $12\frac{1}{2}$-foot rope weighs $8\frac{1}{3}$ pounds. How many pounds per foot is this?

162. A chef uses $\frac{3}{4}$ pound of butter for each cake. How many pounds of butter will she need for 6 cakes?

163. On an architects drawing, $\frac{3}{8}$ inch represents an actual distance of 24 miles. How many inches per mile is this?

164. Shannon's car averages $18\frac{2}{3}$ miles per gallon of gasoline. How many gallons of gas does she need to go 63 miles?

165. Ryan walks $8\frac{2}{5}$ miles each week. How far does he walk in $1\frac{3}{7}$ weeks?

166. During a 30-day period, Alfaro works-out $22\frac{1}{2}$ hours. On the average, how many hours does he work-out each day?

5 Area of a Rectangle

Area is a measure of the extent of a region. A square that measures 1 unit on each side is said to have an area of 1 square unit.

1 unit ⬜ Area = 1 square unit
1 unit

A rectangle that is 3 units wide and 4 units long contains 12 of the 1-square-unit squares, therefore the area is 12 square units.

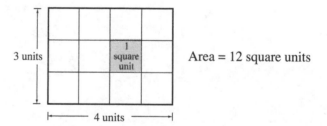

Area = 12 square units

Observe that the area of this rectangle can be obtained by multiplying the length by the width.

$$\begin{aligned} \text{Area} &= \text{length} \times \text{width} \\ &= 4 \times 3 \\ &= 12 \text{ square units} \end{aligned}$$

In general, the area of any rectangle can be computed by multiplying the length by the width.

> *Area of Rectangle*
> The area of a rectangle is the length times the width.
> Area = length × width

EXAMPLE 15   A rectangular flower garden is $16\frac{1}{2}$ feet long and $4\frac{1}{4}$ feet wide. What is the area of the garden?

SOLUTION

$16\frac{1}{2}$ ft

$4\frac{1}{4}$ ft   ? sq ft

$$\begin{array}{ccc} \text{Area} & = & \text{length} \times \text{width} \\ \text{(sq ft)} & & \text{(ft)} \qquad \text{(ft)} \end{array}$$

$$\boxed{} = \quad 16\frac{1}{2} \quad \times \quad 4\frac{1}{4}$$

The answer to the multiplication problem is missing, so multiply.

$$16\frac{1}{2} \times 4\frac{1}{4} = \frac{33}{2} \times \frac{17}{4}$$

$$= \frac{561}{8} \quad \text{or} \quad 70\frac{1}{8}$$

The area of the garden is $70\frac{1}{8}$ square feet.   ◾

EXAMPLE 16   The area of a vacant lot is 540 square meters. The width of the lot is $20\frac{1}{4}$ meters. How long is the lot?

SOLUTION

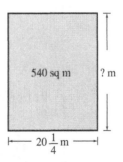

540 sq m   ? m

$20\frac{1}{4}$ m

$$\begin{array}{ccc} \text{Area} & = & \text{length} \times \text{width} \\ \text{(sq m)} & & \text{(m)} \qquad \text{(m)} \end{array}$$

$$540 \quad = \quad \boxed{} \times \quad 20\frac{1}{4}$$

A multiplier is missing, so we divide 540 by $20\frac{1}{4}$.

Try These Problems

29. Andrea wants to carpet her bedroom. The floor of the room is $5\frac{2}{3}$ yards wide and $6\frac{1}{3}$ yards long. How many square yards of carpeting will she need to buy?

30. A tablecloth is 27 square feet in area. It is $4\frac{1}{2}$ feet wide. What is the length of the tablecloth?

31. A rectangular garden is $20\frac{1}{4}$ feet long. How wide is the garden if it contains $337\frac{1}{2}$ square feet?

$$540 \div 20\frac{1}{4} = \frac{540}{1} \div \frac{81}{4}$$
$$= \frac{540}{1} \times \frac{4}{81}$$
$$= \frac{\cancel{9} \times 60}{1} \times \frac{4}{\cancel{9} \times 9}$$
$$= \frac{\cancel{3} \times 20}{1} \times \frac{4}{\cancel{3} \times 3}$$
$$= \frac{80}{3} \quad \text{or} \quad 26\frac{2}{3}$$

The length of the lot is $26\frac{2}{3}$ meters. ■

Try Problems 29 through 31.

6 Problems Involving Translations

In Section 4.4 we saw how translating English phrases to math symbols can be used to solve problems. Now we look at examples involving real-life situations.

EXAMPLE 17 Warren pays $\frac{3}{10}$ of his annual salary in taxes. His annual salary is $70,000. How much does he pay in taxes?

SOLUTION

KEY PHRASE $\rightarrow$ $\frac{3}{10}$ of his annual salary in taxes
$\frac{3}{10}$ × 70,000 = ☐

The answer to the multiplication statement is missing, so multiply $\frac{3}{10}$ by 70,000.

$$\frac{3}{10} \times 70{,}000 = \frac{3}{10} \times \frac{70000}{1}$$
$$= \frac{3}{\underset{1}{\cancel{10}}} \times \frac{\cancel{10} \times 7000}{1}$$
$$= 21{,}000$$

Warren pays $21,000 in taxes. ■

EXAMPLE 18 A certain college conducted a survey that indicates that $\frac{2}{9}$ of the students are smokers. There are 4000 smokers. What is the total number of students?

SOLUTION

KEY PHRASE $\rightarrow$ $\frac{2}{9}$ of the students are smokers.
$\frac{2}{9}$ × ☐ = 4000

Try These Problems

32. Mr. Hummer read $\frac{1}{3}$ of a novel last night. If he read 72 pages, how many pages does the novel have?

33. Darlene spends $\frac{3}{20}$ of her income on food. Her monthly income is $2100. How much does she spend on food in one month?

34. Two-thirds of a bottle of medicine weighs $5\frac{1}{2}$ grams. What does a full bottle weigh?

35. The population of a small town in Texas decreased by 350 persons in 5 years. The original population was 1500. The decrease is what fraction of the original population?

A multiplier is missing, so divide 4000 by $\frac{2}{9}$.

$$4000 \div \frac{2}{9} = \frac{4000}{1} \times \frac{9}{2}$$

$$= \frac{\cancel{2} \times 2000}{1} \times \frac{9}{\cancel{2}}$$

$$= 18,000$$

The total number of students is 18,000. ■

EXAMPLE 19   During last year's football season, Jerry made 81 field goals. The total number attempted was 108. What fractional part of the field goals did he make?

SOLUTION

KEY PHRASE $\rightarrow$ What fractional part of the field goals did he make?

$$\boxed{} \qquad \times \qquad 108 \qquad = \qquad 81$$

A multiplier is missing, so divide 81 by 108.

$$81 \div 108 = \frac{81}{108}$$

$$= \frac{\cancel{9} \times 9}{\cancel{9} \times 12}$$

$$= \frac{\cancel{3} \times 3}{\cancel{3} \times 4}$$

$$= \frac{3}{4}$$

Jerry made $\frac{3}{4}$ of his field goals. ■

 Try Problems 32 through 35.

EXAMPLE 20   Mercy spent $3\frac{3}{4}$ hours reading her history lesson. It took Steven $1\frac{1}{5}$ times as long to read the same lesson. How long did it take Steven to read the lesson?

SOLUTION

KEY PHRASE $\rightarrow$ It took Steven $1\frac{1}{5}$ times as long to read the same lesson.

REPHRASE $\rightarrow$ Steven's time was $1\frac{1}{5}$ times as long as Marcy's time.

$$\downarrow$$

$$\boxed{} \qquad = \qquad 1\frac{1}{5} \qquad \times \qquad 3\frac{3}{4}$$

The answer to the multiplication statement is missing, so multiply $1\frac{1}{5}$ by $3\frac{3}{4}$.

$$1\frac{1}{5} \times 3\frac{3}{4} = \frac{6}{5} \times \frac{15}{4}$$

$$= \frac{\cancel{2} \times 3}{\cancel{5}} \times \frac{3 \times \cancel{5}}{\cancel{2} \times 2}$$

$$= \frac{9}{2} \quad \text{or} \quad 4\frac{1}{2}$$

It took Steven $4\frac{1}{2}$ hours to read the lesson. ■

EXAMPLE 21 An auto mechanic earns $\frac{3}{8}$ as much as a computer programmer. If the auto mechanic earns \$21,000 annually, what is the annual salary of the computer programmer?

SOLUTION

KEY PHRASE → An auto mechanic earns $\frac{3}{8}$ as much as a computer programmer.

	Auto		$\frac{3}{8}$		computer
REPHRASE →	mechanic's	are		as much as	programmer's
	earnings		↓		earnings

$$21{,}000 \quad = \quad \frac{3}{8} \quad \times \quad \boxed{}$$

A multiplier is missing, so divide 21,000 by $\frac{3}{8}$.

$$21{,}000 \div \frac{3}{8} = \frac{21000}{1} \times \frac{8}{3}$$

$$= \frac{7000 \times \cancel{3}}{1} \times \frac{8}{\cancel{3}}$$

$$= 56{,}000$$

The computer programmer earns \$56,000 annually. ■

EXAMPLE 22 The width of a rectangle is $10\frac{3}{4}$ inches. Its length is twice its width. Find the area of the rectangle.

SOLUTION First we find the length of the rectangle.

KEY PHRASE → Length is twice its width.

$$\boxed{} \quad = \quad 2 \times \quad 10\frac{3}{4}$$

To find the length, multiply $10\frac{3}{4}$ by 2.

$$2 \times 10\frac{3}{4} = \frac{\cancel{2}}{1} \times \frac{43}{\cancel{4}}$$

$$= \frac{43}{2} \quad \text{or} \quad 21\frac{1}{2}$$

The length is $\frac{43}{2}$ inches. Now we find the area.

Try These Problems

36. A piano is now worth $2\frac{1}{2}$ times what it was worth 10 years ago. If it is worth $12,000 now, what was it worth 10 years ago?

37. Carl earns $42,000 per year as a computer programmer. José is in business for himself as a tax consultant. José earns $1\frac{1}{4}$ times as much as Carl does. How much does José earn per year?

38. Susan is $2\frac{2}{3}$ feet tall. Her older brother Gary is twice her height. How tall is Gary?

39. The width of a rectangle is $\frac{2}{3}$ as long as the length. If the width is 30 feet, find the area of the rectangle.

$$
\begin{array}{ccc}
\text{Area} & = \text{length} & \times \text{width} \\
\text{(sq in)} & \text{(in)} & \text{(in)}
\end{array}
$$

$$
= \frac{43}{2} \times 10\frac{3}{4}
$$

$$
= \frac{43}{2} \times \frac{43}{4}
$$

$$
= \frac{1849}{8} \quad \text{or} \quad 231\frac{1}{8}
$$

The area of rectangle is $231\frac{1}{8}$ square inches. ■

Try Problems 36 through 39.

EXAMPLE 23   A shipment of fruit contains 500 apples and 850 oranges. What is the ratio of apples to oranges?

SOLUTION

$$
\text{Ratio of apples to oranges} = \frac{\text{number of apples}}{\text{number of oranges}}
$$

$$
= \frac{500}{850}
$$

$$
= \frac{5 \times 10 \times \cancel{10}}{85 \times \cancel{10}}
$$

$$
= \frac{\cancel{5} \times 10}{\cancel{5} \times 17}
$$

$$
= \frac{10}{17}
$$

The ratio of apples to oranges is $\frac{10}{17}$. ■

EXAMPLE 24   There are 210 women present at a convention of 350 persons. What is the ratio of women to men?

SOLUTION   First, determine how many men are at the convention.

$$
\begin{array}{ccc}
\text{Number} & \text{Total} & \text{Number} \\
\text{of men} & = \dfrac{\text{Number}}{} & - \text{of women}
\end{array}
$$

$$
= 350 - 210
$$

$$
= 140
$$

There are 140 men at the convention.

$$
\text{Ratio of women to men} = \frac{\text{number of women}}{\text{number of men}}
$$

$$
= \frac{210}{140}
$$

$$
= \frac{3 \times \cancel{7} \times \cancel{10}}{2 \times \cancel{7} \times \cancel{10}}
$$

$$
= \frac{3}{2}
$$

The ratio of women to men is $\frac{3}{2}$. ■

Try These Problems

40. A vending machine contains 30 nickels, 150 dimes, and 75 quarters. What is the ratio of the number of nickels to the total number of coins?

41. Susan is $5\frac{1}{4}$ feet tall and her daughter is $2\frac{1}{2}$ feet tall. What is the ratio of the daughter's height to Susan's height?

42. The sides of a triangle measure $4\frac{5}{8}$ inches, $5\frac{1}{4}$ inches, and $2\frac{1}{8}$ inches. Find the ratio of the longest side to the shortest side.

EXAMPLE 25   A piece of string is cut into two pieces. One piece measures $2\frac{1}{4}$ yards and the other piece measures $4\frac{4}{5}$ yards. What is the ratio of the longer piece to the shorter piece?

SOLUTION

$$\text{Ratio of longer piece} \atop \text{to shorter piece} = \frac{\text{length of longer piece}}{\text{length of shorter piece}}$$

$$= \frac{4\frac{4}{5} \text{ yards}}{2\frac{1}{4} \text{ yards}} \qquad \text{The yard units cancel and a number without units remains.}$$

$$= 4\frac{4}{5} \div 2\frac{1}{4}$$

$$= \frac{24}{5} \div \frac{9}{4}$$

$$= \frac{24}{5} \times \frac{4}{9}$$

$$= \frac{3 \times 8}{5} \times \frac{4}{3 \times 3}$$

$$= \frac{32}{15}$$

The ratio of the longer piece to the shorter piece is $\frac{32}{15}$. ■

 Try Problems 40 through 42.

Now we summarize the material in this section by giving guidelines that will help you to decide whether to multiply or divide.

Situations Requiring Multiplication

×   **1.** You are looking for a total quantity.

$$\text{Total} \atop \text{quantity} = {\text{size of} \atop \text{each part}} \times {\text{number of} \atop \text{equal parts}}$$

2. You are looking for a total, as in the following examples.

$$\text{Total miles} = \text{miles per hour} \times {\text{number} \atop \text{of hours}}$$

$$\text{Total cost} = \text{cost per item} \times {\text{number} \atop \text{of items}}$$

3. You are looking for a number that is a certain amount times as large as another number.

4. You are looking for the area of a rectangle.

$$\text{Area} = \text{length} \times \text{width}$$

5. You are looking for a fraction of a number.

Situations Requiring Division

÷   **1.** A total quantity is being separated into a number of equal parts.

$$\text{Size of each part} = \text{total quantity} \div \text{number of equal parts}$$

$$= \frac{\text{total quantity}}{\text{number of equal parts}}$$

$$\text{Number of equal parts} = \text{total quantity} \div \text{size of each part}$$

$$= \frac{\text{total quantity}}{\text{size of each part}}$$

2. You are looking for a missing multiplier in a multiplication statement.

$$\text{Missing multiplier} = \text{answer to the multiplication problem} \div \text{given multiplier}$$

3. You are looking for an average.

$$\text{Average cost per item} = \text{total cost} \div \text{number of items}$$

$$\text{Average miles per hour} = \text{total miles} \div \text{number of hours}$$

4. You are looking for what ratio one number is to another number.

Answers to Try These Problems

1. $\frac{2}{3}$ pizza   2. $\frac{3}{2}$ or $1\frac{1}{2}$ pizzas   3. 25 doses   4. $\frac{21}{20}$ or $1\frac{1}{20}$ rn
5. $\frac{8}{25}$ lb   6. 725 oz

29. $\frac{323}{9}$ or $35\frac{8}{9}$ sq yd   30. 6 ft   31. $\frac{50}{3}$ or $16\frac{2}{3}$ ft   32. 216 pages
33. $315   34. $\frac{33}{4}$ or $8\frac{1}{4}$ g   35. $\frac{7}{30}$ 36. $4800   37. $52,500
38. $5\frac{1}{3}$ ft   39. 1350 sq ft   40. $\frac{2}{17}$ 41. $\frac{10}{21}$ 42. $\frac{44}{17}$

EXERCISES 4.5

Solve. Show set ups and calculation steps.

1. Eight persons share equally 12 gallons of water. How much water does each person receive?

2. Twelve persons share equally 8 gallons of water. How much water does each person receive?

3. A loaf of bread 35 centimeters long is to be cut into slices that are $1\frac{1}{4}$ centimeters wide. How many slices can be cut?

4. A truck holds $\frac{7}{8}$ ton of sand. The sand is to be unloaded into barrels that hold $\frac{1}{120}$ ton each. How many barrels can be filled?

5. Three-fourths pound of butter is to be divided into 6 equal parts. How much butter is in each part?

6. Ms. Gamez wants to cut a piece of ribbon into 25 equal parts. If the ribbon is $33\frac{1}{3}$ inches long, how long will each part be?

7. For her party, Ms. Crawford wants 150 servings of punch that each contain $6\frac{1}{2}$ ounces. How much punch does she need?

8. Tony is making drapes for his new house. Each pleat uses $2\frac{3}{4}$ inches of material. How wide must the material be to make 16 pleats?

9. One ounce of gold is worth $648. What is $2\frac{1}{3}$ ounces of gold worth?

10. One full bottle contains $6\frac{3}{4}$ liters. You empty out $\frac{2}{3}$ of the bottle. How many liters did you pour out?

11. Asher can jog $3\frac{1}{2}$ miles in 25 minutes. How long will it take him to jog 1 mile?

12. Fifty-two stones weigh $228\frac{4}{5}$ pounds. How much does each stone weigh?

13. Four-fifths of a can holds $5\frac{3}{8}$ gallon. How much does a full can hold?

14. Ninety thumbtacks weigh 1 pound. How many thumbtacks weigh $\frac{2}{3}$ pound?

Convert each ratio to a rate. Specify both the quantity and the units.

15. $\dfrac{6 \text{ feet}}{1 \text{ second}}$

16. $\dfrac{318 \text{ dollars}}{6 \text{ dresses}}$

17. $\dfrac{12 \text{ gallons}}{50 \text{ persons}}$

18. $\dfrac{6\frac{3}{4} \text{ yards}}{15 \text{ minutes}}$

Solve.

19. In a rural county of Montana, 2000 persons live in a 150-square mile region. How many persons per square mile is this?

20. A faucet leaks $1\frac{1}{2}$ ounces every 5 minutes. How many ounces does the faucet leak per minute?

21. It takes Virna $3\frac{1}{2}$ minutes to type 245 words using her computer. How many words per minute does she type?

22. A chef makes 15 dozen doughnuts using $12\frac{1}{2}$ cups of flour. How many cups of flour does he need to make 1 dozen doughnuts?

23. A watch loses $3\frac{1}{2}$ minutes every day. How many minutes has the watch lost in 12 days?

24. A utility stock is selling for $12\frac{5}{8}$ per share. What is the cost of 800 shares of this stock?

25. Onions cost 24¢ per pound. How many pounds of onions can you buy for 78¢?

26. Joan walks $4\frac{1}{2}$ miles per hour. How long will it take her to walk $1\frac{1}{2}$ miles?

27. Three hundred ninety nails weigh 13 pounds. What is the weight of 1 nail?

28. It takes $8\frac{1}{3}$ minutes for 70 gallons of water to enter a reservoir. How many gallons per minute is this?

29. A desktop measures 4 feet by $3\frac{1}{3}$ feet. What is the area of the desktop?

30. The area of a rectangular window is 38 square feet. The width is 6 feet. How long is the window?

31. A rectangular garden contains 275 square feet. Find the width of the garden if the length is $18\frac{1}{3}$ feet.

32. A rectangular floor is $5\frac{1}{4}$ yards wide and $5\frac{1}{3}$ yards long. How many square yards of carpeting are needed to cover this floor?

33. The St. Louis Cardinals won $\frac{3}{4}$ of their baseball games last season. They played a total of 108 games. How many games did they win?

34. Due to a snowstorm, only $\frac{2}{5}$ of the eligible voters in Chicago voted in the election for mayor. A total of 360,000 people voted. How many eligible voters are there?

35. Howard saves $150 out of his monthly income of $500. What fractional part of his income does he save?

36. An oil tank off the coast of Texas contained 450 tons of oil. During a recent spill, $\frac{1}{30}$ of the oil was lost. How much oil spilled?

37. Asher earned $2400 interest on an investment of $12,000 last year. The interest earned is what fractional part of the investment?

38. A solution that contains acid and water has a total volume of $50\frac{1}{4}$ liters. Three-twentieths of the solution is acid. What is the volume of acid?

39. Brenda works on an assembly line at an auto plant in Detroit. She makes $12 per hour. When she works overtime, they pay her time-and-a-half. This means she is paid $1\frac{1}{2}$ times as much as her regular salary. What does Brenda make each hour when working overtime?

40. A recipe calls for $\frac{1}{8}$ teaspoon of pepper. You wish to double the recipe. How much pepper should you use?

41. Due to inflation, the price of gasoline is $2\frac{1}{2}$ times what it was three years ago. The price three years ago was 16 cents per liter. What is the present price of gasoline?

42. The width of a rectangle is $\frac{2}{3}$ as long as the length. If the length is $37\frac{1}{2}$ feet, what is the perimeter of the rectangle?

43. A shipment of fruit contains 750 oranges and twice as many nectarines. What is the ratio of oranges to the total shipment?

44. A rectangle is $4\frac{1}{2}$ meters wide and $5\frac{1}{4}$ meters long. Find the ratio of the length to the width.

A college in California has 36,000 students. The circle graph indicates the breakdown of the students by ethnic background. Use the graph to answer Exercises 45 and 46.

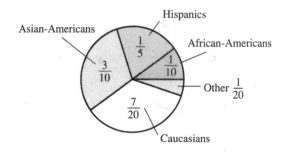

Breakdown of Students by Ethnic Background

45. How many Asian-Americans attend this college?

46. How many Hispanics attend this college?

CHAPTER 4 SUMMARY

KEY WORDS AND PHRASES

reciprocal [4.2]	twice [4.4]	divided into [4.4]
factor [4.3]	half [4.4]	ratio [4.4]
multiplier [4.3]	double [4.4]	rate [4.5]
product [4.3]	divided by [4.4]	area [4.5]

IMPORTANT RULES

How to Multiply Two Fractions [4.1]

▪ Convert the mixed numerals to improper fractions and convert the whole numerals to fractions.

▪ Cancel as much as possible. Each time you cancel a factor from a numerator, you must cancel the same factor from a denominator. (Canceling common factors from the numerator and denominator is equivalent to dividing the numerator and denominator by the same nonzero number.)

▪ Multiply the numerators to obtain the numerator of the answer. Multiply the denominators to obtain the denominator of the answer.

▪ Check to make sure the answer is simplified. If the answer is an improper fraction, you may leave it as an improper fraction or you may convert it to a mixed numeral.

How to Divide Fractions [4.2]

▪ Convert the mixed numerals to improper fractions and convert the whole numerals to fractions.

▪ Change division ($\div$) to multiplication ($\times$) and invert the divisor. The divisor is the second number.

▪ Cancel as much as possible, then multiply the fractions.

▪ Check to make sure the answer is simplified. If the answer is an improper fraction, you may leave it as an improper fraction or you may convert it to a mixed numeral.

How to Find the Missing Number in a Multiplication Statement [4.3]

▪ If you are missing the answer to the multiplication problem (the product), then multiply.

▪ If you are missing one of the multipliers, then divide the answer (or product) by the known multiplier (or factor) to find the missing multiplier.

How to Find a Fraction of a Number [4.4, 4.5]

To find a fraction of a number, multiply the fraction by the number; that is, the word *of* used in this way translates to multiplication.

Situations that Require Multiplication [4.5]

A summary of these situations appears on page 166.

Situations that Require Division [4.5]

A summary of these situations appears on page 167.

CHAPTER 4 REVIEW EXERCISES

Multiply and simplify.

1. $\frac{1}{4} \times 72$ **2.** $\frac{1}{3} \times 61$ **3.** $\frac{2}{5} \times 45$ **4.** $\frac{3}{8} \times 20$

5. $\frac{1}{6} \times \frac{4}{5}$ **6.** $\frac{3}{14} \times \frac{5}{3}$ **7.** $\frac{2}{7} \times 3\frac{1}{4}$ **8.** $5\frac{2}{3} \times \frac{9}{17}$

9. $2\frac{4}{5} \times 1\frac{7}{8}$ **10.** $3\frac{3}{5} \times 2\frac{7}{9}$ **11.** $\frac{36}{20} \times \frac{15}{10}$ **12.** $\frac{12}{14} \times \frac{7}{21}$

13. $\frac{45}{200} \times 80$ **14.** $12\frac{1}{2} \times \frac{3}{325}$ **15.** $66\frac{2}{3} \times 3120$ **16.** $8\frac{7}{8} \times 4\frac{2}{3}$

17. $\frac{3}{4} \times \frac{11}{12} \times 8$ **18.** $6\frac{1}{2} \times \frac{4}{5} \times \frac{3}{26} \times 15$

19. Don bought $5\frac{3}{4}$ yards of fabric that sells for \$12 a yard. How much did he pay for the fabric?

20. Lisa jogged around the lake 5 times. Once around the lake is $\frac{5}{8}$ mile. How far did Lisa jog?

Divide and simplify.

21. $5 \div 9$ **22.** $9 \div 5$ **23.** $\frac{4}{5} \div 3$ **24.** $8\frac{2}{5} \div 5$

25. $13\frac{1}{3} \div 60$ **26.** $\frac{3}{10} \div \frac{3}{4}$ **27.** $\frac{11}{12} \div \frac{1}{8}$ **28.** $\frac{35}{24} \div \frac{42}{30}$

29. $28 \div \frac{4}{7}$ **30.** $3600 \div \frac{90}{12}$ **31.** $15\frac{3}{4} \div \frac{7}{16}$ **32.** $6\frac{1}{4} \div \frac{7}{20}$

33. $7\frac{1}{2} \div 3\frac{1}{3}$ **34.** $\dfrac{\frac{9}{20}}{8}$ **35.** $\dfrac{250}{\frac{4}{5}}$ **36.** $\dfrac{33\frac{1}{3}}{1\frac{1}{9}}$

37. A piece of wire 50 feet long is cut into 75 equal pieces. How long is each piece?

38. A total of $20\frac{1}{4}$ milliliters of medicine is given out in doses of $2\frac{1}{4}$ milliliters each. How many doses can be given?

Find the missing number.

39. $\frac{2}{3} \times 615 = \boxed{}$ **40.** $\frac{1}{4} \times \boxed{} = 8$

41. $\boxed{} \times \frac{4}{5} = \frac{3}{10}$ **42.** $3\frac{1}{2} = \boxed{} \times \frac{3}{4}$

43. $\boxed{} = \frac{3}{7} \times 5\frac{1}{4}$ **44.** $660 = \frac{3}{2} \times \boxed{}$

Solve. Reduce answers to lowest terms. Show set ups and calculation steps.

45. Find $\frac{6}{10}$ of 250.

46. $\frac{9}{4}$ of what number equals 720?

47. What fraction of 25 is $6\frac{1}{4}$?

48. Find $3\frac{1}{2}$ divided by 14.

49. Find half of $\frac{7}{8}$.

50. Find a number that is $4\frac{2}{3}$ times as large as $2\frac{1}{7}$.

51. Find $\frac{4}{5}$ divided into 50.

52. Find the ratio of $\frac{5}{6}$ to $12\frac{1}{2}$.

53. A company conducted a survey indicating that $\frac{3}{20}$ of the workers have young children to care for. There are 240 workers. How many have young children?

54. Barbara paid $\frac{2}{15}$ of her income in federal taxes. She paid \$4000 in taxes. What was her income?

55. Cynthia bought a steak for herself that weighed $\frac{7}{8}$ pound. The steak that she bought for her friend John weighed twice as much. How much did John's steak weigh?

56. Debbie bought $2\frac{1}{2}$ pounds of nails for 60 cents. What is the cost of 1 pound of nails?

57. A carpet is $6\frac{3}{4}$ yards long and 5 yards wide. What is the area of the carpet?

58. Five persons share equally $7\frac{1}{2}$ gallons of water. How much water does each person receive?

59. The owner of a small bakery used a total of $72\frac{1}{2}$ pounds of sugar in 7 days. On the average, how many pounds were used each day?

60. The height of a rectangular window is half its width. If the width of the window is $6\frac{1}{2}$ feet, find the area of the window.

61. A car averages 50 miles per hour. How long will it take it to go 175 miles?

62. One yard of fabric costs \$28. What is the cost of $6\frac{3}{4}$ yards of this fabric?

63. A tabletop contains $16\frac{5}{8}$ square feet. If the width is $3\frac{1}{2}$ feet, find the length.

64. A piece of string $26\frac{1}{4}$ inches long is cut into two pieces. One piece measures 21 inches and the other piece measures $5\frac{1}{4}$ inches. What is the ratio of the shorter piece to the longer piece?

✎ **In Your Own Words**

Write complete sentences to discuss each of the following. Support your comments with examples or pictures, if appropriate.

65. Without actually solving the problem, discuss the procedure you would use to find the missing number in the statement $\frac{4}{5} \times 7\frac{1}{2} = \boxed{}$. Assume that you are working without a calculator.

66. Without actually solving the problem, discuss the procedure you would use to find the missing number in the statement $5\frac{1}{4} = \boxed{} \times 14$. Assume that you are working without a calculator.

67. Give at least three examples where the answer to a multiplication problem is more than either of the multipliers (or factors), then give at least three examples where the answer to a multiplication problem is less than one of the multipliers (or factors). Discuss what you observe.

68. Discuss a real-life situation where a total quantity is being split into a number of equal parts. Choose a situation where the number of equal parts is more than the total quantity.

69. Discuss a real-life situation that would involve finding a fraction of a number.

CHAPTER 4 PRACTICE TEST

Multiply and simplify.

1. $\frac{2}{7} \times \frac{3}{5}$ **2.** $\frac{12}{10} \times \frac{15}{9}$ **3.** $5\frac{2}{3} \times 900$

4. $12\frac{1}{2} \times 4\frac{3}{5}$ **5.** $\frac{7}{10} \times \frac{15}{12} \times \frac{2}{21}$

Divide and simplify.

6. $8 \div 20$ **7.** $\frac{5}{9} \div 60$ **8.** $\frac{16}{30} \div \frac{6}{5}$ **9.** $18 \div 8\frac{4}{5}$ **10.** $\dfrac{7\frac{6}{7}}{3\frac{2}{3}}$

Find the missing number. Simplify.

11. $2\frac{1}{3} \times \boxed{} = 21$ **12.** $\boxed{} = \frac{3}{20} \times 61,500$

Solve. show set ups and calculation steps.

13. Find 4 divided by $3\frac{1}{2}$. $\boxed{} \cdot 4\frac{1}{2} \times 6$

14. Find a number that is $4\frac{1}{2}$ times as large as 6.

15. Four-fifths of what number is 28?

16. What number is twice $\frac{7}{12}$?

17. Bogard is a chef in a small restaurant. He prepares rice using a recipe that yields 25 cups of cooked rice. How many $\frac{2}{3}$-cup servings will he have?

18. One yard of fabric costs \$24. What is the cost of $3\frac{1}{3}$ yards?

19. Earl can run 3 miles in 22 minutes. How long will it take him to run 1 mile?

20. Bette spends $\frac{7}{100}$ of her monthly income on food. Her monthly income is $1200. How much does she spend on food?

21. A wire is $23\frac{1}{3}$ feet long. Bill wants to cut the wire into 35 equal pieces. How long will each piece be?

22. The area of a rectangle is 93 square yards. If the length is $20\frac{2}{3}$ yards, find the width.

23. A solution contains $3\frac{1}{3}$ liters of water and $2\frac{2}{3}$ liters of acid. What is the ratio of acid to water?

24. A faucet leaks $2\frac{1}{3}$ ounces per hour. How long will it take the faucet to leak $8\frac{2}{5}$ ounces?

CHAPTER

5

Fractions: Addition and Subtraction

5.1	ADDING WITH LIKE DENOMINATORS

OBJECTIVES ▌ Add fractions with like denominators.
▌ Add mixed numerals with like denominators.
▌ Solve an application using addition of fractions.

1 Adding Fractions

If you jog $\frac{4}{8}$ mile and then walk $\frac{3}{8}$ mile, how far have you gone? To solve this problem you need to add $\frac{4}{8}$ and $\frac{3}{8}$ because to add means to total or combine.

$$\frac{4}{8} + \frac{3}{8} = \frac{7}{8}$$ ── Add the numerators to obtain the numerator of the answer. $4 + 3 = 7$
── Keep the same denominator.

You have gone a total distance of $\frac{7}{8}$ mile.

Observe that to add fractions with like denominators, add the numerators and keep the same denominator. Here we view a picture of the addition problem $\frac{4}{8} + \frac{3}{8}$; we can see that the result $\frac{7}{8}$ is correct. Assume each separate figure represents 1 whole.

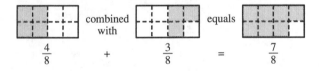

$\frac{4}{8}$	combined with	$\frac{3}{8}$	equals	$\frac{7}{8}$
	+		=	

Here are more examples of adding fractions with like denominators.

Try These Problems

Add and simplify.

1. $\frac{3}{10} + \frac{4}{10}$

2. $\frac{2}{3} + \frac{2}{3}$

3. $\frac{1}{8} + \frac{5}{8}$

4. $\frac{43}{20} + \frac{29}{20}$

5. $\frac{7}{12} + \frac{3}{12} + \frac{2}{12}$

6. $\frac{76}{90} + \frac{29}{90} + \frac{87}{90}$

EXAMPLE 1   Add: $\frac{2}{6} + \frac{5}{6}$

SOLUTION

$$\frac{2}{6} + \frac{5}{6} = \frac{7}{6}$$ —— Add the numerators. $2 + 5 = 7$.
—— Use the *like* denominator.

or $1\frac{1}{6}$ An answer larger than one whole may be left as an improper fraction or a mixed numeral. ■

EXAMPLE 2   Add: $\frac{7}{12} + \frac{1}{12}$

SOLUTION

$$\frac{7}{12} + \frac{1}{12} = \frac{8}{12}$$

$$= \frac{\cancel{4} \times 2}{\cancel{4} \times 3}$$ Always simplify the answer.

$$= \frac{2}{3}$$ ■

EXAMPLE 3   Add: $\frac{25}{27} + \frac{5}{27} + \frac{33}{27}$

SOLUTION

$$\frac{25}{27} + \frac{5}{27} + \frac{33}{27} = \frac{63}{27}$$

$$= \frac{\cancel{9} \times 7}{\cancel{9} \times 3}$$ Simplify the answer.

$$= \frac{7}{3} \quad \text{or} \quad 2\frac{1}{3}$$ The answer may be left as an improper fraction or as a mixed numeral. ■

 Try Problems 1 through 6.

2 | Adding Mixed Numerals

Now we look at examples of adding mixed numerals.

EXAMPLE 4   Add: $1\frac{3}{5} + 2\frac{1}{5}$

SOLUTION
METHOD 1

$$1\frac{3}{5}$$ It can be convenient to align the numbers vertically.

$$+ \ 2\frac{1}{5}$$ Add the fractions. $\frac{3}{5} + \frac{1}{5} = \frac{4}{5}$

$$3\frac{4}{5}$$ Add the wholes. $1 + 2 = 3$

Try These Problems

Add and simplify.

7. $5\frac{2}{8} + 2\frac{3}{8}$

8. $17\frac{1}{4} + \frac{3}{4}$

9. $9\frac{7}{12} + 2\frac{3}{12}$

10. $28\frac{25}{36} + 6\frac{20}{36}$

11. $5\frac{13}{40} + 2\frac{28}{40} + 17\frac{39}{40}$

12. $13\frac{22}{24} + 9\frac{41}{24} + 49\frac{25}{24}$

METHOD 2

$$1\frac{3}{5} + 2\frac{1}{5}$$

$$= \frac{8}{5} + \frac{11}{5} \qquad \text{Convert each mixed numeral to an improper fraction, then add.}$$

$$= \frac{19}{5} \quad \text{or} \quad 3\frac{4}{5} \quad \blacksquare$$

From the above example, observe that it is more efficient to add mixed numerals *without* changing them to improper fractions. Method 1 shows the more efficient method. This method is especially easier with problems like $232\frac{2}{8} + 95\frac{1}{8}$, where there are larger numbers.

EXAMPLE 5   Add: $8\frac{10}{11} + \frac{5}{11}$

SOLUTION

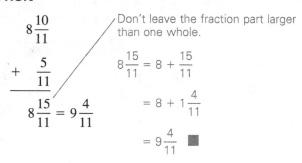

$$
\begin{array}{r}
8\dfrac{10}{11} \\[2mm]
+\quad \dfrac{5}{11} \\[2mm]
\hline
8\dfrac{15}{11} = 9\dfrac{4}{11}
\end{array}
$$

Don't leave the fraction part larger than one whole.

$$8\frac{15}{11} = 8 + \frac{15}{11}$$

$$= 8 + 1\frac{4}{11}$$

$$= 9\frac{4}{11} \quad \blacksquare$$

EXAMPLE 6   Add: $4\frac{16}{21} + 9\frac{12}{21}$

SOLUTION

$$
\begin{array}{r}
4\dfrac{16}{21} \\[2mm]
+\ 9\dfrac{12}{21} \\[2mm]
\hline
13\dfrac{28}{21} = 14\dfrac{7}{21}
\end{array}
$$

Don't leave the fraction part larger than one whole.

$$= 14\frac{1}{3} \quad\text{——— Simplify the fraction.} \quad \blacksquare$$

 Try Problems 7 through 12.

Here we give a rule for adding fractions with like denominators.

> ### Adding Fractions with Like Denominators
>
> **1.** Add the numerators and put the answer over the like denominator. (Always reduce the answer to lowest terms by dividing numerator and denominator by the same nonzero number if possible.)
>
> **2.** To add mixed numbers, add the whole numbers separately from the fractions. (Leave your answer so that the fractional portion is smaller than one and the fraction is reduced to lowest terms.)

 Answers to Try These Problems

1. $\frac{7}{10}$ 2. $\frac{4}{3}$ or $1\frac{1}{3}$ 3. $\frac{3}{4}$ 4. $\frac{18}{5}$ or $3\frac{3}{5}$ 5. 1
6. $\frac{32}{15}$ or $2\frac{2}{15}$ 7. $7\frac{5}{8}$ 8. 18 9. $11\frac{5}{6}$ 10. $35\frac{1}{4}$
11. 26 12. $74\frac{2}{3}$

EXERCISES 5.1

Add and simplify.

1. $\frac{2}{8} + \frac{3}{8}$ **2.** $\frac{4}{15} + \frac{4}{15}$ **3.** $\frac{4}{9} + \frac{2}{9}$ **4.** $\frac{12}{25} + \frac{3}{25}$

5. $\frac{9}{20} + \frac{11}{20}$ **6.** $\frac{8}{7} + \frac{6}{7}$ **7.** $\frac{11}{18} + \frac{12}{18} + \frac{2}{18}$ **8.** $\frac{13}{16} + \frac{14}{16} + \frac{10}{16}$

9. $\frac{2}{3} + 3 + \frac{5}{3}$ **10.** $5 + \frac{1}{6} + \frac{3}{6}$ **11.** $4\frac{3}{4} + 5$ **12.** $6 + 14\frac{2}{5}$

13. $\frac{5}{8} + 2\frac{3}{8}$ **14.** $\frac{7}{10} + 3\frac{1}{10}$ **15.** $\begin{array}{r} 5\frac{5}{24} \\ + \ 3\frac{15}{24} \end{array}$ **16.** $\begin{array}{r} 37\frac{3}{7} \\ + \ \ 3\frac{4}{7} \end{array}$

17. $\begin{array}{r} 28\frac{17}{32} \\ + \ \ 5\frac{20}{32} \end{array}$ **18.** $\begin{array}{r} 2\frac{7}{9} \\ + \ 5\frac{5}{9} \end{array}$ **19.** $\begin{array}{r} 15\frac{27}{40} \\ + \ \ 6\frac{29}{40} \end{array}$ **20.** $\begin{array}{r} 4\frac{19}{21} \\ + \ 78\frac{16}{21} \end{array}$

21. $6\frac{3}{7} + 7\frac{6}{7} + 19\frac{5}{7}$ **22.** $8\frac{11}{12} + 4\frac{8}{12} + 5\frac{9}{12}$

23. $76\frac{2}{39} + 81\frac{24}{39}$ **24.** $135\frac{27}{42} + 256\frac{22}{42}$

Solve.

25. You plan to go on an overnight hiking trip and want to keep your backpack as light as possible. You have packed items weighing $6\frac{3}{4}$ pounds and $2\frac{1}{4}$ pounds. What is the total weight so far?

26. Don had jogged $2\frac{3}{4}$ miles when he ran into Kimberly, a good friend of his. They talked for a while then jogged together for $4\frac{3}{4}$ miles. How far did Don jog?

27. A carpenter cut a piece of wood $27\frac{3}{8}$ inches long. He realized the piece was too short and he needed it to be $\frac{7}{8}$ inch longer. How long should he cut the piece of wood?

28. Tom is reading a book. He read $\frac{1}{8}$ of it on Monday and $\frac{5}{8}$ of it on Tuesday. What fraction of the book did he read in the two days?

5.2 FINDING THE LEAST COMMON MULTIPLE BY PRIME FACTORING

OBJECTIVES ▌ Determine whether a number is prime or not prime.
▌ Write a number as the product of primes.
▌ Find the least common multiple of two or more numbers by prime factoring.

1 Meaning of the Least Common Multiple

You exercised $\frac{1}{4}$ hour on Wednesday and $\frac{5}{6}$ hour on Thursday. How long did you exercise in the two-day period? To solve this problem you need to add $\frac{1}{4}$ and $\frac{5}{6}$.

$$\frac{1}{4} + \frac{5}{6} = ?$$

In Section 5.1 we learned that it is easy to add fractions with *like* denominators. We need to rewrite these fractions so that they have the same denominator, but we do not want to change the value of the fractions. The number we use for a common denominator must be a multiple of both 4 and 6. The multiples of 4 are

4; 8; **12**; 16; 20; **24**; 28; . . .

The multiples of 6 are

6; **12**; 18; **24**; 30; 36; 42; . . .

The common multiples of both 4 and 6 are

12; 24; 36; 48; . . .

Finally, the **least common multiple (LCM)** of 4 and 6 is 12, and this is the denominator that can be used to add $\frac{1}{4}$ and $\frac{5}{6}$. We also call 12 the **least common denominator (LCD).**

$$\frac{1}{4} + \frac{5}{6}$$

$$= \frac{1 \times 3}{4 \times 3} + \frac{5 \times 2}{6 \times 2}$$

What number multiplied by 4 is 12? 3
Multiply the numerator and denominator of the fraction $\frac{1}{4}$ by 3 to obtain $\frac{3}{12}$, a fraction equal to $\frac{1}{4}$.
What number multiplied by 6 is 12? 2
Multiply the numerator and denominator of the fraction $\frac{5}{6}$ by 2 to obtain $\frac{10}{12}$, a fraction equal to $\frac{5}{6}$.

$$= \frac{3}{12} + \frac{10}{12}$$

Now the fractions have a common denominator, so we can see how to add them.

$$= \frac{13}{12} \quad \text{or} \quad 1\frac{1}{12}$$

Add the numerators, 3 + 10 = 13, to obtain the numerator of the answer. Keep the same denominator, 12.

Therefore, if you exercise $\frac{1}{4}$ hour and $\frac{5}{6}$ hour, you have exercised a total of $\frac{13}{12}$ or $1\frac{1}{12}$ hours.

Try These Problems

Write each as the product of prime numbers.

1. 50
2. 54
3. 49
4. 210
5. 195
6. 297

In general, to add fractions with *unlike* denominators, you need to begin by finding the least common multiple of the denominators. In the previous discussion we found the least common multiple of 4 and 6 by listing multiples of each and observing that 12 is the smallest of the common multiples. There are many techniques for finding the least common multiple of two or more numbers. In this section we discuss finding the least common multiple by prime factoring.

2 Writing Numbers as the Product of Primes

Recall from Section 2.3 that a **prime number** is a whole number larger than 1 that is divisible only by itself and 1. The first ten primes are listed here.

First Ten Primes									
2	3	5	7	11	13	17	19	23	29

Also, recall from Section 2.3 that whole numbers larger than 1 that are *not* prime can be written as the product of primes. For example,

$$36 = \underset{\smile}{6 \times 6} \qquad 63 = \underset{\smile}{9} \times 7 \qquad 275 = 5 \times \underset{\smile}{55}$$
$$= 2 \times 3 \times 2 \times 3 \qquad = 3 \times 3 \times 7 \qquad = 5 \times 5 \times 11$$

The process of writing numbers as the product of numbers is called **factoring.** If all of the multipliers (or factors) are prime numbers, then the process is called **prime factoring.** If you need more help with writing numbers as the product of primes, refer to Section 2.3.

 Try Problems 1 through 6.

3 Finding the Least Common Multiple of Two or More Numbers

Now we illustrate how to use prime factoring to find the least common multiple (LCM) of two or more numbers.

EXAMPLE 1 Find the least common multiple of 18, 12, and 40.
SOLUTION Write each number as the product of primes.

$$18 = \underset{\smile}{6} \times 3 \qquad 12 = \underset{\smile}{4} \times 3 \qquad 40 = \underset{\smile}{4} \times \underset{\smile}{10}$$
$$= 2 \times 3 \times 3 \qquad = 2 \times 2 \times 3 \qquad = 2 \times 2 \times 2 \times 5$$

Note that the only prime factors appearing in these numbers are 2, 3, and 5.

Here we explain how to decide how many 2s, 3s, and 5s to multiply to obtain the LCM.

Put 3 factors of 2 in the LCM because that is the **most** factors of 2 that appear in any one of the numbers.

$$\text{LCM} = 2 \times 2 \times 2 \times 3 \times 3 \times 5$$

The **most** factors of 3 that appear in any one of the numbers.

The **most** factors of 5 that appear in any one of the numbers.

$$
\begin{aligned}
\text{LCM} &= 2 \times 2 \times 2 \times 3 \times 3 \times 5 \\
&= \quad 4 \quad \times \quad 6 \quad \times \quad 15 \\
&= \quad 4 \quad \times \quad\quad 90 \\
&= 360
\end{aligned}
$$

Multiply the factors to obtain the LCM. The multiplication can be done in any order. ■

In the previous example we found 360 to be the least common multiple (LCM) of 18, 12, and 40. This means that 360 is the smallest number that is divisible by 18, 12, and 40. Here we perform each of the divisions in two ways. Observe that there is an alternative to using long division; the division can be done by taking advantage of the prime factoring that has already been done.

Dividing 360 by 18.

$$
18\overline{)360} \rightarrow \frac{360}{18} = \frac{2 \times 2 \times 2 \times 3 \times 3 \times 5}{2 \times 3 \times 3}
$$

$$
\begin{aligned}
&= 2 \times 2 \times 5 \\
&= 20
\end{aligned}
$$

Dividing 360 by 18 is equivalent to canceling the factors of 18 from 360.

Dividing 360 by 12.

$$
12\overline{)360} \rightarrow \frac{360}{12} = \frac{2 \times 2 \times 2 \times 3 \times 3 \times 5}{2 \times 2 \times 3}
$$

$$
\begin{aligned}
&= 2 \times 3 \times 5 \\
&= 30
\end{aligned}
$$

Dividing 360 by 12 is equivalent to canceling the factors of 12 from 360.

Dividing 360 by 40.

$$40\overline{)360} \rightarrow \frac{360}{40} = \frac{\cancel{2} \times \cancel{2} \times \cancel{2} \times 3 \times 3 \times \cancel{5}}{\cancel{2} \times \cancel{2} \times \cancel{2} \times \cancel{5}}$$

$\begin{aligned}\phantom{40\overline{)360}} = 3 \times 3\end{aligned}$ Dividing 360 by 40 is

$= 9$ equivalent to canceling the factors of 40 from 360.

Yes, 360 is divisible by the numbers 18, 12, and 40.

Here are more examples of finding the least common multiple by prime factoring.

EXAMPLE 2   Find the least common multiple of 14 and 49.

SOLUTION   Write each number as the product of primes.

$$14 = 2 \times 7 \qquad 49 = 7 \times 7$$

Note that the only prime factors that are needed for the LCM are 2s and 7s.

$$LCM = 2 \times 7 \times 7$$

Put only one factor of 2 because that is the most factors of 2 that appear in 14 or 49.

Put 2 factors of 7 because there are 2 factors of 7 in 49 and that is the most factors of 7 that appear in 14 or 49.

$$\begin{aligned}LCM &= 2 \times 7 \times 7\\ &= 2 \times 49\\ &= 98 \quad \blacksquare\end{aligned}$$

Multiply the factors in any order to obtain the LCM.

EXAMPLE 3   Find the least common multiple of 55 and 33.

SOLUTION   Write each number as the product of primes.

$$55 = 5 \times 11 \qquad 33 = 3 \times 11$$

Note that the only prime factors needed in the LCM are 3s, 5s, and 11s.

$$\begin{aligned}LCM &= 5 \times 3 \times 11\\ &= 15 \times 11\\ &= 165\end{aligned}$$

Put only 1 factor of each because none of the factors appear more than once in 55 or 33. $\blacksquare$

EXAMPLE 4   Find the least common multiple of 7, 72, and 90.

SOLUTION   Write each number as the product of primes.

$$7 \text{ is prime} \qquad\qquad 72 = \underbrace{8}_{} \times \underbrace{9}_{}$$

$$= 2 \times 2 \times 2 \times 3 \times 3$$

$$90 = \underbrace{9}_{} \times \underbrace{10}_{}$$

$$= 3 \times 3 \times 2 \times 5$$

Try These Problems

Find the least common multiple of each group of numbers.

7. 30; 20

8. 28; 49

9. 10; 9

10. 26; 13

11. 8; 12; 9

12. 20; 9; 7

13. 24; 12; 40

14. 81; 18; 8

Note that the only prime factors needed in the LCM are 2s, 3s, 5s, and 7s.

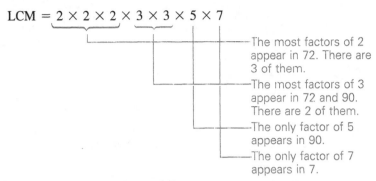

$$LCM = 2 \times 2 \times 2 \times 3 \times 3 \times 5 \times 7$$

The most factors of 2 appear in 72. There are 3 of them.

The most factors of 3 appear in 72 and 90. There are 2 of them.

The only factor of 5 appears in 90.

The only factor of 7 appears in 7.

$$
\begin{aligned}
LCM &= 2 \times 2 \times 2 \times 3 \times 3 \times 5 \times 7 \\
&= \quad 8 \quad \times \quad 9 \quad \times \quad 35 \\
&= \quad 72 \quad \times \quad 35 \\
&= 2520 \ \blacksquare
\end{aligned}
$$

Now we state a rule for finding the least common multiple of two or more numbers.

Finding the Least Common Multiple of Two or More Numbers.

1. Write each number as the product of primes.
2. Each kind of prime factor appearing in step 1 must be a factor in the least common multiple. How many of each prime factor? The greatest number of times the factor appears in any one of the original numbers.

 Try Problems 7 through 14.

 Answers to Try These Problems

1. $2 \times 5 \times 5$ 2. $2 \times 3 \times 3 \times 3$ 3. 7×7
4. $2 \times 3 \times 5 \times 7$ 5. $3 \times 5 \times 13$ 6. $3 \times 3 \times 3 \times 11$
7. 60   8. 196   9. 90   10. 26   11. 72   12. 1260,
13. 120   14. 648

EXERCISES 5.2

Choose the prime numbers in each group.

1. 2; 6; 7; 9   **2.** 3; 9; 11; 15   **3.** 45; 31; 13; 17   **4.** 27; 43; 51; 19

Write each number as the product of primes. If the number is prime, say prime.

5. 9   **6.** 13   **7.** 12   **8.** 27   **9.** 11

10. 24   **11.** 48   **12.** 19   **13.** 64   **14.** 490

15. 125   **16.** 34   **17.** 97   **18.** 84   **19.** 91

20. 147   **21.** 245   **22.** 223

Use prime factoring to find the least common multiple of each group of numbers.

23. 6; 9   **24.** 5; 15   **25.** 30; 24   **26.** 21; 4

27. 28; 12   **28.** 40; 25   **29.** 77; 14   **30.** 39; 52

31. 4; 6; 9   **32.** 10; 12; 15   **33.** 2; 44; 11   **34.** 28; 10; 14

35. 75; 9; 15   **36.** 10; 25; 125   **37.** 65; 25   **38.** 51; 34

39. 52; 68   **40.** 69; 460

5.3   ADDING WITH UNLIKE DENOMINATORS

OBJECTIVES
- Add fractions with unlike denominators.
- Add mixed numerals with unlike denominators.
- Solve an application that involves adding fractions.

1   Working with Easy Denominators

If you complete $\frac{1}{4}$ of a job and your co-worker completes $\frac{3}{10}$ of the job, what fraction of the job have the two of you completed? To solve this problem, we must add $\frac{1}{4}$ and $\frac{3}{10}$.

$$\frac{1}{4} + \frac{3}{10} = ?$$

We must rewrite the fractions so that they have the same denominator. This common denominator is the least common multiple of 4 and 10, which is 20.

$$\frac{1}{4} \quad + \quad \frac{3}{10}$$

$$= \frac{1 \times 5}{4 \times 5} + \frac{3 \times 2}{10 \times 2}$$

Multiply the numerator and denominator of the fraction $\frac{1}{4}$ by 5 to obtain $\frac{5}{20}$, a fraction equal to $\frac{1}{4}$.

Multiply the numerator and denominator of the fraction $\frac{3}{10}$ by 2 to obtain $\frac{6}{20}$, a fraction equal to $\frac{3}{10}$.

$$= \frac{5}{20} + \frac{6}{20}$$

$$= \frac{11}{20}$$

After the fractions have a common denominator, add the numerators and place this over the common denominator.

The two of you completed $\frac{11}{20}$ of the job.

Try These Problems

Add and simplify.

1. $\frac{5}{6} + \frac{3}{8}$

2. $\frac{7}{8} + \frac{3}{40}$

3. $\frac{5}{9} + \frac{11}{6} + \frac{2}{3}$

4. $\frac{1}{2} + \frac{2}{15} + \frac{7}{10}$

Here we look at more examples of adding fractions with unlike denominators.

EXAMPLE 1   Add: $\frac{1}{5} + \frac{7}{15}$

SOLUTION   The least common multiple of 5 and 15 is 15, so raise the fraction $\frac{1}{5}$ to higher terms so that it has a denominator of 15.

$$\frac{1}{5} + \frac{7}{15}$$

The fraction $\frac{7}{15}$ already has the denominator 15 so leave it as it is.

Multiply the numerator and denominator of $\frac{1}{5}$ by 3 to obtain $\frac{3}{15}$, a fraction equal to $\frac{1}{5}$.

$$= \frac{1 \times 3}{5 \times 3} + \frac{7}{15}$$

$$= \frac{3}{15} + \frac{7}{15}$$

$$= \frac{10}{15}$$

$$= \frac{\cancel{5} \times 2}{\cancel{5} \times 3}$$

Reduce the answer to lowest terms.

$$= \frac{2}{3} \ \blacksquare$$

EXAMPLE 2   Add: $\frac{5}{6} + \frac{1}{2} + \frac{3}{4}$

SOLUTION   Find the least common multiple of 6, 2, and 4.

$$\left. \begin{array}{l} 6 = 2 \times 3 \\ 2 \text{ is prime} \\ 4 = 2 \times 2 \end{array} \right\} \quad \begin{array}{l} \text{LCM} = 2 \times 2 \times 3 \\ \quad = 12 \end{array}$$

Rewrite each fraction so they all have the denominator 12, but do not change the values of the fractions.

$$\frac{5}{6} \ + \ \frac{1}{2} \ + \ \frac{3}{4}$$

$$= \frac{5 \times 2}{6 \times 2} + \frac{1 \times 6}{2 \times 6} + \frac{3 \times 3}{4 \times 3}$$

Within each individual fraction, multiply the numerator and denominator by the *same* number so that the value of the fraction does not change. Choose the number to multiply by based on the fact that you want each denominator to be 12.

$$= \frac{10}{12} + \frac{6}{12} + \frac{9}{12}$$

$$= \frac{25}{12} \ \text{or} \ 2\frac{1}{12}$$

You may leave the answer as an improper fraction or as a mixed numeral. ∎

 Try Problems 1 through 4.

EXAMPLE 3 Add: $3\frac{7}{8} + 4\frac{5}{7}$

SOLUTION Find the least common multiple of 8 and 7.

$$\left.\begin{array}{l} 8 = 4 \times 2 \\ = 2 \times 2 \times 2 \\ 7 \text{ is prime} \end{array}\right\} \begin{array}{l} \text{LCM} = 2 \times 2 \times 2 \times 7 \\ \phantom{\text{LCM}} = 8 \times 7 \\ \phantom{\text{LCM}} = 56 \end{array}$$

The numbers can be left in mixed numeral form but the fractional parts must be written with denominator 56.

$$3\frac{7}{8} = 3\frac{7 \times 7}{8 \times 7} = 3\frac{49}{56}$$

$$+\ 4\frac{5}{7} = 4\frac{5 \times 8}{7 \times 8} = 4\frac{40}{56}$$

Do not leave the fractional part more than 1.

$$7\frac{89}{56} = 8\frac{33}{56}\ \blacksquare$$

EXAMPLE 4 Add: $48\frac{2}{9} + 37\frac{10}{21} + 29\frac{6}{7}$

SOLUTION Find the least common multiple of 9, 21, and 7.

$$\left.\begin{array}{l} 9 = 3 \times 3 \\ 21 = 3 \times 7 \\ 7 \text{ is prime} \end{array}\right\} \quad \text{LCM} = 3 \times 3 \times 7 = 63$$

Rewrite the mixed numerals so that the fractional parts each have the denominator 63.

$$48\frac{2}{9} = 48\frac{2 \times 7}{9 \times 7} = 48\frac{14}{63}$$

Because
63 = **3 × 3** × 7
  = 9 × 7,
multiply numerator and denominator of $\frac{2}{9}$ by 7.

$$37\frac{10}{21} = 37\frac{10 \times 3}{21 \times 3} = 37\frac{30}{63}$$

Because
63 = 3 × **3 × 7**
  = 3 × 21,
multiply numerator and denominator of $\frac{10}{21}$ by 3.

$$+\ 29\frac{6}{7} = 29\frac{6 \times 9}{7 \times 9} = 29\frac{54}{63}$$

Because
63 = 3 × 3 × **7**
  = 9 × 7,
multiply numerator and denominator of $\frac{6}{7}$ by 9.

$$114\frac{98}{63}$$

Do not leave the fractional part more than 1.

$$= 115\frac{35}{63}$$

$$= 115\frac{5 \times \cancel{7}}{\cancel{7} \times 9}$$

Reduce the fractional part to lowest terms.

$$= 115\frac{5}{9}\ \blacksquare$$

Try These Problems

Add and simplify.

5. $8\frac{6}{7} + 13\frac{5}{6}$

6. $3\frac{12}{35} + 9\frac{5}{14}$

7. $25\frac{11}{14} + 38\frac{8}{21} + 52\frac{1}{6}$

8. $5\frac{9}{28} + 3\frac{5}{12} + \frac{1}{21}$

▲ **Try Problems 5 through 8.**

2 Working with More Difficult Denominators

The next few examples involve more difficult denominators.

EXAMPLE 5   Add: $\frac{7}{25} + \frac{11}{30}$

SOLUTION   Find the LCM of 25 and 30.

$$25 = 5 \times 5$$
$$30 = 3 \times 10$$
$$ = 3 \times 2 \times 5$$

$$LCM = 2 \times 3 \times 5 \times 5$$
$$= 6 \times 25$$
$$= 150$$

Rewrite each fraction so that they both have a denominator of 150, but do not change the values of the fractions.

$$\frac{7}{25} + \frac{11}{30}$$

$$= \frac{7 \times 6}{25 \times 6} + \frac{11 \times 5}{30 \times 5}$$

Because
$150 = 2 \times 3 \times$ $\boxed{5 \times 5}$
$= 6 \times 25$,
multiply numerator and denominator of $\frac{7}{25}$ by 6.

Because
$150 = \boxed{2 \times 3 \times 5} \times 5$
$= 30 \times 5$,
multiply numerator and denominator of $\frac{11}{30}$ by 5.

$$= \frac{42}{150} + \frac{55}{150}$$

$$= \frac{97}{150}$$

To make sure the fraction is reduced to lowest terms, it is enough to check only the *prime* divisors. We know 2, 3, and 5 are the prime divisors of 150. None of these divide evenly into 97. So the fraction is reduced. ■

EXAMPLE 6   Add: $\frac{5}{21} + \frac{11}{18} + \frac{2}{63}$

SOLUTION   Find the least common multiple of 21, 18, and 63.

$$21 = 3 \times 7$$
$$18 = 3 \times 6$$
$$ = 3 \times 2 \times 3$$
$$63 = 9 \times 7$$
$$ = 3 \times 3 \times 7$$

$$LCM = 2 \times 3 \times 3 \times 7$$
$$= 6 \times 21$$
$$= 126$$

Convert each fraction to an equal fraction with denominator 126.

Try These Problems

Add and simplify.

9. $\frac{11}{32} + \frac{9}{40}$

10. $25\frac{7}{54} + 18\frac{13}{36}$

11. $3\frac{29}{98} + 9\frac{13}{28} + 17\frac{3}{49}$

12. $\frac{23}{50} + \frac{8}{35} + \frac{5}{14}$

$$\frac{5}{21} + \frac{11}{18} + \frac{2}{63}$$

$$= \frac{5 \times 6}{21 \times 6} + \frac{11 \times 7}{18 \times 7} + \frac{2 \times 2}{63 \times 2}$$

Because
$126 = 2 \times 3 \times \boxed{3 \times 7}$
$ = 6 \times 21,$
multiply numerator and denominator by 6.

Because
$126 = \boxed{2 \times 3 \times 3} \times 7$
$ = 18 \times 7,$
multiply numerator and denominator by 7.

Because
$126 = 2 \times \boxed{3 \times 3 \times 7}$
$ = 2 \times 63,$
multiply numerator and denominator by 2.

$$= \frac{30}{126} + \frac{77}{126} + \frac{4}{126}$$

$$= \frac{111}{126}$$

We already know that the prime divisors of 126 are 2, 3, and 7. Do any of these primes divide evenly into 111? Yes, 3 does because the sum of the digits of 111 is 3. We divide 111 by 3 to find the other factor.

$$= \frac{\cancel{3} \times 37}{\cancel{3} \times 42}$$

$$\begin{array}{r} 37 \\ 3\overline{)111} \\ 9 \\ \hline 21 \\ 21 \end{array} \rightarrow 111 = 3 \times 37$$

$$= \frac{37}{42}$$

The fraction is reduced because $42 = 2 \times 3 \times 7$ and none of these prime factors divide evenly into 37. ■

Try Problems 9 through 12.

3 Working with Very Difficult Denominators

Now we look at examples of adding fractions where the denominators contain prime factors that are larger than 7.

EXAMPLE 7 Add: $6\frac{16}{39} + 54\frac{5}{9}$

SOLUTION Find the least common multiple of 39 and 9.

$$\left.\begin{array}{l} 39 = 3 \times 13 \\ \\ 9 = 3 \times 3 \end{array}\right\} \begin{array}{l} \text{LCM} = 3 \times 3 \times 13 \\ \phantom{\text{LCM}} = 9 \times 13 \\ \phantom{\text{LCM}} = 117 \end{array}$$

Try These Problems

Add and simplify.

13. $\frac{17}{22} + \frac{14}{33}$

14. $\frac{5}{68} + \frac{3}{17}$

15. $\frac{7}{26} + \frac{3}{10} + \frac{3}{65}$

16. $2\frac{5}{46} + 5\frac{8}{69} + 8\frac{1}{6}$

Write the fractional parts so that each has a denominator of 117.

$$6\frac{16}{39} = 6\frac{16 \times 3}{39 \times 3} = 6\frac{48}{117}$$

$$+ 54\frac{5}{9} = 54\frac{5 \times 13}{9 \times 13} = 54\frac{65}{117}$$

$$60\frac{113}{117}$$

The fraction is reduced to lowest terms because $117 = 3 \times 3 \times 13$ and neither 3 nor 13 divides evenly into 113. ■

EXAMPLE 8   Add: $\frac{13}{55} + \frac{15}{22} + \frac{9}{10}$

SOLUTION   Find the least common multiple of 55, 22, and 10.

$$\left.\begin{array}{l} 55 = 5 \times 11 \\ 22 = 2 \times 11 \\ 10 = 2 \times 5 \end{array}\right\} \begin{array}{l} \text{LCM} = 2 \times 5 \times 11 \\ = 10 \times 11 \\ = 110 \end{array}$$

Convert each fraction to an equal fraction with denominator 110.

$$\frac{13}{55} + \frac{15}{22} + \frac{9}{10}$$

$$= \frac{13 \times 2}{55 \times 2} + \frac{15 \times 5}{22 \times 5} + \frac{9 \times 11}{10 \times 11}$$

Because $110 = 2 \times 5 \times 11 = 2 \times 55$, multiply numerator and denominator by 2.

Because $110 = 2 \times 5 \times 11 = 5 \times 22$, multiply numerator and denominator by 5.

Because $110 = 2 \times 5 \times 11 = 10 \times 11$, multiply numerator and denominator by 11.

$$= \frac{26}{110} + \frac{75}{110} + \frac{99}{110}$$

$$= \frac{200}{110}$$

$$= \frac{20 \times \cancel{10}}{11 \times \cancel{10}}$$

Cancel the common factor 10 from the numerator and denominator.

$$= \frac{20}{11} \quad \text{or} \quad 1\frac{9}{11} \quad ■$$

 Try Problems 13 through 16.

Now we summarize by stating a rule for adding fractions with unlike denominators.

> *Adding Fractions with Unlike Denominators*
> 1. Find the least common multiple of the denominators. The number is called the least common denominator.
> 2. Convert each fraction to an equivalent fraction that has the common denominator.
> 3. Follow the rules for adding fractions with like denominators.

 Answers to Try These Problems

1. $\frac{29}{24}$ or $1\frac{5}{24}$ 2. $\frac{19}{20}$ 3. $\frac{55}{18}$ or $3\frac{1}{18}$ 4. $\frac{4}{3}$ or $1\frac{1}{3}$ 5. $22\frac{29}{42}$
6. $12\frac{7}{10}$ 7. $116\frac{1}{3}$ 8. $8\frac{11}{14}$ 9. $\frac{91}{160}$ 10. $43\frac{53}{108}$ 11. $29\frac{23}{28}$
12. $\frac{183}{175}$ or $1\frac{8}{175}$ 13. $\frac{79}{66}$ or $1\frac{13}{66}$ 14. $\frac{1}{4}$ 15. $\frac{8}{13}$ 16. $15\frac{9}{23}$

EXERCISES 5.3

Add and simplify.

1. $\frac{5}{9} + \frac{7}{6}$ 2. $\frac{7}{10} + \frac{11}{15}$ 3. $\frac{6}{7} + \frac{29}{56}$ 4. $\frac{3}{14} + \frac{9}{10}$

5. $\frac{3}{20} + \frac{1}{15} + \frac{7}{12}$ 6. $\frac{3}{8} + \frac{13}{10} + \frac{1}{5}$ 7. $\frac{17}{33} + \frac{19}{6}$ 8. $\frac{6}{65} + \frac{4}{13}$

9. $\frac{7}{34} + \frac{3}{4} + \frac{5}{17}$ 10. $\frac{7}{10} + \frac{4}{55} + \frac{13}{22}$ 11. $\frac{6}{35} + \frac{19}{42}$ 12. $\frac{17}{45} + \frac{35}{54}$

13. $27\frac{4}{15} + 8\frac{4}{35}$ 14. $3\frac{5}{22} + 8\frac{8}{9}$ 15. $76\frac{9}{64} + 28\frac{15}{24}$ 16. $9\frac{5}{28} + 53\frac{7}{20}$

17. $28\frac{4}{51} + 36\frac{7}{34}$ 18. $15\frac{5}{7} + 43\frac{39}{91}$

19. $\begin{array}{r} \frac{5}{6} \\ \frac{3}{10} \\ + \frac{4}{15} \end{array}$ 20. $\begin{array}{r} \frac{4}{7} \\ \frac{11}{28} \\ + \frac{1}{2} \end{array}$ 21. $\begin{array}{r} \frac{3}{7} \\ \frac{5}{6} \\ + \frac{4}{5} \end{array}$ 22. $\begin{array}{r} \frac{1}{6} \\ \frac{7}{8} \\ + \frac{11}{16} \end{array}$

23. $\begin{array}{r} 3\frac{8}{11} \\ 4\frac{5}{33} \\ + 6\frac{2}{9} \end{array}$ 24. $\begin{array}{r} 5\frac{3}{49} \\ 26\frac{5}{14} \\ + \frac{1}{7} \end{array}$ 25. $\begin{array}{r} 9\frac{1}{6} \\ 38\frac{3}{7} \\ + 66\frac{3}{10} \end{array}$ 26. $\begin{array}{r} 10\frac{5}{9} \\ 8\frac{11}{15} \\ + 6\frac{4}{7} \end{array}$

27. $\begin{array}{r} 3\frac{17}{24} \\ 7\frac{8}{45} \\ + 9\frac{5}{36} \end{array}$ 28. $\begin{array}{r} 4\frac{8}{35} \\ 12\frac{40}{63} \\ + 7\frac{9}{15} \end{array}$ 29. $\begin{array}{r} 13\frac{7}{20} \\ + 19\frac{8}{65} \end{array}$ 30. $\begin{array}{r} 45\frac{7}{8} \\ + 63\frac{5}{34} \end{array}$

31. A bricklayer worked $4\frac{2}{5}$ hours on Tuesday, $5\frac{1}{4}$ hours on Wednesday, and $6\frac{1}{12}$ hours on Thursday. What was the total time worked for the three-day period?

32. Find the total length of this shaft.

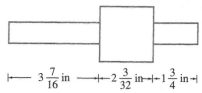

$\longmapsto 3\frac{7}{16}$ in $\longrightarrow$ $\mapsto 2\frac{3}{32}$ in $\mapsto$ $\mid 1\frac{3}{4}$ in $\mid$

33. A rectangular picture window is $6\frac{3}{8}$ feet wide and $4\frac{2}{3}$ feet long. Find the distance around the window.

34. A business is owned by three women. Joan owns $\frac{7}{12}$ of the business, Roberta owns $\frac{1}{4}$ of the business, and Virginia owns the rest. What fraction of the business is owned by Joan and Roberta?

5.4	COMPARING FRACTIONS

OBJECTIVES

- Compare fractions with like denominators.
- Use the comparing symbols to compare fractions.
- Compare fractions with unlike denominators.
- Solve an application that involves comparing fractions.

1 Comparing Fractions with Like Denominators

In the diagram below there are two figures of the same size. The second figure has a larger portion that is shaded.

smaller ⟋ ⬜⬜⬜⬜⬜ $\frac{2}{5}$ of the figure is shaded.

larger ⟋ ▨▨▨▨⬜ $\frac{4}{5}$ of the figure is shaded.

This illustrates that

$$\frac{4}{5} \text{ is larger than } \frac{2}{5} \quad \text{or} \quad \frac{2}{5} \text{ is smaller than } \frac{4}{5}.$$

Observe that when two fractions have the same denominator, the larger fraction has the larger numerator.

> **Comparing Fractions with Like Denominators**
> If two fractions have like denominators, then the larger fraction has the larger numerator.

EXAMPLE 1 Name the larger fraction.

a. $\frac{7}{10}, \frac{3}{10}$ **b.** $\frac{3}{3}, \frac{5}{3}$ **c.** $\frac{6}{9}, \frac{7}{9}$

SOLUTION

a. $\frac{7}{10}$ is larger

b. $\frac{5}{3}$ is larger

c. $\frac{7}{9}$ is larger ∎

EXAMPLE 2 Name the smallest fraction.

a. $\frac{3}{4}, \frac{1}{4}, \frac{7}{4}$ **b.** $\frac{5}{7}, \frac{3}{7}, \frac{2}{7}$

SOLUTION

a. $\frac{1}{4}$ is the smallest

b. $\frac{2}{7}$ is the smallest ∎

EXAMPLE 3 List these fractions from smallest to largest.
$\frac{7}{5}, \frac{3}{5}, \frac{2}{5}, \frac{19}{5}$

SOLUTION Listing from smallest to largest, $\frac{2}{5}, \frac{3}{5}, \frac{7}{5}, \frac{19}{5}$ ∎

Try These Problems

Name the smaller fraction.

1. $\frac{3}{4}, \frac{1}{4}$

2. $\frac{2}{5}, \frac{18}{5}$

3. $\frac{8}{9}, \frac{7}{9}$

Name the largest fraction.

4. $\frac{1}{5}, \frac{4}{5}, \frac{2}{5}$

5. $\frac{2}{18}, \frac{3}{18}, \frac{11}{18}$

List from smallest to largest.

6. $\frac{6}{8}, \frac{3}{8}, \frac{7}{8}, \frac{2}{8}$

7. $\frac{8}{10}, \frac{3}{10}, \frac{12}{10}, \frac{5}{10}$

Solve.

8. Nanda bought a bag of oranges weighing $6\frac{3}{4}$ pounds. Frank bought a bag weighing $6\frac{1}{4}$ pounds. Who bought the heavier bag of oranges?

9. A recipe calls for $\frac{3}{2}$ cups of milk. Ted has $\frac{1}{2}$ cup of milk. Does Ted have enough milk to prepare this recipe?

Use the symbol <, =, or > to compare each pair of numbers.

10. $\frac{3}{5} \underset{(<,\,=,\,>)}{\underline{\quad ? \quad}} \frac{4}{5}$

11. $\frac{7}{12} \underset{(<,\,=,\,>)}{\underline{\quad ? \quad}} \frac{3}{12}$

12. $\frac{11}{5} \underset{(<,\,=,\,>)}{\underline{\quad ? \quad}} 2\frac{1}{5}$

13. $4\frac{5}{10} \underset{(<,\,=,\,>)}{\underline{\quad ? \quad}} 4\frac{3}{10}$

EXAMPLE 4   Allen ran a race in $5\frac{3}{10}$ minutes and Gregory ran the same race in $5\frac{7}{10}$ minutes. Who won the race?

SOLUTION   Compare $5\frac{3}{10}$ with $5\frac{7}{10}$. The number $5\frac{3}{10}$ is less, so Allen won the race. ■

 Try Problems 1 through 9.

2 The Comparing Symbols

The mathematical symbols $>$ and $<$ are used to compare numbers. The following chart gives examples of how to use these symbols correctly.

English	*Math Symbols*
2 is smaller than 4	$2 < 4$
4 is larger than 2	$4 > 2$
$\frac{2}{5}$ is smaller than $\frac{4}{5}$	$\frac{2}{5} < \frac{4}{5}$
$\frac{4}{5}$ is larger than $\frac{2}{5}$	$\frac{4}{5} > \frac{2}{5}$

You should make these observations.

1. $< \quad >$ The pointed side always faces the smaller number.

2. $< \quad >$ The open side always faces the larger number.

EXAMPLE 5   Use the symbol $<$, $=$, or $>$ to compare each pair of numbers.

a. $\frac{3}{8} \underset{(<,\,=,\,>)}{\underline{\quad ? \quad}} \frac{7}{8}$ **b.** $\frac{4}{4} \underset{(<,\,=,\,>)}{\underline{\quad ? \quad}} \frac{2}{4}$ **c.** $1\frac{1}{16} \underset{(<,\,=,\,>)}{\underline{\quad ? \quad}} \frac{17}{16}$

SOLUTION

a. $\frac{3}{8} < \frac{7}{8}$ **b.** $\frac{4}{4} > \frac{2}{4}$ **c.** $1\frac{1}{16} = \frac{17}{16}$ ■

 Try Problems 10 through 13.

3 Comparing Fractions with Unlike Denominators

In the diagram below there are two figures of the same size. The second figure has a smaller portion that is shaded.

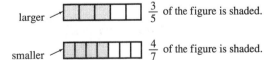

larger $\frac{3}{5}$ of the figure is shaded.

smaller $\frac{4}{7}$ of the figure is shaded.

This illustrates that

$$\frac{3}{5} \text{ is larger than } \frac{4}{7} \quad \text{or} \quad \frac{4}{7} \text{ is smaller than } \frac{3}{5}.$$

If we convert each fraction to an equivalent fraction with denominator 35, we can see that $\frac{3}{5}$ is larger than $\frac{4}{7}$ without viewing a picture.

$$\frac{3}{5} = \frac{3 \times 7}{5 \times 7} = \frac{21}{35} \quad \text{---- larger}$$

$$\frac{4}{7} = \frac{4 \times 5}{7 \times 5} = \frac{20}{35} \quad \text{---- smaller}$$

Because $\frac{21}{35}$ is more than $\frac{20}{35}$, $\frac{3}{5}$ is more than $\frac{4}{7}$.

Comparing Fractions with Unlike Denominators

1. Write each fraction with the same denominator.
2. If two fractions have the same denominator, the larger fraction has the larger numerator.

EXAMPLE 6 List from the smallest to largest: $\frac{1}{2}, \frac{4}{9}, \frac{5}{12}, \frac{17}{36}$

SOLUTION Find the least common multiple of 2, 9, 12, and 36.

$$
\left.
\begin{aligned}
&2 \text{ is prime} \\
&9 = 3 \times 3 \\
&12 = 3 \times 4 \\
&\quad\ = 3 \times 2 \times 2 \\
&36 = \ 6 \ \times \ 6 \\
&\quad\ = 2 \times 3 \times 2 \times 3
\end{aligned}
\right\}
\quad
\begin{aligned}
\text{LCM} &= 2 \times 2 \times 3 \times 3 \\
&= 4 \times 9 \\
&= 36
\end{aligned}
$$

Convert each fraction to an equivalent fraction with denominator 36.

$$\frac{1}{2} = \frac{1 \times 18}{2 \times 18} = \frac{18}{36} \diagdown \text{largest}$$

$$\frac{4}{9} = \frac{4 \times 4}{9 \times 4} = \frac{16}{36}$$

$$\frac{5}{12} = \frac{5 \times 3}{12 \times 3} = \frac{15}{36} \diagdown \text{smallest}$$

$$\frac{17}{36}$$

Listing from smallest to largest, $\frac{5}{12}, \frac{4}{9}, \frac{17}{36}, \frac{1}{2}$ ■

EXAMPLE 7 Beatrice, a mechanic, accidentally picked up a $\frac{7}{16}$-inch wrench to loosen a $\frac{5}{8}$-inch bolt. Was the wrench too large or too small?

Try These Problems

14. Which is larger, $\frac{3}{5}$ or $\frac{7}{12}$?

15. Use the symbol $<$, $=$, or $>$ to compare $\frac{1}{5}$ with $\frac{8}{35}$.

16. List from smallest to largest: $\frac{4}{27}, \frac{7}{54}, \frac{1}{6}, \frac{1}{9}$.

17. In a tennis match, Allanah got $\frac{7}{20}$ of her first serves in and Tina got $\frac{2}{5}$. Which of the women got the larger fractional portion of first serves in?

18. Tim is buying a refrigerator for his kitchen. The space in the kitchen is $2\frac{5}{12}$ feet wide. The refrigerator he likes is $2\frac{3}{4}$ feet wide. Does the refrigerator fit in the space?

SOLUTION Which is larger, $\frac{7}{16}$ or $\frac{5}{8}$?

WRENCH $\quad \frac{7}{16}$

BOLT $\quad \frac{5}{8} = \frac{5 \times 2}{8 \times 2} = \frac{10}{16}$ —— larger

The bolt is larger than the wrench, so the wrench is too small. ■

 **Try Problems 14 through 18.**

Answers to Try These Problems

1. $\frac{1}{4}$ 2. $\frac{2}{5}$ 3. $\frac{7}{9}$ 4. $\frac{4}{5}$ 5. $\frac{11}{18}$ 6. $\frac{2}{8}, \frac{3}{8}, \frac{6}{8}, \frac{7}{8}$ 7. $\frac{3}{10}, \frac{5}{10}, \frac{8}{10}, \frac{12}{10}$

8. Nanda 9. no 10. $<$ 11. $>$ 12. $=$ 13. $>$ 14. $\frac{3}{5}$

15. $\frac{1}{5} < \frac{8}{35}$ 16. $\frac{1}{9}, \frac{7}{54}, \frac{4}{27}, \frac{1}{6}$ 17. Tina 18. no

EXERCISES 5.4

Name the larger fraction.

1. $\frac{2}{3}, \frac{1}{3}$ **2.** $\frac{7}{12}, \frac{9}{12}$ **3.** $\frac{2}{3}, \frac{7}{9}$ **4.** $\frac{3}{10}, \frac{5}{6}$

Name the smaller fraction.

5. $\frac{2}{5}, \frac{4}{5}$ **6.** $\frac{11}{6}, \frac{7}{6}$ **7.** $\frac{7}{20}, \frac{2}{5}$ **8.** $\frac{7}{10}, \frac{7}{9}$

Name the largest fraction in each group.

9. $\frac{2}{12}, \frac{8}{12}, \frac{10}{12}$ **10.** $\frac{17}{36}, \frac{20}{36}, \frac{15}{36}$ **11.** $\frac{1}{4}, \frac{1}{5}, \frac{7}{30}$ **12.** $\frac{5}{6}, \frac{2}{3}, \frac{5}{7}$

Name the smallest fraction in each group.

13. $\frac{7}{6}, \frac{6}{6}, \frac{11}{6}$ **14.** $\frac{15}{24}, \frac{14}{24}, \frac{20}{24}$ **15.** $\frac{9}{20}, \frac{1}{2}, \frac{2}{5}$ **16.** $\frac{5}{8}, \frac{9}{16}, \frac{3}{4}$

List from smallest to largest.

17. $\frac{3}{4}, \frac{1}{4}, \frac{5}{4}, \frac{11}{4}$ **18.** $\frac{9}{5}, \frac{12}{5}, \frac{4}{5}, \frac{10}{5}$ **19.** $\frac{3}{5}, \frac{13}{20}, \frac{1}{2}$ **20.** $\frac{3}{4}, \frac{7}{12}, \frac{2}{3}$

21. $\frac{24}{11}, 3, \frac{11}{24}$ **22.** $5, \frac{17}{3}, \frac{3}{17}$

Use the symbol $>$, $=$, or $<$ to compare each pair of numbers.

23. $2, 7$ **24.** $11, 9$ **25.** $\frac{14}{15}, \frac{8}{15}$ **26.** $\frac{7}{11}, \frac{9}{11}$ **27.** $3\frac{3}{4}, 3\frac{6}{8},$

28. $4\frac{5}{9}, 4\frac{1}{2}$ **29.** $\frac{13}{25}, \frac{3}{5}$ **30.** $\frac{7}{9}, \frac{3}{4}$ **31.** $\frac{11}{11}, \frac{12}{13}$ **32.** $\frac{8}{2}, 4$

Solve.

33. One piece of pipe measures $\frac{5}{8}$ inches in diameter and another piece of pipe measures $\frac{7}{8}$ inches in diameter. Which pipe has the larger diameter?

34. Patricia lives $\frac{8}{10}$ of a mile from school and Agatha lives $\frac{6}{10}$ of a mile from school. Who lives closer to school?

35. Jacqueline receives a weekly salary of $150 and has $10 deducted for health insurance. Paul receives a weekly salary of $100 and has $8 deducted for health insurance. Who pays the larger fractional portion of salary for health insurance?

36. Arthur was comparing his recipe for spaghetti with David's recipe. Arthur's recipe called for $\frac{1}{2}$ cup parsley, whereas David's recipe called for $\frac{1}{4}$ cup parsley. Whose spaghetti recipe contained more parsley?

DEVELOPING NUMBER SENSE #4

COMPARING A FRACTION TO $\frac{1}{2}$

In this feature we look at how to decide if a fraction is less than, equal to, or more than $\frac{1}{2}$. First we look at some fractions that are equal to $\frac{1}{2}$.

$$\frac{1}{2} = \frac{2}{4} = \frac{3}{6} = \frac{4}{8} = \frac{5}{10} = \frac{6}{12} = \frac{7}{14}$$

In each case, observe that the denominator is exactly twice the numerator, or another way to look at it, the numerator is the result of dividing the denominator by 2. For example, in the fraction $\frac{7}{14}$, $14 = 2 \times 7$ or $14 \div 2 = 7$. Using this observation, can you choose the fractions in this list that are exactly equal to $\frac{1}{2}$?

$$\frac{11}{22} \quad \frac{6}{14} \quad \frac{7}{10} \quad \frac{14}{28} \quad \frac{150}{300} \quad \frac{15}{28} \quad \frac{25}{50}$$

The fractions that are equal to $\frac{1}{2}$ are $\frac{11}{22}$, $\frac{14}{28}$, $\frac{150}{300}$, and $\frac{25}{50}$.

Consider the fraction $\frac{6}{14}$. Is it less than or more than $\frac{1}{2}$? Dividing 14 by 2, we see that $\frac{7}{14}$ is equal to $\frac{1}{2}$. Because $\frac{6}{14}$ is less than $\frac{7}{14}$, $\frac{6}{14}$ is less than $\frac{1}{2}$. We write $\frac{6}{14} < \frac{1}{2}$.

Consider the fraction $\frac{14}{25}$. Is it less than or more than $\frac{1}{2}$? Dividing 25 by 2, we see that $\frac{12\frac{1}{2}}{25}$ is exactly equal to $\frac{1}{2}$. Because $\frac{14}{25}$ is more than $\frac{12\frac{1}{2}}{25}$, $\frac{14}{25}$ is more than $\frac{1}{2}$. We write $\frac{14}{25} > \frac{1}{2}$.

Being able to quickly compare a fraction to $\frac{1}{2}$ will help you later when you are rounding off fractions to the nearest whole number.

Number Sense Problems

1. Choose the fractions that are equal to $\frac{1}{2}$.

a. $\frac{4}{7}$ **b.** $\frac{10}{20}$ **c.** $\frac{24}{48}$ **d.** $\frac{13}{37}$ **e.** $\frac{114}{360}$

f. $\frac{47}{91}$ **g.** $\frac{43}{86}$

2. Choose the fractions that are less than $\frac{1}{2}$.

a. $\frac{8}{17}$ **b.** $\frac{24}{47}$ **c.** $\frac{45}{90}$ **d.** $\frac{99}{202}$ **e.** $\frac{87}{180}$

f. $\frac{35}{69}$ **g.** $\frac{305}{610}$

3. Choose the fractions that are more than $\frac{1}{2}$.

a. $\frac{9}{17}$ **b.** $\frac{17}{30}$ **c.** $\frac{20}{48}$ **d.** $\frac{41}{84}$ **e.** $\frac{46}{92}$

f. $\frac{76}{150}$ **g.** $\frac{53}{111}$

Use the symbol <, =, or > to accurately compare each given fraction with $\frac{1}{2}$.

4. $\frac{1}{4}$ **5.** $\frac{5}{8}$ **6.** $\frac{10}{18}$ **7.** $\frac{18}{36}$ **8.** $\frac{34}{70}$ **9.** $\frac{42}{87}$

5.5   SUBTRACTING

OBJECTIVES

▍ Subtract fractions.

▍ Perform subtraction of mixed numerals that involves borrowing.

▍ Find the missing number in an addition statement.

Try These Problems

Subtract and simplify.
1. $\frac{11}{8} - \frac{3}{8}$
2. $\frac{1}{2} - \frac{1}{3}$
3. $\frac{7}{12} - \frac{2}{9}$
4. $\frac{9}{5} - \frac{7}{15}$

Solve.
5. A truck was loaded with $\frac{4}{5}$ ton of sand. If $\frac{3}{10}$ ton was unloaded, what fraction of a ton was left?

1 Subtracting Fractions

Suppose that on Monday you walked $\frac{7}{10}$ mile, and on Tuesday you walked only $\frac{3}{10}$ mile. How much farther did you walk on Monday? To solve this problem we need to subtract $\frac{3}{10}$ from $\frac{7}{10}$. Subtraction is the reverse of addition. To subtract means to take away.

$$\frac{7}{10} - \frac{3}{10} = \frac{4}{10}$$ —— Subtract the numerators. $7 - 3 = 4$
—— Use the common denominator.

$$= \frac{2 \times \cancel{2}}{5 \times \cancel{2}}$$ Simplify the answer.

$$= \frac{2}{5}$$

You walked $\frac{2}{5}$ mile farther on Monday.

Observe that to subtract fractions with like denominators we must subtract the numerators and keep the same denominator. Here we view a picture of the subtraction problem $\frac{7}{10} - \frac{3}{10}$ so that we can see that the result $\frac{2}{5}$ is correct. Assume each separate figure represents 1 whole.

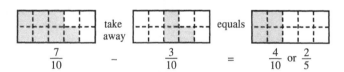

$\frac{7}{10}$ take away $\frac{3}{10}$ equals $\frac{4}{10}$ or $\frac{2}{5}$

Here are more examples of subtracting fractions.

EXAMPLE 1   Subtract: $\frac{3}{4} - \frac{1}{8}$

SOLUTION   The least common multiple of 4 and 8 is 8. Convert $\frac{3}{4}$ to an equivalent fraction with denominator 8 before subtracting.

$$\frac{3}{4} - \frac{1}{8}$$
$$= \frac{3 \times 2}{4 \times 2} - \frac{1}{8}$$ Multiply the numerator and denominator of $\frac{3}{4}$ by 2 so that it has the common denominator 8.
$$= \frac{6}{8} - \frac{1}{8}$$
$$= \frac{5}{8} \blacksquare$$

 Try Problems 1 through 5.

EXAMPLE 2   Subtract: $9\frac{5}{12} - 2\frac{3}{40}$

SOLUTION   Find the least common multiple of 12 and 40.

$$\left. \begin{array}{l} 12 = 3 \times 4 \\ \quad = 3 \times 2 \times 2 \\ 40 = 4 \times 10 \\ \quad = 2 \times 2 \times 2 \times 5 \end{array} \right\} \begin{array}{l} \text{LCM} = 3 \times 2 \times 2 \times 2 \times 5 \\ = 6 \times 4 \times 5 \\ = 6 \times 20 \\ = 120 \end{array}$$

⏵ **Try These Problems**

Subtract and simplify.

6. $4\frac{5}{6} - 1\frac{7}{18}$

7. $42\frac{7}{11} - 17\frac{1}{3}$

8. $15\frac{13}{36} - 9\frac{3}{28}$

Convert each fraction to an equivalent fraction with denominator 120, then subtract.

$$9\frac{5}{12} = 9\frac{5 \times 10}{12 \times 10} = 9\frac{50}{120}$$

$$-\,2\frac{3}{40} = 2\frac{3 \times 3}{40 \times 3} = 2\frac{9}{120}$$

$$7\frac{41}{120}$$

Subtract the whole numbers. $9 - 2 = 7$
Subtract the fractions.
$\frac{50}{120} - \frac{9}{120} = \frac{41}{120}$

The answer $7\frac{41}{120}$ is simplified because 2, 3, and 5 are the only prime divisors of 120 and none of these divide evenly into 41. ∎

⏵ **Try Problems 6 through 8.**

2 | Subtraction Involving Borrowing

Art has a tree that is $3\frac{2}{3}$ feet tall. He wants the tree to be 6 feet tall. How much taller must it grow? To solve this problem you need to subtract $3\frac{2}{3}$ from 6.

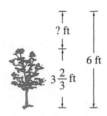

$$6 - 3\frac{2}{3}$$

Because there is no fraction next to 6 to subtract $\frac{2}{3}$ from, we rewrite 6 as $5\frac{3}{3}$.

$$= 5\frac{3}{3} - 3\frac{2}{3}$$

$$= 2\frac{1}{3}$$

Subtract the whole numbers. $5 - 3 = 2$
Subtract the fractions. $\frac{3}{3} - \frac{2}{3} = \frac{1}{3}$

The tree needs to grow $2\frac{1}{3}$ feet.

Now we view a picture of the subtraction problem $6 - 3\frac{2}{3}$ so that we can see that the result $2\frac{1}{3}$ is correct. Assume each separate figure represents 1 whole.

Start with 6.
Take away $3\frac{2}{3}$.
$2\frac{1}{3}$ is left.

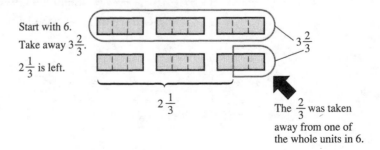

$3\frac{2}{3}$

$2\frac{1}{3}$

The $\frac{2}{3}$ was taken away from one of the whole units in 6.

Subtract and simplify.

9. $8 - 2\frac{3}{4}$

10. $19 - 7\frac{9}{20}$

11. $1 - \frac{5}{8}$

12. $1 - \frac{11}{15}$

Solve.

13. A business is owned by two men. Juan owns $\frac{3}{5}$ of the business and Warren owns the rest. What fraction of the business does Warren own?

14. Betsy read $\frac{1}{4}$ of her book last night. What fraction of the book is left?

15. Karl wants to run 10 miles. So far, he has run $5\frac{3}{8}$ miles. How many miles does he have left to go?

16. Sylvia wants to limit her backpack to 8 pounds. She has already packed items weighing $2\frac{1}{2}$ pounds and $4\frac{3}{4}$ pounds. How many more pounds can she pack without going over her limit?

When we rewrite 6 as $5\frac{3}{3}$, we say that we **borrow** 1 from 6 to make 5 and write the 1 as $\frac{3}{3}$. Here we show the problem $6 - 3\frac{2}{3}$ solved in vertical format.

$$
\begin{array}{rcl}
6 & = & 5\frac{3}{3} \\
-\;3\frac{2}{3} & = & 3\frac{2}{3} \\
\hline
& & 2\frac{1}{3}
\end{array}
$$

Borrow 1 from 6 to make 5 and write 1 as $\frac{3}{3}$.

EXAMPLE 3   Subtract: $9 - 3\frac{7}{12}$

SOLUTION

$$9 - 3\frac{7}{12}$$

$$= 8\frac{12}{12} - 3\frac{7}{12}$$

Because there is no fraction next to 9 to subtract $\frac{7}{12}$ from, rewrite 9 as $8\frac{12}{12}$.

$$= 5\frac{5}{12}$$

Subtract the whole numbers.
$8 - 3 = 5$
Subtract the fractions. $\frac{12}{12} - \frac{7}{12} = \frac{5}{12}$ ■

EXAMPLE 4   Subtract: $1 - \frac{13}{25}$

SOLUTION

$$1 - \frac{13}{25}$$

$$= \frac{25}{25} - \frac{13}{25}$$

Rewrite 1 as $\frac{25}{25}$ so both numbers are in fractional form with denominator 25.

$$= \frac{12}{25}$$ ■

EXAMPLE 5   Dave ate $\frac{1}{3}$ of a pizza. What fraction of the pizza remains?

SOLUTION   The whole pizza is represented by the number 1. Subtract $\frac{1}{3}$ from 1.

$$
\begin{array}{rcl}
1 & = & \dfrac{3}{3} \\
-\;\dfrac{1}{3} & = & \dfrac{1}{3} \\
\hline
& & \dfrac{2}{3}
\end{array}
$$

The whole pizza.

Fraction of the pizza he ate.

Fraction of the pizza that remains.

$\frac{2}{3}$ of the pizza remains.

 Try Problems 9 through 16.

Now consider the following subtraction problem.

$$3\frac{1}{6}$$
$$-1\frac{5}{6}$$

Notice that the fraction $\frac{5}{6}$ is larger than the fraction $\frac{1}{6}$ so we cannot subtract as the problem is written. Before working the problem, view the following picture so that we can see what the answer should be.

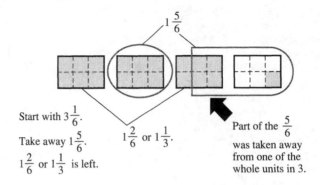

Start with $3\frac{1}{6}$.

Take away $1\frac{5}{6}$.

$1\frac{2}{6}$ or $1\frac{1}{3}$ is left.

$1\frac{5}{6}$

$1\frac{2}{6}$ or $1\frac{1}{3}$.

Part of the $\frac{5}{6}$ was taken away from one of the whole units in 3.

Now here is a procedure that gives the correct result $1\frac{1}{3}$.

$$3\frac{1}{6} = 2\frac{7}{6}$$
$$-1\frac{5}{6} = 1\frac{5}{6}$$
$$\overline{\phantom{-1\frac{5}{6}}}$$
$$1\frac{2}{6} = 1\frac{1}{3}$$

Observe that $\frac{5}{6}$ is larger than $\frac{1}{6}$, so we cannot subtract the fractions. Borrow 1 from 3 to make 2, and combine the 1 you borrowed with $\frac{1}{6}$.
$1 + \frac{1}{6} = \frac{6}{6} + \frac{1}{6} = \frac{7}{6}$
We are rewriting $3\frac{1}{6}$ as $2\frac{7}{6}$ before subtracting.

EXAMPLE 6 Subtract: $43\frac{2}{9} - 12\frac{7}{9}$

SOLUTION

$$43\frac{2}{9} = 42\frac{11}{9}$$
$$-12\frac{7}{9} = 12\frac{7}{9}$$
$$\overline{\phantom{-12\frac{7}{9}}}$$
$$30\frac{4}{9}$$

Note that $\frac{7}{9}$ is larger than $\frac{2}{9}$ so we cannot subtract the fractions. Borrow 1 from 43 to make 42. Combine the 1 you borrowed with $\frac{2}{9}$.
$1 + \frac{2}{9} = \frac{9}{9} + \frac{2}{9} = \frac{11}{9}$
or $1\frac{2}{9} = \frac{11}{9}$ ■

EXAMPLE 7 Subtract: $25\frac{5}{21} - 7\frac{8}{9}$

SOLUTION Find a common denominator.

$$\left.\begin{array}{l} 21 = 3 \times 7 \\ 9 = 3 \times 3 \end{array}\right\} \quad \begin{array}{l} \text{LCM} = 3 \times 3 \times 7 \\ = 63 \end{array}$$

Write each fraction with denominator 63 and subtract.

Try These Problems

Subtract and simplify.

17. $5\frac{2}{7} - 3\frac{5}{7}$

18. $8\frac{3}{12} - 2\frac{7}{12}$

19. $6\frac{1}{4} - 3\frac{7}{8}$

20. $23\frac{5}{24} - 7\frac{15}{16}$

Find the missing number.

21. $\boxed{} + \frac{5}{8} = \frac{9}{8}$

22. $\frac{3}{11} + \boxed{} = \frac{9}{11}$

23. $\frac{2}{3} + \frac{3}{4} = \boxed{}$

24. $\boxed{} = \frac{14}{25} + \frac{3}{10}$

25. $4 = 2\frac{1}{2} + \boxed{}$

26. $\frac{2}{3} = \frac{5}{9} + \boxed{}$

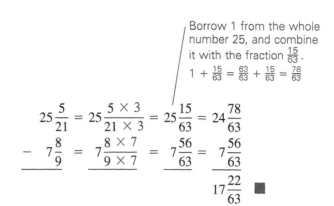

Borrow 1 from the whole number 25, and combine it with the fraction $\frac{15}{63}$.

$1 + \frac{15}{63} = \frac{63}{63} + \frac{15}{63} = \frac{78}{63}$

$$25\frac{5}{21} = 25\frac{5 \times 3}{21 \times 3} = 25\frac{15}{63} = 24\frac{78}{63}$$

$$- \quad 7\frac{8}{9} = 7\frac{8 \times 7}{9 \times 7} = 7\frac{56}{63} = 7\frac{56}{63}$$

$$17\frac{22}{63} \ ∎$$

 Try Problems 17 through 20.

3 The Missing Number in an Addition Statement

The statement $\frac{3}{7} + \frac{2}{7} = \frac{5}{7}$ is an addition statement. If any one of the three numbers is omitted, we can find the missing number. Study the three examples that follow to see how to do this.

1. $\frac{3}{7} + \frac{2}{7} = \boxed{}$ Here the answer to the addition statement is missing, so we *add* to find the missing number.

The missing number is $\frac{5}{7}$.

2. $\boxed{} + \frac{2}{7} = \frac{5}{7}$ Here one of the terms is missing, so we *subtract* to find the missing number.

The missing number is $\frac{5}{7} - \frac{2}{7} = \frac{3}{7}$.

3. $\frac{3}{7} + \boxed{} = \frac{5}{7}$ Here one of the terms is missing, so we *subtract* to find the missing number.

The missing number is $\frac{5}{7} - \frac{3}{7} = \frac{2}{7}$.

 Try Problems 21 through 26.

 Answers to Try These Problems

1. 1   2. $\frac{1}{6}$ 3. $\frac{13}{36}$ 4. $\frac{4}{3}$ or $1\frac{1}{3}$ 5. $\frac{1}{2}$ 6. $3\frac{4}{9}$ 7. $25\frac{10}{33}$

8. $6\frac{16}{63}$ 9. $5\frac{1}{4}$ 10. $11\frac{11}{20}$ 11. $\frac{3}{8}$ 12. $\frac{4}{15}$ 13. $\frac{2}{5}$ of the business

14. $\frac{3}{4}$ of her book   15. $4\frac{5}{8}$ mi   16. $\frac{3}{4}$ lb   17. $1\frac{4}{7}$ 18. $5\frac{2}{3}$

19. $2\frac{3}{8}$ 20. $15\frac{13}{48}$ 21. $\frac{1}{2}$ 22. $\frac{6}{11}$ 23. $\frac{17}{12}$ or $1\frac{5}{12}$ 24. $\frac{43}{50}$

25. $\frac{3}{2}$ or $1\frac{1}{2}$ 26. $\frac{1}{9}$

EXERCISES 5.5

Subtract and simplify:

1. $\frac{5}{6} - \frac{1}{6}$ **2.** $\frac{13}{9} - \frac{4}{9}$ **3.** $\frac{7}{8} - \frac{1}{4}$ **4.** $\frac{10}{21} - \frac{2}{7}$

5. $\frac{7}{9} - \frac{5}{12}$ **6.** $\frac{21}{10} - \frac{3}{8}$ **7.** $15\frac{7}{8} - 4\frac{3}{8}$ **8.** $9\frac{7}{11} - 5\frac{2}{11}$

9. $9\frac{3}{8} - 4$ **10.** $8\frac{5}{16} - 5$ **11.** $5\frac{7}{8} - 2\frac{1}{4}$ **12.** $10\frac{1}{2} - 7\frac{1}{6}$

13. $35\frac{3}{4} - 12\frac{5}{18}$ **14.** $56\frac{7}{13} - 8\frac{8}{39}$ **15.** $8 - 3\frac{4}{5}$ **16.** $72 - 8\frac{1}{3}$

17. $10 - \frac{7}{12}$ **18.** $23 - \frac{8}{15}$ **19.** $1 - \frac{11}{18}$ **20.** $1 - \frac{7}{9}$

21. $\begin{array}{r} 7\frac{1}{3} \\ -\ 2\frac{2}{3} \end{array}$ **22.** $\begin{array}{r} 11\frac{3}{8} \\ -\ 6\frac{7}{8} \end{array}$ **23.** $\begin{array}{r} 10\frac{5}{14} \\ -\ 4\frac{6}{7} \end{array}$ **24.** $\begin{array}{r} 15\frac{1}{3} \\ -\ 7\frac{2}{5} \end{array}$ **25.** $\begin{array}{r} 6\frac{3}{25} \\ -\ 2\frac{11}{15} \end{array}$

26. $\begin{array}{r} 72\frac{4}{45} \\ -\ 12\frac{25}{27} \end{array}$ **27.** $\begin{array}{r} 50\frac{4}{39} \\ -\ \frac{2}{13} \end{array}$ **28.** $\begin{array}{r} 61\frac{4}{33} \\ -\ \frac{13}{22} \end{array}$ **29.** $\begin{array}{r} 12\frac{5}{8} \\ -\ 7\frac{3}{10} \end{array}$ **30.** $\begin{array}{r} 24\frac{5}{12} \\ -\ 17\frac{8}{21} \end{array}$

Solve.

31. A carpenter cuts a piece of wood $7\frac{5}{8}$ feet long. She discovers that it is too long by $\frac{3}{8}$ foot. After she cuts off the extra length, how long will the resulting piece be?

32. The value of a certain stock was $22 at the start of the day. During the day it decreased $\$\frac{7}{8}$. What was the value at the end of the day?

33. The string area of the Prince Pro tennis racket is $10\frac{3}{16}$ inches wide; the string area of the Head Pro racket is only $8\frac{5}{16}$ inches wide. What is the difference in the two widths?

34. Mr. Smiegiel purchased a $3\frac{1}{4}$-pound steak at the meat market. After the butcher trimmed the steak of fat, the steak weighed $2\frac{3}{8}$ pounds. How much fat was trimmed from the steak?

35. Cindy is painting the interior of her apartment. She finished $\frac{1}{6}$ of the job yesterday. What fraction of the job remains?

36. A painter finished $\frac{1}{5}$ of the job the first day. What fraction of the job remains?

37. Sara bought a pizza for herself and several friends. Joe ate $\frac{1}{3}$ of the pizza and Carolyn ate $\frac{1}{8}$ of the pizza. What fraction of the pizza remains?

38. Mr. Winetrub started with a full tank of gas. He used $\frac{1}{4}$ of the tank on Friday and $\frac{2}{3}$ of the tank on Saturday. What fraction of the tank is left?

Find the missing number. Simplify the answer.

39. $\frac{5}{9} + \boxed{} = \frac{8}{9}$ **40.** $\boxed{} + \frac{7}{12} = \frac{11}{12}$ **41.** $\boxed{} = \frac{3}{5} + \frac{7}{15}$

42. $\frac{19}{20} = \boxed{} + \frac{1}{4}$ **43.** $5\frac{1}{4} = \boxed{} + 3\frac{2}{3}$ **44.** $16\frac{2}{9} = 5\frac{5}{6} + \boxed{}$

45. $\frac{10}{13} + \boxed{} = 1$ **46.** $4\frac{3}{5} + \boxed{} = 5$

DEVELOPING NUMBER SENSE #5

APPROXIMATING BY ROUNDING

In this feature we look at approximations that involve computations with fractions. For example, suppose you wanted to approximate this addition problem.

$$2\frac{1}{3} + 5\frac{4}{5} + 9\frac{5}{6}$$

One way to obtain an approximation is to round off each number to the nearest whole number, then add.

$2\frac{1}{3} \approx 2$ $2\frac{1}{3}$ is closer to 2 than 3 because $\frac{1}{3}$ is less than $\frac{1}{2}$.

$5\frac{4}{5} \approx 6$ $5\frac{4}{5}$ is closer to 6 than 5 because $\frac{4}{5}$ is more than $\frac{1}{2}$.

$9\frac{5}{6} \approx 10$ $9\frac{5}{6}$ is closer to 10 than 9 because $\frac{5}{6}$ is more than $\frac{1}{2}$.

Adding the numbers 2, 6, and 10, we obtain 18 for the approximation. The actual sum is $17\frac{29}{30}$.

When approximating with fractions, you do not always have to round off to the nearest whole number. If the numbers are larger, you may want to round off to the the nearest ten, hundred, or thousand as you did when working with whole numbers. For example, suppose you want to approximate this multiplication problem.

$$12\frac{7}{8} \times 36\frac{1}{3}$$

One way to obtain an approximation is to round off each factor to the nearest ten, then multiply.

$$12\frac{7}{8} \approx 10$$ Each number is rounded off to the nearest ten.

$$36\frac{1}{3} \approx 40$$

Multiplying 10 by 40, we obtain 400 for the approximation. The actual product is $467\frac{19}{24}$. Of course, if we had rounded off to the nearest whole number the approximation would have been closer to the actual product, $13 \times 36 = 468$.

Number Sense Problems

Round off each of the following numbers to the nearest whole number.

1. $5\frac{1}{3}$ **2.** $7\frac{3}{4}$ **3.** $12\frac{2}{5}$ **4.** $45\frac{2}{3}$ **5.** $\frac{1}{6}$ **6.** $\frac{11}{13}$

Round off each of the following numbers to the nearest ten.

7. 67 **8.** 153 **9.** $18\frac{1}{4}$
10. $14\frac{7}{8}$ **11.** $53\frac{1}{2}$ **12.** $178\frac{12}{25}$

Approximate by first rounding off each number to the nearest whole number.

13. $4\frac{3}{4} + 2\frac{7}{8} + 7\frac{5}{12}$ **14.** $16\frac{2}{7} - 9\frac{8}{9}$ **15.** $16\frac{7}{8} \times 3\frac{2}{9}$
16. $64\frac{2}{7} \div 3\frac{5}{6}$ **17.** $71\frac{2}{3} \times 12\frac{3}{8}$ **18.** $25\frac{7}{20} + 160\frac{5}{12} + 94\frac{5}{8}$

Approximate by first rounding off each number to the nearest ten.

19. $78\frac{1}{2} + 93$ **20.** $174 - 29\frac{1}{4}$ **21.** $13\frac{6}{7} \times 657$ **22.** $692\frac{5}{6} \div 27\frac{4}{5}$

5.6 LANGUAGE

OBJECTIVES
- Translate an English statement involving addition or subtraction to math symbols.
- Solve problems by using translations.

1 Translating English Statements to Math Symbols

The math symbols that we use often have many translations to the English language. Knowing these translations can help in solving application problems. The following chart gives the many English translations for the symbol $=$.

Math Symbol	English
=	equals
	is equal to
	is the same as
	is the result of
	is
	was
	represents
	gives
	makes
	yields
	will be
	were
	are

The addition statement $\frac{3}{4} + \frac{2}{4} = \frac{5}{4}$ is written using math symbols. Some of the ways to read this in English are given in the following chart.

Math Symbols	English
$\frac{3}{4} + \frac{2}{4} = \frac{5}{4}$	Three-fourths plus two-fourths equals five-fourths.
	Three-fourths added to two-fourths gives five-fourths.
	The *sum* of $\frac{3}{4}$ and $\frac{2}{4}$ is $\frac{5}{4}$.
	$\frac{5}{4}$ represents the total when $\frac{3}{4}$ is added to $\frac{2}{4}$.
	$\frac{5}{4}$ is the result of increasing $\frac{3}{4}$ by $\frac{2}{4}$.
	$\frac{3}{4}$ *increased by* $\frac{2}{4}$ makes $\frac{5}{4}$.
	$\frac{2}{4}$ more than $\frac{3}{4}$ is $\frac{5}{4}$.

Because $\frac{3}{4} + \frac{2}{4}$ equals $\frac{2}{4} + \frac{3}{4}$, the order in which you read the terms $\frac{3}{4}$ and $\frac{2}{4}$ does not matter; however, when reading the subtraction statement $\frac{5}{4} - \frac{2}{4}$, take care to read $\frac{5}{4}$ and $\frac{2}{4}$ in the correct order, because $\frac{5}{4} - \frac{2}{4}$ does not equal $\frac{2}{4} - \frac{5}{4}$.

$$\frac{5}{4} - \frac{2}{4} = \frac{3}{4} \quad \text{but} \quad \frac{2}{4} - \frac{5}{4} = \frac{-3}{4}$$

The numbers $\frac{3}{4}$ and $\frac{-3}{4}$ are not equal. The number $\frac{-3}{4}$ is a negative number. This book covers negative numbers in Chapter 12. The following chart gives several correct ways to read $\frac{5}{4} - \frac{2}{4} = \frac{3}{4}$.

Try These Problems

Translate each English statement to an addition or subtraction statement using math symbols.

1. $\frac{3}{7}$ subtracted from $\frac{5}{7}$ is $\frac{2}{7}$.

2. 8 increased by $7\frac{1}{2}$ is $15\frac{1}{2}$.

3. $1\frac{1}{4}$ decreased by $\frac{3}{4}$ is $\frac{1}{2}$.

4. The sum of $\frac{1}{3}$ and $\frac{1}{2}$ is $\frac{5}{6}$.

Math Symbols	*English*
$\frac{5}{4} - \frac{2}{4} = \frac{3}{4}$	Five-fourths minus two-fourths equals three-fourths.
	$\frac{5}{4}$ take away $\frac{2}{4}$ is $\frac{3}{4}$.
	$\frac{5}{4}$ subtract $\frac{2}{4}$ is $\frac{3}{4}$.
	$\frac{2}{4}$ subtracted from $\frac{5}{4}$ is $\frac{3}{4}$.
	$\frac{2}{4}$ less than $\frac{5}{4}$ is $\frac{3}{4}$.
	The *difference* between $\frac{5}{4}$ and $\frac{2}{4}$ is $\frac{3}{4}$.
	$\frac{5}{4}$ *decreased by* $\frac{2}{4}$ gives $\frac{3}{4}$.
	The result of $\frac{2}{4}$ subtracted from $\frac{5}{4}$ is $\frac{3}{4}$.

Note that when reading the symbol $-$ by using the phrases *subtracted from* or *less than*, the numbers $\frac{5}{4}$ and $\frac{2}{4}$ are read in the reverse order than they are written. That is,

$$\frac{2}{4} \text{ subtracted from } \frac{5}{4} \quad \text{means} \quad \frac{5}{4} - \frac{2}{4}$$

and

$$\frac{2}{4} \text{ less than } \frac{5}{4} \quad \text{means} \quad \frac{5}{4} - \frac{2}{4}$$

 Try Problems 1 through 4.

2 Using Translating to Solve Problems

The following examples illustrate how we can use translating to solve problems.

EXAMPLE 1 Sixty represents $27\frac{1}{3}$ plus what number?

SOLUTION Translate the question into math symbols.

Sixty represents $27\frac{1}{3}$ plus what number?

$$60 = 27\frac{1}{3} + \boxed{}$$

Try These Problems

Solve.

5. Find the sum of $2\frac{1}{8}$ and $\frac{7}{16}$.

6. Find the difference between $8\frac{1}{3}$ and $4\frac{5}{9}$.

7. Subtract $\frac{9}{20}$ from $\frac{1}{2}$.

8. Find $\frac{8}{15}$ plus $\frac{7}{9}$.

9. $2\frac{3}{4}$ increased by what number equals 7?

10. The sum of $\frac{7}{22}$ and $\frac{8}{33}$ is what number?

11. What number represents $5\frac{1}{2}$ less than $7\frac{1}{3}$?

12. Seven-eighths subtracted from nine-tenths yields what number?

The missing number is one of the terms in an addition statement, so we subtract the given term $27\frac{1}{3}$ from the total 60 to find the missing term.

$$
\begin{array}{r}
60 = 59\dfrac{3}{3} \\[2mm]
-27\dfrac{1}{3} = 27\dfrac{1}{3} \\[2mm]
\hline
32\dfrac{2}{3}
\end{array}
$$

The answer is $32\frac{2}{3}$. ■

EXAMPLE 2 $\frac{8}{25}$ subtracted from $\frac{1}{3}$ yields what number?

SOLUTION The question translates to math symbols. Observe that since the phrase *subtracted from* is used, we write $\frac{1}{3}$ first in the symbolic statement.

The missing number is the answer to the subtraction problem, $\frac{1}{3} - \frac{8}{25}$.

$$
\frac{1}{3} - \frac{8}{25} = \frac{1 \times 25}{3 \times 25} - \frac{8 \times 3}{25 \times 3}
$$

$$
= \frac{25}{75} - \frac{24}{75}
$$

$$
= \frac{1}{75}
$$

The answer is $\frac{1}{75}$. ■

 Try Problems 5 through 12.

Answers to Try These Problems

1. $\frac{5}{7} - \frac{3}{7} = \frac{2}{7}$ 2. $8 + 7\frac{1}{2} = 15\frac{1}{2}$ 3. $1\frac{1}{4} - \frac{3}{4} = \frac{1}{2}$ 4. $\frac{1}{3} + \frac{1}{2} = \frac{5}{6}$

5. $2\frac{9}{16}$ 6. $3\frac{7}{9}$ 7. $\frac{1}{20}$ 8. $\frac{59}{45}$ or $1\frac{14}{45}$ 9. $4\frac{1}{4}$ or $\frac{17}{4}$ 10. $\frac{37}{66}$

11. $1\frac{5}{6}$ 12. $\frac{1}{40}$

EXERCISES 5.6

Translate each English statement to an addition or subtraction statement using math symbols.

1. The sum of $2\frac{1}{3}$ and $\frac{2}{3}$ equals 3.

2. $\frac{2}{5}$ increased by $\frac{7}{10}$ is $1\frac{1}{10}$.

3. The difference between 7 and $6\frac{1}{4}$ is $\frac{3}{4}$.

4. $\frac{7}{12}$ subtracted from $\frac{2}{3}$ is equal to $\frac{1}{12}$.

5. $\frac{7}{8}$ plus $\frac{1}{8}$ is 1.

6. The result of $5\frac{1}{2}$ decreased by $\frac{3}{4}$ is $4\frac{3}{4}$.

7. One-half plus three-halves equals two.

8. Thirty-two minus one-fourth is thirty-one and three-fourths.

9. $\frac{3}{10}$ is the result of $\frac{1}{2}$ reduced by $\frac{1}{5}$.

10. $5\frac{6}{7}$ less than 7 is $1\frac{1}{7}$.

Translate to an equation. Then solve.

11. Find the sum of 3 and $2\frac{1}{5}$.

12. Find the difference between 3 and $2\frac{1}{5}$.

13. Subtract $\frac{11}{27}$ from $\frac{4}{9}$.

14. Find the result when $\frac{3}{4}$ is decreased by $\frac{1}{4}$.

15. Find the result when $\frac{3}{4}$ is increased by $\frac{1}{4}$.

16. Find $4\frac{4}{5}$ less than $6\frac{1}{4}$.

17. What number plus $\frac{9}{10}$ yields $3\frac{3}{20}$?

18. $6\frac{5}{8}$ represents $4\frac{2}{3}$ increased by what number?

19. What number is $\frac{17}{20}$ less than $\frac{7}{8}$?

20. $\frac{3}{4}$ subtracted from $\frac{5}{6}$ gives what number?

21. The sum of two-thirds and four-fifths equals what number?

22. What number is the result of subtracting five-twelfths from one?

5.7 APPLICATIONS

OBJECTIVES
- ▌ Solve an application that involves a total as the sum of parts.
- ▌ Find the perimeter of a figure.
- ▌ Solve an application that involves increases or decreases.
- ▌ Solve an application that involves comparisons.
- ▌ Find the average of two or more numbers.
- ▌ Solve an application that involves more than one step.

There are many situations in your daily life in which addition and subtraction of fractions is needed. In this section we look at some of these situations and give guidelines on how to decide whether to add or subtract. At the end of the section we also look at applications that require more than one step. These problems may require multiplication and division, as well as addition and subtraction.

1 Problems Involving a Total as the Sum of Parts

We know that to add means to combine or total. In the addition statement

$$\frac{1}{8} + \frac{6}{8} = \frac{7}{8}$$

the sum $\frac{7}{8}$ is the total and the terms $\frac{1}{8}$ and $\frac{6}{8}$ are parts of the total. Recall from Section 5.5 that if any one of the three numbers is missing, we can find it by using the two given numbers. Here we review the procedure.

Finding the Missing Number in a Basic Addition Statement

1. If the sum (or total) is missing, add the terms (or parts) to find the missing number.
2. If one of the terms (or parts) is missing, subtract the given term from the total to find the missing term.

The following examples illustrate how to use this concept to solve some application problems.

EXAMPLE 1   Ms. Chung purchased a $2\frac{1}{8}$-pound steak at the supermarket. After the butcher trimmed the steak of fat, the steak weighed $1\frac{3}{4}$ pounds. How much fat was trimmed from the original steak?

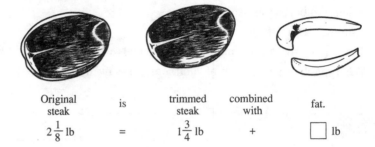

Original steak	is	trimmed steak	combined with	fat.
$2\frac{1}{8}$ lb	=	$1\frac{3}{4}$ lb	+	☐ lb

SOLUTION   We are missing part of the total, so we subtract the given term $1\frac{3}{4}$ from the total $2\frac{1}{8}$.

$$2\frac{1}{8} = 2\frac{1}{8} = 1\frac{9}{8}$$
$$-1\frac{3}{4} = 1\frac{6}{8} = 1\frac{6}{8}$$
$$\frac{3}{8}$$

$\frac{3}{8}$ pound of fat was trimmed from the steak.   ■

EXAMPLE 2   Find the perimeter of this triangle.

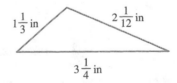

$1\frac{1}{3}$ in $2\frac{1}{12}$ in

$3\frac{1}{4}$ in

SOLUTION   **Perimeter** means the total distance around, so we have the following.

Perimeter = sum of the lengths of the 3 sides

$$\boxed{} = 1\frac{1}{3} + 2\frac{1}{12} + 3\frac{1}{4}$$

We are missing the total, so we add.

Try These Problems

Solve.

1. Ms. Taylor purchased $1\frac{1}{2}$ pounds of Mocha Java coffee beans and $2\frac{1}{2}$ pounds of French Roast coffee beans. What is the total weight of the coffee beans?

2. Sara is hemming drapes for the windows in her apartment. The drapes are now $100\frac{3}{4}$ inches long. They need to be 96 inches long. How wide should she make the hem?

3. Find the distance from B to C.

A   B   C

$\longleftarrow 3\frac{1}{2}$ mi $\longrightarrow$

$\longleftarrow 7\frac{3}{5}$ mi $\longrightarrow$

4. A desk top is $18\frac{1}{2}$ centimeters wide and $120\frac{1}{4}$ centimeters long. What is the perimeter of the desk top?

5. An oil tanker spills $\frac{3}{8}$ of a load. What fraction of the load remains?

6. Elvira owed money on her credit card. She paid $\frac{3}{10}$ of her debt last month. What fraction of her debt remains?

$$1\frac{1}{3} = 1\frac{1\times4}{3\times4} = 1\frac{4}{12}$$

$$2\frac{1}{12} = 2\frac{1}{12} = 2\frac{1}{12}$$

$$+3\frac{1}{4} = 3\frac{1\times3}{4\times3} = 3\frac{3}{12}$$

$$6\frac{8}{12} = 6\frac{4\times2}{4\times3} = 6\frac{2}{3}$$

The perimeter of the triangle is $6\frac{2}{3}$ inches. ■

Try Problems 1 through 4.

EXAMPLE 3 Peggy spends $\frac{1}{5}$ of her take-home pay for rent. What fraction of her take-home pay is left after she pays the rent?

SOLUTION All of her take-home pay is represented by the number 1.

$$\text{Fraction spent for rent} + \text{Fraction that remains} = 1$$

$$\frac{1}{5} + \boxed{} = 1$$

We are missing a term in an addition statement, so subtract the given term $\frac{1}{5}$ from the total 1.

$$1 - \frac{1}{5} = \frac{5}{5} - \frac{1}{5}$$
$$= \frac{4}{5}$$

After she pays the rent, $\frac{4}{5}$ of her take-home pay is left. ■

Try Problems 5 and 6.

2 Problems Involving Increases and Decreases

The price of a transportation stock decreased from $\$36\frac{1}{2}$ to \$34. The amount that the price went down is called the **decrease.** To find the decrease we subtract.

$$\text{Decrease} = \frac{\text{higher}}{\text{price}} - \frac{\text{lower}}{\text{price}}$$
$$= \$36\frac{1}{2} - \$34$$
$$= \$2\frac{1}{2}$$

The decrease in price is $\$2\frac{1}{2}$.

Other language can be used to mean decrease. Here we list some situations where a value has gone down and give the corresponding language.

Try These Problems

7. An entertainment stock sold for 28\frac{1}{8}$ per share last week and 24\frac{1}{2}$ per share this week. Find the decrease in price.

8. A biologist was observing closely a rat in an experiment. The rat's weight dropped from 3$\frac{2}{3}$ pounds to 2$\frac{1}{2}$ pounds in one month. What was the weight loss?

9. The price of a utility stock went from 19\frac{7}{8}$ to 25\frac{1}{2}$. What was the gain in price?

10. A chef increased the amount of chili powder in a chili recipe from $\frac{3}{4}$ teaspoon to 2 teaspoons. What was the increase in the amount of chili powder?

Situation	*Words That Indicate That a Value Went Down*
Last week Cindy's bird weighed 2$\frac{3}{4}$ pounds and this week it weighs only 2$\frac{1}{4}$ pounds.	The *loss* in weight is $\frac{1}{2}$ pound. The *reduction* in weight is $\frac{1}{2}$ pound. The *decrease* in weight is $\frac{1}{2}$ pound.
A chef reduced the amount of milk used in a recipe from 4$\frac{2}{3}$ cups to 3 cups.	The *reduction* is 1$\frac{2}{3}$ cups. The *decrease* is 1$\frac{2}{3}$ cups.

 Try Problems 7 and 8.

A chef increased the amount of paprika used in a recipe from 3$\frac{3}{4}$ cups to 4 cups. The amount that the volume of paprika went up is called the **increase** (or **gain**). To find the increase we subtract.

$$\text{Increase} = \frac{\text{larger}}{\text{amount}} - \frac{\text{smaller}}{\text{amount}}$$

$$= 4 - 3\frac{3}{4}$$

$$= 3\frac{4}{4} - 3\frac{3}{4}$$

$$= \frac{1}{4}$$

The increase in the paprika is $\frac{1}{4}$ cup.

 Try Problems 9 and 10.

3 Problems Involving Comparison

Two unequal numbers, such as 2 and 1$\frac{3}{4}$, can be compared using addition and subtraction. Here is a list of several addition and subtraction statements involving 2 and 1$\frac{3}{4}$, and the corresponding comparison statements in English.

Comparing Two Numbers	
Math Symbols	**English**
$1\frac{3}{4} + \frac{1}{4} = 2$	$\frac{1}{4}$ more than 1$\frac{3}{4}$ is 2.
$2 - \frac{1}{4} = 1\frac{3}{4}$	$\frac{1}{4}$ less than 2 is 1$\frac{3}{4}$.
$2 - 1\frac{3}{4} = \frac{1}{4}$	2 and 1$\frac{3}{4}$ differ by $\frac{1}{4}$.
	The *difference* between 2 and 1$\frac{3}{4}$ is $\frac{1}{4}$.
	1$\frac{3}{4}$ is less than 2 by $\frac{1}{4}$.

Now we solve some problems involving comparisons.

▲ **Try These Problems**

11. Maria uses $2\frac{1}{4}$ cups of Swiss cheese to make a cheese pie that serves 8 persons. José uses half a cup less Swiss cheese when he makes cheese pie for 8. How much cheese does José use in his pie?

12. Manuel studied $3\frac{1}{2}$ hours yesterday. Jamie studied 5 hours. How much longer did Jamie study than Manuel?

13. Stephanie is $1\frac{2}{3}$ feet taller than her younger sister Caitlin. If Stephanie is $5\frac{1}{3}$ feet tall, how tall is Caitlin?

14. Dick has been working at the Stock Investment Company for $4\frac{1}{2}$ years. Rob has worked there $1\frac{1}{2}$ fewer years than Dick. How long has Rob worked at the Stock Investment Company?

EXAMPLE 4   The length of a rectangle is $3\frac{7}{8}$ feet longer than the width. If the length is 8 feet, find the width.

SOLUTION   The first sentence of the problem is comparing the length and width. Translate this sentence to math symbols.

The length	is	$3\frac{7}{8}$ ft longer than	the width.
8	=	$3\frac{7}{8}$ +	☐

We are missing one of the terms, so we subtract the given term from the sum to find the missing term.

$$8 = 7\frac{8}{8}$$
$$-3\frac{7}{8} = 3\frac{7}{8}$$
$$\overline{\qquad 4\frac{1}{8}}$$

The width of the rectangle is $4\frac{1}{8}$ feet. ■

EXAMPLE 5   Mary jogged $2\frac{1}{2}$ miles yesterday. Alex jogged only $1\frac{3}{4}$ miles. How much farther did Mary jog than Alex?

SOLUTION   First we show a picture of the situation.

Mary's path |—— $2\frac{1}{2}$ mi ——|

Alex's path |—— $1\frac{3}{4}$ mi ——| ⏟ ?

We want to know the *difference* between $2\frac{1}{2}$ and $1\frac{3}{4}$, so we subtract.

$$2\frac{1}{2} = 2\frac{2}{4} = 1\frac{6}{4}$$
$$-1\frac{3}{4} = 1\frac{3}{4} = 1\frac{3}{4}$$
$$\overline{\qquad\qquad\qquad \frac{3}{4}}$$

Mary jogged $\frac{3}{4}$ mile farther than Alex. ■

▲ **Try Problems 11 through 14.**

4 | Averaging

Kathy bought 4 steaks weighing $1\frac{1}{4}$ pounds, $1\frac{3}{4}$ pounds, $\frac{3}{4}$ pound, and $2\frac{1}{4}$ pounds. The total weight of the steaks is 6 pounds.

$$1\frac{1}{4} + 1\frac{3}{4} + \frac{3}{4} + 2\frac{1}{4} = 4\frac{8}{4} = 6$$

What same weight could each of the steaks have and still have a total weight of 6 pounds?

$$6 \div 4 = \frac{6}{4} = \frac{3}{2} \text{ or } 1\frac{1}{2}$$

$$\left.\begin{array}{r} 1\frac{1}{2} \\ 1\frac{1}{2} \\ 1\frac{1}{2} \\ + 1\frac{1}{2} \\ \hline \end{array}\right\} \begin{array}{l}\text{Four weights of } 1\frac{1}{2} \\ \text{pounds total 6} \\ \text{pounds.}\end{array}$$

$$4\tfrac{4}{2} = 6$$

The weight $1\frac{1}{2}$ pounds is called the **average** (or **mean**) of the weights $1\frac{1}{4}$, $1\frac{3}{4}$, $\frac{3}{4}$, and $2\frac{1}{4}$. The average of a set of data is a measure of the middle or center of the data. The average of a collection of numbers can be found by adding the numbers, then dividing by how many numbers there are.

Finding the Average of a Collection of Numbers

1. Add all the numbers in the collection.
2. Divide the sum by how many numbers are in the collection.

EXAMPLE 6   Find the average of $20\frac{1}{2}$, $31\frac{3}{4}$, and $18\frac{1}{4}$.

SOLUTION   Add the 3 numbers.

$$
\begin{array}{r}
20\frac{1}{2} = 20\frac{2}{4} \\
31\frac{3}{4} = 31\frac{3}{4} \\
+\ 18\frac{1}{4} = 18\frac{1}{4} \\
\hline
69\frac{6}{4} = 70\frac{2}{4} = 70\frac{1}{2}
\end{array}
$$

Divide the sum $70\frac{1}{2}$ by 3 because there are 3 numbers.

$$70\frac{1}{2} \div 3 = \frac{141}{2} \div \frac{3}{1}$$

$$= \frac{\overset{47}{\cancel{141}}}{2} \times \frac{1}{\underset{1}{\cancel{3}}}$$

$$= \frac{47}{2} \text{ or } 23\frac{1}{2}$$

The average is $\frac{47}{2}$ or $23\frac{1}{2}$. ∎

Try These Problems

15. Find the average of $\frac{1}{3}$, $\frac{1}{4}$, $\frac{3}{4}$, $\frac{2}{3}$, and $\frac{5}{6}$.

16. Ms. Allen is responsible for making the coffee in the faculty lounge this semester. She recorded the following usage of coffee over a 3-week period.
1st Week $2\frac{1}{2}$ pounds
2nd Week $3\frac{3}{4}$ pounds
3rd Week   3 pounds
What was the average amount of coffee used each week?

EXAMPLE 7   During the last month a small neighborhood bakery used the following amounts of sugar.

Week 1 $10\frac{1}{2}$ pounds

Week 2 $12\frac{3}{4}$ pounds

Week 3   8 pounds

Week 4 $11\frac{1}{4}$ pounds

On the average, how many pounds of sugar were used per week?

SOLUTION   Find the total weight.

$$10\frac{1}{2} = 10\frac{2}{4}$$
$$12\frac{3}{4} = 12\frac{3}{4}$$
$$8\phantom{\frac{1}{4}} = 8$$
$$+11\frac{1}{4} = 11\frac{1}{4}$$
$$\rule{4cm}{0.4pt}$$
$$41\frac{6}{4} = 42\frac{2}{4} = 42\frac{1}{2}$$

The total weight is $42\frac{1}{2}$ pounds. Divide $42\frac{1}{2}$ pounds by 4 because there are 4 weeks.

$$42\frac{1}{2} \div 4 = \frac{85}{2} \div \frac{4}{1}$$
$$= \frac{85}{2} \times \frac{1}{4}$$
$$= \frac{85}{8} \quad \text{or} \quad 10\frac{5}{8}$$

The bakery used $10\frac{5}{8}$ pounds of sugar per week.   ■

 **Try Problems 15 and 16.**

5 Problems Involving More Than One Step

Now we put together some of the concepts, language, and procedures we have previously learned to solve problems that involve more than one step. These problems may require multiplication and division as well as addition and subtraction. When solving more complex problems, it is important to label your work clearly with words so that you understand what it is you have obtained at each stage of the problem. Also, if applicable, drawing a picture can be very helpful. Here are some examples.

Try These Problems

17. In the triangle shown here, the longest side is $\frac{7}{8}$ inch longer than the shortest side. The shortest side is $1\frac{3}{8}$ inches long. Find the perimeter of the triangle.

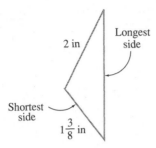

2 in

Longest side

Shortest side

$1\frac{3}{8}$ in

EXAMPLE 8   Shirley is making a rectangular flower bed. The width is $5\frac{1}{3}$ feet. The length is $2\frac{1}{4}$ feet more than the width. Find the perimeter.

SOLUTION   Here we view a picture of the situation.

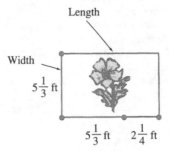

Length

Width

$5\frac{1}{3}$ ft

$5\frac{1}{3}$ ft $2\frac{1}{4}$ ft

Before finding the perimeter, we must find the length. The third sentence in the problem compares the length and width. Translate this sentence to math symbols.

The length	is $2\frac{1}{4}$ ft more than	the width.
$\boxed{}$ = $2\frac{1}{4}$	+	$5\frac{1}{3}$

The length is the sum of $2\frac{1}{4}$ and $5\frac{1}{3}$.

$$5\frac{1}{3} = 5\frac{4}{12}$$
$$+\ 2\frac{1}{4} = 2\frac{3}{12}$$
$$\overline{\phantom{+\ 2\frac{1}{4} =\ } 7\frac{7}{12}}$$

The length of the rectangle is $7\frac{7}{12}$ feet. The perimeter means the total distance around the rectangle, so we add two lengths and two widths.

$$5\frac{1}{3}\ = 5\frac{4}{12}$$
$$5\frac{1}{3}\ = 5\frac{4}{12}$$
$$7\frac{7}{12} = 7\frac{7}{12}$$
$$+\ 7\frac{7}{12} = 7\frac{7}{12}$$
$$\overline{\phantom{+\ 7\frac{7}{12} =\ } 24\frac{22}{12} = 25\frac{10}{12} = 25\frac{5}{6}}$$

The perimeter is $25\frac{5}{6}$ feet. ∎

 Try Problem 17.

EXAMPLE 9   Steven read $\frac{1}{6}$ of his assignment yesterday and $\frac{2}{5}$ of it today. What fraction of his assignment does he have left to read?

Try These Problems

18. Three persons share the ownership of a building. Don's share is $\frac{3}{10}$, Barbara's share is $\frac{1}{4}$, and David owns the rest. What fraction of the building does David own?

1 whole

SOLUTION   First we find the fraction of the assignment he has read in the 2-day period.

$$\frac{1}{6} = \frac{5}{30}$$
$$+ \frac{2}{5} = \frac{12}{30}$$
$$\frac{17}{30} \cdots \text{Fraction he has read}$$

Steven read $\frac{17}{30}$ of his assignment in the two days. The whole assignment is represented by the number 1.

$$1 \quad = \frac{30}{30} \text{——The whole assignment}$$
$$- \frac{17}{30} = \frac{17}{30} \text{——Fraction he has read}$$
$$\frac{13}{30} \text{——Fraction left to read}$$

Steven has $\frac{13}{30}$ of his assignment left to read.   ■

Try Problem 18.

EXAMPLE 10   What is the difference in the areas of these two rectangles?

2½ in ▭ 5 in   ▭ 4¾ in 6½ in

SOLUTION   First we find the areas of each of the rectangles.

$$\text{Area of the smaller rectangle} = \text{length} \times \text{width}$$
$$= 5 \times 2\frac{1}{2}$$
$$= \frac{5}{1} \times \frac{5}{2}$$
$$= \frac{25}{2} \quad \text{or} \quad 12\frac{1}{2} \text{ sq in}$$

$$\text{Area of the larger rectangle} = \text{length} \times \text{width}$$
$$= 6\frac{1}{2} \times 4\frac{3}{4}$$
$$= \frac{13}{2} \times \frac{19}{4}$$
$$= \frac{247}{8} \quad \text{or} \quad 30\frac{7}{8} \text{ sq in}$$

Try These Problems

19. Find the total area of this floor.

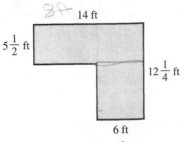

 14 ft

$5\frac{1}{2}$ ft

$12\frac{1}{4}$ ft

6 ft

Hint: Break the region into two rectangular regions.

Now to find the *difference* in the areas, we subtract.

$$\begin{array}{ccc} \text{Difference} & & \text{larger} & \text{smaller} \\ \text{in areas} & = & \text{area} & - & \text{area} \\ \text{(sq in)} & & \text{(sq in)} & \text{(sq in)} \end{array}$$

$$= 30\frac{7}{8} - 12\frac{1}{2}$$

$$= 30\frac{7}{8} - 12\frac{4}{8}$$

$$= 18\frac{3}{8}$$

The difference in the areas is $18\frac{3}{8}$ square inches. ■

 Try Problem 19.

Now we summarize the material presented in this section by giving guidelines that will help you decide whether to add or subtract.

Situations Requiring Addition or Subtraction	
Operation	**Situations**
+	**1.** You are looking for the total or whole.
	2. You are looking for the result when a quantity has been increased.
–	**1.** You are looking for one of the parts in a total or whole.
	2. You are looking for the result when a quantity has been decreased.
	3. You are looking for how much larger one quantity is than another.
	4. You are looking for how much smaller one quantity is than another.

Answers to Try These Problems

1. 4 lb   **2.** $4\frac{3}{4}$ in   **3.** $4\frac{1}{10}$ mi   **4.** $277\frac{1}{2}$ cm   **5.** $\frac{5}{8}$
6. $\frac{7}{10}$ **7.** $3\frac{5}{8}$ **8.** $1\frac{1}{6}$ lb   **9.** $5\frac{5}{8}$ **10.** $1\frac{1}{4}$ t   **11.** $\frac{7}{4}$ or $1\frac{3}{4}$ cups
12. $1\frac{1}{2}$ hr   **13.** $3\frac{2}{3}$ ft   **14.** 3 yr   **15.** $\frac{17}{30}$ **16.** $\frac{37}{12}$ or $3\frac{1}{12}$ lb
17. $5\frac{5}{8}$ in   **18.** $\frac{9}{20}$ **19.** $117\frac{1}{2}$ sq ft

---

EXERCISES 5.7

Solve. Show set ups and calculation steps.

add

1. Carlos paid $\frac{1}{3}$ of a debt in June, $\frac{1}{10}$ in July, and $\frac{2}{5}$ in August. What fraction of the debt was paid in these three months?

2. Find the perimeter of a rectangle that is $5\frac{7}{12}$ feet wide and $8\frac{3}{4}$ feet long.

3. A recipe calls for $1\frac{1}{3}$ cups of milk. Bette has only $\frac{3}{4}$ cup of milk. How much more milk does Bette need?

4. Mr. Nguyen wants to drive 380 miles today. He has already driven $192\frac{3}{4}$ miles. How much farther does he have to drive?

5. Lisa spends $\frac{1}{4}$ of her income on rent. What fraction of her income is left?

6. Dave owns $\frac{7}{10}$ of a building and Ann owns the rest. What fraction of the building does Ann own?

7. You set out to walk a distance of $2\frac{1}{2}$ miles. So far, you have gone $\frac{3}{4}$ mile. How much farther do you have to go?

8. Two years ago, Tish planted a tree that she would like to be 6 feet tall. It is now $3\frac{2}{3}$ feet tall. How much more must the tree grow to reach her goal?

9. A spaghetti recipe for 12 persons calls for $2\frac{1}{2}$ cups of parsley. Bruce is especially fond of parsley, so he decided to increase the amount of parsley by $\frac{1}{2}$ cup. What is the total amount of parsley Bruce puts in the spaghetti?

10. An oil stock was selling for $\$100\frac{3}{4}$ per share, then the price decreased by $\$5\frac{1}{2}$. What is the price after the decrease?

11. A puppy's weight dropped from $8\frac{3}{4}$ pounds to $5\frac{7}{16}$ pounds. Find the weight loss.

12. A chef increased the amount of cheese in a recipe from $5\frac{1}{4}$ cups to 8 cups. What is the increase?

13. Today Mildred worked $3\frac{1}{2}$ hours on her project, which is an increase of $1\frac{3}{4}$ hours over yesterday. How long did she work yesterday?

14. Today the price of a utility stock increased by $\$5\frac{7}{16}$. If the price after the increase is $\$38$, what was the price before the increase?

15. A mechanic cut a piece of wire $5\frac{3}{4}$ inches long, then realized the piece was too short. He needs it to be $\frac{7}{16}$ inch longer. How long should he have cut the piece of wire?

16. A carpenter cut a piece of lumber $6\frac{1}{2}$ feet long. She realized the piece was too long by $\frac{3}{4}$ foot. How long should the piece of lumber be?

17. Harvey accidentally picked up a $\frac{1}{2}$-inch wrench to tighten a $\frac{7}{16}$-inch bolt. Was the wrench too large or too small, and by how much?

18. A microwave oven is $20\frac{1}{4}$ inches wide, and the space in Sam's kitchen for the oven is $20\frac{3}{8}$ inches wide. Will the oven fit in the space; and if so, how much space remains?

19. John worked $5\frac{3}{4}$ hours longer than Steve. If John worked $11\frac{1}{3}$ hours, how long did Steve work?

20. The length of a rectangle is $15\frac{2}{3}$ feet longer than the width. If the length is 38 feet, find the width.

21. Find the average of $\frac{5}{8}$ and $\frac{7}{12}$.

22. Find the average of $\frac{1}{2}$, $\frac{3}{8}$, $\frac{2}{3}$, and $\frac{1}{4}$.

23. Sam hiked $2\frac{1}{2}$ miles the first hour, 4 miles the second hour, and $3\frac{3}{4}$ miles the third hour. On the average, how far did he hike each hour?

24. Five boxes weigh $1\frac{1}{4}$ pounds, $2\frac{1}{10}$ pounds, $1\frac{3}{4}$ pounds, 2 pounds and $2\frac{3}{5}$ pounds. What is the averge weight of the 5 boxes?

25. Three rats weigh $2\frac{1}{3}$ pounds each and another rat weighs $3\frac{1}{4}$ pounds. What is the average weight of the 4 rats?

26. Five boxes weigh $7\frac{1}{2}$ pounds each and three boxes weigh $5\frac{2}{3}$ pounds each. What is the average weight of the 8 boxes?

27. Alice has $500. She spends $\frac{2}{5}$ of it for clothes. How much money is left?

28. A math class has 56 students. Five-eighths of the class are men. How many women are in the class?

29. Sally saved $150 out of a monthly income of $2400. Nancy saved $125 out of a monthly income of $1500. Which person saved the larger fractional portion of her income, and what is the difference in these fractions?

30. A stock decreased in price from $30 to $28\frac{3}{4}$. The decrease in price is what fraction of the original price?

31. Find the perimeter around this floor space.

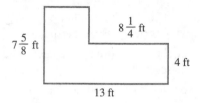

32. Find the total area of this region.

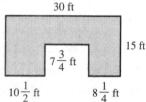

Hannah, Bonnie, Gretchen, and Anna bought some land outside of Washington, D.C. for $72,000. The fractional portion of each person's share is given by the circle graph. Use this information to answer Exercises 33 through 36.

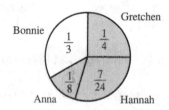

**Fractional Parts of
Land Valued at $72,000**

33. Show that the four fractional parts add up to 1 whole.

34. What fractional part of the land do Gretchen and Hannah together own?

35. How much did Anna pay for her share?

36. How much did Hannah pay for her share?

The bar graph shows the rainfall for a 5-day period in Chicago, Illinois. Use the graph to answer Exercises 37 through 40.

Rainfall for a 5-Day Period

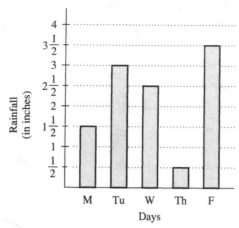

37. Find the total rainfall for the 5-day period.

38. How much more rain fell on Tuesday than on Thursday?

39. On the average, how many inches did it rain each day?

40. Find the ratio of the amount of rain on Friday to the total amount for the 5-day period.

Fractions on the Number Line – Level 1

We like to view fractions on a number line where the numbers are arranged from smallest to largest with uniform distances between adjacent tick marks. A tick mark designates the position of a number. Here we view a number line containing some fractions with denominator 4.

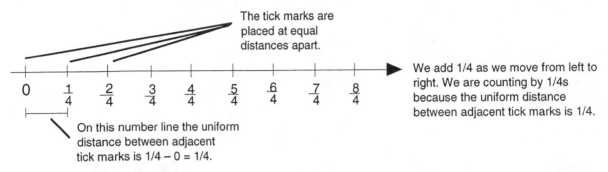

The tick marks are placed at equal distances apart.

We add 1/4 as we move from left to right. We are counting by 1/4s because the uniform distance between adjacent tick marks is 1/4.

On this number line the uniform distance between adjacent tick marks is 1/4 – 0 = 1/4.

Because some of the fractions can be simplified and others can be written as whole or mixed numbers, we can label some positions in more than one way. Here we show the above number line where some of the positions are labeled in more than one way.

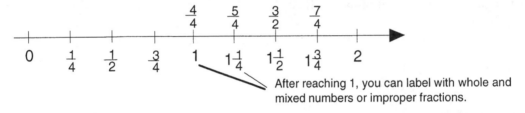

After reaching 1, you can label with whole and mixed numbers or improper fractions.

When you view a number line you are seeing numbers associated with **positions** on the number line as well as **distances** between the numbers. Note that you can obtain the distance between any two numbers by subtracting the smaller number from the larger number. Here we look at an example.

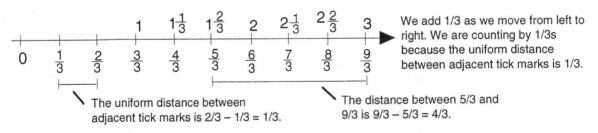

We add 1/3 as we move from left to right. We are counting by 1/3s because the uniform distance between adjacent tick marks is 1/3.

The uniform distance between adjacent tick marks is 2/3 – 1/3 = 1/3.

The distance between 5/3 and 9/3 is 9/3 – 5/3 = 4/3.

The distance between any two positions can be found in two ways. Let's illustrate this by finding the **distance from 5/3 to 9/3**.

Method 1 – Subtract the smaller number from the larger number. $\frac{9}{3} - \frac{5}{3} = \frac{4}{3}$ or $1\frac{1}{3}$

Method 2 – Count the number of segments between the two numbers and multiply that by the length of each segment. $4 \times \frac{1}{3} = \frac{4}{3}$ or $1\frac{1}{3}$ This method is convenient if we already

know the uniform distance between adjacent tick marks.

EXERCISES 5-A

For each number line, label the distance between a pair of adjacent tick marks and label all unlabeled tick marks with the appropriate number. Any fractional form is okay.

1.

$$0 \qquad \frac{1}{2}$$

2.

$$0 \qquad \frac{1}{3}$$

3.

$$0 \qquad \frac{1}{4}$$

4.

$$\frac{5}{3} \qquad \frac{6}{3}$$

5.

$$\frac{7}{4} \qquad \frac{8}{4}$$

6.

$$2\frac{1}{2} \qquad 3$$

7.

$$0 \qquad\qquad \frac{4}{5} \qquad 1$$

8.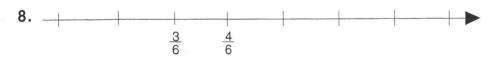

$$\frac{3}{6} \qquad \frac{4}{6}$$

9.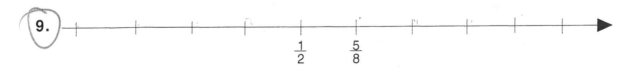

$$\frac{1}{2} \qquad \frac{5}{8}$$

10.

$$1 \qquad 1\frac{1}{7}$$

Fractions on the Number Line – Level 2

Now you want to learn how to label the remaining tick marks on a number line when you are not given two numbers adjacent to one another. First, you will need to find the uniform distance between adjacent tick marks. This can be done as long as you are given at least two numbers. Follow the steps below to see how this is done for the given number line.

Step 1 – Subtract any two given numbers to find out how far apart they are.

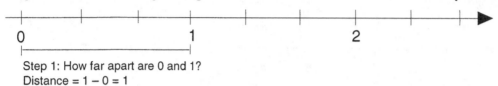

Step 1: How far apart are 0 and 1?
Distance = 1 – 0 = 1

Step 2 – Count the number of spaces between the two numbers.

Step 2: How many spaces are there between 0 and 1? Count them. There are 3. (Don't count the tick marks, count the spaces.)

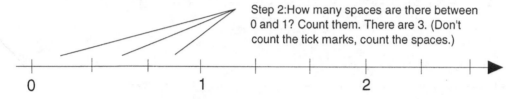

Therefore, a distance of 1 unit is separated into 3 equal parts.

Step 3 – Divide the total distance found in step 1 by the number of equal spaces in step 2.

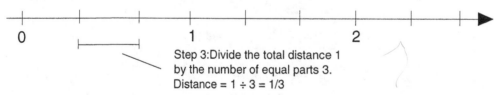

Step 3: Divide the total distance 1 by the number of equal parts 3.
Distance = 1 ÷ 3 = 1/3

This number 1/3 is the uniform distance between adjacent tick marks.

Step 4 – Add the uniform distance to each number on the left to obtain the next number on the right.

0 + 1/3 = 1/3   1/3 + 1/3 = 2/3   2/3 + 1/3 = 3/3 or 1

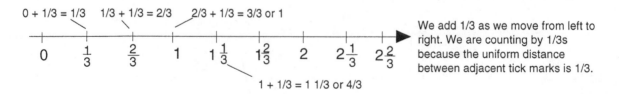

We add 1/3 as we move from left to right. We are counting by 1/3s because the uniform distance between adjacent tick marks is 1/3.

1 + 1/3 = 1 1/3 or 4/3

EXERCISES 5-B

For each number line, label the distance between a pair of adjacent tick marks and label all unlabeled tick marks with the appropriate number. Any fractional form is okay.

1.

0　　　　　　　　1

2.

0　　　　　　1

3.

0　　　　　　　　　1

4.

0　　　　　　　2

5.

0　　　　　　　　　4

6.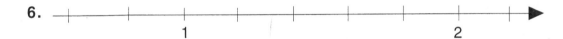

　　1　　　　　　　2

7.

　　$\frac{1}{2}$　　$1-\frac{1}{2}=\frac{1}{2}$　　　1

8.

　$\frac{1}{7}$　　　　　　1

9.

　　$\frac{4}{5}$　　　$1\frac{2}{5}$

10.

0　　　　　　　　1

11.

　　$1\frac{1}{2}$　　　　$2\frac{1}{3}$

CHAPTER 5 SUMMARY

KEY WORDS AND PHRASES

least common multiple (LCM) [5.2]

least common denominator (LCD) [5.2]

prime number [5.2]

prime factoring [5.2]

borrowing [5.3]

sum [5.6]

difference [5.6, 5.7]

perimeter [5.7]

decrease [5.7]

increase (gain) [5.7]

average (mean) [5.7]

SYMBOLS

$2 < 4$ means   2 is less than 4. [5.4]

$4 > 2$ means   4 is more than 2. [5.4]

IMPORTANT RULES

How to Add Fractions [5.1, 5.2, 5.3]

- Find the least common multiple (LCM) of the denominators.
- Convert each fraction to an equivalent fraction that has the common denominator.
- Add the numerators to obtain the numerator of the result. The common denominator is the denominator of the result.
- Simplify the answer.

How to Compare Fractions [5.4]

- Find the least common multiple (LCM) of the denominators.
- Convert each fraction to an equivalent fraction that has the common denominator.
- When two fractions have the same denominator, the larger fraction has the larger numerator.

The Perimeter of a Figure [5.7]

The perimeter of a figure is the distance all the way around the figure.

The Average (or Mean) of a Collection of Numbers [5.7]

- Add all of the numbers in the collection.
- Divide the sum by how many numbers are in the collection.

Situations that Require Addition and Subtraction [5.7]

A summary of the situations that require addition and subtraction is on page 214.

CHAPTER 5 REVIEW EXERCISES

Choose the prime numbers in each group.

1. 9, 13, 23, 51, 38

2. 2, 7, 17, 37, 57

Write each number as the product of primes.

3. 35

4. 72

5. 78

6. 171

Find the least common multiple of each group of numbers.

7. 6, 10

8. 14, 21

9. 5, 15, 9

10. 22, 33, 4

11. 8, 17

12. 9, 4, 5

Add. Simplify if possible.

13. $\frac{3}{4} + \frac{2}{4}$

14. $5\frac{1}{6} + 6\frac{5}{6}$

15. $\frac{29}{60} + \frac{7}{60}$

16. $\frac{2}{3} + \frac{1}{9}$

17. $8\frac{7}{10} + 7\frac{7}{15}$

18. $\frac{2}{3} + \frac{1}{7}$

19. $13\frac{11}{12} + \frac{4}{9}$

20. $\frac{5}{11} + \frac{1}{3}$

21. $6\frac{3}{14} + 29\frac{5}{21}$ **22.** $\begin{array}{r}\frac{5}{16}\\\frac{17}{40}\\+\ \frac{1}{10}\\\hline\end{array}$ **23.** $\begin{array}{r}\frac{1}{2}\\\frac{3}{13}\\+\ \frac{3}{4}\\\hline\end{array}$ **24.** $\begin{array}{r}34\frac{4}{75}\\18\frac{1}{10}\\+\ 5\frac{1}{6}\\\hline\end{array}$

Name the larger fraction.

25. $\frac{3}{9}, \frac{10}{9}$ **26.** $\frac{3}{11}, \frac{1}{5}$ **27.** $\frac{3}{4}, \frac{17}{24}$

List from smallest to largest.

28. $\frac{4}{9}, \frac{1}{3}, \frac{8}{27}$ **29.** $\frac{2}{7}, \frac{2}{3}, \frac{2}{5}$ **30.** $\frac{19}{20}, 1, \frac{47}{50}$

Use the symbol $<$, $=$, or $>$ to accurately compare each pair of fractions.

31. $\frac{5}{7} \underset{(<,\,=,\,>)}{\underline{\quad ? \quad}} \frac{13}{21}$ **32.** $\frac{7}{8} \underset{(<,\,=,\,>)}{\underline{\quad ? \quad}} \frac{11}{12}$ **33.** $6\frac{3}{10} \underset{(<,\,=,\,>)}{\underline{\quad ? \quad}} 6\frac{3}{25}$

34. $3\frac{3}{4} \underset{(<,\,=,\,>)}{\underline{\quad ? \quad}} 3\frac{2}{3}$ **35.** $1 \underset{(<,\,=,\,>)}{\underline{\quad ? \quad}} \frac{99}{100}$

Subtract. Simplify if possible.

36. $\frac{7}{12} - \frac{3}{12}$ **37.** $5\frac{7}{8} - 3\frac{1}{8}$ **38.** $8 - \frac{3}{5}$

39. $17\frac{2}{7} - 5\frac{5}{7}$ **40.** $\frac{7}{8} - \frac{5}{12}$ **41.** $12\frac{5}{9} - 3$

42. $\begin{array}{r}6\frac{3}{10}\\-\ 2\frac{9}{20}\\\hline\end{array}$ **43.** $\begin{array}{r}10\frac{7}{15}\\-\ 3\frac{5}{12}\\\hline\end{array}$ **44.** $\begin{array}{r}28\frac{5}{49}\\-\ 8\frac{3}{14}\\\hline\end{array}$

Translate each of the following to an addition or subtraction statement using math symbols.

45. The difference between $2\frac{1}{3}$ and 2 is $\frac{1}{3}$.

46. When $\frac{3}{5}$ is increased by $\frac{4}{5}$, the result is $\frac{7}{5}$.

47. The sum of $\frac{2}{3}$ and $\frac{5}{3}$ is $\frac{7}{3}$.

48. 5 diminished by $2\frac{1}{3}$ leaves $2\frac{2}{3}$.

49. $\frac{2}{10}$ more than $\frac{3}{10}$ is $\frac{1}{2}$.

Solve.

50. Find the total when $2\frac{1}{7}$ is added to $\frac{3}{7}$.

51. Find the result of $8\frac{1}{5}$ take away 3.

52. What is $\frac{3}{8}$ subtracted from $\frac{3}{4}$?

53. Find the average of $6\frac{5}{6}$, $3\frac{2}{3}$, and $7\frac{1}{2}$.

54. Steven lives $3\frac{7}{10}$ miles from work and Shirley lives $3\frac{4}{5}$ miles from work. Which one lives farther from work?

55. What is the distance from P to Q?

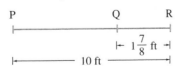

56. Find the perimeter of a rectangle that has a width of $12\frac{1}{3}$ inches and a length of $20\frac{3}{4}$ inches.

57. Marge is half of a foot shorter than Bob. If Bob is 6 feet tall, how tall is Marge?

58. Gloria typed $4\frac{1}{2}$ hours on Wednesday, $6\frac{1}{4}$ hours on Tuesday, and $1\frac{1}{2}$ hours on Monday. What is the total number of hours Gloria typed in the three days?

59. Jean-Louis has a ficus tree in his apartment that is $5\frac{3}{4}$ feet high. He wants the tree to grow to the ceiling, which is 9 feet high. How much higher does the tree need to grow before it reaches the ceiling?

60. Kurt purchased $2\frac{1}{2}$ pounds of ground beef at the meat market. When he got home, he realized he would need 4 pounds to make hamburgers for the barbeque party that evening. How much more meat does he need to buy?

61. Mike was packing his backpack for a hiking trip. He has put in items weighing $5\frac{1}{4}$ pounds, $2\frac{1}{2}$ pounds, and $1\frac{3}{4}$ pounds. What is the total weight so far?

62. An author receives $3000 more of her royalty advance when she has completed $\frac{2}{3}$ of the manuscript. She has completed $\frac{250}{450}$ of the manuscript. Has she completed enough to receive the royalty advance?

63. Ms. Toscano jogged $2\frac{1}{2}$ miles for each of 4 consecutive days, and $4\frac{1}{3}$ miles for each of 3 consecutive days. What was her average daily distance for the 7-day period?

64. In a certain city, $\frac{13}{20}$ of the registered voters are female. What fraction of the voters are male?

65. Doug and Elaine are writing a book. Doug finished $\frac{1}{4}$ of the job and Elaine finished $\frac{2}{3}$ of the job. What fraction of the job is left to do?

66. In a sample of 2700 college students, it was found that $\frac{4}{15}$ of them are smokers. How many students in the sample are nonsmokers?

67. A boat can cruise in still water at the rate of $15\frac{1}{2}$ miles per hour. How fast does the boat go downstream with a current of $2\frac{2}{3}$ miles per hour?

68. The length of a rectangle is $5\frac{3}{8}$ feet more than the width. If the width is $7\frac{1}{2}$ feet, find the area of the rectangle.

69. In a sample of 1500 college students, it was found that $\frac{2}{5}$ of them take public transportation to school. How many students in the sample take public transportation to school?

70. A stock decreased in price from $30 to $28\frac{3}{4}$. The decrease in price is what fraction of the original price?

In Your Own Words

Write complete sentences to discuss each of the following. Support your comments with examples or pictures, if appropriate.

71. Suppose you have a child in school that is having trouble with fractions. The child incorrectly writes $\frac{9}{10}$ as the answer to the problem $\frac{2}{5} + \frac{7}{5}$. Discuss how you would help the child understand the error made.

72. You have a friend who solved a subtraction problem incorrectly as follows.

$$8\frac{1}{3} = 7\frac{11}{3}$$
$$-\,2\frac{2}{3} = 2\frac{2}{3}$$
$$\overline{\phantom{-\,2\frac{2}{3} = }\,5\frac{9}{3} = 8}$$

Discuss how you would help your friend understand the error made.

73. Discuss the procedure you would use to find out which of the fractions, $\frac{13}{24}$ or $\frac{9}{16}$, is smaller?

74. Discuss several ways to read the subtraction statement $5 - 2\frac{3}{4} = 2\frac{1}{4}$.

75. Discuss a real-life situation that would involve finding the average of several numbers where at least one of the numbers is a fraction or mixed numeral.

CHAPTER 5 PRACTICE TEST

1. Choose the prime numbers in this group. 17, 21, 23, 33, 39

Write each number as the product of primes.

2. 42   **3.** 110

Find the least common multiple of each group of numbers.

4. 15, 20   **5.** 6, 27, 8

Add and simplify.

6. $\frac{5}{6} + \frac{3}{6}$ **7.** $\frac{4}{9} + \frac{5}{18}$ **8.** $6\frac{14}{15} + 8\frac{3}{25}$ **9.** $\begin{array}{r} \frac{3}{4} \\ \frac{5}{6} \\ + \frac{5}{9} \end{array}$ **10.** $\begin{array}{r} 3\frac{4}{21} \\ 8\frac{2}{3} \\ + 7\frac{1}{14} \end{array}$

11. Which is larger, $\frac{7}{18}$ or $\frac{1}{2}$?

12. List from smallest to largest: $\frac{2}{3}, \frac{3}{4}, \frac{7}{12}$.

13. Use the symbol $<$, $=$, or $>$ to compare $\frac{17}{24}$ and $\frac{3}{4}$.

Subtract. Simplify if possible.

14. $\frac{3}{4} - \frac{5}{8}$ **15.** $6\frac{4}{15} - \frac{4}{9}$ **16.** $5\frac{7}{11} - 1\frac{3}{22}$

17. $15\frac{5}{12} - 9\frac{1}{8}$ **18.** $10 - 4\frac{2}{3}$

Translate each of the following to an addition or subtraction statement using math symbols.

19. The sum of $\frac{1}{3}$ and $\frac{2}{3}$ is 1.

20. 9 reduced by $1\frac{3}{4}$ is $7\frac{1}{4}$.

Solve.

21. Find the difference between $\frac{2}{3}$ and $\frac{1}{6}$.

22. What is the result when $\frac{4}{5}$ is increased by $\frac{3}{5}$?

23. Find the average of 20, $16\frac{1}{2}$, 12, and $23\frac{3}{4}$.

24. How far is it from B to C?

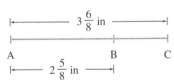

25. Find the perimeter of this rectangle.

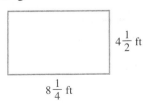

$8\frac{1}{4}$ ft

26. Steven is $\frac{3}{4}$ foot taller than Barbara. Barbara is $5\frac{1}{2}$ feet tall. How tall is Steven?

27. Thuy has already put in $2\frac{1}{4}$ cups of milk in the cream sauce she is making. She realizes that she really wants a total of 3 cups of milk in the cream sauce. How much more milk should she put in?

28. A small hose fills a swimming pool at the rate of $1\frac{1}{2}$ gallons per minute. A large hose fills the pool at $5\frac{3}{4}$ gallons per minute. If both hoses are turned on, how fast is the pool being filled?

29. A manufacturer puts $\frac{2}{5}$ of its soft drinks in bottles and the rest in cans. What fraction of the soft drinks are put in cans?

30. The width of a rectangle is $2\frac{7}{8}$ inches less than its length. If the length is $10\frac{1}{8}$ inches, find the area of the rectangle.

CUMULATIVE REVIEW EXERCISES: CHAPTERS 1–5

1. Write the English name for $\frac{13}{100}$.

2. Convert $5\frac{7}{12}$ to an improper fraction.

3. Convert $\frac{160}{15}$ to a mixed numeral.

4. Reduce to lowest terms: $\frac{1800}{210}$

5. List from smallest to largest: $\frac{3}{5}, \frac{2}{3}, \frac{17}{30}$

6. Find an improper fraction with denominator 9 that has the same value as the whole numeral 7.

Write each number as the product of primes.

7. 690   8. 231   9. 1200   10. 3400

Find the least common multiple of each group of numbers.

11. 45; 63   12. 14; 16; 20   13. 80; 32; 48

Perform the indicated operation.

14. $\frac{2}{5} + 7\frac{2}{3}$ 15. $\frac{8}{15} \times \frac{45}{60}$ 16. $8\frac{1}{3} \div 3\frac{1}{3}$

17. $19 - 6\frac{7}{8}$ 18. $65\frac{1}{4} - 48\frac{5}{6}$ 19. $\frac{40}{100} \times \frac{25}{36} \times \frac{24}{18}$

Find the missing number.

20. $300 \times \boxed{} = 50$ 21. $12\frac{1}{8} + \boxed{} = 25$

22. $6\frac{3}{4} = \boxed{} \times 9\frac{1}{3}$ 23. $\boxed{} = \frac{5}{9} + \frac{7}{12}$

Solve. If the result is not a whole numeral, answer with a fraction that is reduced to lowest terms.

24. Find the quotient and remainder when 7895 is divided by 63.

25. Multiply 680 by 96, then add 758 to the product.

26. Subtract 458 from 4020, then multiply the result by 87.

27. Denise has a piece of ribbon that is 84 inches long.
    a. If she cuts the ribbon into 21 equal pieces, how long will each piece be?
    b. If she cuts the ribbon into 20 equal pieces, how long will each piece be?
    c. If she cuts the ribbon into 90 equal pieces, how long will each piece be?

28. A truck contains 24,000 pounds of vegetables, consisting of tomatoes, broccoli, and squash. There are 10,000 pounds of tomatoes and 7200 pounds of broccoli.
    a. How many pounds of squash are on the truck?
    b. The weight of the broccoli is what fraction of the total load?
    c. Find the ratio of the weight of the tomatoes to the weight of the squash.

29. Scott walks $3\frac{3}{4}$ miles per hour.
   a. How far can he walk in 5 hours?
   b. How far can he walk in $6\frac{1}{2}$ hours?
   c. How long will it take him to walk 1 mile?
   d. How long will it take him to walk 4 miles?

30. An oil tank off the coast of Alaska contained 500 tons of oil. During a recent spill, $\frac{2}{25}$ of the oil was lost.
   a. How much oil spilled?
   b. How much oil remained in the tank?
   c. What fraction of the oil remained in the tank?

31. The width of a rectangular floor is $42\frac{1}{2}$ feet. The length is 3 times the width.
   a. Find the length of the floor.
   b. Find the distance all the way around the floor.
   c. Find the area of the floor.
   d. If tile costs $4 per square foot, how much will it cost to tile this floor?

Decimals: Place Value, Addition, and Subtraction

6.1   AN INTRODUCTION TO DECIMALS

OBJECTIVES
- Specify the digit in a decimal numeral that has a certain place value.
- Specify the place value of a certain digit in a decimal numeral.
- Write the expanded form for a decimal numeral.
- Write a decimal numeral, given its expanded form.
- Convert a decimal fraction from decimal form to fractional form and vice versa.
- Write a decimal numeral when given the English name of the numeral.
- Write the English name of a decimal numeral.

1   Decimal Notation and Place Value

Would you rather have $23 or $8.97? Of course you would rather have the $23 because that is more money. Expressing money values is one of the many uses of decimals.

A **decimal** is simply another way of expressing the numbers we have already studied. For example,

$$0.2 = \frac{2}{10} \quad \text{and} \quad 4.25 = 4\frac{25}{100}$$

The decimal system is an extension of the system used to express whole numbers. Here we show a decimal and its **expanded form.**

DECIMAL   EXPANDED FORM

$$52.469 \quad \text{means} \quad 50 + 2 + \frac{4}{10} + \frac{6}{100} + \frac{9}{1000}$$

The numbers 5, 2, 4, 6, and 9 are called **digits.** Changing the position of a digit changes the value of the decimal. Each position on either side of the decimal point has a **place value.** The place values for the decimal 52.469 are given in the following diagram.

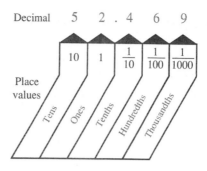

The decimal point is used to separate the whole number portion from the portion that is part of a whole.

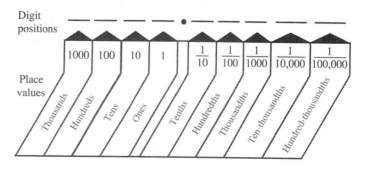

When the decimal has no whole part, we often place a zero in the ones place to bring attention to the decimal point. Here is an example:

$$.18 = 0.18$$

When there is no fractional part to the decimal, we can place one or more zeros past the decimal point to emphasize that there is no fractional part, or we can omit the decimal point and write the number as a whole numeral. Here are some examples:

$$75.00 = 75.0 = 75. = 75$$

$$\$150.00 = \$150. = \$150$$

Here are some more examples of attaching extra zeros to a decimal without changing the value of the decimal.

$$2.6 = 02.6 = 02.600 = 002.6000$$

$$14.709 = 14.70900 = 0014.709$$

Now we look at a diagram that gives more place values. Study this diagram carefully enough so that you make the following observations.

1. As you move from right to left ($\leftarrow$), each place value is 10 times the one before it.
2. As you move from left to right ($\rightarrow$), each place value is $\frac{1}{10}$ of the one before it.
3. The place value nearest the decimal point on the left is *ones*.
4. The place value nearest the decimal point on the right is *tenths*.
5. The English names for the fractional place values $\frac{1}{10}$, $\frac{1}{100}$, $\frac{1}{1000}$, and so on, all end in *ths*. For example, $\frac{1}{1000}$ is read "one thousand*ths.*"

Try These Problems

1. In the decimal 13.82, give the digit in the tenths place.

2. In the decimal 832.754, give the digit in the tens place.

3. Write the decimal for $5000 + 80 + \frac{4}{100} + \frac{7}{1000}$.

4. Write the decimal for $\frac{7}{10} + \frac{2}{1000} + \frac{1}{10000}$.

5. Write 730.04 in expanded form.

6. Write 6.0012 in expanded form.

7. Which of these decimals are equal to 0.07?
   a. 0.007   **b.** .07
   c. .070   **d.** 0.0700

8. Which of these money values is the same as $850?
   a. $.850   **b.** $85.00
   c. $850.00   **d.** $850,000

9. Which of these decimals are equal to 3.0065?
   a. 03.0065   **b.** 3.00065
   c. 3.006500   **d.** 3.6500

 Try Problems 1 through 9.

2 Converting Decimal Fractions from Decimal Form to Fractional Form and Vice Versa

Recall that the expanded form for the decimal 52.469 is as follows.

$$52.469 = 50 + 2 + \frac{4}{10} + \frac{6}{100} + \frac{9}{1000}$$

Observe what we get when we add up the numbers in the expanded form.

$$52.469 = 50 + 2 + \frac{4}{10} + \frac{6}{100} + \frac{9}{1000}$$

Each fraction can be written with common denominator 1000.

$$= 50 + 2 + \frac{400}{1000} + \frac{60}{1000} + \frac{9}{1000}$$

$$= 52 + \frac{469}{1000}$$

$$= 52\frac{469}{1000} \qquad \text{Mixed numeral}$$

$$= \frac{52{,}000}{1000} + \frac{469}{1000}$$

$$= \frac{52{,}469}{1000} \qquad \text{Improper fraction}$$

We say "fifty-two and four hundred sixty-nine thousandths" for 52.469 and $52\frac{469}{1000}$. We say "fifty-two thousand, four hundred sixty-nine thousandths" for $\frac{52{,}469}{1000}$. We call 52.469, $52\frac{469}{1000}$, and $\frac{52{,}469}{1000}$ **decimal fractions.**

$$52.469 = 52\frac{469}{1000} = \frac{52{,}469}{1000}$$

decimal form   fractional forms

Observe how the last place value of the decimal form corresponds to the denominator of the fractional form.

$$52.469 = 52\frac{469}{1000} = \frac{52{,}469}{1000}$$

thousandths

Try These Problems

Write each in fractional form.
10. 0.003

11. 20.17

12. 0.108

13. 8.0731

Write each in decimal form.
14. $\frac{8}{10}$

15. $\frac{28}{1000}$

16. $\frac{704}{100}$

17. $250\frac{17}{10,000}$

EXAMPLE 1 Write each in fractional form.

a. 0.03 **b.** 150.0023

SOLUTION

a. $0.03 = \frac{3}{100}$

hundredths

b. $150.0023 = 150\frac{23}{10,000}$ or $\frac{1,500,023}{10,000}$

ten-thousandths ■

EXAMPLE 2 Write each in decimal form.

a. $\frac{58}{1000}$ **b.** $\frac{375}{100}$ **c.** $26\frac{19}{10,000}$

SOLUTION

The last digit 8 in the numerator must go in the thousandths place.

a. $\frac{58}{1000} = 0.058$

The last digit 5 in the numerator must go in the hundredths place.

b. $\frac{375}{100} = 3\frac{75}{100} = 3.75$

The last digit 9 in the numerator must go in the ten-thousandths place. ■

c. $26\frac{19}{10,000} = 26.0019$

If you have trouble remembering the place value of a digit by its location in the decimal, here is an observation that can help you to convert decimals to fractions and vice versa.

$0.1 = \frac{1}{10}$ One decimal place in the decimal 0.1 One zero in the denominator 10 of the fraction $\frac{1}{10}$.

$0.08 = \frac{8}{100}$ Two decimal places in the decimal 0.08. Two zeros in the denominator 100 of the fraction $\frac{8}{100}$.

$0.015 = \frac{15}{1000}$ Three decimal places in the decimal 0.015. Three zeros in the denominator of the fraction $\frac{15}{1000}$.

The pattern that you observe here continues. That is, 0.00000567 has 8 decimal places, so the fractional form is $\frac{567}{100,000,000}$, which has 8 zeros in the denominator.

 Try Problems 10 through 17.

3 Reading and Writing Decimals

The following chart gives the English names for several decimal fractions. Study the chart carefully enough so that you understand how to read decimal numerals using the English language.

Try These Problems

Write the decimal numeral for each English name.

18. Eight-tenths

19. Eighteen thousandths

20. Eighty

21. Forty and twelve hundredths

22. Nine hundred four tenths

Write the English name for each.

23. 0.027

24. 5.11

25. 120.0083

Decimal Form	Fraction Form	English Name
0.0002	$\frac{2}{10,000}$	Two ten-thousandths
0.016	$\frac{16}{1000}$	Sixteen thousandths
0.50	$\frac{50}{100}$	Fifty hundredths
7.2	$7\frac{2}{10}$ or $\frac{72}{10}$	Seven and two-tenths or Seventy-two tenths
13.08	$13\frac{8}{100}$ or $\frac{1308}{100}$	Thirteen and eight hundredths or One thousand three hundred eight hundredths
920. or 920	$\frac{920}{1}$ or 920	Nine hundred twenty

 Try Problems 18 through 25.

 Answers to Try These Problems

1. 8   2. 3   3. 5080.047   4. 0.7021
5. $700 + 30 + \frac{4}{100}$ 6. $6 + \frac{1}{1000} + \frac{2}{10,000}$
7. b. .07 c. .070 d. 0.0700 8. c. $850.00
9. a. 03.0065 c. 3.006500   10. $\frac{3}{1000}$ 11. $20\frac{17}{100}$ or $\frac{2017}{100}$
12. $\frac{108}{1000}$ 13. $8\frac{731}{10,000}$ or $\frac{80,731}{10,000}$ 14. 0.8   15. 0.028   16. 7.04
17. 250.0017   18. 0.8   19. 0.018   20. 80   21. 40.12
22. 90.4   23. twenty-seven thousandths
24. five and eleven hundredths
25. one hundred twenty and eighty-three ten-thousandths

EXERCISES 6.1

For the decimal 8073.2459, give the digit with the indicated place value.

1. $\frac{1}{10}$ **2.** 1   **3.** 10   **4.** $\frac{1}{100}$

For the decimal 9237.0481, give the digit with the indicated place value.

5. thousandths   **6.** tens   **7.** ten-thousandths   **8.** tenths

Write each decimal in expanded form.

9. 0.238   **10.** 0.035   **11.** 76.008   **12.** 3080.704

Write the decimal whose expanded form is given.

13. $\frac{5}{10} + \frac{7}{100}$ **14.** $\frac{9}{100} + \frac{1}{1000}$

15. $600 + 30 + \frac{8}{10} + \frac{3}{1000}$ **16.** $500 + 7 + \frac{4}{100} + \frac{6}{10,000}$

Write each in fractional form or as a whole numeral. Do not reduce the fractions to lowest terms.

17. 0.3   **18.** 7.8   **19.** 0.58

20. 275.   **21.** 0.006   **22.** 11.0765

Write a decimal numeral for each.

23. $\frac{4}{100}$ **24.** $3\frac{5}{10}$ **25.** $14\frac{32}{1000}$

26. $\frac{45}{10,000}$ **27.** $\frac{2368}{1000}$ **28.** $\frac{351}{10}$

Write a decimal numeral for each.

29. Nine-tenths   **30.** Nineteen hundredths

31. Four hundredths   **32.** Fourteen ten-thousandths

33. Twelve and three-tenths   **34.** Forty and thirteen thousandths

35. Fifty and one-hundred-four thousandths

36. One thousand sixty and thirty-six hundredths

37. Five-hundred-three tenths   **38.** Two-thousand-eight thousandths

Write the English name for each.

39. 0.34   **40.** 0.237   **41.** 0.008   **42.** 0.0002

43. 24.02   **44.** 405.016   **45.** 9.0105   **46.** 7800.0076

47. 9000.   **48.** 50,630.

6.2   MONEY AND CHECK WRITING

OBJECTIVES

- Write the value of a given piece of currency in both cents and dollars.
- Write the name of a single piece of currency with the indicated value.
- Translate a value expressed using English to math symbols.
- Translate a value in symbols to English.
- Complete the writing of a check by giving a value in the appropriate form.

1   The Pieces of United States Currency and Their Values

A common use of decimals is in expressing the value of money. The currency in circulation in the United States consists of paper bills and metal coins. The value of each piece of currency is based on two different units of measurement, dollars and cents.

The currency worth 1 dollar, also written $1 or $1.00, is called a dollar bill. We show a picture of both sides of a dollar bill.

The currency worth 1 cent, also written 1¢ or $.01, is called a penny. We show a picture of both sides of a penny.

The value of the dollar bill is the same as the value of 100 pennies.

$$1 \text{ dollar} = 100 \text{ cents}$$
$$\$1 = 100¢$$
$$1 \text{ cent} = 0.01 \text{ dollar}$$
$$1¢ = \$0.01$$

Here is a list of the most common paper bill currencies in circulation. The value of each is given in both dollars and cents.

Paper Bill Currency			
Name	*Picture*	*Value in Dollars*	*Value in Cents*
One-dollar bill or dollar bill		$1 or $1.00	100¢
Five-dollar bill		$5 or $5.00	500¢
Ten-dollar bill		$10 or $10.00	1000¢
Twenty-dollar bill		$20 or $20.00	2000¢

Here is a list of the most common coins in circulation. The value of each is given in both cents and dollars.

Try These Problems

Write the value *of the given piece of currency in* **a.** *cents and* **b.** *dollars.*

1. ten-dollar bill

2. five-dollar bill

3. quarter

4. nickel

Write the English name *of a single piece of currency with the indicated value.*

5. $0.10

6. 100¢

7. $20.00

8. 1¢

Coin Currency				
Name	*Picture*		*Value in Cents*	*Value in Dollars*
Penny			1¢	$0.01
Nickel			5¢	$0.05
Dime			10¢	$0.10
Quarter			25¢	$0.25
Half-dollar			50¢	$0.50

A common error is to represent 25 cents by using the symbol .25¢. The value .25¢ means $\frac{25}{100}$ of 1 cent which is $\frac{1}{4}$¢ and is, therefore, less than 1¢. As you see in the chart above, 25 cents is written 25¢ or $.25.

 Try Problems 1 through 8.

2 Translating Money Values from English to Symbols and Vice Versa

Combining the currencies in various ways creates different money values. You should become familiar with the English language that is used in reading and writing money values. Here we show two ways to read or write $6.25 using English.

METHOD 1

"Six dollars and twenty-five cents." In this method we read the fractional part of the dollar in cents. This method is used most frequently when speaking.

METHOD 2

"Six and twenty-five hundredths dollars." Here the entire value is read in dollars. This method or a slight variation of it is used in check writing.

Try These Problems

Write the symbol for each in dollars.

9. Six cents

10. Fifteen dollars and seventy-five cents

11. Ten and three hundredths dollars.

12. Nine hundred twelve and twenty-three hundredths dollars

*Write each value using English in two ways: **a.** the fractional part of the dollar in cents and **b.** the entire value in dollars.*

13. $0.19

14. $7.30

15. $1500.08

16. $97.42

The following chart gives more examples.

Symbolic	*English (Fractional part of the dollar in cents)*	*English (Entire value in dollars)*
$0.03	three cents	three hundredths dollars
$0.92	ninety-two cents	ninety-two hundredths dollars
$4.15	four dollars and fifteen cents	four and fifteen hundredths dollars
$28.00	twenty-eight dollars	twenty-eight dollars
$150.07	one hundred fifty dollars and seven cents	one hundred fifty and seven hundredths dollars

 Try Problems 9 through 16.

3 | Writing Checks

Many people deposit their money in a checking account at a bank. When they want to make a purchase or pay a bill they write a check for the amount rather than using cash currency.

Jeff Miller has a checking account with National Bank in Palo Alto, California. He wrote a check to pay his gas and electric bill for the month of May. Here is a copy of the check he wrote.

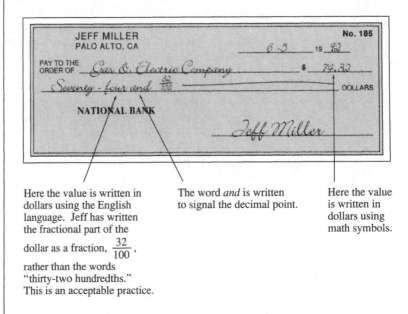

Here the value is written in dollars using the English language. Jeff has written the fractional part of the dollar as a fraction, $\frac{32}{100}$, rather than the words "thirty-two hundredths." This is an acceptable practice.

The word *and* is written to signal the decimal point.

Here the value is written in dollars using math symbols.

The value is written in two different ways on the check so that there is no doubt about the intended value.

Here is another example.

Try These Problems

Give the missing value for each check in the appropriate form.

17. Ms. De Mol wrote a check to pay her water bill. On the check she must express the value in two ways. If she wrote "Thirteen and $\frac{4}{100}$" in the blank that is followed by the word DOLLARS, how must she fill in the blank that follows the dollar symbol $?

$ _____?_____

18. Mr. Moura wrote a check to a financial institution. On the check he must express the value in two ways. If he wrote "10,000.00" in the blank that follows the dollar symbol $, how would he complete the blank that is followed by the word DOLLARS?

_____?_____ DOLLARS

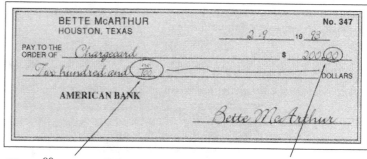

BETTE McARTHUR
HOUSTON, TEXAS

No. 347

PAY TO THE ORDER OF *Chargeard*

$ *200.00*

Two hundred and $\frac{00}{100}$ DOLLARS

AMERICAN BANK

Bette McArthur

$\frac{no}{100}$ or $\frac{00}{100}$ is written to emphasize there is no fractional part of the dollar.

Two zeros are placed past the decimal point to emphasize there is no fractional part of the dollar.

◤ **Try Problems 17 and 18.**

◤ **Answers to Try These Problems**

1. a. 1000¢ b. $10 or $10.00   2. a. 500¢ b. $5 or $5.00
3. a. 25¢ b. $0.25   4. a. 5¢ b. $0.05   5. dime
6. dollar bill   7. twenty dollar bill   8. penny   9. $0.06
10. $15.75   11. $10.03   12. $912.23
13. a. nineteen cents
    b. nineteen hundredths dollars
14. a. seven dollars and thirty cents
    b. seven and thirty hundredths dollars
15. a. fifteen hundred dollars and eight cents
    b. fifteen hundred and eight hundredths dollars
16. a. ninety-seven dollars and forty-two cents
    b. ninety-seven and forty-two hundredths dollars
17. 13.04   18. Ten thousand and $\frac{no}{100}$

EXERCISES 6.2

Write the value *of the given piece of currency in a. cents and b. dollars.*

1. Dollar bill   **2.** Penny   **3.** Twenty-dollar bill
4. Nickel   **5.** Quarter   **6.** Five-dollar bill

Write the English name *of a single piece of currency with the indicated value.*

7. 50¢   **8.** 500¢   **9.** $0.10   **10.** $1.00

Write the symbol for each in dollars.

11. Seventeen cents   **12.** Forty-three cents
13. Forty-six hundredths dollars   **14.** Sixty-two hundredths dollars
15. Twenty-five dollars and eighty-three cents
16. Two hundred five dollars and seventy-one cents
17. Eight hundred and nine hundredths dollars
18. Ninety-eight and fifty-four hundredths dollars

*Write each value using English in two ways: **a.** the fractional part of the dollar in cents and **b.** the entire value in dollars.*

19. $0.55

20. $0.74

21. $8.03

22. $728.14

23. $67.00

24. $5000.00

Complete each check by giving the missing value in the appropriate form.

25.

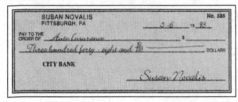

26.

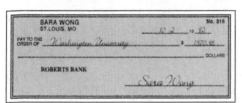

27.

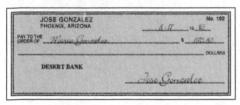

28.

6.3   COMPARING DECIMALS

OBJECTIVES   ▌ Compare decimals.
             ▌ Compare decimals using the comparing symbols <, =, or >.

 Try These Problems

1. Which of these decimals equal 0.6?
   a. 6.   **b.** .6
   c. .60   **d.** .06
   e. 0.60

2. Which of these decimals equal 82?
   a. .82   **b.** 82.
   c. 820   **d.** 82.0
   e. .082

3. Which of these money values are the same as $200.00?
   a. $200   **b.** $2
   c. $200.   **d.** $20,000

1 Attaching Extra Zeros

Sometimes extra zeros are attached to decimal numerals without changing the value of the decimal. Here are some examples.

.53 = 0.53	fifty-three hundredths
7 or 7. = 7.00	seven
2.6 = 2.6000	two and six-tenths
$40 = $40.00	forty dollars

 Try Problems 1 through 3.

Try These Problems

4. Which is larger 0.02 or 0.0154?

5. Which is smaller 0.5 or 0.47?

6. List from smallest to largest.
81.224; 81.2224; 81.2236

2 Comparing Decimals

Now we look at some examples of comparing decimals.

EXAMPLE 1   Which is larger, 0.38 or 0.49?

SOLUTION

$$0.38 = \frac{38}{100}$$

$$0.49 = \frac{49}{100} \text{---- larger}$$

The decimal 0.49 is larger. ■

EXAMPLE 2   Which is smaller, 0.004 or 0.0038?

SOLUTION

$$0.004 = \frac{4}{1000}$$ Before comparing, we need to view them with a common denominator.

$$0.0038 = \frac{38}{10000}$$

$$0.004 = 0.0040 = \frac{40}{10,000}$$ Attach a zero here so that each decimal has four digits past the decimal point.

$$0.0038 = 0.0038 = \frac{38}{10,000}$$

$$\frac{38}{10,000} \text{ is smaller than } \frac{40}{10,000}$$

The decimal 0.0038 is smaller. ■

EXAMPLE 3   List from smallest to largest:
30.05; 30.0467; 30.048

SOLUTION   It can be helpful to arrange the numbers so that decimal points align vertically.

Attach extra zeros so that each decimal has the same number of decimal places.

$$30.05 = 30.0500$$
$$30.0467$$
$$30.048 = 30.0480$$

The numbers are equal out to the tenths place.

Compare 500, 467, and 480, the last three digits of the numbers above. From smallest to largest we have, 467, 480, and 500. Therefore, the decimals listed from smallest to largest are as follows.

$$30.0467; \ 30.0480; \ 30.0500$$

or

$$30.0467; \ 30.048; \ 30.05 \quad ■$$

 Try Problems 4 through 6.

Try These Problems

7. Which is larger, 93.0 or 9.30?

8. Which is smaller, 117.2 or 11.72?

Rewrite each statement using the symbol <, =, or >.

9. 15.2 is larger than 15.02

10. 170 is equal to 170.00

11. 0.0342 is smaller than 0.0351

Use the symbol <, =, or > to compare each pair of numbers.

12. 0.05; 0.50

13. 0.4827; 0.6

14. .42; 0.420

15. 17.81; 17.8099

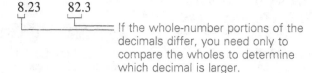 Which is larger, 8.23 or 82.3?

SOLUTION

8.23   82.3

If the whole-number portions of the decimals differ, you need only to compare the wholes to determine which decimal is larger.

Since 82 is larger than 8, we conclude that 82.3 is larger. ■

 Try Problems 7 and 8.

 3 The Comparing Symbols <, =, and >

Special symbols are often used when comparing decimals. Examples of how these symbols are used are given in the following chart.

Math Symbols	English
8 < 20	8 is smaller than 20
20 > 8	20 is larger than 8
20 = 20	20 is equal to 20
0.43 < 0.55	0.43 is smaller than 0.55
0.15 > 0.136	0.15 is larger than 0.136
7.8 = 7.800	7.8 is equal to 7.800

After studying the previous chart, you should make these observations.

1.   < >

The pointed side always faces the smaller number.

2.   < >

The open side always faces the larger number.

 Try Problems 9 through 15.

 Answers to Try These Problems

1. b. .6 c. .60 e. 0.60   2. b. 82. d. 82.0
3. a. $200 c. $200.   4. 0.02   5. 0.47
6. 81.2224; 81.2236; 81.224   7. 93.0   8. 11.72
9. 15.2 > 15.02   10. 170 = 170.00   11. 0.0342 < 0.0351
12. 0.05 < 0.50   13. 0.4827 < 0.6   14. .42 = 0.420
15. 17.81 > 17.8099

EXERCISES 6.3

1. Which of these decimals are equal to 0.43?
   a. .43   b. .043   c. .430   d. 0.430   e. 4.300

2. Which of these decimals are equal to 7.5?
   a. 75.   b. 7.500   c. 7.05   d. 07.50   e. .75

3. Which of these have the same money value as $30?
   a. $3.00   **b.** $300   **c.** $30.00   **d.** $.30   **e.** $30.0

4. Which of these have the same money value as $9.05.
   a. $9.50   **b.** $0.95   **c.** $09.05   **d.** $9.050   **e.** $9.005

Which is the smaller decimal?

5. 2.8; 2.9   **6.** 3.600; 3.489   **7.** 0.3; 0.03
8. 1.399; 2.04   **9.** 132.113; 132.1146   **10.** 5.8607; 58.607

Which is the larger decimal?

11. 8.; .8   **12.** 0.04; 0.40
13. .132; .138   **14.** 83.1784; 83.17828

List from smallest to largest.

15. 5; .5; .55   **16.** .56; 1; 2.3
17. .327; .33; .32   **18.** 53.112244; 53.114422; 53.113

Use the symbol <, =, or > to compare each pair of numbers.

19. 9.00; 9   **20.** 8.8; .88
21. 0.8123; 0.814   **22.** 0.007; 0.000789

6.4   ROUNDING OFF, ROUNDING UP, AND TRUNCATING

OBJECTIVES
- Round off a decimal numeral to a given place value or a given number of decimal places.
- Round up a decimal numeral to a given place value or a given number of decimal places.
- Truncate a decimal numeral to a given place value or a given number of decimal places.

Sometimes the approximate value of a decimal is needed. There are many methods for approximating decimals. We will study three of these methods. The symbol $\approx$ or $\doteq$ is used to mean *approximately equal to*.

1   Rounding Off

Here are some examples that illustrate what it means to **round off** a decimal to a certain place value or to a given number of decimal places.

EXAMPLE 1   Round off 7.1349 to the nearest hundredths place.
SOLUTION

   ┌─────── hundredths place
7.13|49   Because the digit 4 is smaller than 5,
$\approx$ 7.13   we drop the 49 and write 7.13
             for the approximation.

We are saying that 7.1349 is closer to 7.13 than it is to 7.14.
   The answer is 7.13.   ■

Try These Problems

1. Round off 0.2317 at three decimal places.
2. Round off 8.045 at two decimal places.
3. Round off 23.3146 at one decimal place.

Round off each to the nearest cent.
4. $0.057
5. $18.912
6. $285.009

Round off each to the nearest dollar.
7. $12.094
8. $180.75
9. $9.82

EXAMPLE 2   Round off 83.68 to the nearest tenths place.
SOLUTION

```
            ┌─── tenths place
   83.6│8 ──── Because the digit 8 is larger than 5,
              we drop the 8 and write 83.7 for
   ≈ 83.7     the approximation.
```

We are saying that 83.68 is closer to 83.7 than it is to 83.6.
The answer is 83.7. ∎

EXAMPLE 3   Round off 132.6935 at three decimal places.
SOLUTION

```
                ┌─── three decimal places
   132.693│5 ──── Because the digit after 3 is 5, we write
         │        132.694 as the approximation.
         ↓
   ≈ 132.694
```

132.6935 is exactly halfway between 132.693 and 132.694, so we will agree to choose the higher number for the approximation.
The answer is 132.694. ∎

 Try Problems 1 through 3.

When approximating money value, special language is sometimes used. The following examples illustrate this.

EXAMPLE 4   Round off $23.168 to the nearest cent.
SOLUTION   To the nearest cent means to the nearest hundredth of a dollar. We round off at two decimal places.

```
              ┌─── cents place
   $23.16│8       Because 8 is larger than 5, we increase 6
        │         to 7.
        ↓
   ≈ $23.17
```

The answer is $23.17. ∎

EXAMPLE 5   Round off $273.42 to the nearest dollar.
SOLUTION   To the nearest dollar means to the nearest one dollar or to the nearest whole dollar. We round off at the ones place.

```
                 ┌─── dollars place
   $ 273│42
        │
        ↓
   ≈ $ 273 ──── Because 4 is smaller than 5, we leave 3
                as 3 and drop the 42 cents..
```

The answer is $273. ∎

 Try Problems 4 through 9.

Try These Problems

10. Round up $132.081 to the nearest cent.

11. Round up $74.60 to the nearest dollar.

12. Round up 0.0342 at three decimal places.

13. Truncate 17.13891 at three decimal places.

14. Truncate 8.0098 at the hundredths place.

15. Truncate 7.3333 at one decimal place.

2 Rounding Up

Suppose the grocery store is selling bananas at 3 pounds for $1. This means that each pound is selling for approximately $0.333. How much will you be charged for 1 pound of these bananas? Most likely, you will be charged $0.34 or 34¢. The store approximates $0.333 as $0.34. Usually, the business world does not follow the rules for rounding off. They approximate in a way that gives them slightly more money. This type of approximating is called **rounding up.** Here are some examples of approximating decimals by rounding up.

EXAMPLE 6 Round up $24.124 to the nearest cent.
SOLUTION

cents place
$24.12|4
↓
≈ $24.13 —— Increase 2 to 3 even though 4 is smaller than 5.

The answer is $24.13. ■

EXAMPLE 7 Round up 18.32 at one decimal place.
SOLUTION

one decimal place
18.3|2
↓
≈ 18.4 —— Increase 3 to 4 even though 2 is smaller than 5.

The answer is 18.4.

Try Problems 10 through 12.

3 Truncating

The third method for approximating decimals is called **truncating** (or **rounding down**). To truncate means *to chop off* or *to drop off*. This method of approximating is often used by calculators. For example, if a calculator has a display limited to 8 digits, it might display 0.6666666 for the approximation of the decimal 0.6666666666, instead of displaying 0.6666667. The calculator simply chops off the excess digits. The following example illustrates how to approximate decimals by truncating.

EXAMPLE 8 Truncate 87.367 at two decimal places.
SOLUTION

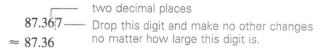

two decimal places
87.36|7 —— Drop this digit and make no other changes no matter how large this digit is.
≈ 87.36

The answer is 87.36.

Try Problems 13 through 15.

Now we summarize the three types of approximating by making a chart that illustrates all three types. Study the following chart carefully enough so that you know the difference between rounding off, rounding up, and truncating.

| Three Types of Rounding | | | |
Decimal	Round off At Two Decimal Places	Round up At Two Decimal Places	Truncate At Two Decimal Places
0.362	0.36	0.37	0.36
0.365	0.37	0.37	0.36
0.368	0.37	0.37	0.36

Answers to Try These Problems

1. 0.232   2. 8.05   3. 23.3   4. $0.06   5. $18.91   6. $285.01
7. $12   8. $181   9. $10   10. $132.09   11. $75   12. 0.035
13. 17.138   14. 8.00   15. 7.3

EXERCISES 6.4

Round off each decimal at the place indicated.

1. 0.316; two decimal places
2. 7.823; one decimal place
3. 732.013569; thousandths place
4. 832.346; tenths place
5. $17.503; nearest dollar
6. $0.1248; nearest cent

Round up each decimal at the place indicated.

7. $0.431; nearest cent
8. $34.00612; nearest cent
9. 9.01392; four decimal places
10. 8.347; one decimal place
11. 2304.191; hundredths place
12. 0.00828; ten-thousandths place
13. 22.079; nearest whole number
14. $186.63; nearest dollar

Truncate each decimal at the place indicated.

15. 0.23691; three decimal places
16. 1.36898; four decimal places
17. 790.364; tenths place
18. 15.0308; hundredths place
19. 75.59; ones place
20. 100.01; nearest whole number

6.5 ADDITION AND SUBTRACTION

OBJECTIVES
▮ Add two or more decimals.
▮ Subtract decimals.
▮ Find the missing number in an addition statement.

 Adding

Cynthia needs to pay the following bills:

Rent $300
Gas and electric $ 31.21
Garbage $ 15.25
Cable TV $ 21.50

What is the total amount of money she needs? To solve this problem we need to add the decimals. We add them similarly to the way we add whole numbers; that is, we add like place values.

> Arrange the decimal points in a vertical line so that digits with like place value will be in the same column.
> Observe that $300 = $300.00

$$
\begin{array}{r}
\$300.00 \\
\$ 31.21 \\
\$ 15.25 \\
+ \$ 21.50 \\
\hline
\$367.96
\end{array}
$$

Cynthia will need $367.96 to pay these bills.

Observe that to add decimals, we arrange the numbers vertically so that the decimal points line up in a vertical line. This forces digits with like place value to form a column. Finally, add digits with like place value and place the decimal point in the answer in line with the other decimal points. Here are more examples of adding decimals.

EXAMPLE 1   Add: 27.5 + 2.346 + 0.0018
SOLUTION

> tens column
> ones column
> DECIMAL POINTS IN A VERTICAL LINE
> tenths column
> hundredths column
> thousandths column
> ten-thousandths column

$$
\begin{array}{r}
27.5 \\
2.346 \\
+ 0.0018 \\
\hline
29.8478
\end{array}
$$

Place the decimal point in the answer in line with the other decimal points. ■

When a column of digits adds up to more than 9, we use carrying as we do when adding whole numbers. Here are some examples:

EXAMPLE 2   Add: 6.5 + 0.846
SOLUTION

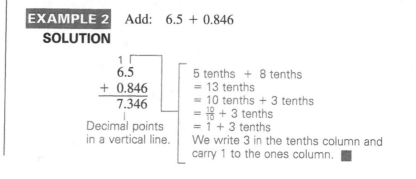

$$
\begin{array}{r}
1 \\
6.5 \\
+ 0.846 \\
\hline
7.346
\end{array}
$$

Decimal points in a vertical line.

5 tenths + 8 tenths
= 13 tenths
= 10 tenths + 3 tenths
= $\frac{10}{10}$ + 3 tenths
= 1 + 3 tenths
We write 3 in the tenths column and carry 1 to the ones column. ■

Try These Problems

Add.

1. $15 + $4.75 + $0.13
2. 703.1 + 0.92 + 2.0008
3. 932.15 + 80.463
4. 56.914 + 870 + 4.061
5. $567.42 + $7.45
6. 0.478 + 2.3 + 7924

EXAMPLE 3   Add: $1.08 + $52.36 + $0.27

SOLUTION

$$
\begin{array}{r}
{}^{2}\\
\$\ 1.08\\
\$52.36\\
+\ \$\ 0.27\\
\hline
\$53.71
\end{array}
$$

8 cents + 6 cents + 7 cents
= 21·cents
= 2 dimes + 1 cent
= 2 tenths dollar + 1 hundredth dollar
We write 1 in the hundredths column and
carry 2 to the tenths column. ■

Decimal points
in a vertical line.

EXAMPLE 4   Add: 172.3 + 79.784 + 1392.007

SOLUTION

$$
\begin{array}{r}
{}^{211}\ {}^{1}\\
172.3\\
79.784\\
+\ 1392.007\\
\hline
1644.091
\end{array}
$$

Decimal points
in a vertical line ■

EXAMPLE 5   Add: 4.13 + 23 + 63.009

SOLUTION   Be careful. The number 23 is a whole numeral. The decimal is placed at the right end. That is, 23 = 23. = 23.000.

$$
\begin{array}{r}
4.13\\
23.000\\
+\ 63.009\\
\hline
90.139
\end{array}
$$

The whole number 23 equals 23. or
23.000.

■

Now we summarize by writing a procedure for adding decimals.

Adding Decimals

1. If any whole numerals are involved, place the decimal point at the right end.
2. Arrange the numerals vertically for convenience. Line up the decimal points in a vertical line so that digits with like place value form a column.
3. Add each column separately, beginning with the column on the right.
4. When a column adds up to more than 9, use carrying.
5. Place the decimal point in the answer in line with the other decimal points.

 Try Problems 1 through 6.

2   Subtracting

Subtracting decimal numerals is similar to adding decimal numerals in that we line up the decimal points in a vertical line so that digits with like place value form a column. Here are some examples.

EXAMPLE 6   Subtract: $7.3 - 0.9$

SOLUTION

$$
\begin{array}{r}
\overset{6}{\cancel{7}}.{}^{1}3 \\
-\ 0.9 \\
\hline
6.4
\end{array}
$$

We do not subtract 9 from 3 because 9 is larger than 3. We borrow 1 from 7, leaving 6. Write 1 in front of 3 to make 13. The 1 we borrow is really $\frac{10}{10}$ or 10 tenths. Then, 10 tenths + 3 tenths = 13 tenths.

CHECK

$$
\begin{array}{r}
{}^{1} \\
0.9 \\
+\ 6.4 \\
\hline
7.3
\end{array}
$$

The answer is 6.4. ■

EXAMPLE 7   Subtract: $18.9 - 0.72$

SOLUTION

$$
\begin{array}{r}
\overset{8}{1\ 8.\cancel{9}}{}^{1}0 \\
-\ \ 0.7\ 2 \\
\hline
1\ 8.1\ 8
\end{array}
$$

Write in a zero place holder. Borrow 1 from 9, leaving 8. Write 1 in front of 0 to make 10. The 1 we borrow is really 1 tenth = $\frac{1}{10} = \frac{10}{100}$ = 10 hundredths.

CHECK

$$
\begin{array}{r}
{}^{1} \\
0.72 \\
+\ 18.18 \\
\hline
18.90 = 18.9
\end{array}
$$

The answer is 18.18. ■

EXAMPLE 8   Subtract: $17.6 - 9.358$

SOLUTION

$$
\begin{array}{r}
\overset{5\ \ 9}{1\ 7.\cancel{6}\ \cancel{0}}{}^{1}0 \\
-\ \ 9.3\ 5\ 8 \\
\hline
8.2\ 4\ 2
\end{array}
$$

Write in two zero place holders. Borrow 1 from 60, leaving 59. Write the 1 in front of the zero to make 10. The 1 we borrow is really 1 hundredth = $\frac{1}{100} = \frac{10}{1000}$ = 10 thousandths.

CHECK

$$
\begin{array}{r}
{}^{1\ 1} \\
9.358 \\
+\ \ 8.242 \\
\hline
17.600 = 17.6
\end{array}
$$

The answer is 8.242. ■

Try These Problems

Subtract.

7. 600.24 − 8.013

8. $1436.89 − $78

9. 7.13 − 0.8482

10. 172 − 9.07

11. 1020 − 96.41

12. 5000 − 7.563

EXAMPLE 9   Subtract: $36 − $4.30

SOLUTION   Observe that $36 is 36 whole dollars. The decimal point is placed at the right end. That is, $36 = $36. or $36.00.

$$
\begin{array}{r}
\overset{5}{\$\ 3\ \cancel{6}.0\ 0} \longleftarrow \$36 = \$36.00. \\
-\ \$\quad 4.3\ 0 \\
\hline
\$\ 3\ 1.7\ 0
\end{array}
$$

CHECK

$$
\begin{array}{r}
\overset{1}{} \\
4.30 \\
+\ 31.70 \\
\hline
36.00
\end{array}
$$

The answer is $31.70. ■

EXAMPLE 10   Subtract: 9000 − 0.064.

SOLUTION   Observe that 9000 is a whole numeral. The decimal point is placed at the right end. That is, 9000 = 9000. = 9000.000.

$$
\begin{array}{r}
8\ 9\ 9\ 9\ 9\ 9 \\
\cancel{9}\ \cancel{0}\ \cancel{0}\ \cancel{0}.\cancel{0}\ \cancel{0}^{1}0 \longleftarrow 9000 = 9000.000 \\
-\qquad\qquad 0.0\ 6\ 4 \\
\hline
8\ 9\ 9\ 9.9\ 3\ 6
\end{array}
$$

CHECK

$$
\begin{array}{r}
1\ 1\ 1\ 1\ 1\ 1 \\
0.0\ 6\ 4 \\
+\ 8\ 9\ 9\ 9.9\ 3\ 6 \\
\hline
9\ 0\ 0\ 0.0\ 0\ 0 = 9000
\end{array}
$$

The answer is 8999.936. ■

Now we summarize by writing a procedure for subtracting decimals.

> ### Subtracting Decimals
> 1. If a whole numeral is involved, place the decimal point at the right end.
> 2. Arrange the numerals vertically for convenience. Line up the decimal points in a vertical line so that digits with like place value form a column.
> 3. Subtract each column separately, beginning with the column on the right.
> 4. When a digit on the bottom is larger than a digit on the top, use borrowing.
> 5. Place the decimal point in the answer in line with the other decimal points.

 Try Problems 7 through 12.

Try These Problems

Find the missing number.

13. 23.86 + ☐ = 45.3

14. ☐ = 245 + 65.09

15. 304 = 76.34 + ☐

16. ☐ + 0.537 = 50.14

3 The Missing Number in an Addition Statement

The statement 5.8 + 2.1 = 7.9 is an addition statement. If any one of the three numbers is omitted, we can find the missing number. Study the three examples that follow to see how to do this.

1. 5.8 + 2.1 = ☐   Here the answer to the addition statement is missing, so we *add* to find the missing number.

The missing number is 7.9.

2. ☐ + 2.1 = 7.9   Here one of the terms is missing, so we *subtract* to find the missing number.

The missing number is 7.9 − 2.1 = 5.8.

3. 5.8 + ☐ = 7.9   Here one of the terms is missing, so we *subtract* to find the missing number.

The missing number is 7.9 − 5.8 = 2.1.

 Try Problems 13 through 16.

Answers to Try These Problems

1. $19.88 2. 706.0208 3. 1012.613 4. 930.975
5. $574.87 6. 7926.778 7. 592.227 8. $1358.89
9. 6.2818 10. 162.93 11. 923.59 12. 4992.437
13. 21.44 14. 310.09 15. 227.66 16. 49.603

EXERCISES 6.5

Add.

1.   43.1
   + 6.23

2.   73.4
   + 8.309

3.   25.345
     56
   + 2.57

4.   456
     8.43
   + 13.952

5. 0.23 + 9.7 + 728.92

6. 0.8 + 9.07 + 1908.62

7. $346.17 + $250 + $3.74

8. $33.90 + $459.09 + $63

9. 2.8 + 73 + 312.643

10. 135 + 15.007 + 234.72

Solve.

11. Ed ran the first mile in 7.83 minutes and the second mile in 6.7 minutes. What is his total time for the 2-mile run?

12. Tina wrote checks for $23, $17.23, and $426.08. What is the total value of the three checks?

Subtract.

13.   8.749
   − 0.68

14.   17.636
   − 5.9

15.   154
   − 8.32

16.   236
   − 37.065

17. 302.9 − 1.353

18. 85.4 − 3.824

19. $400 − $306.79

20. $670 − $19.46

21. 2004.8 − 32.705

22. 3010 − 259.342

23. 5000 − 1230.67

24. 70,000 − 32.046

Solve.

25. How far is it from C to Y?

26. A steak, including the fat, weighs 3.2 pounds. The butcher trims 0.75 pound of fat from the steak. What is the weight of the resulting steak?

Find the missing number.

27. $300 + \boxed{} = 409.67$

28. $\boxed{} + 3.8 = 16.02$

29. $\boxed{} = 35.78 + 9.054$

30. $\boxed{} = 348.7 + 56.238$

31. $2004 = \boxed{} + 805.82$

32. $96.3 + \boxed{} = 101$

6.6	LANGUAGE

OBJECTIVES ▌ Translate an English phrase to math symbols involving addition and subtraction.

▌ Solve problems by using translations.

1 Translating

The math symbols that we use often have many translations to the English language. Knowing these translations can help in solving application problems. The following chart gives the many English translations for the symbol =.

Math Symbol	*English*
=	equals
	is equal to
	is the same as
	is
	was
	were
	are
	will be
	represents
	gives
	makes
	yields
	is the result of

The addition statement $5.6 + 0.7 = 6.3$ is written using math symbols. Some of the ways to read this in English are given in the following chart.

Try These Problems

Translate each English statement to an addition or subtraction statement using math symbols.

1. The sum of 45.5 and 6.4 is 51.9.

2. The difference between 6 and 1.2 equals 4.8.

3. 67.8 subtracted from 100 yields 32.2.

4. 74.14 minus 56.089 is 18.051.

Translate to an equation. Solve.

5. Find 4.5 less than 7.2.

6. Find 34.9 increased by 5.02

7. Find 87.6 more than 3.7.

8. Subtract 455.8 from 500.

Math Symbols	English
5.6 + 0.7 = 6.3	5.6 plus 0.7 equals 6.3
	5.6 added to 0.7 yields 6.3
	5.6 *increased by* 0.7 is 6.3
	0.7 more than 5.6 is equal to 6.3
	The *sum* of 5.6 and 0.7 equals 6.3
	6.3 is the result of adding 5.6 to 0.7

Because 5.6 + 0.7 equals 0.7 + 5.6, the order that you read the terms 5.6 and 0.7 makes no difference; however, when reading the subtraction statement 6.3 − 0.7, take care to read 6.3 and 0.7 in the correct order, because 6.3 − 0.7 does not equal 0.7 − 6.3.

$$6.3 - 0.7 = 5.6 \quad \text{but} \quad 0.7 - 6.3 = -5.6$$

The numbers 5.6 and −5.6 are not equal. The number −5.6 is a negative number. This book covers negative numbers in Chapter 12. The following chart gives several correct ways to read 6.3 − 0.7 = 5.6.

Math Symbols	English
6.3 − 0.7 = 5.6	6.3 minus 0.7 equals 5.6
	6.3 take away 0.7 yields 5.6
	6.3 *decreased by* 0.7 gives 5.6
	6.3 reduced by 0.7 equals 5.6
	6.3 subtract 0.7 is 5.6
	0.7 subtracted from 6.3 is equal to 5.6
	0.7 less than 6.3 gives 5.6
	The *difference* between 6.3 and 0.7 is 5.6

Observe that when reading the symbol − by using the phrases *subtracted from* or *less than,* the numbers 6.3 and 0.7 are read in the reverse order than they are written. That is,

$$0.7 \text{ subtracted from } 6.3 \quad \text{means} \quad 6.3 - 0.7$$

and

$$0.7 \text{ less than } 6.3 \quad \text{means} \quad 6.3 - 0.7$$

 Try Problems 1 through 8.

2 Solving Problems by Using Translations

The following examples illustrate how we can use translating to solve problems.

EXAMPLE 1   The sum of 36.17 and what number is 50.2?

SOLUTION   Translate the question into math symbols.

$$\underbrace{\text{The sum of } 36.17 \text{ and what number}}_{36.17 + \boxed{}} \; \underset{=}{\text{is}} \; \underset{50.2}{50.2?}$$

Try These Problems

Translate to an equation. Solve.

9. 460 represents 348.2 plus what number?

10. What number added to 60.65 yields 120?

11. What number is 75 less than 235.75?

12. What is the difference between 15.1 and 0.35?

The missing number is one of the terms in an addition statement, so we subtract the given term 36.17 from the total 50.2 to find the missing term.

$$\begin{array}{r} \overset{4}{\cancel{5}}0.\overset{1}{\cancel{2}}{}^{1}0 \\ -\ 3\ 6.1\ 7 \\ \hline 1\ 4.0\ 3 \end{array}$$

The answer is 14.03. ■

EXAMPLE 2   What number is 78.4 less than 127.49?

SOLUTION   Translate the question into math symbols.

What number   is   78.4   less than   127.49

□   =   127.49 − 78.4

The missing number is the answer to the subtraction problem, 127.49 − 78.4.

$$\begin{array}{r} 1\ \overset{1}{2}{}^{1}7.4\ 9 \\ -\ \ \ 7\ 8.4\ 0 \\ \hline 4\ 9.0\ 9 \end{array}$$

The answer is 49.09. ■

 Try Problems 9 through 12.

 Answers to Try These Problems

1. 45.5 + 6.4 = 51.9 **2.** 6 − 1.2 = 4.8
3. 100 − 67.8 = 32.2 **4.** 74.14 − 56.089 = 18.051
5. 2.7 **6.** 39.92 **7.** 91.3 **8.** 44.2 **9.** 111.8 **10.** 59.35
11. 160.75 **12.** 14.75

EXERCISES 6.6

Translate each statement to an addition or subtraction statement using math symbols.

1. The sum of 0.8 and 0.4 is 1.2.

2. The difference between 41 and 8.3 is 32.7.

3. 18.7 decreased by 7.3 gives 11.4.

4. 7.75 increased by 0.25 yields 8.

5. The total when 72.8 is added to 0.6 is 73.4.

6. 3 is 0.5 more than 2.5.

7. 8.2 is 0.4 less than 8.6.

8. 99.2 is 100.8 subtracted from 200.

Translate to an equation. Then solve.

9. Find the difference between 0.2 and 7.83.

10. Subtract 0.89 from 2.

11. What number is the sum of 4 and 6.82?

12. 12.82 more than 1.6 is what number?

13. Find 100.1 reduced by 79.93.

14. What number increased by 75.3 yields 98?

15. 7.234 plus what number gives 23.65?

16. 18.04 take away 8.7 gives what number?

17. Find the result when 10 is decreased by 3.4.

18. Find the result when 86.24 is increased by 7.

6.7   APPLICATIONS

OBJECTIVES

▌ Solve an application that involves a total as the sum of parts

▌ Solve an application that involves an increase or decrease.

▌ Solve an application that involves comparisons by addition or subtraction.

▌ Find the perimeter of a figure.

▌ Solve an application that involves more than one step.

There are many situations in your daily life in which addition and subtraction of decimals is needed. In this section we look at some of these situations and give guidelines on how to decide whether to add or subtract.

1   Problems Involving a Total as the Sum of Parts

We know that to add means to combine or total. In the addition statement

$$15.6 + 9.4 = 25$$

the sum 25 is the total and the terms 15.6 and 9.4 are parts of the total. Recall from Section 6.5 that, if any one of the three numbers is missing, we can find it using the two given numbers. Here we review the procedure.

> *Finding the Missing Number in a Basic Addition Statement*
>
> **1.** If the sum (or total) is missing, add the terms (or parts) to find the missing number.
> **2.** If one of the terms (or parts) is missing, subtract the given term from the total to find the missing term.

The following examples illustrate how to use this concept to solve some application problems.

Try These Problems

1. Tom ran a total of 0.3 mile in 2 minutes. The first minute he ran 0.125 mile. How far did he run the second minute?

2. Roberto combined 25.8 gallons of gas with 8.25 gallons of gas. What is the total amount of gas?

3. The total distance from P to N is 7 meters. The distance from P to Q is 3.6 meters. How far is it from Q to N?

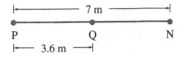

4. Find the perimeter of this triangle.

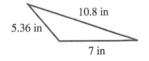

EXAMPLE 1   Arahwana worked on her report 4.5 hours on Monday, 3.75 hours on Tuesday, and 2.25 hours on Wednesday. What is the total time for the three days?

SOLUTION   We are looking for the *total* time, so we add.

$$\begin{array}{r} 1\,1 \\ 4.5 \\ 3.75 \\ +\quad 2.25 \\ \hline 10.50 = 10.5 \end{array}$$

She worked a total of 10.5 hours. ■

EXAMPLE 2   The total distance from the bottom of the vase to the top of the flowers is 38 centimeters. The flowers rise 13.4 centimeters above the vase. How tall is the vase?

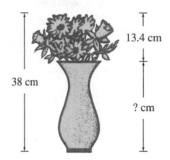

13.4 cm

38 cm

? cm

SOLUTION

$$\text{Total height} = \frac{\text{height of}}{\text{the vase}} + \frac{\text{height of the flowers}}{\text{above the vase}}$$

$$38 \quad = \quad \boxed{} \quad + \quad 13.4$$

We are missing one of the terms in an addition statement, so we subtract 13.4 from 38 to find the missing term.

$$\begin{array}{r} 3\,8.0 \text{——Total height} \\ -\ 1\,3.4 \text{——Part of the total} \\ \hline 2\,4.6 \end{array}$$

The vase is 24.6 centimeters tall. ■

 Try Problems 1 through 4.

2 Problems Involving Increases and Decreases

The price of gasoline increased from $1.20 a gallon to $1.37 during an oil crisis. The amount that the price went up is called the **increase** (or **gain**). What is the increase in price?

$$\frac{\text{Lower}}{\text{price}} + \text{increase} = \frac{\text{higher}}{\text{price}}$$

$$\$1.20 + \boxed{} = \$1.37$$

To find the increase we subtract.

Try These Problems

5. On Monday Alan jogged 5.4 miles. On Tuesday he increased his jogging distance by 2.3 miles over Monday's distance. How far did he jog on Tuesday?

6. The monthly service charge for Roger's checking account increased from $13.75 t0 $15. What was the increase?

7. Mr. Wong purchased a car marked $10,840. The state tax increased the price to $11,761.40. What was the amount of the state tax?

8. Last month gas was selling for $1.85 a gallon and this month the price is $1.58 a gallon. What is the reduction in price?

9. An office supply store is having a sale. A felt tip pen that originally sold for $1.25 is now selling for $0.89. What is the savings on one pen?

$$\text{Increase} = \frac{\text{higher}}{\text{price}} - \frac{\text{lower}}{\text{price}}$$
$$= \$1.37 - \$1.20$$
$$= \$0.17$$

The increase in price is $0.17.

 Try Problems 5 through 7.

Yesterday lettuce was selling for $1.45 a head. Today a head costs $0.85. The amount that the price went down is called the **decrease.** What is the decrease in price?

$$\text{Decrease} = \frac{\text{higher}}{\text{price}} - \frac{\text{lower}}{\text{price}}$$
$$= \$1.45 - \$0.85$$
$$= \$0.60$$

The decrease in price is $0.60.

Other words can be used to mean decrease. Here we list some situations where a value went down and give the corresponding language.

Situation	*Words Indicating the Amount the Value Went Down*
There is a sale on coats. A $100 value is now selling for $75.50.	The *discount* is $24.50 The *savings* is $24.50 The *reduction* in price is $24.50 The *decrease* in price is $24.50
A dog lost weight. The weight dropped from 10.5 pounds to 8.2 pounds.	The *loss* in weight is 2.3 pounds. The *reduction* in weight is 2.3 pounds. The *decrease* is 2.3 pounds.

 Try Problems 8 and 9.

3 Problems Involving Comparisons

Two unequal numbers, such as 30 and 18.6, can be compared using addition and subtraction. Here is a list of several addition and subtraction statements involving 30 and 18.6 and the corresponding comparison statements in English.

Comparing Two Numbers	
Math Symbols	*English*
18.6 + 11.4 = 30	11.4 more than 18.6 is 30.
30 − 11.4 = 18.6	11.4 less than 30 is 18.6.
30 − 18.6 = 11.4	30 and 18.6 differ by 11.4. The *difference* between 30 and 18.6 is 11.4. 30 is more than 18.6 by 11.4. 18.6 is less than 30 by 11.4.

Try These Problems

10. Stephanie has a skirt that is 45.2 centimeters long. Her mother, Tish, wants to lengthen the skirt by 3.5 centimeters. How long will the skirt be after Tish lets the hem out?

11. Betsy mixed a salt solution weighing 50.7 grams. Arthur mixed a salt solution weighing 52 grams. How much lighter is Betsy's solution?

12. Sandy and Leah were in a skiing race. Sandy skied the race in 16.25 seconds. Leah's time was 1.08 seconds less than Sandy's time. How long did it take Leah to ski the race?

Now we look at examples of problems involving comparisons.

EXAMPLE 3   Charlie tried to install a refrigerator that is 62 centimeters wide in a space that is only 61.4 centimeters wide. How much wider is the refrigerator than the space?

SOLUTION   We want to know how much larger 62 is than 61.4. We subtract 61.4 from 62.

$$
\begin{array}{r}
6\ \overset{1}{\cancel{2}}.\overset{1}{\cancel{0}} \\
-\ 6\ 1.4 \\
\hline
0.6
\end{array}
$$

   width of the refrigerator
   width of the space
   difference in the two widths

The refrigerator is 0.6 centimeter wider than the space. ▪

EXAMPLE 4   Lou earns $15.50 per hour. Valerie earns $3.75 less than Lou per hour. How much does Valerie earn each hour?

SOLUTION   Valerie's hourly wage is $3.75 less than Lou's hourly wage. This statement translates to a subtraction statement.

$$
\begin{array}{ccc}
\text{Valerie's} \\ \text{hourly wage}
\end{array}
=
\begin{array}{ccc}
\text{Lou's} \\ \text{hourly wage}
\end{array}
-\ \$3.75
$$

$$
\boxed{} = \$15.50 - \$3.75
$$

To find Valerie's hourly wage we subtract $3.75 from $15.50.

$$
\begin{array}{r}
\$\ 1\ \overset{4}{\cancel{5}}.\overset{4}{\cancel{5}}\overset{1}{0} \\
-\ \$\ \ \ \ 3.7\ 5 \\
\hline
\$\ 1\ 1.7\ 5
\end{array}
$$

Valerie earns $11.75 per hour. ▪

 Try Problems 10 through 12.

4   Applications Requiring More than One Operation

Now we look at an application that requires more than one step to solve.

EXAMPLE 5   The length of a rectangle is 15.6 inches more than its width. The width is 45 inches. Find the perimeter of the rectangle.

SOLUTION   Here we picture the situation.

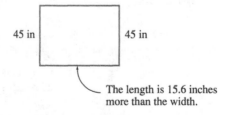

45 in   45 in

The length is 15.6 inches more than the width.

Try These Problems

13. The width of a rectangle is 14.2 centimeters less than the length. If the length is 80 centimeters, find the perimeter of the rectangle.

14. Irene had $412.89 in her checking account. She deposited a check for $356.32 and withdrew $45.79, $124,85, and $68. What is her balance after these transactions?

First, we find the length of the rectangle.

Length is 15.6 inches more than the width

$$\boxed{} = 15.6 + 45$$

To find the length, we must add 15.6 and 45.

$$\begin{array}{r} 15.6 \\ + 45.0 \\ \hline 60.6 \end{array}$$

The length of the rectangle is 60.6 inches.

The **perimeter** of the rectangle is the distance all the way around, so we must add two widths and two lengths together to obtain the perimeter.

$$\begin{array}{r} 60.6 \\ 60.6 \\ 45.0 \\ + 45.0 \\ \hline 211.2 \end{array}$$

The perimeter is 211.2 inches. ■

 Try Problems 13 and 14.

Now we summarize the material presented in this section by giving guidelines that will help you decide whether to add or subtract.

Situations Requiring Addition and Subtraction	
Operation	**Situation**
+	**1.** You are looking for the total or whole.
	2. You are looking for the result when a quantity has been increased.
	3. You are looking for the perimeter of a figure.
−	**1.** You are looking for one of the parts in a total or whole.
	2. You are looking for the result when a quantity has been decreased.
	3. You are looking for how much larger one quantity is than another.
	4. You are looking for how much smaller one quantity is than another.

 Answers to Try These Problems

1. 0.175 mi   2. 34.05 gal   3. 3.4 m   4. 23.16 in
5. 7.7 mi   6. $1.25   7. $921.40   8. $0.27   9. $0.36
10. 48.7 cm   11. 1.3 g   12. 15.17 sec   13. 291.6 cm
14. $530.57

EXERCISES 6.7

1. Nell bought a dress for her granddaughter. The dress was marked $15.95. A tax increased the price by $0.80. What was the total price?

2. Cynthia practiced her piano 2.25 hours on Thursday and 1.75 hours on Friday. How long did she practice during the two days?

3. A lamp has a total height of 82.2 centimeters. From the bottom of the base to the bottom of the shade is 42.4 centimeters. Find the height of the shade.

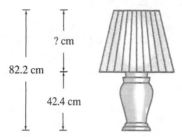

4. Carlos used a 1.2-centimeter screwdriver to loosen a 0.75-centimeter screw. The screwdriver is how much wider than the screw?

5. Find the perimeter of this rectangle.

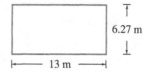

6. Mary bought 10 yards of fabric to make some bicycling clothes for herself and her boyfriend. She used 3.3 yards for herself. How much is left?

7. On a four-day business trip, Ms. Nelle filled her gas tank three times. The amounts were 15.2 gallons, 16 gallons, and 12.9 gallons. How much gasoline did she buy during the trip?

8. Joe bought a portable radio that was marked $85.89. After the tax was added on, it cost $91.37. How much did he pay in tax?

9. Greg jogged a total of 5.4 miles. He jogged 3.6 miles along the highway, then the rest along the river bank. How far did he jog along the river bank?

10. On a two-week trip to Tahiti, Jody encountered the following expenses: $685.75 for air fare, $935.85 for room and board, and $121.60 for miscellaneous other expenses. What was the total cost of the trip?

11. Ms. Taylor bought a microwave oven that was 24.9 inches wide. She put it in a space that was 27.8 inches wide. How much wider was the space than the microwave oven?

12. A cat weighed 5.2 pounds, then lost 1.5 pounds. What was the cat's weight after the weight loss?

13. The price of beans was $1.15 per pound and now is $1.74 per pound. What is the increase in price?

14. Jimmy weighed 8.2 pounds when he was born. Chuck weighed 7.5 pounds at birth. What is the difference in their birth weights?

15. Don is 1.4 feet taller than Richard. If Don is 6.2 feet tall, how tall is Richard?

16. Yesterday the price of oranges was $0.16 per pound less than today. If today's price is $1.25 per pound, what was yesterday's price?

17. The width of a rectangle is 3.5 inches less than the length. If the length is 19.25 inches, find the perimeter of the rectangle.

18. Mr. Stuart has a balance of $500.19 in his checking account. He writes checks for $54.62, $8.74, and $23.91. What is his balance now?

19. Bernice had 450 calories for breakfast, 432 calories for lunch, and 515 calories for supper. That same day, her husband Tom had 520 calories for breakfast, 612 calories for lunch, and 750 calories for supper. How many more calories did Tom have than Bernice for that day?

20. Carlos is taking a 100-mile hike. He hikes 28.5 miles on Monday, 19.8 miles on Tuesday, and 35.2 miles on Wednesday. How much farther does he have to go?

21. What is the difference in the perimeters of these two rectangles?

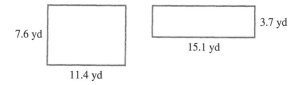

22. A race-car driver wanted to limit total pit-stop time to 50 seconds. He made three pit stops in 16.2 seconds, 15.8 seconds, and 15.6 seconds. How much over or under his desired limit is he?

During an oil crisis the average price per gallon of gasoline fluctuated over a 6-month period as shown in the bar graph. Use the graph to answer Exercises 23 through 26.

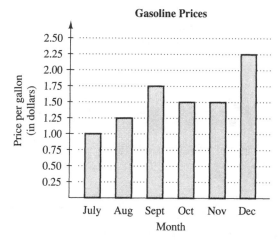

23. What was the average price per gallon for the month of August?

24. For what months was the average price per gallon $1.50?

25. From November to December did the price per gallon increase or decrease, and by how much?

26. From September to October did the price per gallon increase or decrease, and by how much?

CHAPTER 6 SUMMARY

KEY WORDS AND PHRASES

decimal [6.1]

digit [6.1]

expanded form [6.1]

place value [6.1]

decimal fractions [6.1]

round off [6.4]

round up [6.4]

truncate (round down) [6.4]

addition [6.5]

subtraction [6.5]

sum [6.6]

difference [6.6]

increase (gain) [6.7]

decrease [6.7]

perimeter [6.7]

SYMBOLS

3.7   means $3\frac{7}{10}$ [6.1]

$4.12 < 4.3$ means   4.12 is less than 4.3. [6.3]

$4.3 > 4.12$ means   4.3 is more than 4.12. [6.3]

$\approx$ or $\doteq$ means   *is approximately equal to.* [6.4]

IMPORTANT RULES

How to Round Off, Round Up, and Truncate Decimals [6.4]

The chart on page 240 summarizes how to approximate decimals using each of these three methods.

How to Add Decimals [6.5]

The rule for adding decimals is on page 242.

How to Subtract Decimals [6.5]

The rule for subtracting decimals is on page 244.

How to Find the Missing Number in an Addition Statement [6.5]

▌ If the sum (or total) is missing, then add the terms (or parts) to find the sum.

▌ If one of the terms (or parts) is missing, then subtract the known term from the sum (or total) to obtain the missing term.

The Perimeter of a Figure [6.7]

The perimeter of a figure means the total distance around the figure.

Situations Requiring Addition and Subtraction [6.7]

Guidelines for when to add and when to subtract are given in the chart on page 253.

CHAPTER 6 REVIEW EXERCISES

For the decimal 728.10365, give the digit with the indicated place value.

1. hundredths   **2.** hundreds   **3.** $\frac{1}{10,000}$ **4.** $\frac{1}{10}$

Write the decimal whose expanded form is given.

5. $\frac{6}{10} + \frac{9}{1000}$ **6.** $800 + 4 + \frac{3}{100} + \frac{7}{1000}$

Write each decimal as a fraction, mixed numeral, or whole numeral. Do not reduce the fractions to lowest terms.

7. 0.003   **8.** 7.27

Write a decimal numeral for each of the following.

9. $\frac{19}{10,000}$ **10.** $14\frac{15}{100}$

Write the decimal whose English name is given.

11. Sixteen thousand

12. Sixteen thousandths

13. Ninety and two hundred three ten-thousandths

14. Seven hundred fourteen hundredths

Write the English name for each decimal.

15. 0.05   **16.** 50.0002   **17.** 0.304   **18.** 304,000

*Write the value of the given piece of currency in **a.** cents and **b.** dollars.*

19. nickel   **20.** quarter   **21.** dollar bill   **22.** five-dollar bill

Write the English name of a single piece of currency with the indicated value.

23. $0.10   **24.** $0.01   **25.** $10.00   **26.** 50¢

Write the symbol for each in dollars.

27. Forty-seven cents

28. Sixty-two and twelve hundredths dollars

*Write each value using English in two ways: **a.** with the fractional part of the dollar in cents and **b.** with the entire value in dollars.*

29. $0.61   **30.** $200.07

31. Which of these decimals are equal to .580?
     a. .58   **b.** 58.   **c.** 58.0   **d.** 0.58   **e.** 580

32. Which of these have the same money value as $102.00?
     a. $12   **b.** $102   **c.** $102.   **d.** $10.20   **e.** $10,200

List from smallest to largest.

33. 1; 3.9; 0.39   **34.** 73.2323; .732323; 73.23222

Choose the correct symbol $<$, $=$, or $>$ to compare each pair of numbers.

35. 6.03; 6.003   **36.** 7.2; 7.20

37. 19.7; 1.97   **38.** 83.1516; 83.15158

Round off each decimal at the place indicated.

39. 138.137; two decimal places   **40.** $43.49; nearest dollar

Round up each decimal at the place indicated.

41. 0.23117; thousandths place   **42.** $204.833; nearest cent

Truncate each decimal at the place indicated.

43. 9.81768; four decimal places   **44.** 93.1553; hundredths place

Add.

45. 76.7 + 9.682   **46.** 0.8907 + 28.45

47. 26.03 + 66   **48.** 968 + 75.45

49. $13.75 + $704 + $8.36   **50.** $93 + $85.32 + $186.09

Subtract.

51. 76.52 − 5.1   **52.** $70.13 − $9

53. 511.2 − 83.74   **54.** 85.7 − 4.308

55. 9 − 3.6   **56.** 73 − 18.26

57. 3000 − 4.52   **58.** 80,500 − 751.4

Find the missing number.

59. $34.18 + 7.9 = \boxed{}$ **60.** $\boxed{} + 30.6 = 143$

Translate each English statement into an addition or subtraction statement using math symbols.

61. 107 subtracted from 210.8 is 103.8.

62. The sum of 0.7 and 0.6 is 1.3.

63. 4.2 more than 15.8 is 20.

64. 19.7 decreased by 2 gives 17.7.

Solve. Show setups and calculation steps.

65. Find the difference between 2.1 and 0.75.

66. What number increased by 7.2 yields 10.19?

67. Subtract 19.03 from 168.

68. 15 is more than 3.98 by how much?

69. Sam jogged 5.8 miles today and 3.25 miles yesterday. How much farther did he jog today than yesterday?

70. What is the total distance from A to C?

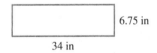

71. A department store is having a sale on television sets. The price of a TV set was marked down from $500 to $465.85. What was the savings?

72. Jan bought a car marked $20,600. A state tax increased the price to $22,505.80. How much was the state tax?

73. Find the perimeter of this rectangle.

6.75 in

34 in

74. Peter has a rope that is 23.6 meters long. He cuts off a piece that is 4.8 meters long. How long is the remaining piece?

✍ In Your Own Words

Write complete sentences to discuss each of the following. Support your comments with examples or pictures, if appropriate.

75. A student incorrectly writes the numeral 35,000 for "thirty-five thousandths." Discuss how you would help this student understand the error made.

76. Discuss how addition of whole numerals is similar to addition of decimals.

77. Discuss the differences in rounding off, rounding up, and truncating.

78. Discuss a real-life situation where rounding up is used.

79. A sign in the post office reads, "Envelopes for 0.69¢ each." You know that they mean to sell these envelopes for 69 cents each. Discuss what is wrong with the sign. How can you help them to understand that 0.69¢ does not represent 69 cents?

CHAPTER 6 PRACTICE TEST

Write a decimal numeral for each.

1. $\frac{934}{10}$

2. $6\frac{19}{10000}$

Write the decimal whose English name is given.

3. Sixty-five hundredths   **4.** Forty-eight and seven thousandths

Write the English name for each.

5. 0.0013

6. 7.2

7. Write the value of a quarter in dollars.

8. Write the value of a five-dollar bill in cents.

9. Which of these decimals are equal to 0.90?
   a. 90   **b.** .900   **c.** 0.9   **d.** .9   **e.** 9.00

10. List from smallest to largest: 1.07; 0.701; 0.079

11. Use the correct symbol $<$, $=$, or $>$ to compare 0.007 and 0.00089.

12. Round off 26.0843 to three decimal places.

13. Round up $78.34 to the nearest dollar.

14. Truncate 0.013456 at the ten-thousandths place.

Add.

15. 6.31 + 129.8

16. 864 + 2.7 + 9 + 0.856

Subtract.

17. 13.8 − 2.403

18. $856.34 − $82

19. 232 − 7.44

20. 5000 − 78.6

Solve. Show setups and calculation steps.

21. Find the sum of 18.6 and 164.82.

22. Find the number that is 2.3 less than 10.

23. Find the perimeter of a rectangle that has width 78.32 feet and length 36.8 feet.

24. A dog weighed 12.4 pounds, then lost 2.8 pounds. What was the dog's weight after the weight loss?

25. Rita paid $7.85 more for a blouse than Britt-Marie. If Rita paid $60.35 for the blouse, what did Britt-Marie pay?

26. Mr. McWilliams was planning to jog a distance of 12 miles. His knee began to hurt after he had gone 8.5 miles, so he walked the rest of the 12 miles. How far did he walk?

CHAPTER

7

Decimals: Multiplication and Division

MULTIPLICATION

OBJECTIVES ▌ Multiply two or more decimals.
▌ Use a shortcut to multiply decimals involving zeros.
▌ Solve an application that involves multiplication of decimals.

1 Multiplying Decimals

At the supermarket, ground beef sells for $4.20 per pound. How much would you pay for 3.2 pounds of ground beef? We have the following.

$$\begin{matrix} \text{Cost per} \\ \text{pound} \end{matrix} \times \begin{matrix} \text{how many} \\ \text{pounds} \end{matrix} = \text{total cost}$$

$$\$4.20 \quad \times \quad 3.2 \quad = \quad \boxed{}$$

To find the total cost, we need to multiply $4.20 by 3.2.

$$
\begin{array}{r}
4.2\,0 \\
\times \quad 3.2 \\
\hline
8\,4\,0 \\
1\,2\,6\,0 \quad\;\; \\
\hline
1\,3.4\,4\,0 \\
\end{array}
$$

2 decimal places
1 decimal place

2 + 1 = 3 decimal places

You would pay $13.44 for 3.2 pounds of ground beef.

Observe that to multiply the two decimals, begin by multiplying 420 by 32 as if they were whole numbers. This gives 13,440. To place the decimal in the answer, count the number of digits in the multipliers that are to the right of the decimal point. In this case, there are a total of 3 decimal places because there are 2 digits to the right of the decimal point in 4.20 and 1 digit to the right of the decimal point in 3.2. Finally, place the decimal in the answer so that there are 3 digits to the right of the decimal point.

Now we will look carefully at the multiplication problem

$$0.02 \times 1.4 = ?$$

Before doing the problem using the procedure discussed in the previous paragraph, we will do the problem using fractions so that you can see why the previously discussed procedure works.

$$0.02 \times 1.4$$

$$= \frac{2}{100} \times 1\frac{4}{10} \qquad \text{Convert each decimal to a fraction.}$$

$$= \frac{2}{100} \times \frac{14}{10}$$

$$= \frac{28}{1000} \qquad \begin{array}{l}\text{Multiply without canceling so that} \\ \text{it will be easy to convert back} \\ \text{to a decimal.}\end{array}$$

$$= 0.028 \qquad \text{Convert back to a decimal.}$$

By solving this problem using fractions, we see that the correct answer should be 0.028. Observe how we can obtain the same answer without using fractions.

Begin by multiplying 2 by 14 to obtain 28.

$$
\begin{array}{r}
1.4 \\
\times\ 0.0\,2 \\
\hline
.0\,2\,8
\end{array}
$$

1 decimal place
2 decimal places
1 + 2 = 3 decimal places. Insert a 0 digit in front of the 2 to make 3 decimal places.

Here are more examples of multiplying decimals.

EXAMPLE 1 Multiply: .069 × .12

SOLUTION Begin by multiplying 69 by 12 as if the numbers were whole numbers. Place the decimal point as indicated here.

$$
\begin{array}{r}
.069 \\
\times\ .12 \\
\hline
138 \\
069 \\
\hline
.00828
\end{array}
$$

3 decimal places
2 decimal places

5 decimal places

Attach the extra 0 to make 5 decimal places.

The answer is 0.00828. ■

Try These Problems

Multiply.
1. .61 × .3
2. 2.5 × 7.8
3. 45 × 8.16
4. .042 × .9
5. .00082 × 3.4
6. .076 × .45

EXAMPLE 2	Multiply: 7.45 × 356.8

SOLUTION

$$
\begin{array}{r}
3\ 5\ 6.8 \\
\times\quad 7.4\ 5 \\
\hline
1\ 7\ 8\ 4\ 0 \\
1\ 4\ 2\ 7\ 2 \\
2\ 4\ 9\ 7\ 6 \\
\hline
2\ 6\ 5\ 8.1\ 6\ 0
\end{array}
$$

1 decimal place
2 decimal places

1 + 2 = 3 decimal places

The answer is 2658.16. ■

EXAMPLE 3	Multiply: 32 × 20.5

SOLUTION

$$
\begin{array}{r}
2\ 0.5 \\
\times\quad 3\ 2 \\
\hline
4\ 1\ 0 \\
6\ 1\ 5 \\
\hline
6\ 5\ 6.0
\end{array}
$$

1 decimal place
0 decimal places

1 decimal place

The answer is 656. ■

EXAMPLE 4	Multiply: .642 × .008

SOLUTION

$$
\begin{array}{r}
.6\ 4\ 2 \\
\times\quad .0\ 0\ 8 \\
\hline
.0\ 0\ 5\ 1\ 3\ 6
\end{array}
$$

3 decimal places
3 decimal places
3 + 3 = 6 decimal places
Attach 2 extra 0s to make 6 decimal places.

The answer is 0.005136. ■

Now we summarize by writing a rule for multiplying decimals.

> *Multiplying Decimals*
> 1. Ignore the decimal points for a moment. Multiply the numbers as if they were whole numbers.
> 2. Place the decimal point in the product by adding the number of decimal places in the multipliers to get the number of decimal places in the product.
> 3. You may have to attach extra zeros on the left end of the product to make enough decimal places.

 Try Problems 1 through 6.

2 Recognizing Unnecessary Zero Digits

The following chart illustrates when a zero digit is necessary and when a zero digit is unnecessary. When we say that a zero digit is unnecessary we mean that omitting it does not change the value of the number, where we are discussing values as exact and not as approximations.

⏷ **Try These Problems**

Multiply.
   7. 0.45 × 0.37
   8. .5400 × 0.82
   9. $132.00 × 0.90

	Decimal	*Location of the Zero Digit*
Necessary Zero Digits	150. = 150 200. = 200 34,000. = 34,000	Zero digits on the right end but before the decimal point.
	.107 208.7 1006.103	Zero digits between nonzero digits.
	.03 = 0.03 .005 = 0.005 .0017 = 0.0017	Zero digits on the left end but after the decimal point.
Unnecessary Zero Digits	0.5 = .5 00.33 = .33 008.134 = 8.134	Zero digits on the left end but before the decimal point.
	22.00 = 22 .50 = .5 .3600 = .36	Zero digits on the right end but after the decimal point.

When a multiplication problem is presented to you with unnecessary zeros, it is more convenient to drop the extra zeros before multiplying. The following examples illustrate this.

EXAMPLE 5 Multiply: 0.75 × 4.600

   SOLUTION Because 0.75 = .75 and 4.600 = 4.6, the problem is .75 × 4.6.

$$
\begin{array}{r}
4.6 \\
\times\ .7\,5 \\
\hline
2\,3\,0 \\
3\,2\,2 \\
\hline
3.4\,5\,0
\end{array}
$$

   4.6   1 decimal place
   × .75   2 decimal places

   3.450   3 decimal places

The answer is 3.45. ■

EXAMPLE 6 Multiply: $26.00 × 8.40

   SOLUTION Because $26.00 = $26 and 8.40 = 8.4, the problem is 26 × 8.4.

$$
\begin{array}{r}
2\,6 \\
\times\ 8.4 \\
\hline
1\,0\,4 \\
2\,0\,8 \\
\hline
2\,1\,8.4
\end{array}
$$

   26   0 decimal places
   × 8.4   1 decimal place

   218.4   1 decimal place

The answer is $218.40. ■

⏷ **Try Problems 7 through 9.**

 **Try These Problems**

Multiply.
10. .007 × 81.04
11. 54.006 × 70004
12. 0.807 × 2.0050

3 Using a Shortcut to Multiply Decimals with Necessary Zero Digits

When a zero digit is between two nonzero digits or is between the decimal point and a nonzero digit, then it is a necessary zero digit and cannot be omitted before multiplying. However, there are some steps in the multiplication process that can be omitted. In the following examples, we solve the problem in two ways: first by the long method and then by the shortcut method.

EXAMPLE 7   Multiply: 305 × 32.626
SOLUTION
LONG METHOD

```
       32.626
   ×      305
     163 130
     000 00 ——— This row of zeros does not add anything to
     9787 8          the product.
    9950.930
```

SHORTCUT

```
       32.626
   ×      305
     163 130
     9787 8 ——— Be sure to begin this row directly under
    9950.930        the digit 3 in 305.
```
Omit the row of zeros.

The answer is 9950.93. ■

EXAMPLE 8   Multiply: 0.0038 × 7.064
SOLUTION Because 0.0038 = .0038, the problem is .0038 × 7.064.
LONG METHOD

```
       7.064
   × .0 038
     56 512
     211 92
     000 0 —— These two rows of zeros do not
     0000       add anything to the product.
    .0268 432
```

SHORTCUT

```
       7.064
   × .0038
     56512
     21192
    .0268432
```
Omit the rows of zeros.

The answer is 0.268432. ■

 **Try Problems 10 through 12.**

Try These Problems

Multiply.

13. 10×18.07

14. 0.041×100

15. 1000×6.7

16. $23.8 \times 10,000$

4 Using a Shortcut to Multiply by a Whole Number Ending in Zero Digits

First we investigate what happens when a decimal is multiplied by 10, 100, 1000, and so on. Here we look carefully at three multiplication problems. First we multiply 3.45 by 10.

$$3.45 \times 10 = 34.5$$

$$\begin{array}{r} 3.45 \\ \times\ \ 10 \\ \hline 0\,00 \\ 34\,5 \\ \hline 34.50 = 34.5 \end{array}$$

Observe that when 3.45 is multiplied by 10, the decimal point moves 1 place to the right, giving the answer 34.5. Next we multiply 3.45 by 100.

$$3.45 \times 100 = 345. \quad \text{or} \quad 345$$

$$\begin{array}{r} 3.45 \\ \times\ \ 1\,00 \\ \hline 0\,00 \\ 00\,0 \\ 345 \\ \hline 345.00 = 345 \end{array}$$

Observe that when 3.45 is multiplied by 100, the decimal point moves 2 places to the right, giving the answer 345. Finally, we multiply 3.45 by 1000.

$$3.45 \times 1000 = 3450$$

$$\begin{array}{r} 3.45 \\ \times\ \ 10\,00 \\ \hline 0\,00 \\ 00\,0 \\ 000 \\ 345 \\ \hline 3450.00 \ = 3450 \end{array}$$

Observe that when 3.45 is multiplied by 1000, the decimal point moves 3 places to the right, giving the answer 3450. The number of places the decimal moves agrees with the number of zeros in 10, 100, 1000, and so forth. We generalize the previous results by stating a shortcut for multiplying by 10, 100, 1000, and so on.

Multiplying a Decimal by 10, 100, 1000, and So On

Move the decimal point to the right
One place when multiplying by 10.
Two places when multiplying by 100.
Three places when multiplying by 1000.
Four places when multiplying by 10,000.
The pattern continues. The decimal point moves to the right the same number of places as there are zeros.

 Try Problems 13 through 16.

Next we look at a shortcut that can be used when multiplying a decimal by any whole number ending in zeros. In the examples that

Try These Problems

Multiply.

17. 5.2 × 600

18. 800,000 × .036

19. 4.55 × 28,000

follow, we solve the problem in two ways: first by the long method and then by the shortcut.

EXAMPLE 9   Multiply: 750,000 × .65

SOLUTION

LONG METHOD

```
        7 5 0 0 0 0
   ×          .6 5
   ─────────────────
      3 7 5 0 0 0 0
    4 5 0 0 0 0 0
   ─────────────────
    4 8 7 5 0 0.0 0
```

The four zero digits at the end of 750,000 caused these four zero digits in the product.

SHORTCUT

```
        7 5 0 0 0 0
   ×  .6 5
   ─────────────
      3 7 5
    4 5 0
   ─────────────
    4 8 7 5 0 0.0 0
```

Bring down the four zeros at the end of 750,000.

The answer is 487,500. ■

EXAMPLE 10   Multiply: 9000 × 2.607

SOLUTION

LONG METHOD

```
        2.6 0 7
   ×  9 0 0 0
   ─────────────
        0 0 0 0
      0 0 0 0
    0 0 0 0
    2 3 4 6 3
   ─────────────
    2 3 4 6 3.0 0 0
```

These three zero digits were caused by the three zero digits at the end of 9000.

SHORTCUT

```
        2.6 0 7
   ×          9 0 0 0
   ─────────────────
    2 3 4 6 3.0 0 0
```

Bring down the three zeros at the end of 9000.

The answer is 23,463. ■

 Try Problems 17 through 19.

5 Multiplying More Than Two Decimals

To multiply more than two numbers, multiply any two of them first, then multiply that result by another one, and continue until all of the numbers have been multiplied. The following examples illustrate the procedure.

▲ **Try These Problems**

Multiply.

20. 5.09 × 10 × 0.8

21. .008 × 3.6 × 300 × 5

EXAMPLE 11 Multiply: 0.7 × 2.1 × 6

SOLUTION It doesn't matter which two numbers are multiplied first. We begin by multiplying 0.7 by 2.1, then we multiply that result by 6.

$$\begin{array}{r} 2.1 \\ \times\ \ .7 \\ \hline 1.4\,7 \end{array} \qquad \begin{array}{r} 1.47 \\ \times\ \ \ \ 6 \\ \hline 8.82 \end{array}$$

The answer is 8.82. ■

EXAMPLE 12 Multiply: 3.75 × 1000 × 4.6 × 3.08

SOLUTION The 4 numbers can be multiplied in any order. We multiply 3.75 by 1000, 4.6 by 3.08, then multiply those two results.

$$3.75 \times 1000 = 3750$$

$$\begin{array}{r} 3.0\,8 \\ \times\ \ \ \ 4.6 \\ \hline 1\,8\,4\,8 \\ 1\,2\,3\,2 \\ \hline 1\,4.1\,6\,8 \end{array} \qquad \begin{array}{r} 1\,4.1\,68 \\ \times\ \ \ \ 3\,750 \\ \hline 7\,0\,8\,400 \\ 9\,9\,1\,7\,6 \\ 4\,2\,5\,0\,4 \\ \hline 5\,3\,1\,3\,0.000 \end{array}$$

The answer is 53,130. ■

▲ **Try Problems 20 and 21.**

▲ **Answers to Try These Problems**

1. .183 or 0.183   **2.** 19.50 or 19.5   **3.** 367.20 or 367.2
4. .0378 or 0.0378   **5.** 0.002788   **6.** 0.0342   **7.** 0.1665
8. 0.4428   **9.** $118.80   **10.** 0.56728   **11.** 3,780,636.024
12. 1.618035   **13.** 180.7   **14.** 4.1   **15.** 6700   **16.** 238,000
17. 3120   **18.** 28,800   **19.** 127,400   **20.** 40.72   **21.** 43.2

EXERCISES 7.1

Multiply.

1. .15 × .6   **2.** .07 × 17.1   **3.** 9.1 × 3.6   **4.** 8 × 2.3

5. 8.6 × 409   **6.** 307.9 × 7.1   **7.** 17.378 × 8.79   **8.** .7 × 4034

9. 6943 × .65   **10.** 92.68 × .47

Multiply. Use a shortcut method when appropriate.

11. 0.4 × 7.50   **12.** 23.00 × 0.80   **13.** .1500 × 3.7

14. 07.30 × 52   **15.** 13.008 × .09   **16.** 746 × 500.8

17. 1200 × .045   **18.** 18,000 × 13.2   **19.** 368,000 × .0625

20. 7,030,000 × 4.40   **21.** 100 × 7.813   **22.** .0816 × 100,000

23. 0.360 × 3.007   **24.** 0.0076 × 0.750   **25.** $73.00 × 190,000

26. 50,300 × $80.70   **27.** 0.78 × 5.2 × 3.2   **28.** 4.02 × 0.007 × 40

29. 500 × 45.2 × 20.03 × 0.6   **30.** 0.0052 × 1000 × 6.7 × 0.3

Solve.

31. Chicken breasts are selling for $3.69 per pound. What do 5.5 pounds of these chicken breasts cost? Round up the answer to the nearest cent.

32. Pens are selling for $1.39 each. How much would you pay for 400 of these pens?

33. In a certain state, the sales tax is computed by multiplying the decimal 0.065 by the marked price. Find the sales tax for a coat that is marked $145.89. Round up the answer to the nearest cent.

34. Each section of a fence is 2.8 meters long. If 507 of these sections are connected, what is the length of the resulting fence?

7.2   DIVISION

OBJECTIVES

▌ Divide a decimal or a whole number by a whole number.
▌ Convert a fraction to decimal form.
▌ Divide a decimal or whole number by a decimal.
▌ Round off, round up, or truncate the answer to a division problem to a specified decimal place.
▌ Divide two places past the decimal point and write the remainder in fractional form.
▌ Write the answer to a division problem as a repeating decimal when specified.
▌ Use a shortcut to divide by 10, 100, 1000, and so on.
▌ Solve an application problem using division of decimals.

A **division** problem can be written in three ways. For example, here are three ways to write *20 divided by 5 is 4,* or *5 divided into 20 is 4.*

$$5\overline{)20}^{\,4} \qquad 20 \div 5 = 4 \qquad \frac{20}{5} = 4 \quad \text{because} \quad 5 \times 4 = 20$$

In each of these problems, the number 5 is called the **divisor,** the number 20 is called the **dividend.** In this section, we will learn how to carry out the division when there are decimals involved. We want the procedure to preserve the fact that division is the reverse of multiplication. This means that the answer to the division problem multiplied by the divisor gives the dividend.

1 Dividing Decimals by Whole Numbers

First we look at a couple of easy division problems so that we can see how to place the decimal point when dividing a decimal by a whole number.

$$2\overline{)8.6}^{\,4.3} \qquad \text{because} \quad 2 \times 4.3 = 8.6$$

$$5\overline{)10.15}^{\,2.03} \qquad \text{because} \quad 5 \times 2.03 = 10.15$$

Observe that when the divisor is a whole number, the decimal point in the answer is placed directly above the decimal point in the dividend.

Try These Problems

Divide as indicated.

1. $6.5 \div 5$

2. $0.15 \div 6$

3. $\frac{67.54}{22}$

4. $\frac{1584.8}{56}$

Here are more examples to illustrate how to divide a decimal by a whole number.

EXAMPLE 1   Divide: $11.6 \div 4$

SOLUTION $11.6 \div 4$ is the same as $4\overline{)11.6}$
— 4 is the divisor.

$$
\begin{array}{r}
2.9 \\
4\overline{)11.6} \\
\underline{8} \\
3\,6 \\
\underline{3\,6}
\end{array}
$$

Place the decimal point in the answer directly above the decimal point in the dividend.

Divide the numbers as whole numbers. Align the digits carefully.

CHECK
$$
\begin{array}{r}
2.9 \\
\times \quad 4 \\
\hline
11.6
\end{array}
$$

The answer is 2.9. ■

EXAMPLE 2   Divide: $43.6 \div 8$

SOLUTION $43.6 \div 8$ is the same as $8\overline{)43.6}$
— 8 is the divisor.

$$
\begin{array}{r}
5.45 \\
8\overline{)43.60} \\
\underline{40} \\
3\,6 \\
\underline{3\,2} \\
40 \\
\underline{40}
\end{array}
$$

— If you are past the decimal point, extra zeros may be attached to the dividend. $43.6 = 43.60$

CHECK
$$
\begin{array}{r}
5.45 \\
\times \quad 8 \\
\hline
43.60 = 43.6
\end{array}
$$

The answer is 5.45. ■

EXAMPLE 3   Divide: $\frac{0.36}{12}$

SOLUTION $\frac{0.36}{12}$ is the same as $12\overline{)0.36}$
— 12 is the divisor.

$$
\begin{array}{r}
.03 \\
12\overline{)0.36} \\
\underline{0} \\
36 \\
\underline{36}
\end{array}
$$

Zero digits on the left end must be written if you are past the decimal point.

The answer is 0.03. ■

 Try Problems 1 through 4.

In the previous three examples, the division came out evenly. This does not always happen. Here are some examples of various ways to leave the answer when the division does not come out evenly. First we look at approximating the answer at a certain decimal place. You should

Try These Problems

Divide and approximate the result as indicated.

5. 624.3 ÷ 8 (Round off at two decimal places.)

6. 0.4 ÷ 65 (Truncate at 4 decimal places.)

7. $\frac{0.508}{36}$ (Round up at 3 decimal places.)

be familiar with the three types of approximating (**rounding off, rounding up, and truncating**) that were covered in Section 6.4.

EXAMPLE 4   Divide: 12.34 ÷ 7 (Round off at 1 decimal place.)

SOLUTION   To round off at 1 decimal place, we will need to see the size of the digit in the 2nd place, so we will divide 2 places past the decimal, then stop and round off as indicated.

$$
\begin{array}{r}
1.76 \approx 1.8 \\
7\overline{)12.34} \\
\underline{7} \\
5\,3 \\
\underline{4\,9} \\
44 \\
\underline{42} \\
2
\end{array}
$$

The answer rounded off at 1 decimal place is 1.8.   ■

EXAMPLE 5   Divide: $\frac{0.04}{18}$ (Round up at 3 decimal places.)

SOLUTION   To round up at 3 decimal places, we will *not* need to look at the size of the digit in the 4th decimal place, so we need only to divide 3 places past the decimal point.

$$
\begin{array}{r}
.002 \approx 0.003 \\
18\overline{)0.040} \\
\underline{0} \\
4 \\
\underline{0} \\
40 \\
\underline{36} \\
4
\end{array}
$$

The answer rounded up at 3 decimal places is 0.003.   ■

 Try Problems 5 through 7.

Another way to leave the answer when the division is not coming out evenly is to stop dividing at some point and write the remainder in a fractional form. The following example illustrates this.

EXAMPLE 6   Divide: 423.1 ÷ 36   (Stop dividing 2 places past the decimal and write the answer in fractional form.)

SOLUTION

$$
\begin{array}{r}
1\,1.7\,5\frac{10}{36} = 11.75\frac{5}{18} \\
36\overline{)4\,2\,3.1\,0} \\
\underline{3\,6} \\
6\,3 \\
\underline{3\,6} \\
2\,7\,1 \\
\underline{2\,5\,2} \\
1\,9\,0 \\
\underline{1\,8\,0} \\
1\,0
\end{array}
$$

$$\text{Fraction} = \frac{\text{remainder}}{\text{divisor}}$$

Try These Problems

Divide. Stop dividing 2 places past the decimal and write the remainder in fractional form.

8. 2.34 ÷ 28

9. 19.8 ÷ 16

Divide. Write the answer as a repeating decimal.

10. 10.4 ÷ 9

11. 0.4 ÷ 33

The notation $11.75\frac{5}{18}$ is ambiguous. Although it is often used in business, it is seldom used by mathematicians. Here is what it means.

$$11.75\frac{5}{18} \quad \text{means} \quad 11\frac{75\frac{5}{18}}{100}$$

The fraction $\frac{5}{18}$ is not in the thousandths place, it is associated with the digit 5 that is in the hundredths place.

 Try Problems 8 and 9.

The answer to a division problem can be a repeating decimal. Sometimes the repeating pattern is easy to see after a few division steps. Here is an example:

EXAMPLE 7   Divide: $\frac{5.5}{6}$ (Write the answer as a repeating decimal.)

SOLUTION $\frac{5.5}{6}$ is the same as $6\overline{)5.5}$

$$
\begin{array}{r}
.9\ 1\ 6\ 6 = .91\overline{6} \\
6\overline{)5.5\ 0\ 0\ 0} \\
\underline{5\ 4} \\
1\ 0 \\
\underline{6} \\
4\ 0 \\
\underline{3\ 6} \\
4\ 0 \\
\underline{3\ 6} \\
4
\end{array}
$$

The digit 6 continues to repeat no matter how far we carry out the division.

A bar written above the 6 indicates this digit repeats.

The answer is $0.91\overline{6}$. ∎

 Try Problems 10 and 11.

2   Dividing a Whole Number by a Whole Number

Recall from Chapter 6 that the decimal point in a whole numeral is placed at the right end. For example,

$$5 = 5. = 5.00 \qquad \text{Five}$$
$$40 = 40. = 40.000 \qquad \text{Forty}$$
$$128 = 128. = 128.0 \qquad \text{One hundred twenty-eight}$$

Any number of zeros can be placed past the decimal point without changing the value of the whole number.

Now we look at examples of dividing a whole number by a whole number, where we write the answer as a decimal.

EXAMPLE 8   Divide: 32 ÷ 5

SOLUTION   32 ÷ 5 is the same as $5\overline{)32}$

$$
\begin{array}{r}
6.4 \\
5\overline{)32.0} \\
\underline{30} \\
2\ 0 \\
\underline{2\ 0}
\end{array}
$$

Every whole number can be written as a decimal. The decimal point is placed at the right end.

$32 = 32. = 32.0$

Try These Problems

Divide as indicated.

12. 15 ÷ 6

13. 6 ÷ 15

14. 7 ÷ 125

15. 125 ÷ 7 (Truncate at 2 decimal places.)

CHECK

$$\begin{array}{r} 6.4 \\ \times 5 \\ \hline 32.0 = 32 \end{array}$$

The answer is 6.4. ■

EXAMPLE 9 Divide: 5 ÷ 32

SOLUTION 5 ÷ 32 is the same as 32)5

In this book, you will be expected to continue dividing until the division comes out evenly unless told otherwise.

$$\begin{array}{r} .1\ 5\ 6\ 2\ 5 \\ 32\overline{)5.0\ 0\ 0\ 0\ 0} \\ \underline{3\ 2} \\ 1\ 8\ 0 \\ \underline{1\ 6\ 0} \\ 2\ 0\ 0 \\ \underline{1\ 9\ 2} \\ 8\ 0 \\ \underline{6\ 4} \\ 1\ 6\ 0 \\ \underline{1\ 6\ 0} \end{array}$$

If you are past the decimal point, attach as many zeros as needed to continue the division.
5 = 5. = 5.00000

CHECK

$$\begin{array}{r} .15625 \\ \times 32 \\ \hline 31250 \\ 4\ 6875 \\ \hline 5.00000 = 5 \end{array}$$

The answer is 0.15625. ■

Compare Examples 8 and 9. In Example 8, the divisor is 5 and the dividend is 32; however, in Example 9 we have the reverse situation. Observe that when using the division symbol ÷, the second number is always the divisor.

 Try Problems 12 through 15.

3 Converting Fractions to Decimals

Now that we can divide whole numbers by whole numbers, we can convert fractions to decimals, because the fraction bar means division.

EXAMPLE 10 Convert $\frac{5}{8}$ to a decimal.

SOLUTION $\frac{5}{8}$ means 8)5

The denominator is always the divisor.

$$\frac{5}{8} \rightarrow 8\overline{)5.0\ 0\ 0}\quad\begin{array}{r}.6\ 2\ 5\\ \underline{4\ 8}\\ 2\ 0\\ \underline{1\ 6}\\ 4\ 0\\ \underline{4\ 0}\end{array}$$

The denominator is always the divisor.

The decimal form is 0.625. ■

◢▲ **Try These Problems**

Convert each of these fractions to a decimal.

16. $\frac{4}{5}$

17. $\frac{5}{4}$

18. $\frac{3}{40}$

19. $\frac{40}{3}$ (Write the answer as a repeating decimal.)

EXAMPLE 11   Convert $\frac{70}{33}$ to a decimal.

SOLUTION $\frac{70}{33}$ means $33\overline{)70}$

└─ The denominator is always the divisor.

$$\frac{70}{33} \rightarrow \begin{array}{r} 2.1212 = 2.\overline{12} \\ 33\overline{)70.0000} \\ \underline{66} \\ 40 \\ \underline{33} \\ 70 \\ \underline{66} \\ 40 \\ \underline{33} \\ 70 \\ \underline{66} \\ 4 \end{array}$$

The digit pattern 12 continues to repeat no matter how far we carry out the division.

A bar written above 12 indicates that the digit pattern 12 repeats.

The decimal form is $2.\overline{12}$. ■

EXAMPLE 12   Convert $\frac{4}{53}$ to a decimal. Truncate at 4 decimal places.

SOLUTION $\frac{4}{53}$ means $53\overline{)4}$

└─The denominator is always the divisor.

To truncate at 4 decimal places, we do *not* need to see the size of the digit in the 5th decimal place, so we divide 4 places past the decimal point.

$$\begin{array}{r} .0754 \approx 0.0754 \\ 53\overline{)4.0000} \\ \underline{3\ 71} \\ 290 \\ \underline{265} \\ 250 \\ \underline{212} \\ 38 \end{array}$$

The decimal truncated at 4 decimal places is 0.0754. ■

◢▲ **Try Problems 16 through 19.**

4   Dividing a Decimal by a Decimal

So far we have divided whole numbers and decimals by *whole numbers.* How do we divide by *decimals?* Here we look carefully at the following problem.

$$0.48 \div 0.2 \quad \text{or} \quad 0.2\overline{)0.48}$$

The divisor 0.2 is not a whole number, but we can convert this division problem to an equivalent division problem where the divisor is a whole number. First we view the division problem as a fraction.

$$0.48 \div 0.2 = \frac{0.48}{0.2}$$

We know that if we multiply the numerator and denominator of a fraction by the same nonzero number, we do not change the value of the fraction. So if we multiply the numerator and denominator by 10, we will have a division problem that has the divisor a whole number.

$$
\begin{aligned}
0.48 \div 0.2 &= \frac{0.48}{0.2} \\
&= \frac{0.48 \times 10}{0.2 \times 10} \\
&= \frac{4.8}{2}
\end{aligned}
$$

Multiplying by 10 shifts the decimal point 1 place to the right.

Therefore, dividing 0.48 by 0.2 is the same as dividing 4.8 by 2. Our procedure could have been as follows.

$$0.2\overline{)0.4\,8}$$

Step 1: Make the divisor a whole number by moving the decimal point 1 place to the right.

Step 2: Move the decimal point in the dividend, 0.48, 1 place to the right also.

$$
\begin{array}{r}
2.4 \\
0\,2.\overline{)0\,4\,!8}
\end{array}
$$

Step 3: Place the decimal point in the quotient directly above the new decimal point in the dividend.

Step 4: Divide the numbers as whole numbers. Align the digits carefully.

The result is 2.4.

Now we look at more examples where both the divisor and the dividend contain a decimal point.

EXAMPLE 13   Divide: $50.75 \div 2.5$

SOLUTION   The second number 2.5 is the divisor. It is placed outside the division symbol $\overline{)}$.

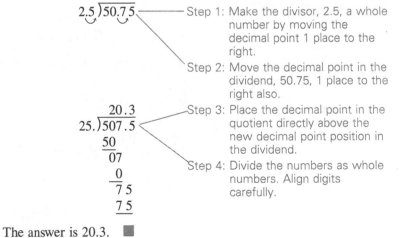

Step 1: Make the divisor, 2.5, a whole number by moving the decimal point 1 place to the right.

Step 2: Move the decimal point in the dividend, 50.75, 1 place to the right also.

Step 3: Place the decimal point in the quotient directly above the new decimal point position in the dividend.

Step 4: Divide the numbers as whole numbers. Align digits carefully.

The answer is 20.3. ■

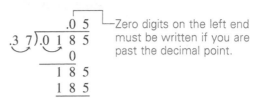

Try These Problems

Divide as indicated.

20. $0.756 \div .06$

21. $0.171 \div 4.5$

22. $\frac{10.5}{.015}$

23. $\frac{302.8}{.009}$ (Round off at 3 decimal places.)

EXAMPLE 14   Divide: $.0185 \div .37$

SOLUTION   The second number .37 is the divisor. It is placed outside the division symbol $\overline{)}$.

```
            . 0 5
   .3 7 ) . 0 1 8 5
              0
          1 8 5
          1 8 5
```
Zero digits on the left end must be written if you are past the decimal point.

The answer is 0.05. ■

EXAMPLE 15   Divide: $\frac{4.2}{2.03}$ (Round off at 2 decimal places.)

SOLUTION   The denominator 2.03 is the divisor. It is placed outside the division symbol $\overline{)}$.

```
              2. 0 6 8  ≈ 2. 0 7
   2.0 3 ) 4. 2 0 0 0 0
              4 0 6
              1 4 0
                  0
              1 4 0 0
              1 2 1 8
                1 8 2 0
                1 6 2 4
                  1 9 6
```
Extra zeros may be attached to the dividend if you are past the decimal point.

The answer rounded off at 2 decimal places is 2.07. ■

Try Problems 20 through 23.

5   Dividing a Whole Number by a Decimal

Remember that the decimal point in a whole numeral is placed at the right end. For example,

$$62 = 62. = 62.00$$
$$450 = 450. = 450.000$$
$$3482 = 3482. = 3482.0$$

Any number of zeros can be placed after the decimal point without changing the value of the whole number. Here are some examples of dividing a whole number by a decimal.

EXAMPLE 16   Divide: $23 \div 9.2$

SOLUTION   Write the whole numeral 23 as a decimal before beginning the division process. $23 = 23. = 23.00$

```
              2. 5
   9.2 ) 2 3. 0 0
            1 8 4
              4 6 0
              4 6 0
```
Write the whole number 23 as a decimal before moving the decimal point.
$23 = 23. = 23.00$

The answer is 2.5. ■

Try These Problems

Divide as indicated.

24. 27 ÷ .08

25. 153 ÷ 1.7

26. $\frac{8}{24}$ (Write the answer as a repeating decimal.)

27. $\frac{801}{0.028}$ (Round up at 2 decimal places.)

EXAMPLE 17 Divide: $\frac{7}{.033}$ (Write the answer as a repeating decimal.)

SOLUTION Write the whole numeral 7 as a decimal before beginning the division process. 7 = 7. = 7.000.

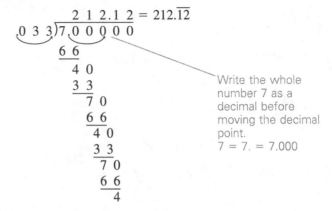

$$2\ 1\ 2.1\ 2 = 212.\overline{12}$$

Write the whole number 7 as a decimal before moving the decimal point.
7 = 7. = 7.000

The repeating decimal is 212.$\overline{12}$. ■

 Try Problems 24 through 27.

6 Paying Special Attention to Zeros in the Quotient

A common error that students make is to omit necessary zero digits in the quotient. Here are some examples to help you with this problem.

EXAMPLE 18 Divide: 195,000 ÷ 2.6

SOLUTION Write the whole numeral 195,000 as a decimal before beginning the division process.
195,000 = 195,000. = 195,000.0

```
           7 5 0 0 0.
  2,6)1 9 5 0 0 0.0        Be sure to include these zero
      1 8 2                digits.
        1 3 0
        1 3 0
```

The answer is 75,000. ■

EXAMPLE 19 Divide: 0.027 ÷ 45

SOLUTION

```
       .0 0 0 6     Be sure to include these zero digits.
  4 5).0 2 7 0
        2 7 0
```

The answer is 0.0006. ■

Try These Problems

Divide as indicated.

28. 7.2 ÷ .008

29. 11,100 ÷ .74

30. .00225 ÷ 12.5

31. 1002 ÷ 500

32. $\frac{21}{400.2}$ (Truncate at 3 decimal places.)

33. $\frac{53,352}{76}$

EXAMPLE 20   Divide: $\frac{240.123}{.06}$

SOLUTION

```
              4 0 0 2.0 5
    .0 6 ) 2 4 0.1 2 3 0
            2 4
            0 0 1 2
                1 2
                  0 3 0
                    3 0
```

Be sure to include these zero digits.

The answer is 4002.05.   ■

 Try Problems 28 through 33.

7   Using a Shortcut to Divide by 10, 100, or 1000

Here we show the result when dividing the numbers 25 and 3.7 by 10.

```
        2.5                 .37
  10)25.0            10)3.70
     20                  3 0
      5 0                  70
      5 0                  70
```

Observe that in each case, dividing a number by 10 causes the decimal point to shift 1 place to the left. Here we show the results.

$$25 ÷ 10 = 2.5 \qquad\qquad 3.7 ÷ 10 = 0.37$$

Similarly, dividing a decimal by 100 causes the decimal point to shift 2 places to the left. Here we show the results of dividing the numbers 25 and 3.7 by 100.

$$25 ÷ 100 = 0.25 \qquad\qquad 3.7 ÷ 100 = 0.037$$

As you might predict, dividing a decimal by 1000 causes the decimal point to shift 3 places to the left. Here we show the results of dividing the numbers 25 and 3.7 by 1000. This time we use the fraction bar to indicate the division.

$$\frac{25}{1000} = 0.025 \qquad\qquad \frac{3.7}{1000} = 0.0037$$

We generalize the previous results by stating a shortcut for dividing by 10, 100, 1000 and so on.

Dividing a Decimal by 10, 100, 1000, and So On

Move the decimal point to the left
    one place when dividing by 10,
    two places when dividing by 100,
    three places when dividing by 1000,
    four places when dividing by 10,000.
The pattern continues. The decimal point moves to the left the same number of places as there are zeros.

 **Try These Problems**

Divide as indicated without using long division. Answer with a decimal.

34. 673.8 ÷ 10

35. 0.9 ÷ 100

36. $\frac{728}{100}$

37. $\frac{9.76}{1000}$

 Try Problems 34 through 37.

Answers To Try These Problems

1. 1.3   2. 0.025   3. 3.07   4. 28.3   5. 78.04
6. 0.0061   7. 0.015   8. 0.08$\frac{5}{14}$ 9. 1.23$\frac{3}{4}$ 10. 1.1$\overline{5}$
11. 0.01$\overline{2}$ 12. 2.5   13. 0.4   14. 0.056   15. 17.85
16. 0.8   17. 1.25   18. 0.075   19. 13.$\overline{3}$ 20. 12.6
21. 0.038   22. 700   23. 33,644.444   24. 337.5   25. 90
26. 33.$\overline{3}$ 27. 28,607.15   28. 900   29. 15,000
30. 0.00018   31. 2.004   32. 0.052   33. 70,200
34. 67.38   35. 0.009   36. 7.28   37. 0.00976

EXERCISES 7.2

Divide. Continue dividing until the remainder is zero.

1. 8.4 ÷ 6   **2.** 6.7 ÷ 50   **3.** 8 ÷ 50   **4.** 3 ÷ 8

5. 0.65 ÷ 0.5   **6.** 0.11 ÷ 5.5   **7.** 6.3 ÷ 0.15   **8.** 5.7 ÷ 0.125

9. 21 ÷ 0.06   **10.** 3 ÷ 0.12   **11.** 1244 ÷ .625   **12.** 555 ÷ .185

13. 6030 ÷ .09   **14.** 34.8 ÷ .058   **15.** 107.92 ÷ .0568 **16.** 16.2024 ÷ .03

17. 45,093 ÷ 15   **18.** 20.3203 ÷ 4.06   **19.** .244 ÷ 8   **20.** 3624 ÷ 300

21. $\frac{30400.2}{50}$ **22.** $\frac{562.5}{.0625}$ **23.** $\frac{.02197}{8.45}$ **24.** $\frac{1}{32}$

25. $\frac{14}{.035}$ **26.** $\frac{31}{12.4}$

Divide. Write the answer as a repeating decimal.

27. 26.8 ÷ 3   **28.** 95 ÷ 12   **29.** 125 ÷ .9

30. $\frac{2}{.003}$ **31.** $\frac{1}{90}$ **32.** $\frac{21.3}{.99}$

Convert each of these fractions to decimal form.

33. $\frac{7}{8}$ **34.** $\frac{3}{16}$ **35.** $\frac{7}{400}$ **36.** $\frac{13}{250}$

37. $\frac{50}{48}$ **38.** $\frac{458}{90}$ **39.** $\frac{3}{11}$ **40.** $\frac{5}{27}$

Divide. Approximate the answer as indicated.

41. 82.9 ÷ 6   (Round off at 3 decimal places.)

42. 930 ÷ 64   (Round off at 1 decimal place.)

43. 63.13 ÷ 8.3   (Truncate at 3 decimal places.)

44. 315 ÷ .073   (Truncate at 2 decimal places.)

45. 3 ÷ 360   (Round up at 3 decimal places.)

46. .01 ÷ .62   (Round up at 3 decimal places.)

47. $\frac{.0034}{7.7}$ (Round off at 4 decimal places.)

48. $\frac{2990.069}{4.6}$ (Truncate at 2 decimal places.)

49. $\frac{63}{4.03}$ (Round up at 2 decimal places.)

50. $\frac{40}{13}$ (Truncate at 2 decimal places.)

Divide. Stop dividing 2 places past the decimal point and write the remainder in fractional form.

51. $18.3 \div 7$

52. $40 \div 62$

53. $2.15 \div .03$

54. $\frac{8}{.28}$

55. $\frac{18}{6.3}$

56. $\frac{31}{7}$

Use a shortcut to do each indicated division. Answer with a decimal.

57. $4.56 \div 100$

58. $0.08 \div 10$

59. $8976 \div 1000$

60. $45.3 \div 1000$

61. $\frac{0.075}{1000}$

62. $\frac{45}{10}$

Solve. Write the answer as a decimal.

63. A string is 30.8 inches long. You cut the string into 8 equal pieces. How long is each piece?

64. In San Francisco, the sales tax is computed by multiplying the decimal 0.085 by the marked price of an item. If the sales tax on an item was $52.70, what was the marked price of this item?

65. The length of a rectangle is 12.8 meters. If the area is 83.2 square meters, how wide is the rectangle?

66. A wire is 3.8 feet long. Sasha wants to cut the wire into 0.04-foot pieces. How many pieces can she cut?

DEVELOPING NUMBER SENSE #6

MULTIPLYING BY 0.1, 0.01, AND 0.001 MENTALLY

Multiplying by the decimal 0.1 is the same as multiplying by the fraction $\frac{1}{10}$, and thus is equivalent to dividing by 10. Therefore, this should cause the decimal point to move 1 place to the left. Here we show some examples:

$$36 \times 0.1 = 3.6$$
$$75.8 \times 0.1 = 7.58$$
$$0.07 \times 0.1 = 0.007$$

Similarly, multiplying by the decimal 0.01 is the same as multiplying by the fraction $\frac{1}{100}$, and thus is equivalent to dividing by 100. Therefore, this should cause the decimal point to move 2 places to the left. Here are some examples:

$$36 \times 0.01 = 0.36$$
$$75.8 \times 0.01 = 0.758$$
$$0.07 \times 0.01 = 0.0007$$

The pattern observed above continues. Multiplying by 0.001 causes the decimal point to move 3 places to the left.

Number Sense Problems

Compute each of the following mentally.

1. 0.1×340

2. 0.1×78.4

3. 0.1×0.659

4. 0.1×9.2

5. 0.01×84

6. 0.01×8.75

7. 0.01×0.006

8. 0.01×12.45

9. 0.001×3

10. 0.001×57

11. 0.001×45.7

12. 0.001×0.5

13. 0.01×3.67

14. 0.1×0.786

15. 0.01×80

16. 0.1×1200

7.3   THE MISSING NUMBER IN A MULTIPLICATION STATEMENT

OBJECTIVE   ▌   Find the missing number in a multiplication statement.

In the multiplication statement

$$9 \times 3 = 27 \quad \text{or} \quad 27 = 9 \times 3$$

the numbers 9 and 3 are called **multipliers** or **factors.** The answer to the multiplication problem, 27, is called the **product** of 9 and 3. Note that the statement can be written with the product located after the equality symbol or before the equality symbol.

Three questions can be asked by omitting any one of the three numbers.

1. $9 \times 3 = \boxed{}$

Missing number is 27.

We are missing the answer to a multiplication problem, so we *multiply* to find the missing number.

2. $9 \times \boxed{} = 27$

$$9 \overline{)27}$$ with quotient 3

known multiplier — answer to the multiplication problem

We are missing one of the multipliers, so we divide to find the missing number.

3. $\boxed{} \times 3 = 27$

$$3 \overline{)27}$$ with quotient 9

known multiplier — answer to the multiplication problem

We are missing one of the multipliers, so we *divide* to find the missing number.

In the multiplication statement $9 \times 3 = 27$, the product 27 is larger than either one of the multipliers. Do not expect this to always be true. Here we look at more examples.

$$2.5 \times 400 = 1000$$

Here the product 1000 is larger than either multiplier because both multipliers are larger than 1.

$$0.5 \times 400 = 200$$

Here the product 200 is less than the multiplier 400 because the other multiplier, 0.5, is less than 1.

EXAMPLE 1 $0.85 \times 908 = \boxed{}$

SOLUTION   We are missing the answer to the multiplication problem, so we multiply to find the missing number.

$$
\begin{array}{r}
9\,08 \\
\times\ .85 \\
\hline
45\,40 \\
726\,4 \\
\hline
771.80 = 771.8
\end{array}
$$

The missing product is 771.8.   ▌

Try These Problems

Find the missing number. Write the answer as a decimal.

1. 70 × 0.3 = ☐

2. ☐ = 16 × 0.83

3. 0.72 = 18 × ☐

4. ☐ × 700 = 35

5. ☐ × 82.5 = 0.66

6. 120,000 = 0.375 × ☐

Note in Example 1 that we expected the product to be less than 908 because 0.85 is less than 1.

 Try Problems 1 and 2.

EXAMPLE 2   12 = 0.25 × ☐

SOLUTION   One of the multipliers is missing, so we divide to find the missing number.

$$\text{Missing multiplier} = \frac{\text{answer to the multiplication problem}}{} \div \text{known multiplier}$$

☐ = 12 ÷ 0.25

known multiplier
$$.25\overline{)12.00}$$
$$\underline{100}$$
$$200$$
$$\underline{200}$$
48. = 4 8 — missing multiplier
answer to the multiplication problem

CHECK
$$\begin{array}{r} 48 \\ \times\ .25 \\ \hline 2\ 40 \\ 9\ 6 \\ \hline 12.00 = 12 \end{array}$$

The missing multiplier is 48. ■

In Example 2 note that the multiplier we found, 48, is more than the product 12. This happened because the other multiplier, 0.25, is less than 1.

EXAMPLE 3   6.8 × ☐ = 20.74

SOLUTION   One of the multipliers is missing, so we divide to find the missing number.

$$\text{Missing multiplier} = \frac{\text{answer to the multiplication problem}}{} \div \text{known multiplier}$$

☐ = 20.74 ÷ 6.8

$$6.8\overline{)20.740}$$
$$\underline{20\ 4}$$
$$3\ 4$$
$$\underline{0}$$
$$3\ 4\ 0$$
$$\underline{3\ 4\ 0}$$
3.05

The missing multiplier is 3.05. ■

 Try Problems 3 through 6.

Now we summarize the procedure for finding the missing number in a multiplication statement.

Finding the Missing Number in a Multiplication Statement

1. If you are missing the answer to the multiplication problem, then **multiply.**
2. If you are missing one of the multipliers, then **divide.** Take care to divide in the correct order. Here is how it works.

known
multiplier ⟍ missing multiplier
            ⟍ answer to the
            / multiplication
            / problem

⬛ Answers to Try These Problems

1. 21   **2.** 13.28   **3.** 0.04   **4.** 0.05   **5.** 0.008   **6.** 320,000

EXERCISES 7.3

Find the missing number. Write the answer as a decimal.

1. $0.065 \times \boxed{} = 1.508$

2. $72.45 = 0.35 \times \boxed{}$

3. $1800 \times \boxed{} = 36.9$

4. $48 = 0.6 \times \boxed{}$

5. $76.2 \times 0.05 = \boxed{}$

6. $\boxed{} = 2.3 \times 0.047$

7. $4.75 = \boxed{} \times 380$

8. $\boxed{} \times 5200 = 16{,}380$

9. $900 = 2.5 \times \boxed{}$

10. $32.4 \times \boxed{} = 200.88$

11. $\boxed{} = 150.20 \times 0.065$

12. $600 \times 8.3 = \boxed{}$

13. $91 = 7 \times \boxed{}$

14. $\boxed{} \times 6000 = 15$

15. $985.32 = 122.4 \times \boxed{}$

16. $5000 = 3.125 \times \boxed{}$

17. $0.95 \times \boxed{} = 0.9785$

18. $30.4 \times 720 = \boxed{}$

19. $65 = \boxed{} \times 0.13$

20. $31.59 = 4050 \times \boxed{}$

DEVELOPING NUMBER SENSE #7

MULTIPLYING AND DIVIDING BY A DECIMAL LESS THAN, EQUAL TO, OR MORE THAN 1

Here we look at the number 480 multiplied by 2.4, 1, and 0.75. Observe how the answers compare with 480.

$$480 \times 2.4 = 1152$$
$$480 \times 1 = 480$$
$$480 \times 0.75 = 360$$

The first result 1152 is more than 480 because the factor 2.4 is more than 1. The second result 480 is equal to 480 because the factor being multiplied by 480 is 1. The third result 360 is less than 480 because the factor 0.75 is less than 1. This property of numbers was also observed in Developing Number Sense #3 with relation to fractions.

What happens with *division* by numbers less than, equal to, or more than 1? Here we divide the number 480 by the numbers 2.4, 1, and 0.75. Observe how the answers compare with 480.

$$480 \div 2.4 = 200$$
$$480 \div 1 = 480$$
$$480 \div 0.75 = 640$$

The first result 200 is less than 480 because the divisor 2.4 is more than 1. The second result is 480 because the divisor is 1. The third result 640 is more than 480 because the divisor 0.75 is less than 1.

Cont. page 283

Number Sense Problems

Without computing, decide whether the result is less than, equal to, or more than 850.

1. 850×7.5 **2.** 850×0.98 **3.** 0.005×850 **4.** 1.86×850

5. $850 \div 1$ **6.** $850 \div 1.7$ **7.** $850 \div 0.64$ **8.** $850 \div 0.005$

Without computing, decide whether the result is less than, equal to, or more than 47.2.

9. $47.2 \div 0.16$ **10.** 47.2×0.16 **11.** 47.2×56.8 **12.** $47.2 \div 56.8$

7.4	LANGUAGE

OBJECTIVES

▮ Find a decimal of a number.

▮ Translate an English phrase to math symbols involving multiplication and division.

▮ Solve problems by using translations.

 Try These Problems

Solve.

1. 0.25 of 68.5

2. 4.5 of 4600

3. 0.076 of 30.6

4. 5.09 of 0.7

1 Finding a Decimal of a Number

Recall from Section 4.4 that to find a fraction of a number we multiply the fraction by the number. For example,

$$\frac{3}{4} \text{ of } 20$$
$$\downarrow$$
$$= \frac{\overset{1}{\cancel{3}}}{\cancel{4}} \times \frac{\overset{5}{\cancel{20}}}{1} \qquad \text{The word } of \text{ used in this way translates to multiplication.}$$
$$= 15$$

Also to find a decimal of a number we multiply the decimal by the number. For example,

$$0.75 \text{ of } 20$$
$$\downarrow$$
$$= 0.75 \times 20 \qquad \text{The word } of \text{ used in this way translates to multiplication.}$$
$$= 15.00$$
$$= 15$$

Finding a Decimal of a Number

To find a decimal of a number, multiply the decimal by the number, that is, the word *of* used in this way translates to multiplication.

 Try Problems 1 through 4.

2 Translating English to Multiplication

Here is a review of the many English translations for the symbol =.

Math Symbol	English
=	equals
	is equal to
	is the same as
	is the result of
	is
	are
	was
	were
	will be
	represents
	gives
	makes
	yields

The multiplication statement $1.5 \times 3 = 4.5$ or $4.5 = 1.5 \times 3$ is written with math symbols. Some of the ways to read this statement in English are given in the following chart.

Math Symbols	English
$1.5 \times 3 = 4.5$	1.5 times 3 equals 4.5.
$4.5 = 1.5 \times 3$	1.5 multiplied by 3 is 4.5.
	1.5 of 3 yields 4.5.
	4.5 is 3 times as large as 1.5.
	The *product* of 1.5 and 3 is 4.5.

Because 1.5×3 equals 3×1.5, the order that you say the multipliers does not matter.

The following examples illustrate how to use translating to solve problems.

EXAMPLE 1   What number represents the product of 4.05 and 60?

SOLUTION   The question translates to a multiplication statement.

What number	represents	the product of 4.05 and 60	?
☐	↓ =	4.05×60	

The answer to the multiplication statement is missing, so we multiply to find the missing number.

$$\begin{array}{r} 4.0\,5 \\ \times\quad 60 \\ \hline 24\,3.00 \end{array} = 243$$

The missing product is 243. ∎

Try These Problems

5. What number is 5 times as large as 43.2?

6. 65 represents the product of 12.5 and what number?

7. What decimal of 700.5 is 5.604?

8. 15.7 times 50.9 yields what number?

EXAMPLE 2   0.75 of what number is 300?

SOLUTION   The question translates to a multiplication statement.

$$0.75 \quad \text{of} \quad \begin{array}{c}\text{what} \\ \text{number}\end{array} \quad \text{is} \quad 300?$$
$$\quad\quad\quad\quad\quad \downarrow \quad\quad\quad\quad\quad \downarrow$$
$$0.75 \quad \times \quad \boxed{} \quad = \quad 300$$

A multiplier is missing, so divide the answer 300 by the given multiplier 0.75 to find the missing multiplier.

$$0.75\overline{)300} \atop \underline{300}^{\displaystyle 4}$$

The missing number is 4. ■

 Try Problems 5 through 8.

Special language is used when the number 2 or the number 0.5 is a multiplier.

Math Symbols	*English*
$2 \times 8.6 = 17.2$	*Twice* 8.6 is 17.2.
	Doubling 8.6 gives 17.2.
	2 times 8.6 equals 17.2.
$0.5 \times 8.6 = 4.3$	*Half of* 8.6 is 4.3.
	0.5 times 8.6 gives 4.3.

EXAMPLE 3   What number is half of 0.35?

SOLUTION   The question translates to a multiplication statement.

$$\text{What number} \quad \text{is} \quad \text{half} \quad \text{of} \quad 0.35?$$
$$\boxed{} \quad\quad = \quad 0.5 \quad \times \quad 0.35$$

The answer to the multiplication statement is missing, so we multiply to find the missing number.

$$\begin{array}{r} 0.3\,5 \\ \times\ \ 0.5 \\ \hline .17\,5 \end{array}$$ ■

EXAMPLE 4   1.21 equals twice what number?

SOLUTION   The question translates to a multiplication statement.

$$1.21 \quad \text{equals} \quad \text{twice} \quad \begin{array}{c}\text{what} \\ \text{number}\end{array}?$$
$$1.21 \quad = \quad 2 \times \quad \boxed{}$$

A multiplier is missing, so divide the answer 1.21 by the given multiplier 2 to find the missing multiplier.

Try These Problems

Solve. Answer with a decimal.

9. 8.15 is half of what number?

10. What is the result when 3.8 is doubled?

11. Find twice 0.056.

12. Find half of 45.9.

13. Divide 500 by 3.2.

14. Divide 500 into 3.2.

15. Divide 1.2 into 0.15.

16. Divide 1.2 by 0.15.

17. Find the ratio of 50 to 0.32.

18. Find the ratio of 0.32 to 50.

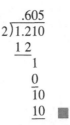

$$
\begin{array}{r}
.605 \\
2\overline{)1.210} \\
\underline{1\ 2} \\
1 \\
\underline{0} \\
10 \\
\underline{10}
\end{array}
$$

 Try Problems 9 through 12.

3 Translating English to Division

When reading the division statement 80 ÷ 0.4, take care to say 80 and 0.4 in the correct order because 80 ÷ 0.4 does not equal 0.4 ÷ 80. Here we illustrate the division done in both ways.

$$
80 \div 0.4 \rightarrow 0.4\overline{)80.0} \quad \frac{200.}{} = 200
$$

$$
0.4 \div 80 \rightarrow 80\overline{)0.400} \quad .005
$$
$$
\underline{400}
$$

Observe that the results are different. The following chart gives correct ways to read the division statement 80 ÷ 0.4 = 200.

Math Symbols	English
80 ÷ 0.4 = 200	80 *divided by* 0.4 equals 200. 0.4 *divided into* 80 is 200. The *ratio* of 80 to 0.4 is 200.

Note that the word *by* is used when the statement is read from left to right as you read words in a book; however, the word *into* is used if you read the divisor first. The divisor is the number after the division symbol.

Recall that the fraction bar is also used to indicate division. For example,

$$
\frac{80}{0.4} = 80 \div 0.4
$$

The following chart gives correct ways to read the division statement $\frac{80}{0.4} = 200$.

Math Symbols	English
$\frac{80}{0.4} = 200$	80 *divided by* 0.4 is 200. 0.4 *divided into* 80 equals 200. The *ratio* of 80 to 0.4 is 200.

Note that the word *by* is used when the numerator is read first, but the word *into* is used when the denominator is read first.

 Try Problems 13 through 18.

Answers to Try These Problems

1. 17.125   2. 20,700   3. 2.3256   4. 3.563   5. 216
6. 5.2   7. 0.008   8. 799.13   9. 16.3   10. 7.6   11. 0.112
12. 22.95   13. 156.25   14. 0.0064   15. 0.125   16. 8
17. 156.25   18. 0.0064

EXERCISES 7.4

Translate each of these statements to a multiplication or division statement using math symbols.

1. The product of 0.3 and 0.2 equals 0.06.
2. 0.5 divided by 0.2 equals 2.5.
3. 45.2 is 5 times as large as 9.04.
4. 19.5 is half of 39.
5. 41.6 is twice 20.8.
6. 450 represents 0.75 of 600.

Translate to an equation. Then solve.

7. Find the product of 4.7 and 200.
8. 0.875 is the product of 2.5 and what number?
9. Divide 0.4 by 16.
10. Divide 0.4 into 16.
11. Find half of 30.5.
12. Half of what number is 67.5?
13. 9.45 represents 0.07 of what number?
14. Find 0.035 of 46,000.
15. What decimal of 60.4 is 392.6?
16. 32,500 equals 1.25 of what number?
17. Divide 0.075 into 37.5.
18. Divide 0.075 by 37.5.
19. What number is twice 18.09?
20. Twice what number is 1.05?
21. Find the ratio of 81 to 4.05.
22. What number is 8.5 times as large as 55?
23. 300 is what decimal of 3750?
24. Find the ratio of 18 to 0.036.

7.5 APPLICATIONS

OBJECTIVES
- Solve an application involving equal parts in a total quantity.
- Solve an application involving equivalent rates.
- Convert a rate to an equivalent rate.
- Solve an application by interpreting a rate as a ratio.
- Solve an application by using a rate as a multiplier.
- Solve an application involving the area of a rectangle.
- Solve an application by using translations.
- Find the average (or mean) of a collection of numbers.

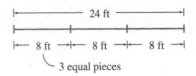

1 Solving Problems Involving Equal Parts in a Total Quantity

Suppose you have a string that is 24 feet long. If you cut the string into 3 equal pieces, then each piece is 8 feet. Here is a picture of the situation.

$$\vdash\!\!\!\longleftarrow 24\ \text{ft} \longrightarrow\!\!\!\dashv$$

$$\vdash\!\!\!- 8\ \text{ft} \longrightarrow\!\!+\!\!\longleftarrow 8\ \text{ft} \longrightarrow\!\!+\!\!\longleftarrow 8\ \text{ft} \longrightarrow\!\!\dashv$$

3 equal pieces

Observe that the numbers are related as follows.

$$\begin{matrix} \text{Size of} \\ \text{each part} \\ \text{(ft)} \end{matrix} \times \begin{matrix} \text{number of} \\ \text{equal parts} \end{matrix} = \begin{matrix} \text{total} \\ \text{quantity} \\ \text{(ft)} \end{matrix}$$

$$8 \quad \times \quad 3 \quad = \quad 24$$

In general, if a situation involves a total quantity being split into a number of equal parts, the following always applies.

$$\begin{matrix} \textbf{Size of} \\ \textbf{each part} \end{matrix} \times \begin{matrix} \textbf{number of} \\ \textbf{equal parts} \end{matrix} = \begin{matrix} \textbf{total} \\ \textbf{quantity} \end{matrix}$$

A problem can be presented by giving any two of the three quantities and asking for the third quantity. The following examples illustrate this.

EXAMPLE 1   A board 6 feet long is cut into 24 equal pieces. How long is each piece?

    SOLUTION   Here we picture the situation.

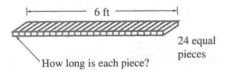

$$\vdash\!\!\!\longleftarrow 6\ \text{ft} \longrightarrow\!\!\!\dashv$$

24 equal pieces

How long is each piece?

We use the formula

$$\begin{matrix} \text{Size of} \\ \text{each part} \\ \text{(ft)} \end{matrix} \times \begin{matrix} \text{number of} \\ \text{equal parts} \end{matrix} = \begin{matrix} \text{total} \\ \text{quantity} \\ \text{(ft)} \end{matrix}$$

$$\boxed{} \quad \times \quad 24 \quad = \quad 6$$

A multiplier is missing, so we divide 6 by 24 to find the missing multiplier.

$$\begin{array}{r} .25 \\ 24\overline{)6.00} \\ \underline{48} \\ 120 \\ \underline{120} \end{array}$$

.25 —— length of each piece in feet
6.00 —— total length in feet

number of equal pieces

Each piece is 0.25 foot long. ■

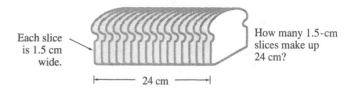
Try These Problems

Solve.

1. A rope that is 45 inches long is cut into 36 equal pieces. How long is each piece?

2. A rope that is 36 inches long is cut into 45 equal pieces. How long is each piece?

3. Medicine is given out in doses that each contain 1.8 centiliters. How many doses can be given from a bottle that contains 45 centiliters?

4. Twelve children share equally 2.4 gallons of milk. How much milk does each child receive?

5. Mr. Henry pays off a debt by making 40 equal payments. If the total debt is $4370, what is each payment?

6. Linda is preparing punch for a party. She wants to have 75 servings that each contain 6.5 ounces. How many ounces of punch does she need?

EXAMPLE 2   A slicing machine for a baking company slices a 24-centimeter loaf of bread into slices that are each 1.5 centimeters wide. How many slices can be cut from the loaf of bread?

SOLUTION   Here we picture the situation.

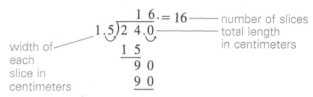

Each slice is 1.5 cm wide.

How many 1.5-cm slices make up 24 cm?

|←——— 24 cm ———→|

We use the formula

$$\begin{array}{ccc} \text{Size of} & \text{number of} & \text{total} \\ \text{each part} \times \text{equal parts} = \text{quantity} \\ \text{(cm)} & & \text{(cm)} \\ 1.5 \times \boxed{} = 24 \end{array}$$

A multiplier is missing, so we divide 24 by 1.5 to find the missing multiplier.

$$\begin{array}{r} 1\ 6. = 16 \\ 1.5\overline{)2\ 4.0} \\ \underline{1\ 5} \\ 9\ 0 \\ \underline{9\ 0} \end{array}$$

— number of slices
— total length in centimeters

width of each slice in centimeters

16 slices can be cut from the loaf. ■

EXAMPLE 3   Theresa pays off a debt by making 60 equal payments of $230.70. What is the total debt?

SOLUTION   We use the formula

$$\begin{array}{ccc} \text{Size of} & \text{number of} & \text{total} \\ \text{each part} \times \text{equal parts} = \text{quantity} \\ \text{(\$)} & & \text{(\$)} \\ 230.70 \times 60 = \boxed{} \end{array}$$

We are missing the answer to the multiplication problem, so we multiply to find the total debt.

$$\begin{array}{r} 230.7 \\ \times\ \ \ 6\ 0 \\ \hline 1384\ 2.0 = 13,842 \end{array}$$

The total debt is $13,842. ■

 Try Problems 1 through 6.

Generating Equivalent Rate Phrases

Rate phrases and **rates** give us one way to compare two quantities. Suppose you earn $16 for every 1 hour. The phrase, "*$16 for every 1 hour*," is a **rate phrase**. We are comparing the quantity $16 to the quantity 1 hour. We are saying that for every $16 in pay you must work 1 hour or for every 1 hour you work you get paid $16. When this rate phrase is put in a single quantity form, it is called a **rate** or **rate quantity**.

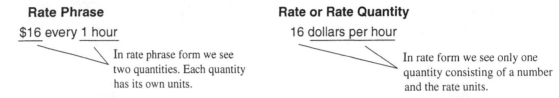

Rate Phrase	Rate or Rate Quantity
$16 every 1 hour	16 dollars per hour

In rate phrase form we see two quantities. Each quantity has its own units.

In rate form we see only one quantity consisting of a number and the rate units.

Observe that **rates** and **rate quantities** have units like, "dollars per hour," "diapers per day," "pounds per cubic foot," "miles an hour", "persons per square mile," and "pounds per carton." Make certain that you know how to convert a rate quantity to a rate phrase. Refer to Chapter 4 Custom Enhancement if you need more help. Here are more examples of **rate phrases**.

- $8.50 for 1 share
- 1 nail weighs 0.04 pound
- 1.5 miles in 3 minutes

Recall from Chapter 4 Custom Enhancement that we can generate equivalent rate phrases by **multiplying or dividing both quantities in a rate phrase by the same nonzero number**. Here we look at generating some rate phrases that are equivalent to, "1.5 *miles in 3 minutes.*"

1.5 miles in 3 minutes	1.5 miles in 3 minutes	1.5 miles in 3 minutes
x 2 x 2	÷ 3 ÷ 3	÷ 1.5 ÷ 1.5
3 miles in 6 minutes	0.5 mile in 1 minute	1 mile in 2 minutes

$$1.5\overline{)3.0} \quad \overset{2.}{}$$

> ### Rule for Generating Equivalent Rate Phrases
> Multiply or divide both quantities in a rate phrase by the same nonzero number to generate an equivalent rate phrase.

Now we look at finding a missing quantity in a rate phrase. We will use our knowledge of how to generate equivalent rate phrases.

EXAMPLE   Find the missing quantity that makes the second rate phrase equivalent to the first one.

$400 every 1 week

   _?_   for   8 weeks

Solution   Write down the given rate phrase. Write the rate phrase with missing quantity under the given one so that like units align.

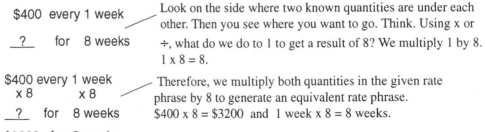

$400   every 1 week

   _?_   for   8 weeks

Look on the side where two known quantities are under each other. Then you see where you want to go. Think. Using x or ÷, what do we do to 1 to get a result of 8? We multiply 1 by 8. 1 x 8 = 8.

$400 every 1 week
   x 8   x 8

   _?_   for   8 weeks

Therefore, we multiply both quantities in the given rate phrase by 8 to generate an equivalent rate phrase. $400 x 8 = $3200 and 1 week x 8 = 8 weeks.

Answer $3200   for 8 weeks

EXAMPLE   Find the missing quantity that makes the second rate phrase equivalent to the first one.

6 hours for 19.2 miles

1 hour   for   ___?___

Solution   Write down the given rate phrase. Write the rate phrase with missing quantity under the given one so that like units align.

6 hours for 19.2 miles

1 hour for   ___?___

Look on the side where two known quantities are under each other. Then you see where you want to go. Think. Using x or ÷, what do we do to 6 to get a result of 1? We divide 6 by 6.
6 ÷ 6 = 1.

6 hours for 19.2 miles
÷ 6   ÷ 6

1 hour for   ___?___

Therefore, we divide both quantities in the given rate phrase by 6 to generate an equivalent rate phrase. The calculation 19.2 divided by 6 is shown to the right. Show your calculation steps clearly when the work cannot be done mentallly.

$$6 \overline{)\begin{array}{l} 3.2 \\ 19.2 \\ \underline{18} \\ 12 \\ \underline{12} \\ 0 \end{array}}$$

Answer   1 hour for 3.2 miles

EXAMPLE   Find the missing quantity that makes the second rate phrase equivalent to the first one.

$10.20   for   8.5 pounds

___?___   for   1 pound

Solution   Write down the given rate phrase. Write the rate phrase with missing quantity under the given one so that like units are under each other.

$10.20 for 8.5 pounds

___?___ for 1 pound

Look on the side where two known quantities are under each other. Then you see where you want to go. Think. Using x or ÷, what do we do to 8.5 to get a result of 1? We divide 8.5 by 8.5 to get 1.

$10.20 for 8.5 pounds
÷ 8.5   ÷ 8.5

___?___ for 1 pound

Therefore, we divide both quantities in the given rate phrase by 8.5 to generate an equivalent rate phrase. The calculation 10.20 divided by 8.5 is shown to the right. Show your calculation steps clearly when the work cannot be done mentally.

$$8.5 \overline{)\begin{array}{l} 1.2 \\ 10.2\,0 \\ \underline{85} \\ 170 \\ \underline{170} \\ 0 \end{array}}$$

Answer $1.20   for   1 pound

▶ **Try These Problems**

Find the missing quantity that makes the two rate phrases equivalent. Show clearly the number you choose to multiply or divide by. Also, show your calculation steps neatly when the work cannot be done mentally.

1. $48   for   8 hours
    ___?___   for   1 hour

2. 120 gallons every 1 minute
    ___?___   in   3.2 minutes

3. $6.50 for 5 pounds
    ___?___ for 1 pound

4. 1.4 meters weigh 2.1 pounds
    1 meter weighs ___?___

5. 0.8 liter in   20 minutes
    1 liter in   ___?___

6. $3.25   per 1 pound
    ___?___   for 6.8 pounds

7. 30.25 pounds for 1 carton
    ___?___   for 17 cartons

8. 0.018 ton for 9 barrels
    1 ton for   ___?___

9. 54.4 liters in 40.8 seconds
    1 liter in   ___?___

Solving Applications using Equivalent Rate Phrases

Now we look at solving applications using equivalent rate phrases.

EXAMPLE   Vernon earns $212.40 each week. How much money does he earn in 16 weeks?

Solution   Write the rate, "$212.40 each week," ⟶ $212.40 each 1 week   Using x or ÷, what do we
in rate phrase form.   do to 1 to get 16? We

Write the question as a rate phrase ⟶ _____ ? in 16 weeks   multiply 1 by 16 to get 16.
with missing quantity. Be sure to   1 x 16 = 16
arrange like units under each other.

Multiply both quantities in the given rate phrase by 16 to generate an equivalent rate phrase.

$212.40 each 1 week   212.40   Show the calculation steps when the
    x 16   x 16   x   16   work cannot be done mentally.
_____ ? in 16 weeks   1274 40
                                             2124 0
                                             3398.40

Answer $3398.40 in 16 weeks

EXAMPLE   The cost of 5.5 pounds of bananas is $6.60. What is the cost per pound?

Solution   Write down the given rate phrase. ⟶ 5.5 pounds for $6.60   Using x or ÷, what do we
                                                                                        do to 5.5 to get 1? We
Write the question as a rate phrase   divide 5.5 by 5.5 to get 1.
with missing quantity. Note that, ⟶ 1 pound costs _____ ?   5.5 ÷ 5.5 = 1
"cost per pound," means cost for
1 pound. Be sure to align like units.

Divide both quantities in the given rate phrase by 5.5 to generate an equivalent rate phrase.

5.5 pounds for $6.60   1.2   Show the calculation steps when the
    ÷ 5.5   ÷ 5.5   5.5) 6.6,0   work cannot be done mentally.
1 pound costs _____ ?   55
                                               11 0
                                               11 0
                                                  0

Answer   1 pound costs $1.20

▶ **Try These Problems**

Solve each of these applications by generating equivalent rate phrases. Show steps clearly.

10. One nail weighs 0.03 pound. What do 75 nails weigh?

11. One share of utility stock sells for $35.40. What is the cost of 27 shares?

12. Dana paid $42.60 for 7.5 yards of fabric. What is the cost of 1 yard of fabric?

13. A watch loses 3 minutes every 4.8 hours. How much does the watch lose in 1 hour?

14. A faucet leaks 3.4 ounces per hour. How many ounces does the faucet leak in 8.6 hours?

15. It takes you 35 minutes to drive 21 miles. How many miles do you drive per minute?

16. Fifty cartons have a total weight of 1030 pounds. What is the weight of each carton?

17. An airplane travels 600 miles per hour. How far can the airplane travel in 7.5 hours?

18. Hal can jog 3.5 miles in 25.9 minutes. At this rate, how many minutes does it take him to jog 1 mile?

19. A car uses 5.6 gallons of gas to go 226.8 miles. How far can the car go on 1 gallon of gas?

Generating Equivalent Rate Phrases - 2 Steps

Now we look at some examples of solving equivalent rate phrase
problems that require more than one step.

EXAMPLE   Find the missing quantity that makes the second
rate phrase equivalent to the first one.

2 liters   for   6.25 minutes

____?____   for   9 minutes

Solution   Using x or ÷, it's not easy to see what to do to 6.25 to get 9.
Therefore, we insert a rate phrase to find how many liters ⟶
for 1 minute.

2 liters for 6.25 minutes

____?____   for   1 minute

____?____   for   9 minutes

Step 1: Divide both quantities in the first rate
phrase by 6.25 to find the liters for 1 minute.

2 liters for 6.25 minutes
÷ 6.25   ÷ 6.25

$$\begin{array}{r} 0.32 \\ 6.25\,\overline{)\,2.0000} \\ \underline{1875} \\ 1250 \\ \underline{1250} \\ 0 \end{array}$$

Step 2: Multiply both quantities in the inserted
rate phrase by 9 to find the liters for 9 minutes.

0.32 liter for   1 minute
x 9   x 9
____?____   for   9 minutes

0.32
x   9
2.88 liters

Answer   <u>2.88 liters</u>   for   9 minutes

EXAMPLE   Find the missing quantity that makes the second
rate phrase equivalent to the first one.

2.8 gallons   for   85.4 miles

5.2 gallons for   ____?____

Solution   Using x or ÷, it's not easy to see what to do 2.8 to get 5.2.
Therefore, we insert a rate phrase to find how many ⟶
miles for 1 gallon.

2.8 gallons for 85.4 miles

1 gallon   for   __?__

5.2 gallons for   __?__

Step 1: Divide both quantities in the first rate
phrase by 2.8 to find the miles for 1 gallon.

2.8 gallons for 85.4 miles
÷ 2.8   ÷ 2.8

$$\begin{array}{r} 30.5 \\ 2.8\,\overline{)\,85.40} \\ \underline{84} \\ 14 \\ \underline{0} \\ 140 \\ \underline{140} \\ 0 \end{array}$$

Step 2: Multiply both quantities in the inserted
rate phrase by 5.2 to find the miles for 5.2 gallons.

1 gallon for   30.5 miles
x 5.2   x 5.2
5.2 gallons   for   __?__

30.5
x   5.2
61 0
1525
158.6 0 miles

Answer   5.2 gallons   for   <u>158.6 miles</u>

▶ **Try These Problems**

Find the missing quantity that makes the two rate phrases equivalent. Show your steps clearly.

20. $30   for   15 pens

____?____   for   20 pens

21.   72 gallons every 3 hours

_____?_____   in   1.2 hours

22.   12 meters weigh 3 pounds

20 meters weigh____?____

23.   1.8 liters in   90 minutes

10.6 liters in ____?____

24. $6.20 for 0.8 pound

____?____   for 2 pounds

25.   2.1 seconds every 24 hours

_____?_____   every 160 hours

26.   8 pounds in 3 weeks

6 pounds in ____?____

27.   7.2 feet in 360 seconds

____?____   in 50 seconds

28.   0.05 ounce costs $1

0.14 ounce costs ____?____

Solving Applications Using Equivalent Rate Phrases – 2 Steps

Now we look at solving applications using equivalent rate phrases that require two steps.

EXAMPLE   Ms. Yeh earns $442.50 in 30 hours. How much does she earn in 8 hours?

Solution   Write down the given rate phrase. $\longrightarrow$ $442.50 in 30 hours

Write the question as a rate phrase with missing quantity. Be sure to arrange like units under each other. $\longrightarrow$ _____ in 8 hours

Using x or ÷, it is not easy to see what to do to 30 to get 8. Therefore, we insert a rate phrase to find how much she earns in 1 hour.

$442.50 in 30 hours
_____?_____ in 1 hour
_____?_____ in 8 hours

Step 1: Divide both quantities in the first rate phrase by 30 to find the money for 1 hour.

$442.50 in 30 hours
÷ 30   ÷ 30

$14.75 in 1 hour

Step 2: Multiply both quantities in the inserted rate phrase by 8 to find the money for 8 hours.

$14.75 in 1 hour
x 8   x 8
___?___ in 8 hours

14.75
x   8
$118.00

```
        14.75
30 ) 442.50
       30
       142
       120
         225
         210
          150
          150
            0
```

Answer $118 in 8 hours

EXAMPLE   Kerin types 420 words in 10.5 minutes. How long will it take her to type 750 words?

Solution   Write down the given rate phrase. $\longrightarrow$ 420 words in 10.5 minutes

Write the question as a rate phrase with missing quantity. Be sure to arrange like units under each other. $\longrightarrow$ 750 words in ____?____

Using x or ÷, it is not easy to see what to do to 420 to get 750. Therefore, we insert a rate phrase to find how many minutes for 1 word.

420 words in 10.5 minutes
1 word in ___?___
750 words in ___?___

Step 1: Divide both quantities in the first rate phrase by 420 to find the minutes for 1 word.

420 words in 10.5 minutes
÷ 420   ÷ 420

1 word in 0.025 minute
x 750   x 750

Step 2: Multiply both quantities in the inserted rate phrase by 750 to find the minutes for 750 words.

750 words in ___?___

0.025
x   750
1 250
17 5
18.750 min = 18.75 min

```
         0.025
420 ) 10.500
        840
       2100
       2100
          0
```

Answer   750 words in 18.75 minutes

▶ Try These Problems

Solve each of these applications by generating equivalent rate phrases. Show steps clearly.

29. Six nails weigh 7.2 ounces. What do 25 nails weigh?

30. Jim paid $93.60 for 12 shares of energy stock. What is the cost of 50 shares of this stock?

31. Mailinh paid $63.25 for 5.5 hours of babysitting. What does she pay for 8 hours of babysitting?

32. A watch loses 6 seconds every 2.4 hours. How many hours does it take the watch to lose 7.5 seconds?

33. A cable that is 5.2 feet long weighs 26 pounds. What is the weight of 3.9 feet of this cable?

34. Bob stuffs 24 envelopes in 60 seconds. How long does it take him to stuff 50 envelopes?

35. Water enters a tank at the rate of 37.8 gallons in 3.5 hours. How many gallons enter the tank in 9.5 hours?

36. A fish swims 0.2 mile each minute. How many minutes does it take the fish to swim 9.7 miles?

Rate as a Multiplier

Suppose you earn 15 dollars per hour and you work for 8 hours. If we multiply 15 by 8, we get the total amount of money earned in 8 hours. Let's look at the multiplication statement with the units attached.

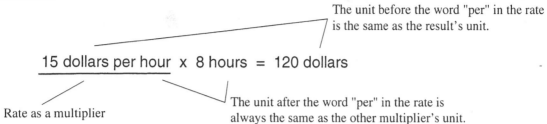

The unit before the word "per" in the rate is the same as the result's unit.

15 dollars per hour x 8 hours = 120 dollars

Rate as a multiplier

The unit after the word "per" in the rate is always the same as the other multiplier's unit.

When the rate, 15 dollars per hour, is multiplied by 8 hours, the "hour" unit cancels and we end up with "dollars." Here are more examples. Study carefully how the units work. It can help you with setting up application problems.

$2.50 per pen x 10 pens = $25

1.5 feet per minute x 5 minutes = 7.5 feet

14 liters = 2.8 liters per week x 5 weeks

4 pounds = 80 nails x 0.05 pound per nail

In each equation note the following:
1) The rate is one of the multipliers.
2) The unit after the word "per" in the rate is the same as the other multiplier's unit.
3) The unit before the word "per" in the rate is the same as the result's unit.

To focus on the units more carefully, here we look at the above equations without the numbers.

$ per pen x pens = $

feet per minute x minutes = feet

liters =   liters per week x weeks

pounds = nails x pound per nail

One multiplier has a rate unit. The other multiplier's unit is the same as the unit after the word "per" in the rate.

EXAMPLE   Find the missing quantity that makes the equation true. Give both the number and units.
12 yards = 2.4 minutes x _____

Solution   First, we can see the following unit structure. ⟶ **yards = minutes x yards per minute**

Therefore, the missing multiplier is a rate.
The units are "yards per minute."

Because we are missing the multiplier, we divide the result 12 by the given multiplier 2.4 to obtain the missing multiplier.

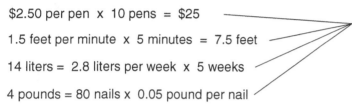

$12 \div 2.4$ ⟶

Answer   5 yards per minute

► Try These Problems

Find the missing quantity that makes the statement true. Include both the number and units.

37. $15.60 per hour x 9 hours = _____

38. 24.8 pounds per carton x 12 cartons = _____

39. 6.4 miles per hour x _____ = 16 miles

40. _____ x 9.8 feet per minute = 2.45 feet

41. _____ = 300 nails x 0.07 pound per nail

42. _____ = 2.6 inches per day x 16 days

43. 2100 calories = _____ x 3 meals

44. $1.53 = _____ x $0.085 per ounce

Rate Applications - Rate Given or Rate Missing

There are some cases where you may want to set up a multiplication statement, using the rate as a multiplier, to solve an application problem. This is particularly helpful when the rate is given or when you are looking for the rate. Here we look at three examples.

EXAMPLE Kniesha earns $12.50 per hour. How many hours does she have to work to earn $600?

Solution We are given the rate, "$12.50 per hour."
We are looking for the number of hours to earn $600.

Set up the structure using ⟶ **$ per hour x hours = $**
"$ per hour" as a multiplier.

Put the known quantities ⟶ 12.50 x _____?_____ = 600
in the appropriate positions.

Because we are missing a multiplier, we divide 600 ÷ 12.50
the result 600 by the given multiplier 12.50.

$$\begin{array}{r} 48. \\ 12.5\overline{)600.0} \\ \underline{500} \\ 100\ 0 \\ \underline{100\ 0} \\ 0 \end{array}$$

Answer Kniesha needs to work 48 hours to earn $600.

EXAMPLE Canned peaches cost $0.18 per ounce. What is the cost of 16 ounces?

Solution We are given the rate, $0.18 per ounce.

Set up the structure. ⟶ **$ per ounce x ounces = $**

Put the known quantities ⟶ 0.18 x 16 = _____?_____
in the appropriate positions.

$$\begin{array}{r} 0.18 \\ \times\ 16 \\ \hline 1\ 08 \\ 1\ 8 \\ \hline 2.88 \end{array}$$

Answer 16 ounces cost $2.88.

EXAMPLE 5.6 gallons of water enter a tank every 0.35 hour. How many gallons per hour is this?

Solution We are looking for the number of "gallons per hour."
Therefore, we are looking for the rate.

Set up the structure. ⟶ **gallons per hour x hours = gallons**

Put the known quantities
in the appropriate positions. ⟶ _____?_____ x 0.35 = 5.6

Because we are missing the multiplier, we divide the
result 5.6 by the given multiplier 0.35 to obtain the
missing multiplier.

$$\begin{array}{r} 16. \\ 0.35\overline{)5.60} \\ \underline{3\ 5} \\ 2\ 10 \\ \underline{2\ 10} \\ 0 \end{array}$$

Answer Water enters the tank at a rate of 16 gallons per hour.

✳ ▶**Try These Problems**

Solve each of these applications by setting up a multiplication equation with the rate as a multiplier.

45. You walk 4.5 miles each hour. How many miles can you walk in 3.8 hours?

46. A watch loses 6.2 seconds each day. How many seconds has the watch lost in 9 days?

47. A fish swims 2.4 meters per second. How many seconds will it take the fish to swim 6 meters?

48. A clerk earns $6.25 per hour. How many hours does it take the clerk to earn $80?

49. A 12.5-foot rope weighs 16 pounds. How many pounds per foot is this?

50. Green peppers cost $35 for 9.5 pounds. What is the cost of 1 pound? (Round up to the nearest cent.)

51. Thirty-six loads of dirt weigh 0.18 ton. What is the weight of 1 load?

52. A faucet leaks 3.6 centiliters every minute. How long does it take the faucet to leak 8.1 centiliters?

5 Area of a Rectangle

The **area** of a rectangle is a measure of the extent of the region inside the boundary. A square that measures 1 unit on each side is said to have an area of 1 square unit.

1 unit [ ] Area = 1 square unit
1 unit

A rectangle that is 3 units wide and 4 units long contains 12 of the 1-square-unit squares, therefore the area is 12 square units.

3 units Area = 12 square units

4 units

Observe that the area of this rectangle can be obtained by multiplying the length by the width.

$$\text{Area} = \text{length} \times \text{width}$$
$$= \quad 4 \quad \times \quad 3$$
$$= 12 \text{ square units}$$

In general, the area of any rectangle can be computed by multiplying the length by the width.

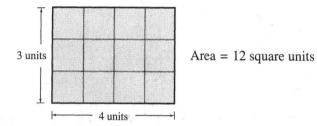

Area of a Rectangle
The area of a rectangle is the length times the width.
Area = length × width

EXAMPLE 14 Find the area of a rectangle that has length 65.4 feet and width 40.5 feet.

SOLUTION We use the following formula.

Area = length × width
(sq ft)   (ft)   (ft)
[ ]   = 65.4 × 40.5

We multiply 65.4 by 40.5 to find the area.

```
        6 5.4
      × 4 0.5
       32 7 0
      2616
      2648.7 0 = 2648.7
```

The area is 2648.7 square feet. ■

26. The area of a plot of land is 1.76 square miles. The length is 2.2 miles. How wide is the plot?

27. The rectangular floor of a room measures 7.5 yards by 8.4 yards. How many square yards does this floor contain?

EXAMPLE 15   The area of a rectangle is 54.4 square meters. The width is 6.4 meters. Find the length.

   SOLUTION   We use the following formula.

$$\begin{array}{ccc} \text{Area} & = \text{length} \times \text{width} \\ \text{(sq m)} & \text{(m)} \quad\quad \text{(m)} \\ 54.4 & = \boxed{} \times \quad 6.4 \end{array}$$

A multiplier is missing, so we divide the answer 54.4 by the given multiplier 6.4 to find the missing multiplier.

$$\begin{array}{r} 8.5 \text{——length in meters} \\ 6.4{\overline{\smash{\big)}\,5\,4.4\,0}} \\ \underline{5\,1\,2} \\ 3\,2\,0 \\ \underline{3\,2\,0} \end{array}$$

The length is 8.5 meters. ■

▲ **Try Problems 26 and 27.**

6 Solving Problems Involving Translations

In Section 7.4 we saw how translating English phrases to math symbols can be used to solve problems. Now we look at examples involving real-life situations.

EXAMPLE 16   This week apples cost 1.5 times as much as they did last week. This week apples cost $0.89 a pound. What was the cost last week? (Round off to the nearest cent.)

   SOLUTION   The first sentence translates to a multiplication statement.

$$\begin{array}{ccccc} \text{Cost} & & & & \text{cost} \\ \text{this week} & \text{is} & 1.5 & \text{times} & \text{last week} \\ \text{(\$)} & \downarrow & & \downarrow & \text{(\$)} \\ 0.89 & = & 1.5 & \times & \boxed{} \end{array}$$

A multiplier is missing, so we divide the answer, 0.89, by the given multiplier, 1.5, to find the missing multiplier.

$$\begin{array}{r} .5\,9\,3 \approx 0.5\,9 \\ 1.5{\overline{\smash{\big)}\,0.8\,9\,0\,0}} \\ \underline{7\,5} \\ 1\,4\,0 \\ \underline{1\,3\,5} \\ 5\,0 \\ \underline{4\,5} \\ 5 \end{array}$$

The apples cost $0.59 a pound last week. ■

EXAMPLE 17   Margaret pays 0.35 of her take-home pay for rent. How much does she pay for rent if her take-home pay is $800?

SOLUTION   The first sentence translates to a multiplication statement.

	her		
0.35 of	take-home pay ($)	is	rent ($)
↓		↓	
0.35 ×	800	=	☐

The answer to the multiplication problem is missing, so we multiply to find the rent.

$$
\begin{array}{r}
800 \\
\times\ 0.35 \\
\hline
40\ 00 \\
240\ 0 \\
\hline
280.00 = 280
\end{array}
$$

Margaret pays $280 in rent.   ■

EXAMPLE 18   At City College, 0.15 of the students are over 25 years old. If 2250 students are over the age of 25, how many students does the college have?

SOLUTION   The first sentence translates to a multiplication statement.

0.15	of	all the students	are	over 25 years old
		↓	↓	
0.15	×	☐	=	2250

A multiplier is missing, so we divide the answer 2250 by the given multiplier to find the missing multiplier.

$$
\begin{array}{r}
1\ 5\ 0\ 0\ 0. = 1\ 5,0\ 0\ 0 \\
0.1\ 5\overline{)2\ 2\ 5\ 0.0\ 0} \\
\underline{1\ 5} \\
7\ 5 \\
\underline{7\ 5}
\end{array}
$$

There are 15,000 students.   ■

EXAMPLE 19   In a recent football game, a quarterback completed 20 out of 32 passes. The number of completions is what decimal of the total number of passes?

SOLUTION   The last sentence translates to a multiplication statement.

Number of completions	is	what decimal	of	total passes
	↓		↓	
20	=	☐	×	32

A multiplier is missing, so we divide the answer 20 by the given multiplier 32 to obtain the missing multiplier.

Try These Problems

Solve. Answer with a decimal.

28. Mr. Stribolt cut two pieces of wire. The shorter piece is 0.75 times as long as the longer piece. The shorter piece is 12.3 meters long. What is the length of the longer piece?

29. The price of gasoline is 1.2 times as much as it was last year. Last year the price was $0.54 per liter. What is the price this year? (Truncate to the nearest cent.)

30. A company conducted a survey indicating that 0.4 of the workers have young children at home to care for. There are 1600 workers. How many have young children?

31. Ms. Cruz pays 0.30 of her income in federal taxes. If she pays $7680 in taxes, what is her income?

32. A baseball player was up to bat 150 times. He got 33 hits. His hits are what decimal part of his times at bat? (The answer is called his batting average.)

33. Six-tenths of a bottle of medicine weighs 3.45 grams. How much does the full bottle weigh?

34. Find the average of 6.25; 8.75; 10.5; and 12.95.

35. Mr. Lau earns $45.30 per hour, Ms. Tomm earns $52.65 per hour, and Mr. Pearson earns $80.75 per hour. What is the average of these three rates of pay? (Truncate to the nearest cent.)

$$
\begin{array}{r}
0.625 \\
32\overline{)20.000} \\
\underline{192} \\
80 \\
\underline{64} \\
160 \\
\underline{160}
\end{array}
$$

He completed 0.625 of his passes. ■

 Try Problems 28 through 33.

7 Averaging

Recall from Sections 2.5 and 5.7 that the **average** (or **mean**) of a set of data is a measure of the middle or center of the data. The average of a collection of numbers can be found by adding the numbers, then dividing by how many numbers there are.

Finding the Average of a Collection of Numbers

1. Add all the numbers in the collection.

2. Divide the sum by how many numbers are in the collection.

 EXAMPLE 20 Find the average of 34.2, 65.85, and 56. (Round up at 2 decimal places.)

SOLUTION First add the numbers, then divide the sum by 3.

$$
\begin{array}{r}
34.20 \\
65.85 \\
+\ 56.00 \\
\hline
156.05
\end{array}
\qquad
\begin{array}{r}
52.01 \approx 52.02 \\
3\overline{)156.05} \\
\underline{15} \\
6 \\
\underline{6} \\
05 \\
\underline{3} \\
2
\end{array}
$$

The average is 52.02. ■

EXAMPLE 21 The rainfall in Atlanta for a 5-day period was as follows.

1.7 in   2.4 in   0.65 in   0.84 in   2.1 in

What was the average rainfall for the 5-day period? (Truncate at 1 decimal place.)

SOLUTION Add the 5 numbers, then divide the total by 5.

$$
\begin{array}{r}
1.7 \\
2.4 \\
0.65 \\
0.84 \\
+\ 2.1 \\
\hline
7.69
\end{array}
\qquad
\begin{array}{r}
1.5 \\
5\overline{)7.69} \\
\underline{5} \\
2\ 6 \\
\underline{2\ 5} \\
1
\end{array}
$$

Because we want the answer truncated at 1 decimal place, we do not need to divide any further.

The average rainfall is 1.5 inches. ■

 Try Problems 34 and 35.

Now we summarize the material in this section by giving guidelines that will help you to decide whether to multiply or divide.

Situations Requiring Multiplication

×   1.   You are looking for a total quantity.

$$\text{Total quantity} = \text{size of each part} \times \text{number of equal parts}$$

      2.   You are looking for a total, as in the following examples.

$$\text{Total miles} = \text{miles per hour} \times \text{number of hours}$$

$$\text{Total cost} = \text{cost per item} \times \text{number of items}$$

      3.   You are looking for a number that is a certain amount times as large as another number.

      4.   You are looking for the area of a rectangle.

$$\text{Area} = \text{length} \times \text{width}$$

      5.   You are looking for a decimal of a number.

Situations Requiring Division

÷   1.   A total quantity is being separated into a number of equal parts.

$$\text{Size of each part} = \text{total quantity} \div \text{number of equal parts}$$

$$= \frac{\text{total quantity}}{\text{number of equal parts}}$$

$$\text{Number of equal parts} = \text{total quantity} \div \text{size of each part}$$

$$= \frac{\text{total quantity}}{\text{size of each part}}$$

      2.   You are looking for a missing multiplier in a multiplication statement.

$$\text{Missing multiplier} = \text{answer to the multiplication problem} \div \text{given multiplier}$$

      3.   You are looking for an average.

$$\text{Average cost per item} = \text{total cost} \div \text{number of items}$$

$$\text{Average miles per hour} = \text{total miles} \div \text{number of hours}$$

$$\text{Average of a collection of numbers} = \text{sum of the numbers} \div \text{how many numbers}$$

      4.   You are looking for what ratio one number is to another number.

▲ Answers to Try These Problems

1. 1.25 in 2. 0.8 in 3. 25 doses 4. 0.2 gal
5. $109.25 6. 487.5 oz 7. 2.25 lb 8. $955.80
9. $5.68 10. 0.625 min 11. 29.24 oz 12. 0.6 mi
13. 5 lb per wk 14. 2.25 gal per hr 15. 6.5¢ per oz
16. $1.25 per lb 17. 0.125 m 18. 0.02 lb 19. $14.75
20. $0.08 21. 51 mi 22. 8.6 lb 23. 187.5. min 24. 125 sec
25. 19.5 lb 26. 0.8 mi 27. 63 sq yd 28. 16.4 m
29. $0.64 per ℓ 30. 640 workers 31. $25,600 32. 0.22 or 0.220
33. 5.75 g 34. 9.6125 35. $59.56 per hr

EXERCISES 7.5

Solve. Show setups and calculation steps.

1. Cathy earned $3829.50 over a 9-month period. How much did she earn each month?

2. Four persons share an apartment that rents for $323 per month. If they split the rent equally, what does each pay per month?

3. One hundred twenty strips of metal are laid one right after the other. If each strip is 4.05 meters long, what is the resulting total length?

4. A large container of milk is distributed equally among 24 persons. If each person receives 6.5 ounces, how much milk was in the original large container?

5. How many 1.2-foot pieces of wood can be cut from a board that is 21.6 feet long?

6. A chef made 975 ounces of spaghetti sauce. How many 7.5-ounce servings is this?

7. Find the cost of 4 pounds of meat at $4.15 per pound.

8. Lumber costs $0.82 per foot. What is the cost of 36.5 feet of this lumber?

9. Nancy can go 148.8 miles in 3 hours. How far can she go in 1 hour?

10. Jack paid $4.95 for 5 pounds of bananas. How much does 1 pound cost?

11. Rene jogs 3.5 miles in 32.2 minutes. How long does it take her to jog 1 mile?

12. A jar of mushrooms containing 8.6 ounces costs $0.69. What is the cost per ounce? (Truncate to the nearest cent.)

13. If sales tax is 0.055 of the marked price, what is the sales tax on a TV set marked $495? (Round off to the nearest cent.)

14. Bill's take-home pay for one month is $1475. He pays $354 in rent. What decimal part of his take-home pay is his rent?

15. Today radishes cost 0.8 times as much as they did yesterday. Today the cost is $0.85 a bunch. What was the cost yesterday? (Truncate to the nearest cent.)

16. Susan has a charge account at a department store. The store charges a service charge which is 0.015 multiplied by the unpaid balance. What is the service charge if her unpaid balance is $180?

17. A baseball player had 32 hits out of 95 times at bat. What is the ratio of hits to times at bat? (Round off at 3 decimal places.)

18. A solution contains 960 centiliters of water and 4.5 centiliters of acid. What is the ratio of acid to water? (Truncate at 4 decimal places.)

19. The area of a rectangle is 70.68 square feet. If the length is 7.6 feet, find the width.

20. The length of a rectangle is 12.03 centimeters and the width is 4.8 centimeters. Find the area of the rectangle.

21. Gordon bought three suits at the following prices: $475.80, $395.60, and $419.20. What is the average price of the suits?

22. A statistician measured the weight of drained peaches in 5 randomly selected 15-ounce cans packed by the Sunny Fruit Company. The weights (in ounces) were as follows.
10.9   11.4   11.3   12.4   10.8
Compute the average of these 5 weights.

23. A bottle of medicine contains 36 centiliters. A nurse needs to give out doses of this medicine, each containing 2.4 centiliters. How many doses can be given from the bottle?

24. A pile of sand weighs 0.5 ton. The sand is to be relocated using barrels that each hold 0.025 ton of sand. How many barrels are needed?

25. Susan's car averages 35.8 miles per gallon. How far can she go on a full tank of 15 gallons?

26. If Joe bicycles 0.4 mile each minute, how far can he bicycle in 12 minutes?

27. Gary wants to drive from Houston to New Orleans, which is a distance of 359 miles. If his car averages 24.6 miles per gallon, how many gallons of gas does he need to make the one-way trip? (Round up at 1 decimal place.)

28. Peter walks at the rate of 5.2 miles per hour. How long will it take him to walk 160 miles? (Truncate at 1 decimal place.)

29. Five pens weigh 32 grams. What is the weight of 19 pens?

30. Fifteen ounces of a product cost $1.20. What is the cost of 24 ounces?

31. In a tennis match, Tracy got 0.65 of her first serves in. If she got 78 first serves in, how many first serves did she attempt?

32. Today the price of oil is 0.75 of what it was last year. If the price today is $36 a barrel, what was the price last year?

33. You buy 1.5 pounds of mushrooms for $3.27. What is the cost per pound?

34. A watch loses 4 seconds every 25 hours. How much time does the watch lose per hour?

35. Betsy cuts a 4.5-meter wire into 30 equal pieces. How long is each piece?

36. Chuck wants to practice his piano for 24 hours during the next 15 days. If he spreads the time equally over the 15 days, how many hours will he practice each day?

37. The width of a rectangle is 45.3 feet. The length is twice the width. Find the area of the rectangle.

38. A rectangular floor contains 400 square feet. If the length is 27.5 feet, find the width. (Round off at 1 decimal place.)

39. Lou bought 3 steaks. The prices were $3.75, $4.20, and $5.15. What was the average price? (Round off to the nearest cent.)

40. The hourly wages of 5 workers were as follows.
$16.75 $18.45 $20.75 $32.60 $17.50
What is the average of these wages?

41. A basketball team won 0.75 of the total games played. If they won 96 games, how many games have they played?

42. The price of a computer decreased from $4200 to $3360. The decrease is what decimal of the original price?

The cost per pound for fresh asparagus fluctuated during a 5-month period as shown in the bar graph. Use the graph to answer Exercises 43 through 46.

Price of Asparagus

43. What was the cost per pound for asparagus in August?

44. What was the cost of 20 pounds of asparagus in June?

45. Find the average cost per pound for the 5-month period.

46. The decrease in price from August to September is what decimal of the August price? (Round off at 2 decimal places.)

CHAPTER 7 SUMMARY

KEY WORDS AND PHRASES

multiplication [7.1]
division [7.2]
divisor [7.2]
dividend [7.2]
quotient [7.2]
round off [7.2]
round up [7.2]

truncate [7.2]
repeating decimal [7.2]
multiplier [7.3]
factor [7.3]
product [7.3, 7.4]
twice [7.4]
half of [7.4]

divided by [7.4]
divided into [7.4]
ratio [7.4, 7.5]
rate [7.5]
area of a rectangle [7.5]
average (mean) [7.5]

SYMBOLS

$8.4\overline{56}$ means $8.456565656\ldots$

$0.33\frac{1}{3}$ means $\dfrac{33\frac{1}{3}}{100}$

There are three ways to indicate the division problem 42 divided by 6.

$$42 \div 6 = 7 \qquad 6\overline{)42}\,^{7} \qquad \frac{42}{6} = 7$$

IMPORTANT RULES

How to Multiply Two Decimals [7.1]

▌ Ignore the decimal points and multiply the numbers as if they were whole numbers.

▌ Place the decimal point in the product by adding the number of decimal places in the multipliers to get the number of decimal places in the product.

How to Multiply a Decimal by 10, 100, 1000, and so on [7.1]
The rule for how to multiply a decimal by 10, 100, 1000, and so on is on page 265.

How to Divide Decimals [7.2]

▮ If the divisor is a whole number, place the decimal point in the quotient directly above the decimal point in the dividend.

▮ If the divisor is not a whole number, move the decimal point in the divisor to the right as many places as it takes to make a whole number. Move the decimal in the dividend the same number of places as was moved in the divisor. Place the decimal point in the quotient directly above the new decimal point in the dividend.

How to Divide a Decimal by 10, 100, 1000, and so on [7.2]
The rule for how to divide a decimal by 10, 100, 1000, and so on is on page 277.

How to find the Missing Number in a Multiplication Statement [7.3]

▮ If you are missing the answer to the multiplication problem (the product), then multiply.

▮ If you are missing one of the multipliers, then divide the answer (or product) by the known multiplier (or factor) to find the missing multiplier.

How to find a Decimal of a Number [7.4, 7.5]
To find a decimal of a number, multiply the decimal by the number, that is, the word *of* used in this way translates to multiplication.

Situations Requiring Multiplication [7.5]
A summary of these situations appears on page 301.

Situations Requiring Division [7.5]
A summary of these situations appears on page 301.

CHAPTER 7 REVIEW EXERCISES

Multiply.

1.
$$\begin{array}{r} .7\,5 \\ \times\quad .8 \\ \hline \end{array}$$

2.
$$\begin{array}{r} .1\,2 \\ \times\ .6\,4 \\ \hline \end{array}$$

3.
$$\begin{array}{r} 3\,5 \\ \times\ 6.3 \\ \hline \end{array}$$

4.
$$\begin{array}{r} 3\,0\,7 \\ \times\quad 8.4 \\ \hline \end{array}$$

5. 0.83×54.0 **6.** 92.40×0.70 **7.** 593.00×0.065

8. 12×8.20 **9.** $.600 \times 0.360$ **10.** $.090 \times 705$

11. 3050×60.5 **12.** 60.70×0.103 **13.** $950,000 \times 2.50$

14. $3600 \times .045$ **15.** 9000×11.2 **16.** $120,000 \times .009$

17. $.086 \times 1000$ **18.** $0.78 \times 100,000$

19. $700 \times 4.5 \times 0.5$ **20.** $506 \times 3.4 \times 0.23 \times 6$

Divide. Continue dividing until the remainder is zero.

21. $48.6 \div 120$ **22.** $0.185 \div 74$ **23.** $17 \div 5$

24. $16 \div 64$ **25.** $2.268 \div 40.5$ **26.** $0.1456 \div 0.07$

27. $83.12 \div 0.004$ **28.** $2737.5 \div 0.375$ **29.** $4440 \div 0.12$

30. $\frac{90}{3.2}$ **31.** $\frac{2.22}{0.6}$ **32.** $\frac{3}{400}$

Divide. Express the answer as a repeating decimal.

33. $5 \div 9$ **34.** $26 \div 3$ **35.** $3.85 \div 3.3$ **36.** $43 \div 0.075$

Divide two places past the decimal and write the remainder in fractional form.

37. $468.3 \div 56$ **38.** $620 \div 6$ **39.** $\frac{0.4}{6.5}$ **40.** $\frac{50}{0.48}$

Divide. Approximate the answer as indicated.

41. $490.3 \div 16$ (Truncate at 3 decimal places.)

42. $4 \div 6.9$ (Truncate at 2 decimal places.)

43. $7 \div 26$ (Round off at 4 decimal places.)

44. $5.2 \div 20.5$ (Round off at 3 decimal places.)

45. $\frac{35}{6}$ (Round up at 3 decimal places.)

46. $\frac{7.08}{0.38}$ (Round up at 2 decimal places.)

Convert each of these fractions to a decimal.

47. $\frac{3}{4}$ **48.** $\frac{210}{8}$ **49.** $\frac{62}{25}$ **50.** $\frac{7}{40}$

51. $\frac{53}{6}$ **52.** $\frac{5}{120}$ **53.** $\frac{19}{27}$ **54.** $\frac{93}{11}$

Find the missing number. Write the answer in decimal form.

55. $8.5 \times 9 = \boxed{}$ **56.** $8 \times \boxed{} = 201$

57. $33 = 0.48 \times \boxed{}$ **58.** $299 = 0.065 \times \boxed{}$

59. $\boxed{} \times 6.4 = 0.08$ **60.** $0.35 \times 27{,}000 = \boxed{}$

Solve. Write the answer in decimal form. Show setups and calculation steps.

61. Find 0.015 of 650.

62. Divide 3.51 by 2.7.

63. Divide 2500 into 93.

64. What decimal of 2400 is 144?

65. Find twice 8.6.

66. What number is half of 17.73?

67. Find the ratio of 4.5 to 12.

68. Find the average of 0.17 and 2.89.

69. Twelve families share equally 8.7 pounds of cheese. How much cheese does each family receive?

70. How many 0.8-foot pieces of wood can be cut from a log that is 10.4 feet long?

71. A program consists of 9 segments that are each 3.75 minutes long. What is the total length of the program?

72. Find the cost of 7.2 pounds of chicken at $3.28 per pound. (Round up to the nearest cent.)

73. Six loads of dirt weigh 0.09 ton. What is the weight of 1 load?

74. Ching earns $24.75 per hour. At this rate, how many hours must he work to earn $1980?

75. Water enters a tank at the rate of 56 gallons every 3.5 minutes. How many gallons per minute is this?

76. If sales tax is 0.085 of the marked price, what is the sales tax on a microwave oven that is marked $380?

77. Ms. Gomez has a charge account at a department store. The store charges a service charge which is 0.015 of the unpaid balance. If the service charge is $6.12, what is the unpaid balance?

78. At an auto plant outside of Detroit, 76 out of 3800 workers called in sick. What decimal of the workers called in sick?

79. The price of sugar has doubled in the past ten years. If the price now is $5.68 per pound, what was the price ten years ago?

80. Stanley, an auto mechanic, earns $42 per hour. His girlfriend Edna is a lawyer making 3.5 times as much as Stanley. What does Edna make per hour?

81. One side of a box is 35.8 centimeters wide and 60 centimeters long. What is the area of this one side?

82. A rectangular wall is 9.5 feet high and contains 200 square feet. How wide is the wall? (Round up at 1 decimal place.)

83. The hourly wages for 4 workers are as follows.
$13.80 $15 $16.75 $20.50
Find the average of 4 hourly wages. (Round off to the nearest cent.)

84. The price of gas decreased from $1.89 per gallon to $1.50 per gallon in one week. Find the ratio of the decrease in price to the original price. (Round off at 2 decimal places.)

85. A watch loses 4.8 minutes in 8 hours. How much time does the watch lose in 12 hours?

86. On a map 1.25 inches represents 20 miles. How many miles does 2 inches represent?

✎ In Your Own Words

Write complete sentences to discuss each of the following. Support your comments with examples or pictures, if appropriate.

87. Discuss how the following two problems are similar and how they differ.
  a. $2.5 \times \boxed{} = 0.4$ **b.** $0.4 \times \boxed{} = 2.5$

88. Discuss how you decide whether a decimal is less than or more than the number 1.

89. A rectangle is 8.5 feet long and 4.2 feet wide. Discuss how the procedure for finding the perimeter of this rectangle is different than the procedure for finding the area.

90. Give examples of at least three different rates that you experience in your life. Choose examples that involve decimals.

91. Discuss how you can always find the decimal representation for a fraction.

CHAPTER 7 PRACTICE TEST

Multiply.

1. 7.2×8.6 **2.** 208.30×0.603 **3.** $60{,}000 \times 7.5$
4. 0.0608×1000 **5.** 0.0013×9 **6.** $0.8 \times 3.4 \times 50$

Divide. Continue dividing until the remainder is zero.

7. $230 \div 80$ **8.** $2.1654 \div 5.4$ **9.** $\frac{1404}{0.004}$

Divide. Express the answer as a repeating decimal.

10. $2 \div 3$ **11.** $21.4 \div 12$ **12.** $\frac{1300}{2.7}$

Divide two places past the decimal and write the remainder in fractional form.

13. $7.82 \div 0.3$ **14.** $1.2 \div 64$ **15.** $\frac{18.9}{0.81}$

Divide. Approximate the answer as indicated.

16. $28.023 \div 0.7$ (Round off at 3 decimal places.)

17. $8 \div 4.25$ (Truncate at 4 decimal places.)

18. $\frac{2.3}{0.72}$ (Round up at 3 decimal places.)

Convert each of these fractions to a decimal.

19. $\frac{5}{8}$ **20.** $\frac{43}{25}$ **21.** $\frac{5}{18}$ **22.** $\frac{208}{33}$

Find the missing number. Write the answer as a decimal.

23. $16 \times \boxed{} = 8$ **24.** $\boxed{} \times 6.4 = 32$

25. $\boxed{} = 0.07 \times 415$ **26.** $128 = 0.08 \times \boxed{}$

Solve. Write the answer as a decimal. Show setups and calculation steps.

27. What is 12 divided by 0.03?   **28.** Find 6.2 of 500.

29. Divide 16 into 0.05.   **30.** What decimal of 125 is 8.2?

31. Kathy earns $250.60 each week. How much money will she earn in 12 weeks?

32. Bob pays 0.08 of his take-home pay for food each month. He spends $60 on food. How much is his take-home pay?

33. Lieu bought an unsliced loaf of bread from the neighborhood bakery. It was 21 centimeters long. She wants to cut slices that are 1.4 centimeters wide. How many slices can she cut from the loaf of bread?

34. The length of a rectangle is 80 feet and the width is 17.3 feet. What is the area of the rectangle?

35. Anthony drove a total of 238 miles in 5 hours. How many miles per hour is this?

36. An airplane flies 2478 miles in 3.5 hours. How far does it go in 6.7 hours?

37. The amount of snow that fell in a 5-day period at a ski resort in Utah was as follows.
6.8 in   10.9 in   24.5 in   36.6 in   48 in
What was the average amount for the 5-day period? (Round off at 1 decimal place.)

CUMULATIVE REVIEW EXERCISES: CHAPTERS 1–7

Convert each of these decimals to a fraction. Reduce to lowest terms.

1. 3.6   **2.** 0.85   **3.** 0.0025   **4.** 2.125

Convert each of these fractions to a decimal.

5. $\frac{3}{8}$ **6.** $\frac{11}{200}$ **7.** $\frac{302}{4}$ **8.** $\frac{354}{15}$

Find the missing number. Answer with a fraction.

9. $4\frac{2}{3} + \boxed{} = 24$ **10.** $\boxed{} \times \frac{7}{100} = 140$

11. $\boxed{} = \frac{27}{45} \times \frac{65}{26}$ **12.** $\frac{3}{14} + \frac{7}{8} + \frac{11}{28} = \boxed{}$

Solve. Show setups and calculation steps.

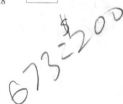

13. Find the difference between 20.1 and 5.76.

14. Find the average of 4.3, 12.8, and 6.

15. Twice what number yields $7\frac{1}{2}$?

16. Find the ratio of $12\frac{1}{2}$ to 100.

17. Find the product of 39.78 and 10,000.

18. Divide 400 into 2.5.

19. Divide 400 by 2.5.

20. Aritha purchased items costing $4.58, $12.96, and $23.79. How much change does she receive from a $100 bill?

21. Bernice and Tom planned to work on a project for 20 hours this week. On Monday they worked $5\frac{1}{2}$ hours; on Tuesday, they worked $4\frac{1}{4}$ hours; and on Wednesday, they worked $3\frac{3}{4}$ hours. How many more hours do they need to work to reach their goal?

22. A rectangular piece of land is 40 feet wide and 65 feet long.
   a. What is the area of this plot?
   b. What is the perimeter of this plot?
   c. If 64 fluid ounces of fertilizer are needed to fertilize each 1000 square feet of land, how many fluid ounces of fertilizer are needed to fertilize this plot?
   d. If you build a fence around the plot at $24.75 per foot, what is the total cost of the fence?

23. An elderly couple inherits $60,000. They invest $\frac{4}{5}$ of the money and divide the rest equally among their 8 grandchildren. How much does each grand-child receive?

Problem Solving: Whole Numbers, Fractions, and Decimals

8.1 THE NUMBER LINE

OBJECTIVES ▌ Name whole numbers that are associated with points on a number line.
▌ Name fractions that are associated with points on a number line.
▌ Name decimals that are associated with points on a number line.

1 Whole Numbers on the Number Line

We picture numbers associated with points along a line. Here is a **number line** containing some whole numbers.

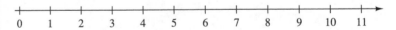

The arrow at the right end indicates the direction in which the numbers get larger. On this number line the numbers are increasing by 1 unit as we move to the right so that the length of each of the smaller segments is 1. Observe that the **distance** between any two points can be found by subtracting the numbers associated with these points. Subtract the smaller number from the larger number to obtain the distance between them.

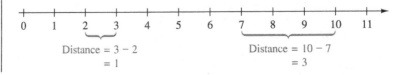

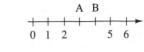 **Try These Problems**

Label all tick marks. Then give the numbers for A and B.

1.

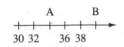

2.

3.

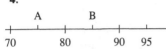

4.

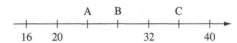

EXAMPLE 1   Give the numbers associated with points A, B, and C.

SOLUTION   First we need to find the length of each of the smaller segments. Because the distance between 202 and 203 is 1 unit, each of the smaller segments has length 1 unit.

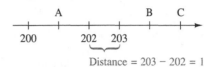

Now we fill in the missing numbers. As we move from left to right, we add 1 unit.

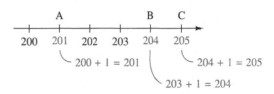

A. 201   **B.** 204   **C.** 205   ■

EXAMPLE 2   Give the numbers associated with points A, B, and C.

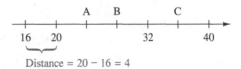

SOLUTION   First we find the length of each of the smaller segments. Because the distance between 16 and 20 is 4, each of the smaller segments has a length of 4 units.

Now we fill in the missing numbers by adding 4 as we move from left to right.

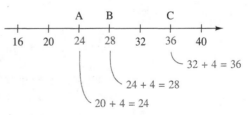

A. 24   **B.** 28   **C.** 36   ■

▲ **Try Problems 1 through 4.**

EXAMPLE 3 Give the numbers associated with points A and B.

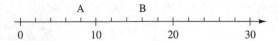

SOLUTION First find the distance between two of the given numbers. For example, the distance between 20 and 30 is 10 units.

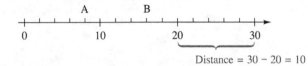

Now count the number of segments between 20 and 30. There are 5 segments between 20 and 30. If a 10-unit length is divided into 5 equal parts then each part has length 2 units. Thus each of the smaller segments has length 2 units.

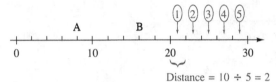

Now fill in the missing numbers by adding 2 as you move from left to right from one tick mark to the next.

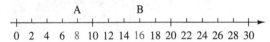

A. 8 **B.** 16 ◼

EXAMPLE 4 Give the numbers associated with points A, B, and C.

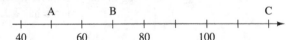

SOLUTION First, find the distance between two of the given numbers. For example, the distance between 80 and 100 is 20.

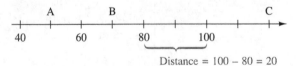

Second, count the number of segments between 80 and 100. There are 2 segments between 80 and 100. If a 20-unit length is divided into 2 equal parts then each part has length 10 units. Thus each of the smaller segments has length 10 units.

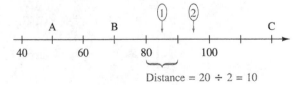

Try These Problems

Label all tick marks. Then give the numbers for A and B.

5.

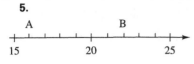

15   20   25

6.

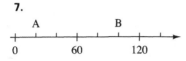

0   100   200

7.

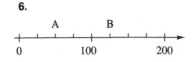

0   60   120

8.

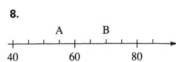

40   60   80

Finally, we fill in the missing numbers by adding 10 as we move left to right from one tick mark to the next.

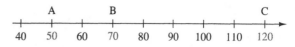

A   B   C
40   50   60   70   80   90   100   110   120

A. 50 **B.** 70 **C.** 120 ■

Try Problems 5 through 8.

---

2 Fractions on the Number Line

We also picture fractions on a number line. Here we show a number line where we look at some fractions with denominator 2.

$$
\begin{array}{cccccccccccc}
0 & & 1 & & 2 & & 3 & & 4 & & 5 \\
\frac{0}{2} & \frac{1}{2} & \frac{2}{2} & \frac{3}{2} & \frac{4}{2} & \frac{5}{2} & \frac{6}{2} & \frac{7}{2} & \frac{8}{2} & \frac{9}{2} & \frac{10}{2}
\end{array}
$$

The fractions get larger as we move in the direction of the arrow. On this number line, the numbers are increasing by $\frac{1}{2}$ unit as we move from left to right, so that the length of each of the smaller segments is $\frac{1}{2}$ unit. Observe that the distance between any two points can be found by subtracting the numbers associated with these points. Subtract the smaller number from the larger number to obtain the distance.

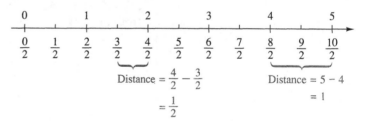

$$
\text{Distance} = \frac{4}{2} - \frac{3}{2} = \frac{1}{2}
$$

$$
\text{Distance} = 5 - 4 = 1
$$

EXAMPLE 5   Give the fractions associated with points A, B, and C.

$$
\begin{array}{ccccccc}
6 & & & A & & 7 & B & C \\
\frac{30}{5} & \frac{31}{5} & \frac{32}{5} & & \frac{34}{5} & \frac{35}{5} &
\end{array}
$$

SOLUTION   We can see that each of the smaller segments has length $\frac{1}{5}$ by subtracting any two numbers that are associated with adjacent tick marks. For example, the distance between $\frac{30}{5}$ and $\frac{31}{5}$ is $\frac{1}{5}$.

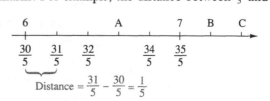

$$
\text{Distance} = \frac{31}{5} - \frac{30}{5} = \frac{1}{5}
$$

Now fill in the missing numbers by adding $\frac{1}{5}$ as you move from left to right from one tick mark to the next.

Try These Problems

Label all tick marks. Then give the fractions for A and B.

9.

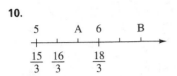

10.

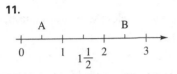

11.

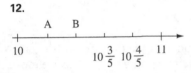

12.

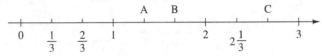

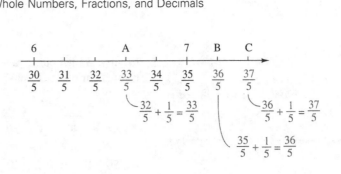

$$\frac{32}{5} + \frac{1}{5} = \frac{33}{5} \qquad \frac{36}{5} + \frac{1}{5} = \frac{37}{5}$$

$$\frac{35}{5} + \frac{1}{5} = \frac{36}{5}$$

A. $\frac{33}{5}$ or $6\frac{3}{5}$ **B.** $\frac{36}{5}$ or $7\frac{1}{5}$ **C.** $\frac{37}{5}$ or $7\frac{2}{5}$ ■

EXAMPLE 6 Give the fractions associated with points A, B, and C.

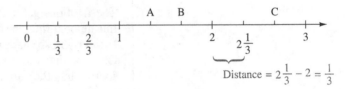

SOLUTION We can see that each of the smaller segments has length $\frac{1}{3}$ by subtracting any two numbers that are associated with adjacent tick marks. For example, the distance between 2 and $2\frac{1}{3}$ is $\frac{1}{3}$.

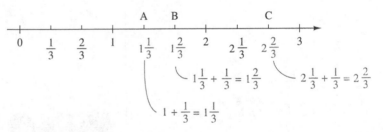

Fill in the missing numbers by adding $\frac{1}{3}$ as you move from left to right from one tick mark to the next.

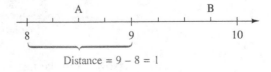

A. $1\frac{1}{3}$ or $\frac{4}{3}$ **B.** $1\frac{2}{3}$ or $\frac{5}{3}$ **C.** $2\frac{2}{3}$ or $\frac{8}{3}$ ■

Try Problems 9 through 12.

EXAMPLE 7 Give the fractions associated with points A and B.

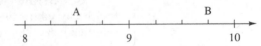

SOLUTION First, find the distance between two given numbers. For example, the distance between 8 and 9 is 1.

Second, count the number of segments between 8 and 9. There are 4 segments between 8 and 9. If a 1-unit length is divided into 4 equal parts then each part has length $\frac{1}{4}$ unit. Thus each of the smaller segments has length $\frac{1}{4}$ unit.

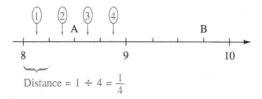

Finally, fill in the missing numbers by adding $\frac{1}{4}$ as you move from left to right from one tick mark to the next.

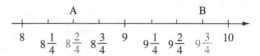

A. $8\frac{1}{2}$ or $\frac{17}{2}$ **B.** $9\frac{3}{4}$ or $\frac{39}{4}$ ■

EXAMPLE 8   Give the fractions associated with points A and B.

SOLUTION   First, find the distance between two given numbers. For example, the distance between 2 and 3 is 1.

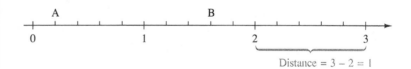

Second, count the number of segments between 2 and 3. There are 5 segments between 2 and 3. If a 1-unit length is divided into 5 equal parts then each part has length $\frac{1}{5}$ unit. Thus each of the smaller segments has length $\frac{1}{5}$ unit.

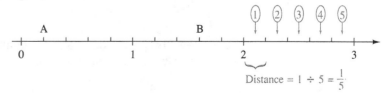

Finally, fill in the missing numbers by adding $\frac{1}{5}$ as you move from left to right from one tick mark to the next.

0    $\frac{1}{5}$ $\frac{2}{5}$ $\frac{3}{5}$ $\frac{4}{5}$ 1 $1\frac{1}{5}$ $1\frac{2}{5}$ $1\frac{3}{5}$ $1\frac{4}{5}$ 2 $2\frac{1}{5}$ $2\frac{2}{5}$ $2\frac{3}{5}$ $2\frac{4}{5}$ 3

A. $\frac{1}{5}$ **B.** $1\frac{3}{5}$ or $\frac{8}{5}$ ■

◄ **Try These Problems**

Label all tick marks. Then give the fractions for A and B.

13.

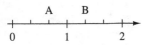

0   1   2

14.

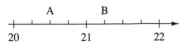

20   21   22

15.

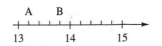

13   14   15

16.

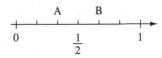

0          $\frac{1}{2}$ 1

EXAMPLE 9 Give the fractions associated with points B and C.

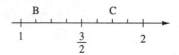

1          $\frac{3}{2}$ 2

SOLUTION First, find the distance between two given numbers. For example, the distance between 1 and 2 is 1.

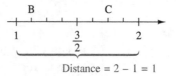

Distance = 2 − 1 = 1

Second, count the number of segments between 1 and 2. There are 8 segments between 1 and 2. If a 1-unit length is divided into 8 equal parts then each part has length $\frac{1}{8}$ unit. Thus each of the smaller segments has length $\frac{1}{8}$ unit.

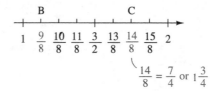

Distance = 1 ÷ 8 = $\frac{1}{8}$

Finally, fill in the missing numbers by adding $\frac{1}{8}$ as you move from left to right from one tick mark to the next.

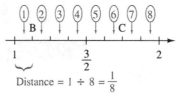

1 $\frac{9}{8}$ $\frac{10}{8}$ $\frac{11}{8}$ $\frac{3}{2}$ $\frac{13}{8}$ $\frac{14}{8}$ $\frac{15}{8}$ 2

$\frac{14}{8} = \frac{7}{4}$ or $1\frac{3}{4}$

B. $1\frac{1}{8}$ or $\frac{9}{8}$ **C.** $1\frac{3}{4}$ or $\frac{7}{4}$ ■

◄ **Try Problems 13 through 16.**

3 Decimals on the Number Line

We also picture decimals on a number line. Here is a number line with some decimals between 0 and 1.

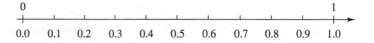

0   1

0.0 0.1 0.2 0.3 0.4 0.5 0.6 0.7 0.8 0.9 1.0

The decimals get larger as we move in the direction of the arrow. On this number line the numbers are increasing by 0.1 as we move to the right so that the length of each of the smaller segments is 0.1. Observe that the distance between any two points can be found by subtracting the numbers associated with these points. Subtract the smaller number from the larger number to obtain the distance.

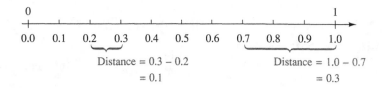

EXAMPLE 10 Give the decimals associated with points A, B, and C.

SOLUTION We can see that each of the smaller segments has length 0.5 by subtracting any two numbers that are associated with adjacent tick marks. For example, the distance between 5 and 5.5 is 0.5.

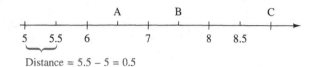

Now fill in the missing numbers by adding 0.5 as you move from left to right from one tick mark to the next.

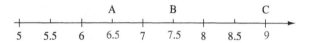

A. 6.5 **B.** 7.5 **C.** 9 ■

EXAMPLE 11 Give the decimals associated with points A, B, and C.

SOLUTION We can see that each of the smaller segments has length 0.2 by subtracting any two numbers that are associated with adjacent tick marks. For example, the distance between 4.6 and 4.8 is 0.2.

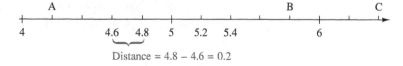

Now fill in the missing numbers by adding 0.2 as you move from left to right from one tick mark to the next.

A. 4.2 **B.** 5.8 **C.** 6.4 ■

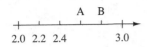 **Try These Problems**

Label all tick marks. Then give the decimals for A and B.

17.

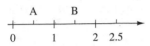

2.0 2.2 2.4   3.0

18.

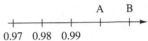

0.97 0.98 0.99

19.

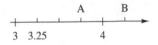

0   1   2 2.5

20.

3   3.25   4

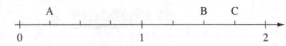 **Try Problems 17 through 20.**

EXAMPLE 12   Give the decimals associated with points A, B, and C.

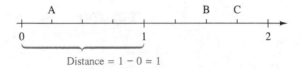

SOLUTION   First, find the distance between two given numbers. For example, the distance between 0 and 1 is 1.

Distance = 1 − 0 = 1

Second, count how many segments are between 0 and 1. There are 4 segments between 0 and 1. If a 1-unit segment is divided into 4 equal parts then each part has length $\frac{1}{4}$ or 0.25 unit.

Distance = 1 ÷ 4 = $\frac{1}{4}$ = 0.25

Now fill in the missing numbers by adding 0.25 as you move from left to right from one tick mark to the next.

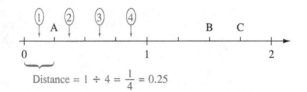

A   B   C

0   0.25   0.5   0.75   1   1.25   1.5   1.75   2

A. 0.25   **B.** 1.50 or 1.5   **C.** 1.75   ■

EXAMPLE 13   Give the decimals associated with points A, B, and C.

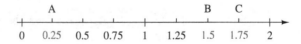

SOLUTION   First, find the distance between two given numbers. For example, the distance between 3 and 4 is 1.

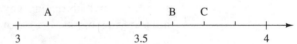

Distance = 4 − 3 = 1

Second, count the number of segments between 3 and 4. There are 8 segments between 3 and 4. If a 1-unit length is divided into 8 equal parts then each part has length $\frac{1}{8}$ or 0.125. Thus each of the smaller segments has length 0.125.

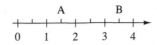 **Try These Problems**

Label all tick marks. Then give the decimals for A and B.

21.

A   B

0   1   2   3   4

22.

A   B

4   5

23.

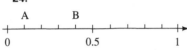

A   B

8   9   10

24.

A   B

0   0.5   1

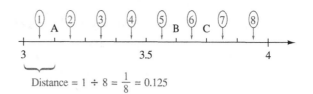

Distance = 1 ÷ 8 = $\frac{1}{8}$ = 0.125

Now fill in the missing numbers by adding 0.125 as you move from left to right from one tick mark to the next.

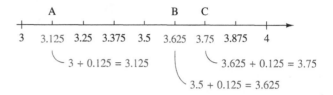

A   B   C

3   3.125 3.25 3.375 3.5   3.625 3.75 3.875   4

3 + 0.125 = 3.125

3.5 + 0.125 = 3.625

3.625 + 0.125 = 3.75

A. 3.125   **B.** 3.625   **C.** 3.75   ■

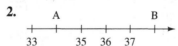 **Try Problems 21 through 24.**

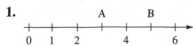 **Answers to Try These Problems**

1. A. 3 B. 4   2. A. 13 B. 18
3. A. 34 B. 40   4. A. 75 B. 85
5. A. 16 B. 22   6. A. 50 B. 125
7. A. 20 B. 100   8. A. 55 B. 70
9. A. $1\frac{1}{4}$ or $\frac{5}{4}$ B. $1\frac{3}{4}$ or $\frac{7}{4}$
10. A. $\frac{17}{3}$ or $5\frac{2}{3}$ B. $\frac{20}{3}$ or $6\frac{2}{3}$
11. A. $\frac{1}{2}$ B. $2\frac{1}{2}$ or $\frac{5}{2}$ 12. A. $10\frac{1}{5}$ B. $10\frac{2}{5}$
13. A. $\frac{2}{3}$ B. $1\frac{1}{3}$ or $\frac{4}{3}$ 14. A. $20\frac{1}{2}$ B. $21\frac{1}{4}$
15. A. $13\frac{1}{5}$ B. $13\frac{4}{5}$ 16. A. $\frac{2}{6}$ or $\frac{1}{3}$ B. $\frac{4}{6}$ or $\frac{2}{3}$
17. A. 2.6 B. 2.8   18. A. 1.00 or 1 B. 1.01
19. A. 0.5 B. 1.5   20. A. 3.75 B. 4.25
21. A. 1.5 B. 3.5   22. A. 4.25 B. 4.75
23. A. 7.8 B. 9.4   24. A. 0.1 B. 0.4

EXERCISES 8.1

Give the numbers associated with points A and B. First label all tick marks.

1.

A   B

0   1   2   4   6

2.

A   B

33   35 36 37

3.

A B

10 13 16 19   28

4. A   B

250 300 350 400

5. A   B

0   10   20

6.   A   B

50   70   90   120

7. A   B

0   10   20   30

8. A   B

100   200   300

Give the fractions associated with points A and B. First label all tick marks.

9.

A   B

0 $\frac{1}{8}$ $\frac{3}{8}$ $\frac{4}{8}$ $\frac{5}{8}$ $\frac{6}{8}$ 1

10.

5 A   6   B   8

$\frac{10}{2}$ $\frac{12}{2}$ $\frac{13}{2}$ $\frac{16}{2}$

11.

A   B

4   5   6

12.

A   B

16   17

13.

A   B

0   1

14.

A   B

0   2

15.

A   B

2   $2\frac{1}{2}$ 3 $3\frac{1}{2}$

16.

A   B

0   $\frac{1}{2}$ 1 $1\frac{1}{2}$

Give the decimals associated with points A and B. First label all ticks.

17.

A B

2.8   3.1 3.2 3.3

18.

A B

0.70 0.75 0.80   0.95

19.

A   B

8   9   10

20.

A   B

0   1   2   3

21.

A B

13   14   15

22.

A   B

0   1

23. A   B

4   4.5   5

24. A   B

50   51

The bar graph gives the fraction of administrative positions held by women at a large university for each of four years. Use the graph to answer Exercises 25 through 28.

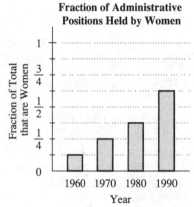

Fraction of Administrative Positions Held by Women

25. In 1960 what fraction of the administrative positions were held by women?

26. In 1990 what fraction of the administrative positions were held by women?

27. In 1970 what fraction of the administrative positions were held by men?

28. In 1980 what fraction of the administrative positions were held by men?

8.2	COMPARING NUMBERS

OBJECTIVES
- Convert fractions, decimals, and whole numbers from one form to another.
- Compare decimals with decimals.
- Compare fractions with fractions.
- Compare fractions with decimals.

1 Equality of Numbers

A number can be written in many forms without changing its value. For example,

$$\frac{1}{2} = \frac{2}{4} = \frac{3}{6} = \frac{4}{8} = \frac{5}{10} = 0.5 = 0.50$$

Here we picture the number $\frac{1}{2}$ in various forms on the number lines that follow.

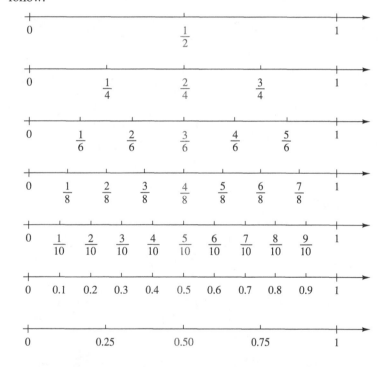

Observe that the position of the number $\frac{1}{2}$ remains halfway between the numbers 0 and 1 regardless of its form. In general, equal numbers occupy the same position on the number line.

When problem solving, it is often necessary to convert numbers from one form to another. Here is a review of the various techniques of **converting** a number; that is, changing its form without changing its value.

CONVERTING NUMBERS FROM ONE FORM TO ANOTHER

1. Reduce a fraction to lower terms by dividing the numerator and denominator by the same nonzero number, or by canceling common factors from the numerator and denominator.

   Example: $\dfrac{21}{28} = \dfrac{3 \times \cancel{7}}{4 \times \cancel{7}} = \dfrac{3}{4}$

2. Raise a fraction to higher terms by multiplying the numerator and denominator by the same nonzero number.

   Example: $\dfrac{2}{3} = \dfrac{2 \times 4}{3 \times 4} = \dfrac{8}{12}$

3. Convert a mixed numeral to an improper fraction.

   Example: $3\dfrac{1}{5} = 3 + \dfrac{1}{5} = \dfrac{15}{5} + \dfrac{1}{5} = \dfrac{16}{5}$

4. Convert an improper fraction to a mixed numeral.

   Example: $\dfrac{18}{7} \rightarrow 7\overline{)18}$ with quotient 2, $\dfrac{14}{4}$ Therefore, $\dfrac{18}{7} = 2\dfrac{4}{7}$

5. Write a mixed numeral so that the fractional part is smaller than one whole.

   Example: $9\dfrac{8}{5} = 9 + \dfrac{8}{5} = 9 + 1\dfrac{3}{5} = 10\dfrac{3}{5}$

   └─ Fractional part is larger than one whole.

   \ Fractional part is smaller than one whole.

6. Write a mixed numeral so that the fractional part is larger than one whole.

   Example: $7\dfrac{3}{8} = 6 + 1\dfrac{3}{8} = 6 + \dfrac{11}{8} = 6\dfrac{11}{8}$

   └─ Fractional part is smaller than one whole.

   \ Fractional part is larger than one whole.

7. Convert a fraction to a decimal.

   Example: $\dfrac{9}{20} \rightarrow 20\overline{)9.00}$ with quotient $.45$, $\dfrac{80}{100}$, $\dfrac{100}{}$ Therefore, $\dfrac{9}{20} = 0.45$

8. Convert a decimal to a fraction.

Example: $0.125 = \dfrac{125}{1000} = \dfrac{5 \times \cancel{25}}{40 \times \cancel{25}} = \dfrac{5}{40} = \dfrac{1 \times \cancel{5}}{8 \times \cancel{5}}$

$\qquad\qquad\qquad = \dfrac{1}{8}$

9. Convert a whole numeral to a decimal or vice versa.

Examples: $\quad 3 = 3.$

$\qquad\qquad 182 = 182.$

$\qquad\qquad 75. = 75$

10. Attach extra zeros to a decimal or remove extra zeros.

Examples: $\quad 6.5 = 6.50$

$\qquad\qquad .823 = 0.823000$

$\qquad\qquad 4 = 4.00$

$\qquad\qquad 12.300 = 12.3$

The symbol $=$ is used to indicate that two numbers are equal and the symbol $\neq$ is used to indicate that two numbers are not equal. For example,

$$0.3 = 0.30 \quad \text{0.3 equals 0.30}$$
$$3 \neq 0.3 \quad \text{3 does not equal 0.3}$$

EXAMPLE 1 Which of these numbers are equal to $\frac{3}{20}$?

a. $6\frac{2}{3}$ **b.** 0.203 **c.** $\frac{27}{180}$

SOLUTION

a. Does $6\frac{2}{3} = \frac{3}{20}$? $6\frac{2}{3}$ is larger than 1 and $\frac{3}{20}$ is smaller than 1.

$$6\frac{2}{3} \neq \frac{3}{20}$$

b. Does $0.203 = \frac{3}{20}$? Convert $\frac{3}{20}$ to a decimal.

$$\frac{3}{20} \rightarrow 20\overline{)3.00}^{\;.15} \quad \text{Therefore, } \frac{3}{20} = 0.15$$

$$\begin{array}{r} .15 \\ 20\overline{)3.00} \\ \underline{2\,0} \\ 1\,00 \\ \underline{1\,00} \end{array}$$

Smaller than 0.203

$$\frac{3}{20} \neq 0.203$$

c. Does $\frac{27}{180} = \frac{3}{20}$? Reduce $\frac{27}{180}$ to lowest terms.

$$\frac{27}{180} = \frac{3 \times \cancel{9}}{20 \times \cancel{9}} = \frac{3}{20}$$

$$\frac{27}{180} = \frac{3}{20}$$

Answer **c.** $\frac{27}{180}$ ■

Try These Problems

1. Which of these numbers are equal to $\frac{3}{8}$?
   a. $\frac{12}{32}$ **b.** $\frac{8}{3}$
   c. 0.375   **d.** 2.66

2. Which of these numbers are equal to $12\frac{2}{5}$?
   a. $\frac{29}{5}$ **b.** $10\frac{12}{5}$
   c. 12.4   **d.** $\frac{62}{5}$

3. Which of these numbers are equal to 8.3?
   a. $8\frac{1}{3}$ **b.** 0.083
   c. $\frac{83}{10}$ **d.** 8.300

4. Which of these numbers are equal to 0.008?
   a. $\frac{8}{100}$ **b.** 0.0080
   c. $\frac{8}{1000}$ **d.** $\frac{4}{500}$

EXAMPLE 2   Which of these numbers are equal to 7.8?
a. $6\frac{18}{10}$ **b.** $7\frac{4}{5}$ **c.** $\frac{115}{15}$
SOLUTION

a. Does $6\frac{18}{10} = 7.8$? Write $6\frac{18}{10}$ so that the fraction part is smaller than one whole, then convert to a decimal.

$$6\frac{18}{10} = 6 + \frac{18}{10} = 6 + 1\frac{8}{10} = 7\frac{8}{10} = 7.8$$

$6\frac{18}{10} = 7.8$

b. Does $7\frac{4}{5} = 7.8$? Convert 7.8 to a mixed numeral.

$$7.8 = 7\frac{8}{10} = 7\frac{4 \times 2}{5 \times 2} = 7\frac{4}{5}$$

$7\frac{4}{5} = 7.8$

c. Does $\frac{115}{15} = 7.8$? Convert $\frac{115}{15}$ to a decimal.

$$\begin{array}{r} 7.66 \\ 15\overline{)115.00} \\ \underline{105} \\ 10\,0 \\ \underline{9\,0} \\ 1\,00 \\ \underline{90} \\ 10 \end{array} \rightarrow \frac{115}{15} = 7.\overline{6}$$

└── Smaller than 7.8

$\frac{115}{15} \neq 7.8$

Answer **a.** $6\frac{18}{10}$ **b.** $7\frac{4}{5}$ ■

 Try Problems 1 through 4.

2 Comparing Decimals

Decimals on the number line are arranged in order. As you move from left to right the decimals get larger. For example, this picture illustrates that 0.6 is more than 0.58.

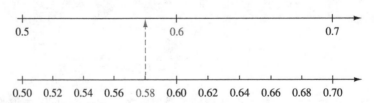

The symbols $<$ and $>$ are used to **compare** numbers that are not equal. For example,

$0.6 > 0.58$ 0.6 is more than 0.58

$0.58 < 0.6$ 0.58 is less than 0.6

Remember that the pointed side of the symbol always points toward the smaller number.

Try These Problems

In Problems 5 and 6, use the symbol < or > to compare each pair of numbers.

5. 0.3, 0.256

6. 5.14, 5.014

7. Which is less, 0.00786 or 0.007849?

8. Which is more, 8.508 or 8.50799?

9. Which is less, 0.35$\overline{2}$ or 0.3$\overline{5}$?

10. Which is more, 13.45 or 13.$\overline{435}$?

One method of comparing decimals is to write each of them with the same number of decimal places, then compare. Here we compare 0.6 with 0.58 using this method.

$$0.6 \; = 0.60 = \frac{60}{100} \quad \text{60 hundredths}$$

$$0.58 = 0.58 = \frac{58}{100} \quad \text{58 hundredths}$$

Because $\frac{60}{100}$ is more than $\frac{58}{100}$, 0.6 is more than 0.58. This method for comparing decimals is discussed carefully in Section 6.3.

 Try Problems 5 and 6.

It is possible to compare decimals without writing each decimal with the same number of decimal places. Here are examples to illustrate the technique.

EXAMPLE 3   Which is less, 7.132876 or 7.1345?

SOLUTION   Arrange the numbers so that decimal points are aligned vertically and digits with the same place value form a column. Compare digits with like place value, starting on the left.

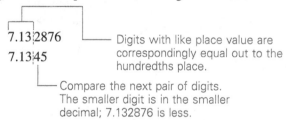

The decimal 7.132876 is less.   ■

 Try Problems 7 and 8.

EXAMPLE 4   Which is more, 12.438 or 12.43$\overline{8}$?

SOLUTION   Arrange the numbers so that decimal points are aligned vertically, and digits with the same place value form a column. Compare digits with like place value, starting on the left.

```
12.438
12.43̄8
```
Digits with like place value are correspondingly equal out to the thousandths place.

After the thousandths place the digits will not be equal so write the decimals so that you can view these digits carefully.

$$12.438 \; = 12.438|0$$

$$12.43\overline{8} = 12.438|888\ldots$$

Compare the next pair of digits. The larger digit is in the larger decimal. 12.43$\overline{8}$ is more.

The decimal 12.43$\overline{8}$ is more.   ■

Try Problems 9 and 10.

Try These Problems

List from smallest to largest.

11. 0.75; 7.52; 7.5; 7.499

12. 22.36; 22.$\overline{3}$; 2.236; 2.$\overline{23}$

Use the symbol < or > to compare each pair of numbers.

13. $\frac{9}{20}$, $\frac{3}{5}$

14. $2\frac{1}{3}$, $2\frac{2}{7}$

EXAMPLE 5 List from smallest to largest: 3.$\overline{7}$, 3.76, 3.$\overline{75}$

SOLUTION First, recall that 3.$\overline{7}$ means 3.7777777. . . . . and 3.$\overline{75}$ means 3.7575757575 . . . . .

When there are more than two decimals to compare, it can be helpful to picture the approximate positions of the decimals on the number line.

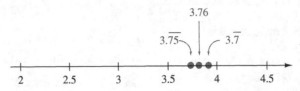

From smallest to largest the numbers are; 3.$\overline{75}$, 3.76, and 3.$\overline{7}$. ■

 Try Problems 11 and 12.

3 Comparing Fractions

Fractions on the number line are arranged in order. As you move from left to right the fractions get larger. For example, this picture illustrates that $\frac{7}{10}$ is less than $\frac{4}{5}$.

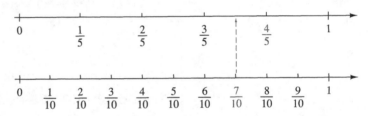

The symbols < and > can be used to compare fractions. For example,

$$\frac{7}{10} < \frac{4}{5} \qquad \text{$\frac{7}{10}$ is less than $\frac{4}{5}$}$$

$$\frac{4}{5} > \frac{7}{10} \qquad \text{$\frac{4}{5}$ is more than $\frac{7}{10}$}$$

One method of comparing fractions is to write them with the same denominator, then compare. Here we compare $\frac{7}{10}$ and $\frac{4}{5}$ using this method. The least common multiple of 5 and 10 is 10, so we convert $\frac{4}{5}$ to a fraction with denominator 10.

$$\frac{4}{5} = \frac{4 \times 2}{5 \times 2} = \frac{8}{10} \qquad \text{8 tenths}$$

$$\frac{7}{10} \qquad\quad = \frac{7}{10} \qquad \text{7 tenths}$$

Because $\frac{8}{10}$ is more than $\frac{7}{10}$ and $\frac{4}{5} = \frac{8}{10}$, then $\frac{4}{5}$ is more than $\frac{7}{10}$. Using symbols, we write $\frac{4}{5} > \frac{7}{10}$. This method of comparing fractions is discussed thoroughly in Section 5.4.

 **Try Problems 13 and 14.**

Try These Problems

15. Which is less, $\frac{1}{2}$ or $\frac{2}{5}$?

16. Which is more, $\frac{8}{10}$ or $\frac{31}{39}$?

17. Which is less, $3\frac{7}{11}$ or $3\frac{19}{30}$?

18. Which is more, $5\frac{2}{17}$ or $5\frac{29}{250}$?

Another way to compare fractions is change each to a decimal, then compare. Here are examples to illustrate the technique.

EXAMPLE 6   Which is less, $\frac{9}{20}$ or $\frac{21}{50}$?

SOLUTION   Convert each fraction to a decimal.

$$
20\overline{)9.00}^{\,.45} \rightarrow \frac{9}{20} = 0.45
$$
$$
\begin{array}{r} 8\,0 \\ \hline 1\,00 \\ 1\,00 \\ \hline \end{array}
$$

$$
50\overline{)21.00}^{\,.42} \rightarrow \frac{21}{50} = 0.42 \text{ —— This number is less.}
$$
$$
\begin{array}{r} 20\,0 \\ \hline 1\,00 \\ 1\,00 \\ \hline \end{array}
$$

The fraction $\frac{21}{50}$ is less.   ■

 Try Problems 15 and 16.

EXAMPLE 7   Which is more, $5\frac{3}{8}$ or $5\frac{7}{18}$?

SOLUTION   Convert each mixed numeral to a decimal.

$$
8\overline{)3.000}^{\,.375} \rightarrow 5\frac{3}{8} = 5.375
$$
$$
\begin{array}{r} 2\,4 \\ \hline 60 \\ 56 \\ \hline 40 \\ 40 \\ \hline \end{array}
$$

$$
18\overline{)7.000}^{\,.388} \rightarrow 5\frac{7}{18} = 5.38\overline{8} \text{ —— This number is more.}
$$
$$
\begin{array}{r} 5\,4 \\ \hline 1\,60 \\ 1\,44 \\ \hline 160 \\ 144 \\ \hline 16 \\ \end{array}
$$

The number $5\frac{7}{18}$ is more.   ■

Try Problems 17 and 18.

EXAMPLE 8   List from smallest to largest: $\frac{3}{2}, \frac{5}{7}, \frac{3}{4}$

SOLUTION   Convert each of the fractions to a decimal, then compare.

$$
2\overline{)3.0}^{\,1.5} \rightarrow \frac{3}{2} = 1.5
$$
$$
\begin{array}{r} 2 \\ \hline 1\,0 \\ 1\,0 \\ \hline \end{array}
$$

Try These Problems

In Problems 19 and 20, list from smallest to largest.

19. $\frac{180}{200}, \frac{3}{8}, \frac{7}{5}$

20. $\frac{211}{40}, \frac{79}{13}, \frac{50}{9}, \frac{61}{10}$

21. Which is more, $\frac{8}{13}$ or 0.62?

22. Which is less, 5.8724 or $5\frac{7}{8}$?

$$
\begin{array}{r}
.71 \\
7\overline{)5.00} \\
4\,9 \\
\hline
10 \\
7 \\
\hline
3
\end{array}
\quad \rightarrow \quad \frac{5}{7} \approx 0.71
$$

$$
\begin{array}{r}
.75 \\
4\overline{)3.00} \\
2\,8 \\
\hline
20 \\
20 \\
\hline
\end{array}
\quad \rightarrow \quad \frac{3}{4} \approx 0.75
$$

When comparing more than two numbers, it can be helpful to picture the numbers on the number line.

From smallest to largest the numbers are $\frac{5}{7}, \frac{3}{4}$, and $\frac{3}{2}$. ■

 Try Problems 19 and 20.

4 Comparing Fractions to Decimals

If you need to compare numbers where some of them are written as fractions and others are written as decimals, write them all as decimals then compare. The following examples illustrate this.

EXAMPLE 9 Which is more, $\frac{7}{11}$ or 0.6367?

SOLUTION Convert $\frac{7}{11}$ to a decimal.

$$
\begin{array}{r}
.6363 \\
11\overline{)7.0000} \\
6\,6 \\
\hline
40 \\
33 \\
\hline
70 \\
66 \\
\hline
40 \\
33 \\
\hline
7
\end{array}
\quad \rightarrow \quad \frac{7}{11} = 0.\overline{63}
$$

Now compare the two decimals carefully. It helps to arrange them so that the decimal points align vertically and digits with like place value form a column.

$$\frac{7}{11} = 0.\overline{63} = 0.636\vert363\ldots$$

$$0.6367 \quad = 0.636\vert700 \underline{\quad\quad} \text{This number is more.}$$

The number 0.6367 is more. ■

 Try Problems 21 and 22.

Try These Problems

23. List from smallest to largest:
1.09, 0.916, $\frac{11}{12}$, $\frac{9}{10}$

EXAMPLE 10 List from smallest to largest: $\frac{2}{9}$, 0.22, 1.2, $\frac{1}{4}$

SOLUTION Convert $\frac{2}{9}$ and $\frac{1}{4}$ to decimals.

$$9\overline{)2.00} \to \frac{2}{9} = 0.\overline{2}$$
$$\underline{18}$$
$$20$$
$$\underline{18}$$
$$2$$

$$4\overline{)1.00} \to \frac{1}{4} = 0.25$$
$$\underline{8}$$
$$20$$
$$20$$

When there are more than two numbers it helps to picture the numbers on the number line.

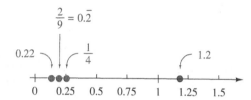

From smallest to largest the numbers are 0.22, $\frac{2}{9}$, $\frac{1}{4}$, and 1.2. ∎

 Try Problem 23.

 Answers to Try These Problems

1. a. $\frac{12}{32}$ c. 0.375   2. b. $10\frac{12}{5}$ c. 12.4 d. $\frac{62}{5}$ 3. c. $\frac{83}{10}$ d. 8.300
4. b. 0.0080 c. $\frac{8}{1000}$ d. $\frac{4}{500}$ 5. >   6. >   7. 0.007849
8. 8.508   9. 0.352   10. 13.45   11. 0.75; 7.499; 7.5; 7.52
12. 2.23; 2.236; 22.3; 22.36   13. <   14. >   15. $\frac{2}{5}$
16. $\frac{8}{10}$ 17. $3\frac{19}{30}$ 18. $5\frac{2}{17}$ 19. $\frac{3}{8}, \frac{180}{200}, \frac{7}{5}$
20. $\frac{211}{40}, \frac{50}{9}, \frac{79}{13}, \frac{61}{10}$ 21. 0.62   22. 5.8724
23. $\frac{9}{10}$, 0.916, $\frac{11}{12}$, 1.09

EXERCISES 8.2

Use the symbol <, =, or > to compare each pair of numbers.

1. 23.54, 23.268
2. 0.0076, 0.012
3. $\frac{5}{12}, \frac{3}{4}$
4. $8\frac{7}{50}, 8\frac{2}{10}$
5. $14\frac{12}{4}, 17$
6. $9\frac{6}{4}, 10\frac{1}{2}$
7. 0.78, $\frac{7}{9}$
8. $\frac{2}{13}$, 0.154
9. 16.25, $16\frac{11}{48}$
10. $\frac{104}{5}$, 20.8
11. Which of these numbers are equal to $\frac{7}{25}$?
    a. $\frac{28}{100}$ b. 0.725   c. $\frac{35}{125}$ d. 0.28
12. Which of these numbers are equal to $9\frac{3}{16}$?
    a. $\frac{147}{16}$ b. 9.316   c. $8\frac{19}{16}$ d. 9.1875

13. Which of these numbers are equal to 0.06?
    a. $\frac{3}{500}$ **b.** $\frac{3}{50}$ **c.** 0.0600   **d.** $\frac{60}{1000}$

14. Which of these numbers are equal to 7.4?
    a. 7.400   **b.** $\frac{37}{5}$ **c.** $\frac{74}{100}$ **d.** $\frac{296}{40}$

15. Which of these numbers are equal to 12?
    a. $\frac{60}{5}$ **b.** $\frac{2}{24}$ **c.** 0.12   **d.** 12.0

16. Which of these numbers are equal to 35?
    a. $34\frac{6}{6}$ **b.** $\frac{1220}{4}$ **c.** 35.00   **d.** $\frac{420}{12}$

Which number is less?

17. 8.16394, 8.1638109

18. $\frac{3}{1000}$, $\frac{1}{33}$

19. 1.75, $1\frac{13}{18}$

20. $\frac{5}{34}$, 0.148

Which number is greater in value?

21. $8\frac{1}{12}$, $8\frac{2}{25}$

22. $25.\overline{3}$, 25.3378

23. $\frac{52}{50}$, 1.3

24. $\frac{5}{17}$, 0.29

List from smallest to largest.

25. 21.5; 2.1; 20.75; 21.6

26. $7.\overline{7}$; 7.7; 0.7; $0.\overline{7}$

27. $1\frac{1}{4}, \frac{3}{4}, \frac{4}{3}, 1$

28. $\frac{14}{33}, \frac{2}{50}, \frac{2}{5}, \frac{5}{2}$

29. $0.64, \frac{3}{5}, \frac{23}{40}, 0.63\overline{7}$

30. $3.6, 3.628, 3\frac{2}{3}, 3\frac{17}{27}$

31. $20\frac{11}{18}, 20.6, 2.06, 20\frac{2}{3}$

32. $0.114, \frac{1}{10}, \frac{10}{1}, 9.8$

8.3   LANGUAGE

OBJECTIVE   ▌   Solve problems by using translations.

In this section we review the language that has been introduced throughout this book and look at some examples of solving problems by using translations. The first chart gives many English words or phrases that often translate to the equality symbol $=$.

Math Symbol	*English*
=	equals
	is equal to
	is the same as
	is the result of
	is
	are
	was
	were
	will be
	represents
	gives
	makes
	yields

1 Translating English to Addition and Subtraction

The addition statement $3.2 + 0.4 = 3.6$ is written using math symbols. Some of the ways to read this statement using English are given in the chart that follows.

Math Symbols	English
$3.2 + 0.4 = 3.6$	3.2 plus 0.4 equals 3.6.
	3.2 added to 0.4 gives 3.6.
	3.2 *increased by* 0.4 yields 3.6.
	The *sum* of 3.2 and 0.4 is 3.6.
	0.4 more than 3.2 is 3.6.
	3.6 is the result of adding 3.2 and 0.4.

The subtraction statement $3.2 - 0.4 = 2.8$ is written using math symbols. Some of the ways to read this statement using English are given in the following chart.

Math Symbols	English
$3.2 - 0.4 = 2.8$	3.2 minus 0.4 is 2.8
	3.2 take away 0.4 equals 2.8.
	3.2 *decreased by* 0.4 gives 2.8.
	0.4 subtracted from 3.2 is 2.8.
	0.4 less than 3.2 is equal to 2.8.
	The *difference* between 3.2 and 0.4 is 2.8.
	2.8 is the result of subtracting 0.4 from 3.2.

Observe that when reading the subtraction symbol $-$ using the phrases *subtracted from* or *less than*, the numbers are read in the reverse order than they are written. Here is a closer look at translations that involve these phrases.

$$\underbrace{0.4 \text{ subtracted from } 3.2}_{3.2 - 0.4} \qquad \underbrace{0.4 \text{ less than } 3.2}_{3.2 - 0.4}$$

Here is an example of using translations to help with problem solving.

EXAMPLE 1   What number increased by $\frac{3}{4}$ gives $7\frac{5}{18}$?

SOLUTION   The question translates to an addition statement.

$$\text{What number}\quad \underbrace{\text{increased by}}\quad \frac{3}{4}\quad \text{gives}\quad 7\frac{5}{18}?$$

$$\square \quad + \quad \frac{3}{4} \quad = \quad 7\frac{5}{18}$$

Try These Problems

Translate to an equation. Solve.

1. Find the difference between 230 and 1.98.
2. Find the sum of $3\frac{1}{12}$ and $6\frac{3}{20}$.
3. What number plus 0.86 yields 9.7?
4. 16 represents $12\frac{3}{5}$ more than what number?

One of the parts is missing so we subtract to find the missing number.

$$7\frac{5}{18} - \frac{3}{4}$$

$$= 7\frac{5 \times 2}{18 \times 2} - \frac{3 \times 9}{4 \times 9}$$

Convert each fraction to an equivalent fraction with denominator 36.

$$= 7\frac{10}{36} - \frac{27}{36}$$

$$= 6\frac{46}{36} - \frac{27}{36}$$

$$= 6\frac{19}{36}$$

The missing number is $6\frac{19}{36}$. ■

If you need to see more examples of translation problems involving addition and subtraction, refer to Sections 1.3, 5.6, and 6.6.

 Try Problems 1 through 4.

2 Translations Involving Multiplication and Division

The multiplication statement $\frac{3}{4} \times 200 = 150$ is written using math symbols. The chart that follows illustrates many correct ways to read the statement using English.

Math Symbols	English
$\frac{3}{4} \times 200 = 150$	$\frac{3}{4}$ times 200 is 150.
	$\frac{3}{4}$ of 200 equals 150.
	$\frac{3}{4}$ multiplied by 200 gives 150.
	The *product* of $\frac{3}{4}$ and 200 is 150.
	150 represents $\frac{3}{4}$ of 200.
	150 is the result of multiplying $\frac{3}{4}$ by 200.

EXAMPLE 2   What fraction of 60 is 2.4?

SOLUTION   The question translates to a multiplication statement.

What fraction   of   60   is   2.4?
$\square$ ×   60   =   2.4

Translate to an equation. Solve.

5. Find 0.15 of 460.

6. Find the product of $\frac{1}{30}$ and $8\frac{1}{3}$.

7. 115 represents 0.005 multiplied by what number?

8. What fraction of $45\frac{1}{2}$ is $9\frac{1}{10}$?

9. Find the ratio of 0.45 to 30.

10. Find the result when $3\frac{3}{4}$ is divided by $1\frac{1}{2}$.

11. Divide 0.125 into 16.

12. Divide $\frac{2}{5}$ into 80.

A multiplier is missing, so we divide 2.4 by 60 to find the missing multiplier.

$$60\overline{)2.40}\;\;\begin{array}{c}.04\\ \end{array}$$

The product 2.4 is written inside the division symbol.

$$\begin{array}{r} .04 \\ 60\overline{)2.40} \\ 0 \\ \hline 2\,40 \\ 2\,40 \end{array}$$

The answer is 0.04 or $\frac{4}{100}$. ■

Now that we have studied both fractions and decimals, it is correct to answer the question, "what fraction of," with either a fraction or decimal.

If you need to see more examples of problems that translate to a multiplication statement, refer to Sections 2.4, 4.4, and 7.4.

◢◣ **Try Problems 5 through 8.**

When reading the division statement $12 \div 3$, take care to read the numbers in the correct order, because $12 \div 3$ does not equal $3 \div 12$.

$$12 \div 3 = \frac{12}{3} = 4 \quad \text{but} \quad 3 \div 12 = \frac{3}{12} = \frac{1}{4} \text{ or } 0.25$$

Larger than 1.   Smaller than 1.

The following chart gives several correct ways to read each of these division statements using English.

Math Symbols	English
$12 \div 3 = 4$ or $\frac{12}{3} = 4$	12 *divided by* 3 is 4. The *ratio* of 12 to 3 is 4. 3 *divided into* 12 equals 4. 4 is the result of dividing 12 by 3.
$3 \div 12 = \frac{1}{4}$ or 0.25	3 *divided by* 12 is 0.25.
$\frac{3}{12} = \frac{1}{4}$ or 0.25	The *ratio* of 3 to 12 is $\frac{1}{4}$. 12 *divided into* 3 is $\frac{1}{4}$. 0.25 is the result of dividing 3 by 12.

If you need more help with the language related to division, refer to Sections 2.4, 4.4, and 7.4.

◢◣ **Try Problems 9 through 12.**

◢◣ Answers to Try These Problems

1. 228.02   2. $9\frac{7}{30}$ 3. 8.84   4. $3\frac{2}{5}$ 5. 69   6. $\frac{5}{18}$
7. 23,000   8. $\frac{1}{5}$ or 0.2   9. 0.015   10. $\frac{5}{2}$ or $2\frac{1}{2}$ or 2.5
11. 128   12. 200

EXERCISES 8.3

Translate to an equation. Then solve.

1. Find the product of 4.5 and 300.
2. Find the sum of 23.9 and 360.
3. Find the difference between $2\frac{1}{3}$ and $\frac{3}{4}$.
4. Find the ratio of $3\frac{1}{2}$ to $10\frac{1}{2}$.
5. Divide 40 into 3.4.
6. Subtract 9.45 from 82.
7. What number is $5\frac{5}{8}$ more than $7\frac{3}{4}$?
8. Find $\frac{7}{8}$ of 320.
9. 50 equals 1.6 times what number?
10. Divide 8 by 3.2.
11. What number is $3\frac{8}{9}$ less than $8\frac{13}{20}$?
12. What number plus $\frac{4}{3}$ yields $\frac{13}{7}$?
13. What fraction of 84 is 2.1?
14. 0.02 of what number gives 0.15?
15. 14 is what fraction of 56?
16. Find the ratio of 13 to 104.
17. $12\frac{5}{6}$ decreased by $4\frac{2}{3}$ yields what number?
18. 36 represents $2\frac{1}{2}$ of what number?
19. Divide $3\frac{1}{5}$ by 200.
20. Divide $3\frac{1}{5}$ into 200.

USING THE CALCULATOR # 8

MULTIPLYING AND DIVIDING FRACTIONS AS DECIMALS

When we use a calculator to compute mathematics problems, we are often satisfied with the answer in decimal form even if the original problem was given in fractional form and even if the answer is only an approximation. In this feature, we look at operating with fractions without the use of the $\boxed{a\text{\%}}$ key.

Of course, you can convert a fraction to a decimal on the calculator by dividing the numerator by the denominator. For example, here we convert $\frac{3}{4}$ to a decimal.

To Convert to a Decimal	$\dfrac{3}{4}$
Enter	3 $\boxed{\div}$ 4 $\boxed{=}$
Result	0.75

Therefore, the fraction $\frac{3}{4}$ is equal to the decimal 0.75. The procedure for converting a fraction to a decimal is the same for both the scientific and the basic calculator.

Next we look at multiplying two fractions on the calculator. The procedure is the same for both the scientific and the basic calculator. For example, here we compute $\frac{5}{8} \times \frac{2}{5}$.

To Compute	$\dfrac{5}{8} \times \dfrac{2}{5}$
Enter	5 $\boxed{\div}$ 8 $\boxed{\times}$ 2 $\boxed{\div}$ 5 $\boxed{=}$
Result	0.25

Dividing two fractions on the calculator is not as straightforward as multiplying two fractions. If you enter the $\boxed{\div}$ key instead of the $\boxed{\times}$ key in the previous procedure, you do not get the result of $\frac{5}{8} \div \frac{2}{5}$. The reason has to do with the order in which the calculator is doing the repeated division.

Probably the safest way for you to divide two fractions on the calculator is first to change the problem to multiplication, then use the procedure for multiplication. Here we show how to compute $\frac{5}{8} \div \frac{2}{5}$.

To Compute	$\dfrac{5}{8} \div \dfrac{2}{5}$
Change to	$\dfrac{5}{8} \times \dfrac{5}{2}$
Enter	5 $\boxed{\div}$ 8 $\boxed{\times}$ 5 $\boxed{\div}$ 2 $\boxed{=}$
Result	1.5625

Cont. page 338.

Calculator Problems

Convert each fraction to a decimal. If the decimal representation goes beyond 3 decimal places, round off at 3 decimal places.

1. $\frac{7}{8}$ **2.** $\frac{8}{7}$ **3.** $\frac{35}{13}$ **4.** $\frac{13}{35}$ **5.** $\frac{250}{6000}$ **6.** $\frac{6000}{250}$

Evaluate each without using the $\boxed{a^{b/c}}$ *key. If the decimal representation goes beyond 3 decimal places, round off at 3 decimal places.*

7. $\frac{5}{6} \times \frac{3}{4}$ **8.** $\frac{15}{38} \times \frac{75}{41}$ **9.** $678 \times \frac{97}{186}$ **10.** $\frac{85}{300} \times 45$

11. $\frac{5}{6} \div \frac{3}{4}$ **12.** $\frac{15}{38} \div \frac{75}{41}$ **13.** $678 \div \frac{97}{186}$ **14.** $\frac{85}{300} \div 45$

Convert the mixed numerals to improper fractions, then use the procedure discussed in this feature to evaluate. If the decimal representation goes beyond 3 decimal places, round off at 3 decimal places.

15. $8\frac{4}{5} \times 3\frac{6}{7}$ **16.** $8\frac{4}{5} \div 3\frac{6}{7}$ **17.** $78\frac{17}{456} \times 27\frac{45}{88}$ **18.** $78\frac{17}{456} \div 27\frac{45}{88}$

8.4   APPLICATIONS: CHOOSING THE CORRECT OPERATION

OBJECTIVES

▮ Solve an application that involves a total as the sum of parts.
▮ Solve an application that involves equal parts in a total quantity.
▮ Solve an application that involves the perimeter of a figure.
▮ Solve an application that involves the area of a rectangle.
▮ Solve an application that involves translating.
▮ Solve an application that involves rates or ratios.

In this section we look at the various types of applications that have been introduced throughout the text thus far. Also we refer you to the appropriate previous sections where more detailed instruction is given on a particular type of problem.

1 Problems Involving a Total as the Sum of Parts

EXAMPLE 1   Dick wanted to jog a total distance of 8 miles. After jogging 6.4 miles, his foot began to hurt and he walked the rest of the way. How far did he walk?

SOLUTION   First picture the situation.

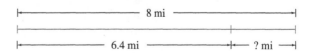

Observe that we are missing one of the parts in a total quantity, so we have the following.

$$\begin{array}{ccc} \text{Jogging} & \text{walking} & \text{total} \\ \text{distance} + \text{distance} = \text{distance} \\ \text{(mi)} & \text{(mi)} & \text{(mi)} \\ 6.4 & + \boxed{} & = \quad 8 \end{array}$$

Try These Problems

Solve. Show setups.

1. Ms. Rodriquez, the vice-president of finance for a small company, wrote checks for $456.96, $365.75, and $1087.54. What is the total amount of the checks?

2. Doug has a piece of wire that is 18.2 meters long. He cuts off a piece that is 9.75 meters long. How long is the remaining piece?

3. On a vacation Bette spent $\frac{1}{3}$ of her money on air fare. What fraction of her money was left for other expenses?

4. Jose received a bonus from his employer. He invested $\frac{2}{5}$ of it in a money market fund, $\frac{1}{4}$ of it in municipal bonds, and spent the rest on furniture for his new home. What fraction of his bonus did he invest?

To find the missing part, subtract the given part 6.4 from the total 8.

$$
\begin{array}{r}
8.0 \\
-6.4 \\
\hline
1.6
\end{array}
\quad
\begin{array}{l}
\text{Total} \\
\text{Jogging part} \\
\text{Walking part}
\end{array}
$$

Dick walked 1.6 miles. ∎

EXAMPLE 2   An engineer completed $\frac{2}{15}$ of a job. What fraction of the job is left?

SOLUTION   The whole job is represented by the number 1, thus we have the following.

$$
\begin{array}{ccc}
\text{Fraction} & & \text{fraction} \\
\text{completed} & + & \text{left}
\end{array}
= \text{total}
$$

$$
\frac{2}{15} \quad + \quad \boxed{} \quad = \quad 1
$$

To find the missing part, subtract the given part $\frac{2}{15}$ from the total 1.

$$
1 - \frac{2}{15}
$$

$$
= \frac{15}{15} - \frac{2}{15} \qquad \text{Convert 1 to } \tfrac{15}{15}.
$$

$$
= \frac{13}{15}
$$

$\frac{13}{15}$ of the job is left. ∎

If you need to see additional examples of problems involving a total as the sum of parts; the list that follows gives the section of the text where the specified examples can be found.

Section	Examples
1.4	1, 2, and 3
5.7	1, 2, and 3
6.7	1 and 2

 Try Problems 1 through 4.

2 Problems Involving Equal Parts in a Total Quantity

Suppose you have a rope that is 3 feet in length. If you cut the rope into 12 equal pieces, then the length of each piece is $\frac{1}{4}$ or 0.25 foot. Here is a picture of the situation.

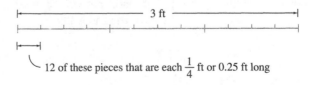

12 of these pieces that are each $\frac{1}{4}$ ft or 0.25 ft long

Observe that the numbers are related as follows.

$$\underset{\substack{\text{(ft)}}}{\substack{\text{Size of} \\ \text{each part}}} \times \substack{\text{number of} \\ \text{equal parts}} = \underset{\substack{\text{(ft)}}}{\substack{\text{total} \\ \text{quantity}}}$$

$$0.25 \times 12 = 3$$

In general, if a situation involves a total quantity being split into a number of equal parts, the following always applies.

$$\substack{\text{Size of} \\ \text{each part}} \times \substack{\text{number of} \\ \text{equal parts}} = \substack{\text{total} \\ \text{quantity}}$$

When using this formula be careful not to assume that the total quantity is always the largest of the three numbers. Notice in the situation above, the total quantity is 3, and the number of equal parts is a larger number, 12. The total quantity is always larger than the size of each part but may or may not be larger than the number of equal parts.

A problem can be presented by giving any two of the three quantities and asking for the third quantity. The following examples illustrate this.

EXAMPLE 3   A nurse needs to give a patient 42 doses of medicine. Each dose contains 2.7 centiliters. How much medicine does the nurse need for this patient?

SOLUTION   This problem involves a total quantity that is made up of a number of equal parts. The following formula applies.

$$\underset{\substack{\text{(c}\ell\text{)}}}{\substack{\text{Size of} \\ \text{each part}}} \times \substack{\text{number of} \\ \text{equal parts}} = \underset{\substack{\text{(c}\ell\text{)}}}{\substack{\text{total} \\ \text{quantity}}}$$

$$2.7 \times 42 = \boxed{}$$

To find the total amount of medicine, multiply the number of doses 42 by the size of each dose, 2.7 centiliters.

$$
\begin{array}{rl}
4\,2 & \text{Number of doses} \\
\underline{\times\ 2.7} & \text{Size of each dose in centiliters} \\
29\,4 & \\
\underline{84} & \\
113.4 & \text{Total amount in centiliters.}
\end{array}
$$

The nurse needs a total of 113.4 centiliters. ∎

EXAMPLE 4   A chef prepared 174 cups of pudding. How many $\frac{2}{3}$-cup portions can she serve?

SOLUTION   We want to know how many $\frac{2}{3}$-cup servings are in the total quantity, 174 cups. The following formula applies.

$$\underset{\substack{\text{(cups)}}}{\substack{\text{Size of} \\ \text{each part}}} \times \substack{\text{number of} \\ \text{equal parts}} = \underset{\substack{\text{(cups)}}}{\substack{\text{total} \\ \text{quantity}}}$$

$$\frac{2}{3} \times \boxed{} = 174$$

Try These Problems

5. A bookshelf is 57 inches wide. Books that are each 0.6 inch thick are to stand on the shelf. How many books fit on the shelf?

6. The cost of putting in a new road through a residential area was $19,800. The 55 home-owners who live in the area shared the cost equally. What was each homeowner's share?

7. Janet is making drapes for a very wide window. If she sews together 12 panels that are each $3\frac{5}{8}$ feet wide, what is the total width of the resulting drapes?

A multiplier is missing, so we divide 174 by $\frac{2}{3}$ to find the missing multiplier.

$$174 \div \frac{2}{3} = \frac{\overset{87}{\cancel{174}}}{1} \times \frac{3}{\underset{1}{\cancel{2}}} = 261$$

Total amount in cups — Size of each serving in cups — Number of servings

The chef can serve 261 of the $\frac{2}{3}$-cup portions. ■

If you need to see additional examples involving equal parts in a total quantity, the following list gives the section of the text where the specified examples can be found.

Section	Examples
2.5	1, 2, and 3
3.6	1, 2, and 3
4.5	1, 2, 3 and 4
7.5	1, 2, and 3

 Try Problems 5 through 7.

3 Perimeter and Area

The segment shown here has a length of 1 centimeter.

——— Length = 1 centimeter

Here is a square that has each side measuring 1 centimeter.

1 cm [square] 1 cm   Area = 1 square centimeter
Perimeter = 4 centimeters

We say that the **area** of this square measures 1 square centimeter. However, the **perimeter** of this square is 4 centimeters. Area is the measure of the extent of a region on a flat surface, while perimeter is the total distance around the boundary of the region. Consider a rectangular region that has a width of 3 centimeters and a length of 4 centimeters.

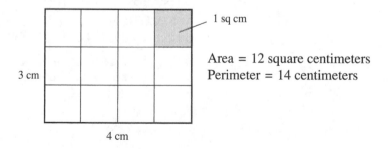

Area = 12 square centimeters
Perimeter = 14 centimeters

The area of each of the smaller squares inside measures 1 square centimeter, and there are 12 of these squares inside. Therefore, the area of the entire rectangle is 12 square centimeters. Because the distance around the rectangle is 14 centimeters, the perimeter of the rectangle is 14 centimeters. Observe that the area of this rectangle can be found by multiplying the width by the length.

$$\text{Area} = 3 \text{ cm} \times 4 \text{ cm} = 12 \text{ sq cm}$$

Also, observe that the perimeter of this rectangle can be found by adding the lengths of all four sides.

$$\text{Perimeter} = 3 \text{ cm} + 3 \text{ cm} + 4 \text{ cm} + 4 \text{ cm}$$
$$= 14 \text{ cm}$$

In general the area of any rectangle can be found by multiplying the width by the length. Before multiplying, the distances must be written using the same unit of measurement. The perimeter of a rectangle can be found by adding the lengths of all four sides.

> *Area of a Rectangle*
>
> The area of a rectangle is the length times the width.
> Area = length × width
>
> *Perimeter of a Rectangle*
>
> Perimeter = length + length + width + width
> = twice the length + twice the width

EXAMPLE 5   A rectangular window is $6\frac{1}{2}$ feet wide and $3\frac{3}{4}$ feet high.

a. Find the perimeter of the window.

b. Find the area of the window.

SOLUTION

a. Perimeter $= 6\dfrac{1}{2} + 6\dfrac{1}{2} + 3\dfrac{3}{4} + 3\dfrac{3}{4}$
(ft)

$\qquad = 6\dfrac{2}{4} + 6\dfrac{2}{4} + 3\dfrac{3}{4} + 3\dfrac{3}{4}$

$\qquad = 18\dfrac{10}{4}$

$\qquad = 20\dfrac{2}{4}$

$\qquad = 20\dfrac{1}{2} \quad \text{or} \quad 20.5$

b.   Area $\; = 6\dfrac{1}{2} \times 3\dfrac{3}{4}$
(sq ft)

$\qquad = \dfrac{13}{2} \times \dfrac{15}{4}$

$\qquad = \dfrac{195}{8} \quad \text{or} \quad 24\dfrac{3}{8} \quad \text{or} \quad 24.375$

The perimeter is $20\frac{1}{2}$ feet and the area is $24\frac{3}{8}$ square feet. ■

Try These Problems

8. A rectangular piece of fabric is $17\frac{3}{8}$ inches wide and $35\frac{1}{3}$ inches long.
   a. Find the perimeter of the piece.
   b. Find the area of the piece.

9. Find the perimeter of a triangle whose sides have lengths of 28 centimeters, 5.7 centimeters, and 18.73 centimeters.

10. The length of a sheet of metal is 8.6 meters. The sheet consists of 54.61 square meters.
    a. What is the width of the sheet?
    b. What is the perimeter of the sheet?

EXAMPLE 6   A rectangular lot contains 1020 square yards. If the width of the lot is 25 yards, find the length.

SOLUTION   The quantity *1020 square yards* is the area of the lot. This should be obvious because of the units *square yards* attached to the 1020. We have the following:

$$\text{Area} = \text{length} \times \text{width}$$
$$(\text{sq yd}) \quad (\text{yd}) \quad (\text{yd})$$
$$1020 = \boxed{} \times 25$$

A multiplier is missing, so we divide 1020 by 25 to find the missing multiplier.

```
              40.8 ——— Length in yards
        25)1020.0 ——— Area in square yards
Width       100
in yards     20
              0
             20 0
             20 0
```

The length of the lot is 40.8 yards. ■

If you need to see more examples related to perimeter or area, the following list gives the location of these examples.

Section	Examples
1.4	2
2.5	11, 12, 17, and 18
4.5	15 and 16
5.7	2, 8, and 10
6.7	5
7.5	14 and 15

 Try Problems 8 through 10.

4 Problems Involving Translations

EXAMPLE 7   A certain stock opened for $18\frac{3}{8}$ a share. At the end of the day the price was $19\frac{5}{8}$. What was the increase in price?

SOLUTION $18\frac{3}{8}$ is the original price and $19\frac{5}{8}$ is the price after the increase. We have the following:

$$\begin{array}{ccccc} \text{Original} & + & \text{Increase} & = & \text{final} \\ \text{price} & & \text{in price} & & \text{price} \\ (\$) & & (\$) & & (\$) \end{array}$$

$$18\frac{3}{8} + \boxed{} = 19\frac{5}{8}$$

We are missing one of the terms, so we subtract to find the missing term.

$$19\frac{5}{8} - 18\frac{3}{8}$$

$$= 19\frac{5}{8} - 18\frac{3}{8}$$

$$= 1\frac{2}{8}$$

$$= 1\frac{1}{4}$$

The increase in price is $1\frac{1}{4}$ or $1.25. ■

EXAMPLE 8   Dorothy worked for 3.5 hours on Tuesday. Steve worked 2.25 times as long as Dorothy. How long did Steve work?

SOLUTION   The sentence, "Steve worked 2.25 times as long as Dorothy," really means that Steve's time is 2.25 times as long as Dorothy's time, and can be translated to a multiplication statement.

Steve's time	is	2.25	times as long as	Dorothy's time
↓	↓			
☐	=	2.25	×	3.5

The answer to the multiplication problem is missing, so we multiply to find the answer.

$$\begin{array}{r} 2.25 \\ \times\ 3.5 \\ \hline 1125 \\ 675 \\ \hline 7.875 \end{array}$$

Steve worked 7.875 hours. ■

EXAMPLE 9   Ms. Tang pays 0.4 of her annual gross salary in taxes. She paid $24,000 in taxes last year. What is her annual gross salary?

SOLUTION   The phrase *0.4 of her annual gross salary in taxes* really means that 0.4 of her annual gross salary is the amount paid in taxes, and can be translated to a multiplication statement.

0.4	of	her salary ($)	is	taxes ($)
↓		↓	↓	
0.4	×	☐	=	24,000

A multiplier is missing, so we divide to find the missing multiplier.

$$0.4\,\overline{)2\,4\,0\,0\,0\,0.0}\quad\overset{6\,0\,0\,0\,0.}{}$$

Her salary was $60,000. ■

Try These Problems

11. A coat is marked $165. Tax increases the price by $9.90. What is the total price of the coat?

12. Kathy earns 0.04 of her total sales in commissions. She sells $2600 worth of merchandise. How much does she earn in commissions?

13. A carpenter has one board that is $5\frac{3}{8}$ feet long and another board that is $12\frac{2}{3}$ feet long.
a. What is the difference in the lengths of these two boards?
b. What is the ratio of the shorter board to the longer board?

14. Cyrus earns 1.8 times as much as Betsy earns. Cyrus earns $900 each month. What is Betsy's monthly salary?

15. Seven-thirtieths of the workers in a factory were out with the flu last week. There were 490 workers out with the flu. How many workers are employed by this factory?

If you need additional examples related to solving problems using translations, the following list gives the location of these examples.

Section	Examples
1.4	4, 5
2.5	13, 14
3.6	4–8
4.5	17–25
5.7	4, 5
6.7	3, 4, 5
7.5	16–19
8.3	1, 2

 Try Problems 11 through 15.

 Answers to Try These Problems

1. $1910.25   2. 8.45 m   3. $\frac{2}{3}$ 4. $\frac{13}{20}$ 5. 95 books
6. $360   7. $\frac{87}{2}$ or $43\frac{1}{2}$ ft
8. a. $105\frac{5}{12}$ in b. $\frac{7367}{12}$ or $613\frac{11}{12}$ sq in   9. 52.43 cm
10. a. 6.35 cm b. 29.9 cm   11. $174.90   12. $104
13. a. $7\frac{7}{24}$ ft b. $\frac{129}{304}$ 14. $500   15. 2100 workers

Overview of Unit Analysis

Some numbers have **units** attached to them. Here are three examples.

60 dollars or $60   **$14\frac{2}{3}$ feet**   **15.6 pounds**
$\searrow$ unit $\searrow$ unit $\searrow$ unit $\searrow$ unit

Here we look at operating with quantities that have units. Study carefully the patterns.
It can help you in setting up word problems.

Introduction

5 tons + 6 tons = 11 tons
12 hours − 7 hours = 5 hours

When adding or subtracting quantities with like units, the result's unit is the same as the other units.

3 x 7 days = 21 days
$60 ÷ 8 = $7.50

When multiplying or dividing a quantity with units by a number with no units, the result's unit is the same as the quantity's unit.

5 cartons ÷ 6 cartons = 5/6
4 pounds ÷ 0.5 pound = 8

When dividing two quantities with like units, the result is a number with no units.

Distance & Area

1.5 feet + 2.6 feet = 4.1 feet
50 square inches + 32 square inches = 18 square inches
6.2 meters − 0.35 meter = 5.85 meters

When adding or subtracting quantities with like units, the result's unit is the same as the other units.

4.5 meters x 2 meters = 9 square meters
3/4 inch x 8 inches = 6 square inches

Distance times distance equals area.

Rates

6 miles per hour x 4.5 hours = 27 miles
1.75 feet per second x 8 seconds = 14 feet

Here are two examples of a rate as a multiplier. The unit before the word "per" in the rate is the same as the result's unit.

150 miles ÷ 5 hours = 50 miles per hour
$300 ÷ 15 shirts = $20 per shirt

Dividing two quantities with unlike units gives a rate. The divisor's unit is the same as the unit after the word "per" in the resulting rate.

▶ **Try These Problems**

Calculate the following. Give both the number and unit.

1. 9 pounds + 8 pounds
2. 15 years − 6 years
3. 7 x 8 miles
4. 2 pounds ÷ 5 pounds
5. 35 ounces ÷ 7
6. 9 miles x 8 miles
7. 90 pints ÷ 18 pints
8. 300 years − 68 years
9. 70 miles ÷ 2 hours
10. 3.2 ounces ÷ 0.8 day
11. 42.5 meters per day x 8.2 days
12. 0.6 hour + 1.25 hour
13. 20.3 minutes − 7.75 minutes
14. 18 feet ÷ 3.6 seconds
15. 45 hours ÷ 1.25 hour
16. $1\frac{1}{3}$ inches + $\frac{3}{4}$ inch
17. 8 feet ÷ $12\frac{1}{2}$ feet
18. $5\frac{2}{3}$ cartons x 6
19. $5\frac{1}{3}$ feet x $\frac{7}{8}$ dollars per foot
20. $9\frac{1}{2}$ inches per week x 4 weeks
21. 5 tons ÷ $6\frac{2}{3}$ barrels
22. $6\frac{1}{4}$ yards − $1\frac{7}{8}$ yards
23. $\frac{1}{2}$ child per year x $2\frac{1}{4}$ years
24. 80 yards x $3\frac{1}{8}$ yards

Fill in the blank with the appropriate unit that makes the statement true.

25. minutes + minutes = _____
26. inches x inches = _____
27. miles x miles = _____
28. pounds per carton x cartons = _____
29. feet ÷ seconds = _____
30. $ per person x persons = _____
31. miles per hour x _____ = miles
32. feet x _____ = square feet
33. _____ = pounds per week x weeks
34. _____ = square feet − square feet
35. gallons = _____ x hours
36. square meters = meters x _____
37. days x gallons per day = _____
38. _____ x meals = calories

Rates in Ratio Form

You have learned that the fraction bar represents division. For example

$$\frac{8}{2} = 8 \div 2 = 4 \qquad\qquad \frac{2}{8} = 2 \div 8 = \frac{1}{4} \text{ or } 0.25$$

Observe that the numerator is divided by the denominator to get the result.

Recall that 12 feet divided by 2.5 seconds will produce a rate with units feet per second. We often set up the rate in a ratio (or fractional) form to define the direction of the division. Here are two examples.

Numerator units.
Denominator units.

$$\frac{12 \text{ ft}}{2.5 \text{ sec}} = 12 \div 2.5 \text{ ft per sec}$$

$$= 4.8 \text{ ft per sec}$$

Divide the numerator by the denominator.

$$2.5\overline{)12.0\,0} \;\; 4.8$$
$$\underline{10\,0}$$
$$2\,0\,0$$
$$\underline{2\,0\,0}$$
$$0$$

$$\frac{8\frac{1}{3} \text{ ounces}}{10 \text{ minutes}} = 8\frac{1}{3} \div 10 \text{ oz per min}$$

$$= \frac{5}{6} \text{ oz per min} \qquad \text{It's okay to leave the answer in fractional form.}$$

$$8\frac{1}{3} \div 10 = \frac{25}{3} \div \frac{10}{1}$$
$$= \frac{25}{3} \times \frac{1}{10}$$
$$= \frac{5 \times 5}{3} \times \frac{1}{2 \times 5} = \frac{5}{6}$$

▶ **Try These Problems**

Convert each ratio to a simplified rate. Your answer should include both a number and the appropriate rate unit. You may leave the number portion in decimal or fractional form.

39. $\dfrac{150 \text{ miles}}{3 \text{ hours}}$ 40. $\dfrac{75 \text{ dollars}}{5 \text{ shirts}}$ 41. $\dfrac{18 \text{ pounds}}{24 \text{ weeks}}$ 42. $\dfrac{21 \text{ feet}}{35 \text{ seconds}}$

43. $\dfrac{60 \text{ ounces}}{3.2 \text{ hours}}$ 44. $\dfrac{15.9 \text{ ounces}}{3 \text{ dollars}}$ 45. $\dfrac{\$0.06}{2.4 \text{ cups}}$ 46. $\dfrac{\$0.54}{0.25 \text{ gallon}}$

47. $\dfrac{5\frac{1}{4} \text{ ounces}}{7 \text{ seconds}}$ 48. $\dfrac{\$42}{\frac{2}{3} \text{ yard}}$ 49. $\dfrac{2\frac{4}{5} \text{ tons}}{3\frac{1}{3} \text{ loads}}$ 50. $\dfrac{\frac{7}{8} \text{ pound}}{3 \text{ weeks}}$

A rate phrase like, 8 miles every 2 minutes, can be put in a ratio form in two ways.

8 miles every 2 hours $\longrightarrow$ $\dfrac{8 \text{ miles}}{2 \text{ hours}} = 8 \div 2 \text{ mi per hr} = 4 \text{ mi per hr}$

8 miles every 2 hours $\longrightarrow$ $\dfrac{2 \text{ hours}}{8 \text{ miles}} = 2 \div 8 \text{ hr per mi} = \dfrac{1}{4} \text{ or } 0.25 \text{ hr per mi}$

If we put 8 miles over 2 hours, we end up with 4 miles per hour. In this case, we see how many miles for 1 hour. If we put 2 hours over 8 miles, we end up with 1/4 or 0.25 hour per mile. We see here the amount of time it takes to go 1 mile. These two rates are different rate quantities; however, they are expressing the same rate situation.

▶ **Try These Problems**

Write each of these rate phrases in a ratio form so that the resulting rate quantity has units, **"inches per day."** Finally, simplify the rate. Give both the number and rate unit.

51. 20 inches every 6 days 52. $7\frac{1}{2}$ inches every 12 days

53. 4.5 days every 15 inches 54. $\frac{3}{4}$ day per $1\frac{1}{2}$ inches

Write each of these rate phrases in a ratio form so that the resulting rate quantity has units, **"gallons per mile."** Finally, simplify the rate. Give both the number and rate unit.

55. 300 miles on 15 gallons 56. 8.4 miles every 2.1 gallons

57. $\frac{5}{8}$ gallon every $6\frac{1}{4}$ miles 58. 30 gallons every $4\frac{1}{2}$ miles

Rate Applications - Setting Up a Ratio

We will now look at solving some applications by setting up the rate in ratio form. This technique is very convenient when you are looking for the rate. You will need to pay close attention to the units so that you set up the ratio in the correct order. This will tell you which order to do the division. Here are two examples.

EXAMPLE Carlos can jog $\frac{7}{8}$ mile in 7 minutes. How many minutes will it take him to go 1 mile?

Solution We want to know the number of minutes for 1 mile. That is, we want to know the "minutes per mile."

minutes per mile $\longrightarrow$ $\dfrac{\text{minutes}}{\text{mile}}$

Therefore, we divide minutes by miles to get "minutes per mile."

$\dfrac{7 \text{ minutes}}{\frac{7}{8}\text{ mile}} = 7 \div \frac{7}{8}$ minutes per mile

$= 8$ minutes per mile

$7 \div \frac{7}{8} = \frac{7 \times 1}{1} \times \frac{8}{7 \times 1}$

$= \frac{8}{1} = 8$

Show the calculation steps when the work cannot be done mentally.

Answer It takes Carlos 8 minutes to jog 1 mile.

EXAMPLE The cost of 2.5 pounds of blueberries is $9? What is the cost per pound?

Solution We want to know the "cost per pound."

cost per pound $\longrightarrow$ $\dfrac{\$}{\text{pound}}$

Therefore, we divide dollars by pounds to get "$ per pound."

$\dfrac{\$9}{2.5 \text{ pounds}} = 9 \div 2.5$ $ per pound

$= \$3.60$ per pound

$2.5\overline{)9.0\,0}$ with quotient 3.6
$\quad \underline{75}$
$\quad 15\,0$
$\quad \underline{15\,0}$
$\quad\quad 0$

Show the calculation steps when the work cannot be done mentally.

Answer The blueberries cost $3.60 per pound.

▶ **Try These Problems**

Set up a rate as a ratio to solve each of these applications.

59. Three pounds of apples cost $3.57. What is the cost of one pound of these apples?

60. On a map, 4.2 centimeters represent 210 miles. How many centimeters represent 1 mile?

61. Alicia can jog $3\frac{3}{4}$ miles in $22\frac{1}{2}$ minutes. How many minutes will it take her to jog 1 mile?

62. Water leaks from a faucet at the rate of $4\frac{2}{3}$ ounces every 42 minutes. How many minutes per ounce is this?

63. Ninety nails weigh 3.6 pounds. What does 1 nail weigh?

64. Snow was falling at the rate of 3.2 feet every 0.8 of an hour. How many feet per hour was this?

65. Billy can walk $9\frac{2}{3}$ miles in 58 minutes. How many miles per minute is this?

66. A clock loses $4\frac{1}{6}$ seconds every 12 hours. How many hours does it take the clock to lose 1 second?

67. Mr. Jefferson paid $885 for 60 square yards of carpeting. What is the cost per square yard?

68. Frank bought 6.5 pounds of lettuce for $11.70. What is the cost per pound?

Writing a Rate in Ratio Form

Now let's look at writing rates in a ratio form. Here we show some examples.

RATE	RATE PHRASE FORM	RATIO FORM
5 feet per minute	5 feet in 1 minute	$\dfrac{5 \text{ feet}}{1 \text{ minute}}$
$6.50 per ticket	$6.50 for each 1 ticket	$\dfrac{\$6.50}{1 \text{ ticket}}$
$\frac{5}{6}$ yard an hour	$\frac{5}{6}$ yard for 1 hour	$\dfrac{\frac{5}{6} \text{ yard}}{1 \text{ hour}}$ or $\dfrac{5 \text{ yards}}{6 \text{ hours}}$
$3\frac{1}{3}$ gallons each mile	$3\frac{1}{3}$ gallons each 1 mile	$\dfrac{3\frac{1}{3} \text{ gallons}}{1 \text{ mile}}$ or $\dfrac{\frac{10}{3} \text{ gallons}}{1 \text{ mile}}$ or $\dfrac{10 \text{ gallons}}{3 \text{ miles}}$

▶ **Try These Problems**

Write each of these rates in a ratio form.

69. 20 gallons each mile
70. 36 pounds per carton
71. $14.20 per calculator
72. $0.65 per minute
73. $\frac{3}{4}$ ton per barrel
74. $6\frac{2}{3}$ inches every day

Rate as a Multiplier

You have learned to set up a multplication equation with a rate as a multiplier. For example,

$$7 \text{ miles per hour} \times 4 \text{ hours} = 28 \text{ miles}$$

Now we want to learn to write this equation with the rate in a ratio form. For example,

$$\frac{7 \text{ miles}}{1 \text{ hour}} \times \frac{4 \text{ hours}}{1} = 28 \text{ miles}$$

Observe that the "hour" units cancel similar to the way multipliers cancel in multiplication of fractions. Here are two more examples.

$$\frac{9 \text{ bikes}}{1 \text{ week}} \times \frac{7 \text{ weeks}}{1} = 63 \text{ bikes}$$

$$\frac{11 \text{ cents}}{2 \text{ pounds}} \times \frac{6 \text{ pounds}}{1} = \frac{11}{2 \times 1} \times \frac{2 \times 3}{1} \text{ cents} = 33 \text{ cents}$$

▶ **Try These Problems**

Calculate each. Give both the number and units.

75. $\dfrac{\$36}{1 \text{ shirt}} \times \dfrac{8 \text{ shirts}}{1}$

76. $\dfrac{\$8.90}{1 \text{ hour}} \times \dfrac{5.2 \text{ hours}}{1}$

77. $\dfrac{9 \text{ days}}{1} \times \dfrac{0.06 \text{ meter}}{3 \text{ days}}$

78. $\dfrac{3 \text{ miles}}{1} \times \dfrac{12 \text{ gallons}}{\frac{3}{8} \text{ mile}}$

79. $\dfrac{3\frac{1}{5} \text{ feet}}{1 \text{ minute}} \times \dfrac{15 \text{ minutes}}{1}$

80. $\dfrac{\frac{5}{6} \text{ inch}}{10 \text{ weeks}} \times \dfrac{1\frac{3}{4} \text{ weeks}}{1}$

Each of these unit equations has a rate as a multiplier. Fill in the blank with the missing unit.

81. $\dfrac{\text{miles}}{\text{hour}} \times \text{hours} = \underline{\hspace{1cm}}$

82. $\dfrac{\text{feet}}{\text{day}} \times \text{days} = \underline{\hspace{1cm}}$

83. $\dfrac{\$}{\text{car}} \times \underline{\hspace{1cm}} = \$$

84. $\text{meters} = \dfrac{\text{meters}}{\text{second}} \times \underline{\hspace{1cm}}$

85. $\$ = \underline{\hspace{1cm}} \times \text{hours}$

86. $\text{minutes} \times \underline{\hspace{1cm}} = \text{gallons}$

87. $\dfrac{\text{gallons}}{\text{day}} \times \underline{\hspace{1cm}} = \text{gallons}$

88. $\dfrac{\text{minutes}}{\$} \times \$ = \underline{\hspace{1cm}}$

89. $\text{liters} = \underline{\hspace{1cm}} \times \text{bottles}$

Rate Applications - Rate Given or Rate Missing

Here are some examples of solving applications involving rates.

EXAMPLE Debra paid $101.43 for fabric that cost $8.05 per yard. How many many yards did she buy?

Solution We are given the rate, "$8.05 per yard."
We are looking for the number of yards she bought with $101.43.

Set up the structure using "$ per yard" as a multiplier. $\longrightarrow$ $\dfrac{\$}{\text{yard}} \times \text{yards} = \$$

Put the known quantities in the appropriate positions. $\longrightarrow$ $8.05 \times \underline{\quad ? \quad} = 101.43$

Because we are missing a multiplier, we divide the result 101.43 by the given multiplier 8.05. $101.43 \div 8.05$

$$\begin{array}{r} 12.6 \\ 8.05\overline{)101.430} \\ \underline{80\ 5} \\ 20\ 93 \\ \underline{16\ 10} \\ 4\ 830 \\ \underline{4\ 830} \end{array}$$

Answer Debra bought 12.6 yards of fabric.

EXAMPLE On a map $13\frac{1}{2}$ miles is represented by $20\frac{1}{4}$ inches. How many inches per mile is this?

Solution We are looking for the rate, "inches per mile."
Set up the appropriate ratio to see the direction of the division. **inches per mile** $\longrightarrow$ $\dfrac{\text{inches}}{\text{mile}}$

$\dfrac{13\frac{1}{2}\text{ inches}}{20\frac{1}{4}\text{ miles}} = 13\frac{1}{2} \div 20\frac{1}{4}$ inch per mile

$= \frac{2}{3}$ inch per mile

Show calculation steps.

$13\frac{1}{2} \div 20\frac{1}{4} = \frac{27}{2} \div \frac{81}{4}$

$= \frac{27}{2} \times \frac{4}{81}$

$= \frac{3 \times 9}{2} \times \frac{2 \times 2}{9 \times 9}$

Leave the answer in fractional form because it's decimal form repeats.

$= \frac{3 \times 1}{1} \times \frac{2}{3 \times 3} = \frac{2}{3}$

Answer On the map, every 2/3 inch represents 1 mile.

EXAMPLE Water enters a tank at the rate of $8\frac{1}{6}$ gallons every 1 hour.
How many gallons have entered the tank in 12 hours?

Solution You are given the rate phrse, "$8\frac{1}{6}$ gallons every 1 hour."
The rate is, "$8\frac{1}{6}$ gallons per hour." Note the rate unit is "gallons per hour."

Write an equation with the rate as a multiplier. $\longrightarrow$ $\dfrac{\text{gallons}}{\text{hour}} \times \text{hours} = \text{gallons}$

Put the known quantities in the appropriate positions. $\longrightarrow$ $8\frac{1}{6} \times 12 = \underline{\quad ? \quad}$

Multiply the two factors. $8\frac{1}{6} \times 12 = \frac{49}{6} \times \frac{12}{1}$ $\longleftarrow$ Show calculation steps.

$= \frac{7 \times 7}{6} \times \frac{2 \times 6}{1} = 98$

Answer 98 gallons of water enter the tank in 12 hours.

▶ Try These Problems

Solve each of these applications. Use methods as shown above. Show set ups and calculation steps.

90. Joshua hikes 3.6 miles each hour. How many miles does he hike in 20.5 hours?

91. Alfaro works out in the gym 1.25 hours each day. How many days will it take him to total 50 hours in the gym?

92. A faucet leaks $9\frac{1}{3}$ ounces every $3\frac{1}{2}$ seconds. How many ounces per second is this?

93. It took Zhi 12 minutes to run $1\frac{1}{8}$ miles. How far can he go in 1 minute?

94. Rain fell at the rate of $2\frac{1}{3}$ inches per hour. How many hours did it take to rain 56 inches?

95. Svetlana earns $60.52 in 8.5 hours. How much does she earn each hour?

Rate Applications - Equivalent Rate Phrases – 2 Steps

Now we look at solving applications using equivalent rate phrases that require two steps.

EXAMPLE **Ashley earns $533 in 26 hours. How much does she earn in 12 hours?**

Solution Write down the given rate phrase. $\longrightarrow$ $533 in 26 hours

Write the question as a rate phrase with missing quantity. Be sure to arrange like units under each other. $\longrightarrow$ _____?_____ in 12 hours

Using x or ÷, it is not easy to see what to do to 26 to get 12. Therefore, we insert a rate phrase to find how much she earns in 1 hour.

$533 in 26 hours
____?____ in 1 hour
____?____ in 12 hours

Step 1: Divide both quantities in the first rate phrase by 26 to find her pay for 1 hour.

$533 in 26 hours
÷ 26   ÷ 26

$14.75 in 1 hour
x 12   x 12

Step 2: Multiply both quantities in the inserted rate phrase by 12 to find the pay for 12 hours.

____?____ in   12 hours

Show calculation steps.

```
      14.75
  x       8
   118.00
```

```
        20.5
26 ) 533.0
       52
       13
        0
      130
      130
        0
```

Answer Ashley earns $20.50 in 12 hours. $\longleftarrow$ $20.50

EXAMPLE Kerin types 420 words in 10.5 minutes. How long will it take her to type 750 words?

Solution Write down the given rate phrase. $\longrightarrow$ 420 words in 10.5 minutes

Write the question as a rate phrase with missing quantity. Be sure to arrange like units under each other. $\longrightarrow$ 750 words in ____?____

Using x or ÷, it is not easy to see what to do to 420 to get 750. Therefore, we insert a rate phrase to find how many minutes for 1 word.

420 words in 10.5 minutes
1 word   in ____?____
750 words in ____?____

Step 1: Divide both quantities in the first rate phrase by 420 to find the minutes for 1 word.

420 words in 10.5 minutes
÷ 420   ÷ 420

1 word in 0.025 minute
x 750   x 750

Step 2: Multiply both quantities in the inserted rate phrase by 750 to find the minutes for 750 words.

750 words in ____?____

```
        0.025
420 ) 10.500
        8 4 0
        2100
        2100
           0
```

```
        0.025
  x     750
    1 250
   17 5
   18.750 = 18.75
```

Answer Kerin types 750 words in 18.75 minutes. $\longleftarrow$ 18.75 minutes

▶ **Try These Problems**

Solve each of these applications by generating equivalent rate phrases. Show steps clearly.

96. Six nails weigh 7.2 ounces. What do 25 nails weigh?

97. Jim paid $93.60 for 12 shares of energy stock. What is the cost of 50 shares of this stock?

98. Mailinh paid $63.25 for 5.5 hours of babysitting. What does she pay for 8 hours of babysitting?

99. A watch loses 6 seconds every 2.4 hours. How many hours does it take the watch to lose 7.5 seconds?

100. A cable that is 5.2 feet long weighs 26 pounds. What is the weight of 3.9 feet of this cable?

101. Bob stuffs 24 envelopes in 60 seconds. How long does it take him to stuff 50 envelopes?

102. Water enters a tank at the rate of 37.8 gallons in 3.5 hours. How many gallons enter the tank in 9.5 hours?

103. A fish swims 0.2 mile each minute. How many minutes does it take the fish to swim 9.7 miles?

EXERCISES 8.4

Solve. Show setups and calculation steps.

1. How far is it from A to B?

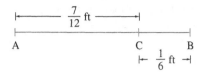

2. How far is it from X to Y?

3. A painter used $\frac{3}{4}$ of a bucket of paint. What fraction of the paint remained?

4. Roger, Ted, and Claudia own an apartment building together. Ted owns $\frac{1}{3}$ of the property and Claudia owns $\frac{4}{9}$ of it. What fraction of the property do Ted and Claudia together own?

5. Four hundred forty pounds of candy are packaged in boxes each weighing 0.8 pound. How many boxes of candy can be packaged?

6. A wire that is 3 meters long is cut into 12 equal pieces. How long is each piece?

7. How many 6.5-ounce servings can a chef get from 200 ounces of rice? (Truncate to the nearest whole number.)

8. Mr. Wilson built a fence along one side of his backyard by joining together 15 segments of fencing that were each $7\frac{1}{3}$ feet. What is the total length of this fence?

9. A rectangular piece of paper is $8\frac{1}{2}$ inches wide and 11 inches long.
   a. What is the area of the piece of paper?
   b. What is the perimeter of the piece of paper?

10. The width of a rectangular garden is 12.8 feet. The garden contains 262.4 square feet.
    a. Find the length of the garden.
    b. Find the perimeter of the garden.

11. Find the perimeter of this triangle.

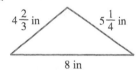

12. The width of a rectangle is 0.6 of the length. The length is 80 meters.
    a. Find the width of the rectangle.
    b. Find the area of the rectangle.

13. Because of inflation, the price of steak has risen from $2.75 per pound to $5.29 per pound. What is the increase in the price per pound?

14. A construction worker earned $17.50 an hour last year. This year she got a raise of $1.65 an hour. What is her hourly wage now?

15. A plane flew to New York and back. Because of weather conditions, the return trip took 1.2 times as long as the trip to New York. The return trip took 6.3 hours. How long was the flight to New York?

16. In a certain state, sales tax is 0.056 of the marked price. The tax paid on a textbook was $1.96. Find the marked price of the textbook.

17. A student got 168 questions correct out of 180.
 a. What fraction of the questions did the student get correct?
 b. How many questions did the student get wrong?

18. Karl traveled a total distance of 5800 miles. Eight-tenths of the distance was by airplane. How far did he travel by plane?

19. A factory employs 3500 workers. There are 500 African-Americans and 800 Hispanics.
 a. What is the ratio of African-Americans to total workers?
 b. What is the ratio of Hispanics to African-Americans?

20. A chemist mixes 2.5 liters of acid with 8 liters of water.
 a. What is the total volume of this solution?
 b. Find the ratio of the acid volume to the total volume. (Round off at 2 decimal places.)

21. Jeff types 208 words in 4 minutes. On average, how many words per minute does he type?

22. Carpeting sells for $23.50 per square yard. What is the cost of $7\frac{1}{4}$ square yards of carpeting? (Round up to the nearest cent.)

23. You buy 8 heads of lettuce that sell for $0.89 per head. What is the total cost of the lettuce?

24. John pays $107.10 for 8.5 yards of fabric. What is the cost per yard?

25. On a map $\frac{3}{4}$ inch represents 25 miles. How many miles do 6 inches represent?

26. A watch loses 2 minutes every 12 hours. At this rate, how much time does the watch lose in 51 hours?

8.5 APPLICATIONS: MORE THAN ONE STEP

OBJECTIVES
▊ Solve an application requiring more than one step that involves addition and subtraction.

▊ Solve an application requiring more than one step that involves multiplication and division.

▊ Solve an application requiring more than one step that involves multiplication and addition.

▊ Solve an application requiring more than one step that involves a combination of any of the four operations: multiplication, division, addition, or subtraction.

In this section we look at applications that require more than one step to solve. We will present these problems in four different categories as stated in the objectives. When solving more complex problems, it is important to label your work clearly with words so that you understand what it is you have obtained at each stage of the problem. Also, if applicable, drawing a diagram can be very helpful. Here are some examples.

Try These Problems

Solve. Show setups.

1. Your checking account shows a balance of $538.24. What is your checking account balance after you write checks for $28.30, $95.64, and $260?

2. At the hardware store Henry buys items marked $3.98, $2.76, and $13.89. A tax of $1.34 is added to the bill. Henry gives the clerk $25. How much change does he receive?

3. A triangular plot of land has sides measuring $2\frac{3}{4}$ feet, $4\frac{1}{4}$ feet, and $5\frac{3}{4}$ feet. Mr. Nelson buys 14 feet of fencing to put around the border of the plot. How much fencing is left over?

4. Carmen, Patricia, and Tosca own a small business together. Carmen owns $\frac{1}{4}$ of it, Tosca owns $\frac{2}{5}$ of it, and Patricia owns the rest. What fraction of the business does Patricia own?

1 Applications Involving Addition and Subtraction

EXAMPLE 1   Carol buys the following items at the grocery store:

Milk	$2.39
Potatoes	$4.90
Meat	$9.64

If we assume no tax is added, how much change does she receive from a $20 bill?

SOLUTION   First find the total cost of the three items by adding.

$$
\begin{array}{r}
2.39 \\
4.90 \\
+\ 9.64 \\
\hline
16.93
\end{array}
$$
—— Total cost in dollars

Carol paid a total of $16.93 for the three items. To find how much change she received from a $20 bill, subtract 16.93 from 20.

$$
\begin{array}{r}
20.00 \\
-\ 16.93 \\
\hline
3.07
\end{array}
$$
—— Change she received in dollars

Carol received $3.07 in change.   ■

EXAMPLE 2   One rectangle has width $19\frac{1}{3}$ feet and length $20\frac{2}{3}$ feet. Another rectangle has width $16\frac{1}{2}$ feet and length 18 feet. What is the difference in the perimeters of these two rectangles?

SOLUTION   First find the perimeter of each of the rectangles.

$$
\begin{aligned}
\text{Perimeter of rectangle \#1 (ft)} &= 19\frac{1}{3} + 19\frac{1}{3} + 20\frac{2}{3} + 20\frac{2}{3} \\
&= 78\frac{6}{3} \\
&= 80
\end{aligned}
$$

$$
\begin{aligned}
\text{Perimeter of rectangle \#2 (ft)} &= 16\frac{1}{2} + 16\frac{1}{2} + 18 + 18 \\
&= 68\frac{2}{2} \\
&= 69
\end{aligned}
$$

Now subtract to find the difference in the perimeters.

$$80 - 69 = 11$$

The difference in the two perimeters is 11 feet.   ■

Try Problems 1 through 4.

2 Applications Involving Multiplication and Division

EXAMPLE 3   Bob can jog 4 miles in 38 minutes. How long does it take him to jog 6 miles?

SOLUTION

METHOD 1   The phrase *4 miles in 38 minutes* is a rate and can be written as a ratio.

$$4 \text{ miles in 38 minutes} = \frac{4 \text{ miles}}{38 \text{ minutes}}$$

$$= \frac{2 \text{ miles}}{19 \text{ minutes}}$$

Now set up a multiplication statement using this rate so that units in the denominator cancel.

$$\frac{\text{miles}}{\cancel{\text{minute}}} \times \cancel{\text{minutes}} = \text{miles}$$

$$\frac{2}{19} \times \boxed{} = 6$$

A multiplier is missing, so divide 6 by $\frac{2}{19}$ to find the missing multiplier.

$$6 \div \frac{2}{19} = \frac{\overset{3}{\cancel{6}}}{1} \times \frac{19}{\underset{1}{\cancel{2}}}$$

$$= 57$$

It takes Bob 57 minutes to jog 6 miles.

METHOD 2   The phrase *4 miles in 38 minutes* can be written as a ratio so that miles are in the denominator instead of minutes.

$$4 \text{ miles in 38 minutes} = \frac{38 \text{ minutes}}{4 \text{ miles}}$$

$$= \frac{9.5 \text{ minutes}}{1 \text{ mile}}$$

Now set up a multiplication statement using this rate so that units in the denominator cancel.

$$\frac{\text{minutes}}{\cancel{\text{mile}}} \times \cancel{\text{miles}} = \text{minutes}$$

$$9.5 \times 6 = \boxed{}$$

The answer to the multiplication statement is missing so multiply 6 by 9.5 to obtain the answer.

$$9.5 \times 6 = 57.0 = 57$$

It takes Bob 57 minutes to jog 6 miles. ■

Try These Problems

5. Seventy-five nails weigh 15 ounces. What is the weight of 101 nails?

6. The dosage of a certain medicine is $\frac{2}{3}$ ounce for each 100 pounds of body weight. How much medicine is required for a person who weighs 240 pounds?

7. Mohammed wants to cover a rectangular floor with tile that costs $12.70 per square foot. If the floor is 10.2 feet wide and 14.5 feet long, what is the total cost of the tile? Do not include tax.

8. A real estate agent sells a piece of property for $250,000. She receives 0.06 of the selling price. She then must turn over 0.25 of her money to the company she works for. How much money does the agent give to the company?

EXAMPLE 4   The floor of a rectangular room measures 4.75 yards by 6 yards. You want to carpet the floor with carpeting that costs $11.95 per square yard. Without including tax, what is the total cost of carpeting the floor? (Round up the answer to the nearest cent.)

SOLUTION   The carpeting sells for $11.95 *per square yard*. We need to find out how many square yards this floor covers; that is, we need to find out the area of the floor.

$$\begin{aligned} \text{Area} &= \text{length} \times \text{width} \\ \text{(sq yd)} &\quad \text{(yd)} \quad\;\; \text{(yd)} \\ &= \quad 6 \quad \times \quad 4.75 \\ &= 28.5 \end{aligned}$$

The floor covers an area of 28.5 square yards. Set up a multiplication statement using the rate *$11.95 per square yard*.

$$\begin{aligned} \frac{\text{total cost}}{(\$)} &= \frac{\text{cost (\$)}}{\text{square yard}} \times \text{square yards} \\ &= \quad 11.95 \quad \times \quad 28.5 \\ &= 340.575 \\ &\approx 340.58 \end{aligned}$$

The total cost is $340.58.   ■

EXAMPLE 5   A machine fills and caps 250 bottles of mineral water each hour. After 24 hours, how many 6-packs of mineral water have been filled and capped?

SOLUTION   The phrase *250 bottles every hour* is a rate. Set up a multiplication statement using this rate.

$$\begin{aligned} \frac{\text{Total number}}{\text{of bottles}} &= \frac{\text{bottles}}{\text{hour}} \times \text{number of hours} \\ &= \quad 250 \quad \times \quad\;\; 24 \\ &= 6000 \end{aligned}$$

In 24 hours the machine has filled and capped a total of 6000 bottles. Now we want to know how many 6-packs can be made from the 6000 bottles. That is, we want to separate 6000 into a number of equal parts. The size of each part is 6.

$$\begin{aligned} \text{Total quantity} &= \frac{\text{size of}}{\text{each part}} \times \frac{\text{number of}}{\text{equal parts}} \\ 6000 \quad\;\; &= \quad\;\; 6 \quad\;\; \times \quad \boxed{} \end{aligned}$$

A multiplier is missing so we divide 6000 by 6 to find the missing multiplier.

$$6000 \div 6 = 1000$$

In 24 hours 1000 6-packs can be filled and capped.   ■

 Try Problems 5 through 8.

Try These Problems

9. Nanda bought 7 yards of fabric selling for $9.69 per yard and $5\frac{1}{2}$ yards of fabric selling for $7.98 per yard. What is the total cost of the fabric? Do not include tax.

10. The marked price of a tennis racket is $89.95. The store adds a sales tax, which is 0.065 of the marked price. What is the total cost of the tennis racket? (Round up the answer to the nearest cent.)

11. Chuck is reading a book that has 860 pages. He read $\frac{1}{4}$ of the book on Saturday and $\frac{2}{5}$ of the book on Sunday. How many pages has he read?

12. A taxi charges $1.20 in addition to $0.85 per mile. What is the cost of a 5-mile taxi ride?

3 Applications Involving Multiplication and Addition

EXAMPLE 6   David bought two shirts at $26.50 each and three ties at $22.85 each. What is the total cost of these items?

SOLUTION   First find the total cost of the shirts.

$$\begin{array}{c}\text{Total cost} \\ \text{of the shirts} \\ (\$)\end{array} = \begin{array}{c}\text{cost} \\ \text{per shirt} \\ (\$)\end{array} \times \begin{array}{c}\text{how many} \\ \text{shirts}\end{array}$$
$$= 26.50 \times 2$$
$$= 53$$

Next find the total cost of the ties.

$$\begin{array}{c}\text{Total cost} \\ \text{of the ties} \\ (\$)\end{array} = \begin{array}{c}\text{cost} \\ \text{per tie} \\ (\$)\end{array} \times \begin{array}{c}\text{how many} \\ \text{ties}\end{array}$$
$$= 22.85 \times 3$$
$$= 68.55$$

Last find the total cost of the shirts and the ties.

$$\begin{array}{c}\text{Total cost} \\ (\$)\end{array} = \begin{array}{c}\text{cost of} \\ \text{the shirts} \\ (\$)\end{array} + \begin{array}{c}\text{cost of} \\ \text{the ties} \\ (\$)\end{array}$$
$$= 53 + 68.55$$
$$= 121.55$$

The total cost of all the items is $121.55. ∎

EXAMPLE 7   The marked price of a pair of running shoes is $65.80. The store adds a sales tax, which is 0.065 of the marked price. What is the total cost of the shoes? (Round up the answer to the nearest cent.)

SOLUTION   First find the sales tax. The problem states the following.

$$\begin{array}{ccccc}\text{Sales tax} & \text{is} & 0.065 & \text{of} & \begin{array}{c}\text{the marked} \\ \text{price (\$)}\end{array} \\ (\$) & & \downarrow & & \downarrow \end{array}$$
$$= 0.065 \times 65.80$$
$$= 4.277 \qquad \text{Do not round until the end.}$$

The sales tax is $4.277. The sales tax is added to the marked price to obtain the final selling price.

$$\begin{array}{ccc}\text{Total cost} = & \text{marked price} & + & \text{sales tax} \\ (\$) & (\$) & & (\$)\end{array}$$
$$= 65.80 + 4.277$$
$$= 70.077$$
$$\approx 70.08$$

The total cost of the shoes is $70.08. ∎

 Try Problems 9 through 12.

EXAMPLE 8   A carpenter wants to put weather stripping around the border of a rectangular window that is 3.4 feet wide and 2.5 feet high. If the weather stripping sells for $2.45 per foot, what is the total cost of the weather stripping? Do not include tax.

SOLUTION   The weather stripping sells for $2.45 per foot. First we must find out how many feet are around the border of the window; that is, we want the perimeter of the window.

$$\text{Perimeter (ft)} = 3.4 + 3.4 + 2.5 + 2.5$$
$$= 11.8$$

The total distance around the window is 11.8 feet. Because each foot of weather stripping costs $2.45, we multiply 11.8 by $2.45 to find the total cost.

$$\text{Total cost (\$)} = \frac{\text{cost per foot (\$)}}{} \times \frac{\text{how many feet}}{}$$
$$= 2.45 \times 11.8$$
$$= 28.91$$

The total cost is $28.91. ■

EXAMPLE 9   Find the total area of this region.

4.2 yd
3.2 yd
4.5 yd
3.5 yd

SOLUTION   View the region as two rectangular regions.

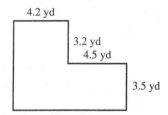

3.2 + 3.5
= 6.7 yd

4.2 yd
3.2 yd
4.5 yd
Rect 1
Rect 2
3.5 yd

Observe that the length of rectangle #1 is not given but we can find it by adding 3.2 yards to 3.5 yards. Now find the areas of each of the two rectangular regions.

$$\text{Area of rectangle \#1 (sq yd)} = \text{length (yd)} \times \text{width (yd)}$$
$$= 6.7 \times 4.2$$
$$= 28.14$$

$$\text{Area of rectangle \#2 (sq yd)} = \text{length (yd)} \times \text{width (yd)}$$
$$= 4.5 \times 3.5$$
$$= 15.75$$

Try These Problems

13. Carlos wants to put a fence around a rectangular piece of land that is 8.5 feet wide and 20.8 feet long. The fencing material costs $4.59 per foot. What is the total cost of the fence? (Round up the answer to the nearest cent.)

14. Find **a.** the perimeter and **b.** the area of this region.

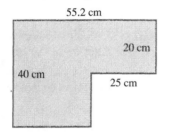

55.2 cm

20 cm

40 cm

25 cm

15. Joanne jogged these distances during the last five days:

Monday   3.5 mi
Tuesday   4.7 mi
Wednesday   4.6 mi
Thursday   5.2 mi
Friday   6.2 mi

What is her average daily jogging distance? (Round off at one decimal place.)

To find the total area of the region, add the area of rectangle #1 to the area of rectangle #2.

$$\begin{array}{c} \text{Total area} \\ \text{of the region} \\ \text{(sq yd)} \end{array} = \begin{array}{c} \text{area of} \\ \text{rectangle \#1} \\ \text{(sq yd)} \end{array} + \begin{array}{c} \text{area of} \\ \text{rectangle \#2} \\ \text{(sq yd)} \end{array}$$

$$= \qquad 28.14 \quad + \quad 15.75$$

$$= 43.89$$

The total area of the region is 43.89 square yards. ■

 Try Problems 13 and 14.

4 Applications Involving Multiplication, Division, Addition, and Subtraction

EXAMPLE 10   Lula bowled four games with the following scores.

132   146   127   137

What was her average score? (Round off to the nearest whole number.)

SOLUTION   Find the sum of the 4 scores.

$$132 + 146 + 127 + 137 = 542$$

Divide the sum 542 by 4 to find the average of the 4 scores.

$$\begin{array}{r} 135.5 \approx 136 \\ 4\overline{)542.0} \\ \underline{4} \\ 14 \\ \underline{12} \\ 22 \\ \underline{20} \\ 2\,0 \\ \underline{2\,0} \end{array}$$

The average is 136. ■

 Try Problem 15.

EXAMPLE 11   The Anderson Food Company sells 7.2 ounces of canned apricots for $2.81. The Justrite Food Company sells 6.5 ounces of canned apricots for $2.60. Which company has the better price per ounce? (Round off to the nearest cent.)

SOLUTION   Find the price per ounce for each. The lower rate is the better price per ounce.

ANDERSON FOOD COMPANY

7.2 ounces for $2.81

$$= \frac{\$2.81}{7.2 \text{ ounces}}$$

$$\approx \$0.39 \text{ per ounce}$$

Put the price in the numerator and ounces in the denominator to find the price per ounce.

Divide 2.81 by 7.2 to obtain 0.39.

Try These Problems

16. James earned $235 in 20 hours and Rebecca earned $188.10 in 15 hours. Who earns more money per hour?

17. Last week Olga purchased 6 ounces of gold for $2604. This week she purchased 5.5 ounces for $2365. Did the price per ounce increase or decrease during the week and by how much?

18. The price of gasoline increased from $1.20 per gallon to $1.50 per gallon. The increase in price is what fraction of the original price?

19. A utility stock decreased in price from $20 per share to $18¾ per share. The decrease in price is what fraction of the original price?

JUSTRITE FOOD COMPANY

6.5 ounces for $2.60

$$= \frac{\$2.60}{6.5 \text{ ounces}}$$

$$= \$0.40 \text{ per ounce}$$

Put the price in the numerator and ounces in the denominator to find the price per ounce.

Divide 2.60 by 6.5 to obtain 0.40.

The Anderson Food Company has the better price per ounce at approximately $0.39 per ounce. ■

 Try Problems 16 and 17.

EXAMPLE 12 During a sale, the price of a pair of shoes is reduced from $85 to $50. The decrease is what fraction of the original price?

SOLUTION First find out how much the price decreased by subtracting $50 from $85.

$$\text{Decrease in price} = \$85 - \$50 = \$35$$

The question is, "The decrease is what fraction of the original price?" This sentence can be translated to a multiplication statement.

The decrease	is	what fraction	of	original price
↓		↓		↓
35	=	☐	×	85

A multiplier is missing, so divide 35 by 85 to find the missing multiplier.

$$35 \div 85 = \frac{35}{85} = \frac{\cancel{5} \times 7}{\cancel{5} \times 17} = \frac{7}{17}$$

The decrease in price is $\frac{7}{17}$ of the original price. ■

Try Problems 18 and 19.

EXAMPLE 13 A large tank is leaking water out of two different holes. The larger hole is leaking water at the rate of 2 gallons each hour. The smaller hole is leaking water at the rate of $\frac{1}{2}$ gallon each hour. After $5\frac{1}{2}$ hours, how many more gallons of water have leaked through the larger hole than through the smaller hole?

SOLUTION First find out how many gallons of water have leaked through each of the holes in $5\frac{1}{2}$ hours.

LARGER HOLE

$$\begin{aligned} \frac{\text{Total}}{\text{gallons}} &= \frac{\text{gallons}}{\text{per hour}} \times \frac{\text{number}}{\text{of hours}} \\ &= 2 \times 5\frac{1}{2} \\ &= \frac{2}{1} \times \frac{11}{2} \\ &= 11 \end{aligned}$$

Try These Problems

20. Two airplanes started from the same airport and flew in different directions. One plane flew for 3 hours at a rate of 350 miles per hour. The other plane flew for $5\frac{1}{2}$ hours at a rate of 470 miles per hour. How much farther did the second plane fly?

SMALLER HOLE

$$\frac{\text{Total}}{\text{gallons}} = \frac{\text{gallons}}{\text{per hour}} \times \frac{\text{number}}{\text{of hours}}$$

$$= \frac{1}{2} \times 5\frac{1}{2}$$

$$= \frac{1}{2} \times \frac{11}{2}$$

$$= \frac{11}{4} = 2\frac{3}{4}$$

After $5\frac{1}{2}$ hours, 11 gallons of water have leaked through the larger hole and $2\frac{3}{4}$ gallons have leaked through the smaller hole. Subtract $2\frac{3}{4}$ from 11 to find out how many more gallons have leaked through the larger hole.

$$11 - 2\frac{3}{4} = 10\frac{4}{4} - 2\frac{3}{4} = 8\frac{1}{4}$$

$8\frac{1}{4}$ gallons more have leaked through the larger hole.   ■

 Try Problem 20.

 Answers to Try These Problems

1. $154.30   2. $3.03   3. $1\frac{1}{4}$ ft   4. $\frac{7}{20}$ 5. 20.2 oz
6. $1\frac{3}{5}$ or 1.6 oz   7. $1878.33   8. $3750   9. $111.72
10. $95.80   11. 559 pages   12. $5.45   13. $268.98
14. a. 190.4 cm   b. 1708 sq cm   15. 4.8 mi
16. Rebecca at $12.54 per hr   17. decreased by $4 per oz
18. $\frac{1}{4}$ or 0.25   19. $\frac{1}{16}$ or 0.0625   20. 1535 mi

EXERCISES 8.5

Solve. Show set ups and calculation steps.

1. Your checking account shows a balance of $1290.45. After you write checks for $235.15 and $76.98 and you deposit your paycheck of $800.35, what is your balance?

2. How far is it from A to B?

|← 26.8 ft →|← 46.2 ft ───────→|
A   B   C   D
|←────────── 93.8 ft ──────────→|

3. Cynthia bought five pens at $0.69 each and two tablets at $1.29 each. She is charged a sales tax that is 0.06 times the marked price. How much change does she receive from a 10-dollar bill? (Round off to the nearest cent.)

4. Lucinda completed $\frac{1}{3}$ of the job yesterday and $\frac{1}{4}$ of the job today. What fraction of the job does she have left to do?

5. A watch loses $3\frac{3}{4}$ minutes every 24 hours. At this rate, how much time does the watch lose in 40 hours?

6. Five pounds of oranges cost $2.45. How much do $3\frac{1}{2}$ pounds cost? (Round up the answer to the nearest cent.)

7. Yesterday Mr. Yee paid $4062.50 for 250 shares of an energy stock. Today he paid $7000 for 400 shares of the same stock. Did the price per share increase or decrease and by how much?

8. Machine A can print 460 pages in 50 minutes and Machine B can print 540 pages in 60 minutes. Which machine is faster; that is, which one prints more pages per minute?

9. The length of a rectangle is 1.8 times as long as the width. The width is 38.7 feet. What is **a.** the perimeter, and **b.** the area of the rectangle?

10. What is the total cost of tiling this floor if tile sells for $3.79 per square foot? (Round up the answer to the nearest cent.)

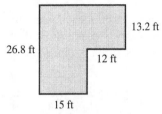

11. A stock increased in value from $35\frac{3}{8}$ dollars to $36\frac{1}{2}$ dollars. The increase in value is what fraction of the original value?

12. The price of a computer decreased from $4000 to $3400. What fraction of the original is the decrease?

13. A Tennessee farmer has a total of 2500 acres to plant some rice, cotton, and corn. He uses $\frac{1}{4}$ of the land for rice, $\frac{3}{5}$ of it for cotton, and the rest for corn. How many acres of corn did he plant?

14. A salesperson earns a commission that is $\frac{6}{100}$ of the first $3000 in sales combined with $\frac{9}{100}$ of the sales over $3000. How much commission does the person receive for sales of $5400?

15. Three suitcases weigh $82\frac{3}{4}$ pounds, $50\frac{1}{2}$ pounds, and $63\frac{1}{4}$ pounds. What is the average weight of the suitcases?

16. Anna has 6 quarters and 12 nickels. How much money does Anna have?

17. Ms. Truong left on a trip at 8 AM in the morning. The odometer on her car read 55140. At 1 PM, when she stopped for lunch, the odometer read 55409. How many miles per hour did she average?

18. Mr. Hsu sells flowers. He put 1545 roses in bunches with 18 roses in each bunch. After making as many bunches as possible, he took home the leftover roses and distributed them equally among his three children. How many roses did each child receive?

19. A parking lot charges $1.50 for the first hour, then $0.65 for each additional half hour. You enter the lot at a 9 AM and leave at 2:30 PM. How much is your parking fee?

20. Inez wants to put a fence around the border of this triangular plot of land. If the fencing material costs $3.85 per foot, find the total cost of the fence.

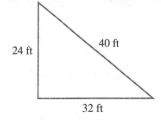

A statistician for a local car dealer made this double-bar graph that indicates the number of new cars sold during each quarter of 1992 and 1993. Use the graph to answer Exercises 21 through 24.

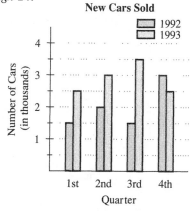

21. How many new cars did the company sell during the 3rd quarter of 1993?

22. How many new cars did the company sell during the 4th quarter of 1992?

23. Find the average number of new cars sold per quarter in 1993.

24. Find the average number of new cars sold per quarter in 1992.

CHAPTER 8 SUMMARY

KEY WORDS AND PHRASES

number line [8.1]

distance [8.1]

converting numbers [8.2]

comparing numbers [8.2]

increased by [8.3]

sum [8.3]

decreased by [8.3]

difference [8.3]

product [8.3]

ratio [8.3, 8.6]

divided by [8.3]

divided into [8.3]

area [8.4]

perimeter [8.4]

rate [8.4, 8.5, 8.6]

cross products [8.6]

proportion [8.6]

solving a proportion [8.6]

SYMBOLS

$0.9 < 5$ means 0.9 is less than 5

$\frac{3}{4} > \frac{1}{4}$ means $\frac{3}{4}$ is more than $\frac{1}{4}$

$19.\overline{6}$ means $19.66666666\ldots$

IMPORTANT RULES

Converting Numbers From One Form to Another [8.2]

A summary of the different techniques for changing a number from one form to another is on pages 322 and 323.

Area of a Rectangle [8.4]

The area of a rectangle measures the number of square units inside the rectangle. The area can be found by multiplying the length by the width.

Area = length $\times$ width

Perimeter of a Rectangle [8.4]
The perimeter of a rectangle is the distance all the way around it. The perimeter can be found by adding the lengths of the four sides.
Perimeter = length + length + width + width

Choosing the Correct Operation [8.4]
Table 5 at the end of the book reviews the operations that correspond to various situations.

CHAPTER 8 REVIEW EXERCISES

Label all tick marks. Then give the numbers for A and B.

1.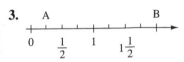
A   B
20   25   30

2.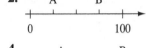
A   B
0   100

3.
A   B
0    $\frac{1}{2}$ 1 $1\frac{1}{2}$

4.
A   B
4   5   7

5. A   B
7 7.1 7.2   8

6. A   B
0.50   0.55   0.60

7. Which of these numbers are equal to $\frac{9}{50}$?
   a. $5.\overline{5}$ **b.** 0.18   **c.** 0.1800   **d.** $\frac{27}{150}$

8. Which of these numbers are equal to 7.8?
   a. 7.08   **b.** $\frac{39}{5}$ **c.** $7\frac{8}{100}$ **d.** $7\frac{32}{40}$

9. Which of these numbers are equal to 25?
   a. $\frac{3}{75}$ **b.** $\frac{75}{3}$ **c.** 25.00   **d.** 0.25

Use the symbol <, =, or > to compare each pair of numbers.

10. $13\frac{4}{9}\underset{(<,\,=,\,>)}{?}13.45$

11. $8.2\overline{3}\underset{(<,\,=,\,>)}{?}8.\overline{23}$

12. $\frac{5}{24}\underset{(<,\,=,\,>)}{?}\frac{1}{4}$

13. $\frac{7}{16}\underset{(<,\,=,\,>)}{?}0.4375$

List from smallest to largest.

14. $\frac{7}{8}$, $0.8\overline{7}$, $\frac{31}{36}$ **15.** $4\frac{2}{5}$, 0.44, 0.044, $\frac{4}{90}$

16. $8\frac{5}{6}$, $8\frac{2}{3}$, $8\frac{3}{4}$ **17.** 0.58, $\frac{5}{8}$, 0.5625

Solve. **Show setups and calculation steps.**

18. Find the difference between 32 and 4.8.

19. Find the ratio of $3\frac{1}{5}$ to 8.

20. Divide $4\frac{1}{2}$ into $\frac{2}{3}$.

21. Find $\frac{5}{6}$ of $7\frac{1}{2}$.

22. 0.075 of what number is 30?

23. What number increased by $22\frac{1}{3}$ yields 50?

24. 12 is what decimal of 750?

25. The profit for a company was $450,000 last year. This year the profit is 0.7 times as large as last year. Find the profit this year.

26. Pedro takes home $1512 each month. He spends $630 on rent. What fraction of his take-home pay is spent on rent? Simplify your answer.

27. A painter has $6\frac{1}{2}$ gallons of paint. He needs an additional $3\frac{3}{4}$ gallons to do his job. How much paint does it take to do the job?

28. A bakery makes a loaf of bread that is 34 centimeters long. How many slices can be cut from one loaf if each slice is 1.7 centimeters wide?

29. Sandra spent $\frac{2}{3}$ of her vacation in Hawaii. She spent the rest in Vancouver. What fraction of her vacation was spent in Vancouver?

30. A picture is 28.2 inches wide and 36.5 inches long.
   a. Find the perimeter around the picture.
   b. Find the area of the picture.

31. Water enters a tank at the rate of 4.5 gallons per hour. How much water has entered the tank after 7.5 hours?

32. A fish swims 210 yards in 50 seconds. How many yards per second is this?

33. A rectangular plot of land is 34.6 feet wide and 60.8 feet long. Jack buys 200 feet of fencing to put around the lot. How much fencing is left over?

34. Janet buys $4\frac{1}{3}$ yards of fabric at $12.60 per yard and 5 yards of fabric at $7.25 per yard. The store adds a sales tax that is 0.058 of the marked price. Find the total cost of the fabric. (Round up at two decimal places.)

35. Due to a sale the price of a television decreased from $600 to $450. The decrease in price is what fraction of the original price?

36. The width of a rectangle is 6.8 feet less than the length. If the length is 12 feet, what is the area of the rectangle?

37. A rectangular mirror is 4.5 feet wide and 3 feet high. You put a frame around the mirror that costs $5.75 per foot. What is the total cost of the frame?

38. Find the total cost of carpeting this floor if the carpeting costs $17.95 per square yard.

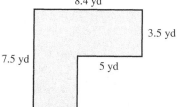

39. Bob saved the following amounts the last four months:
   April $300
   May $260
   June $400
   July $150
On average, how much did he save each month?

40. A parking lot charges $1.00 for the first half hour, then $0.80 for each additional half hour. You enter the garage at 11 AM and leave at 2 PM. How much is your parking fee?

41. A watch loses 6.5 seconds every 5 hours. At this rate, how much time does the watch lose in 24 hours?

42. Blanca types 276 words in 5 minutes and Natalie types 222 words in 4 minutes. Who types faster and at what rate?

43. If Stephanie can walk 13 miles in 3 hours, how long will it take her to walk 52 miles?

44. The area of a rectangle is 32 square yards and the length is $13\frac{1}{3}$ yards. Find the perimeter of the rectangle.

The rainfall for the first 5 months of a year for a certain city is given in the bar graph. Use the graph to answer Exercises 45 through 50.

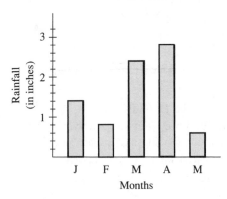

Monthly Rainfall

45. How much rain fell in February?

46. How much rain fell in March?

47. What was the total rainfall for the 5-month period?

48. What was the average rainfall per month for the 5-month period?

49. The amount of rainfall in May is what fraction of the total rainfall for the 5-month period?

50. Which month had the least amount of rain?

In Your Own Words

Write complete sentences to discuss each of the following. Support your comments with examples or pictures, if appropriate.

51. Discuss at least two ways of showing that the decimal 12.4 is equal to the fraction $\frac{620}{50}$.

52. Matthew is building a fence around a rectangular plot of land. Discuss whether he should find the perimeter or the area of this rectangular plot before buying the fencing materials.

53. A committee consists of 4 men and 6 women. Discuss at least two ways to compare the number of women and men by using addition or subtraction. Also, discuss at least two ways to compare the number of men and women by using division or a ratio.

54. Discuss how you can decide, before dividing, how the answers to these two problems should compare with the number 200.
   a. $200 \div 2.5$ **b.** $200 \div 0.25$

55. Discuss how you would decide which one of the following is the better buy.
   a. 14.5-ounce can of beans for $1.19
   b. 16-ounce can of the same beans for $1.29

CHAPTER 8 PRACTICE TEST

Label all tick marks. Then give the numbers for A and B.

1.
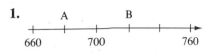

2.
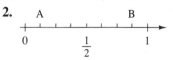

3.

4. Which of these numbers are equal to $9\frac{7}{25}$?
  a. 9.14   **b.** 9.357   **c.** $\frac{232}{25}$ **d.** $8\frac{32}{25}$

Use the symbol $<$, $=$, or $>$ to compare each pair of numbers.

5. $12\frac{5}{8}$, 12.625

6. 0.65, $0.\overline{6}$

7. List from smallest to largest: $9\frac{1}{4}$, $\frac{46}{5}$, 9.14

8. List from smallest to largest: $\frac{83}{10}$, $7\frac{4}{3}$, 0.95, 9.2

Solve. Show setups and calculation steps.

9. Find the sum of $5\frac{1}{6}$ and $2\frac{2}{3}$.

10. Find the ratio of 5.2 to 12.5.

11. Sales tax is 0.058 of the marked price. If the marked price of a stereo is $450, how much is the sales tax?

12. A chef prepared 57 ounces of rice. How many $\frac{3}{4}$-ounce portions can he serve?

13. A rectangular sheet of metal measures 7.9 feet by 18.7 feet. What is the area of the sheet of metal?

14. Jennifer filled $\frac{2}{5}$ of a bucket with water. What fraction of the bucket has no water?

15. Cindy studied for $5\frac{3}{4}$ hours and Roger studied for $7\frac{1}{4}$ hours. How much longer did Roger study than Cindy?

16. Ms. Wilson pays $\frac{1}{3}$ of her take-home pay in mortgage payments each month. If her monthly mortgage payment is $725.50, how much is her take-home pay?

17. Four pounds of coffee cost $21. How much of this coffee can you buy for $45.15?

18. A watch loses 4 seconds every 6 hours. At this rate, how many seconds does the watch lose in 10 hours?

19. The area of a rectangle is 170 square meters. The width is 8.5 meters. Find the perimeter of this rectangle.

20. The price of a certain stock increased from $13\frac{1}{8}$ to $15\frac{3}{4}$. The increase in price is what fraction of the original price?

21. You buy 6 pairs of socks at $5.75 each and 5 scarves at $12.50 each. If $5.82 in tax is added to the cost, how much change do you receive from $120?

22. What is the total cost of tiling this floor space if the tile costs $8.60 per square foot?

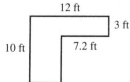

Percent

OBJECTIVES ▮ Recognize whether a percent is less than, equal to, or more than 1.
▮ Convert a percent to a decimal.
▮ Convert a percent to a fraction.

1   Introduction

Most people encounter **percents** in their everyday life. You probably have seen a sign similar to this one in a department store.

SWEATER SALE
40% OFF

The sign indicates that the store management has reduced the price of some sweaters. Percents are being used to tell the customer how much the price has been reduced. We will take a closer look at this and other applications later in the chapter.

    Why do we need percents? Percents were introduced in an attempt to standardize the arithmetic numbers by thinking of all of them with the same denominator so that they are easier to compare. The number 100 was chosen as the common denominator. Why was 100 chosen? Perhaps because it is convenient to work with and fits well with the decimal system. The symbol, %, read "percent," was introduced and is used in the place of the fraction bar and the denominator 100.

$$\frac{50}{100} = 50\%$$

Observe that the symbol % was chosen very cleverly. The slash (/) between the two 0s symbolizes the fraction bar or division. The 0s on each side of the slash symbolize the two 0s in the denominator 100.

The word *percent* comes from the Latin phrase *per centum.*

Per means **For each** or **Divide by**

Centum means **100** or **One hundred**

Therefore, percent means *per 100* or *divide by 100.*

The percent, 50%, is simply another way to write the number $\frac{50}{100}$ or 0.50 or $\frac{1}{2}$. Study the following chart to see how $\frac{1}{2}$ or .50 changes to percent.

Fraction to Percent	Decimal to Percent
$\frac{1}{2}$ one-half	0.5 five-tenths
$= \frac{50}{100}$ fifty hundredths	$= 0.50$ fifty hundredths
$= 50$ per 100	$= 50$ per 100
$= 50$ percent	$= 50$ percent
$= 50\%$	$= 50\%$

All numbers can be written in percent form. We now have three ways to write each number. Each number can be written as a fraction, as a decimal, or as a percent. A few examples are given in the table below.

Fraction	Decimal	Percent
$\frac{1}{100}$	0.01	1%
$\frac{1}{10} = \frac{10}{100}$	$0.1 = 0.10$	10%
$\frac{1}{4} = \frac{25}{100}$	0.25	25%
$\frac{1}{2} = \frac{50}{100}$	$0.5 = 0.50$	50%
$\frac{3}{4} = \frac{75}{100}$	0.75	75%
$1 = \frac{1}{1} = \frac{100}{100}$	$1 = 1.00$	100%
$1\frac{1}{2} = \frac{3}{2} = \frac{150}{100}$	$1.5 = 1.50$	150%
$2 = \frac{2}{1} = \frac{200}{100}$	$2 = 2.00$	200%
$3\frac{1}{4} = \frac{13}{4} = \frac{325}{100}$	3.25	325%

Observe from the previous table that the number 1 is the same as 100%, that a number less than 1 is less than 100%, and a number more than 1 is more than 100%.

Try These Problems

Indicate whether each percent is less than, equal to, or more than the number 1.

1. 35%

2. 180%

3. 6%

4. 100%

Convert each percent to a decimal.

5. 4%

6. 39%

7. 100%

8. 375%

A Useful Observation

1. 100% = 1

2. A percent that is less than 100% represents a number less than 1.

3. A percent that is more than 100% represents a number more than 1.

 Try Problems 1 through 4.

2 | Converting Percents to Decimals

The percent symbol, %, means *per 100* or *divide by 100*. Therefore to convert a percent to a decimal, drop the percent symbol and divide by 100. For example,

$$50\% = 50 \div 100 = \frac{50}{100} = 0.50$$

Converting a Percent to a Decimal

To convert a percent to a decimal, drop the percent symbol and divide by 100.

Here are more examples that illustrate how to use this rule to convert percents to decimals.

EXAMPLE 1 Convert 3% to a decimal.

SOLUTION

3% = 3 ÷ 100	% means divided by 100.
= 3. ÷ 100	Because 3 is a whole number, the decimal point is placed at the right end. 3. = 3
= .03	Dividing a decimal by 100 moves the decimal point 2 places to the left.
= .03 or 0.03	The digit 0 before the decimal point is not necessary but helps bring attention to the decimal point. ■

EXAMPLE 2 Convert 425% to a decimal.

SOLUTION

425% = 425 ÷ 100	% means divided by 100.
= 425. ÷ 100	
= 4.25	Dividing the decimal by 100 moves the decimal point 2 places to the left. ■
= 4.25	

 Try Problems 5 through 8.

◢◤ Try These Problems

Convert each percent to a decimal.

9. 8.05%

10. 0.25%

11. 62.5%

12. 200.8%

13. $\frac{1}{2}$%

14. $\frac{5}{80}$%

EXAMPLE 3   Convert 5.2% to a decimal.

SOLUTION

$5.2\% = 5.2 \div 100$	% means divided by 100.
$= .052$	Dividing a decimal by 100 moves the decimal point 2 places to the left.
$= .052$ or 0.052	The digit 0 before the decimal point is not necessary but helps bring attention to the decimal point.

EXAMPLE 4   Convert 0.06% to a decimal.

SOLUTION

$0.06\% = 0.06 \div 100$	% means divided by 100.
$= .0006$	Dividing a decimal by 100 moves the decimal point 2 places to the left.
$= .0006$ or 0.0006	The digit 0 before the decimal point is not necessary but helps bring attention to the decimal point.

◢◤ **Try Problems 9 through 12.**

EXAMPLE 5   Convert $\frac{1}{4}$% to a decimal.

SOLUTION   Be careful here. The percent, $\frac{1}{4}$%, is not the same as the number $\frac{1}{4}$.

$\frac{1}{4}\% = 0.25\%$	Convert $\frac{1}{4}$ to a decimal before dropping the percent symbol and dividing by 100.
	$\begin{array}{r} .25 \\ 4\overline{)1.00} \\ \underline{8} \\ 20 \\ \underline{20} \end{array} \rightarrow \frac{1}{4} = 0.25$
$= 0.25 \div 100$	Drop the percent symbol and divide by 100.
$= .0025$	Dividing a decimal by 100 moves the decimal point 2 places to the left.
$= .0025$ or 0.0025 ◼	

◢◤ **Try Problems 13 and 14.**

Try These Problems

Convert each percent to a decimal.

15. $12\frac{1}{2}\%$

16. $4\frac{7}{8}\%$

17. $66\frac{2}{3}\%$

18. $5\frac{1}{6}\%$

19. $\frac{1}{3}\%$

20. $4\frac{7}{11}\%$

EXAMPLE 6   Convert $6\frac{3}{8}\%$ to a decimal.

SOLUTION

$$6\frac{3}{8}\% = 6.375\%$$

Convert $6\frac{3}{8}$ to a decimal before dropping the percent symbol and dividing by 100.

$$8)\overline{3.000} \rightarrow \frac{3}{8} = 0.375$$
$$\underline{24}$$
$$60$$
$$\underline{56}$$
$$40$$
$$\underline{40}$$

$= 6.375 \div 100$

Drop the percent symbol and divide by 100.

$= .06375$

$= .06375$ or 0.06375

Dividing a decimal by 100 moves the decimal point 2 places to the left. ■

 Try Problems 15 and 16.

EXAMPLE 7   Convert $33\frac{1}{3}\%$ to a decimal.

SOLUTION
METHOD 1

$$33\frac{1}{3}\% = 33.\overline{3}\%$$

Convert $33\frac{1}{3}$ to a decimal before dropping the percent symbol and dividing by 100.

$$3)\overline{1.000} \rightarrow \frac{1}{3} = 0.33333\ldots$$
$$\underline{9} \qquad\qquad = 0.\overline{3}$$
$$10$$
$$\underline{9}$$
$$10$$
$$\underline{9}$$
$$1$$

$= 33.\overline{3} \div 100$

Drop the percent symbol and divide by 100.

$= .33\overline{3}$

$= 0.\overline{3}$

Dividing a decimal by 100 moves the decimal point 2 places to the left.

METHOD 2   When the percent converts to a repeating decimal, we often write it as a decimal with fraction rather than a repeating decimal.

$$33\frac{1}{3}\% = \frac{33\frac{1}{3}}{100} = 0.33\frac{1}{3} \quad ■$$

Repeating decimals like $0.\overline{3}$ and decimals with fractions like $0.33\frac{1}{3}$ are not convenient to work with. As you will see later in the chapter, it is better to convert percents like $33\frac{1}{3}\%$ to fractions rather than decimals.

 Try Problems 17 through 20.

▲ Try These Problems

Convert each percent to a fraction.
21. 2%
22. 80%
23. 420%

3 Converting Percents to Fractions

To convert a percent to a decimal, we dropped the percent symbol and divided by 100. This same rule can be used to convert a percent to a fraction. For example,

$$50\% = 50 \div 100 = \frac{50}{100} = \frac{1}{2}$$

> *Converting a Percent to a Fraction*
>
> **To convert a percent to a fraction, drop the percent symbol and divide by 100.**

Here are some examples to illustrate how to use this rule.

EXAMPLE 8   Convert 35% to a fraction.

SOLUTION

$$35\% = 35 \div 100$$ Drop the percent symbol and divide by 100.

$$= \frac{35}{100}$$

$$= \frac{5 \times 7}{5 \times 20}$$ Reduce the fraction to lowest terms.

$$= \frac{7}{20} \quad\blacksquare$$

EXAMPLE 9   Convert 250% to a fraction.

SOLUTION

$$250\% = 250 \div 100$$ Drop the percent symbol and divide by 100.

$$= \frac{250}{100}$$

$$= \frac{25 \times 10}{10 \times 10}$$

$$= \frac{25}{10}$$

$$= \frac{5 \times 5}{2 \times 5}$$ Reduce the fraction to lowest terms.

$$= \frac{5}{2} \quad\text{or}\quad 2\frac{1}{2}$$ The answer may be expressed as an improper fraction or as a mixed numeral.

 Try Problems 21 through 23.

Try These Problems

Convert each percent to a fraction.

24. $\frac{1}{4}\%$

25. $\frac{3}{10}\%$

26. $3\frac{1}{5}\%$

27. $6\frac{2}{3}\%$

28. $12\frac{1}{2}\%$

29. $10\frac{2}{3}\%$

EXAMPLE 10 Convert $\frac{3}{4}\%$ to a fraction.

SOLUTION Be careful here. The percent, $\frac{3}{4}\%$, is not the same as the number $\frac{3}{4}$.

$$\frac{3}{4}\% = \frac{3}{4} \div 100$$
Drop the percent symbol and divide by 100.

$$= \frac{3}{4} \times \frac{1}{100}$$
Dividing by 100 is the same as multiplying by $\frac{1}{100}$.

$$= \frac{3}{400} \blacksquare$$

 Try Problems 24 and 25.

EXAMPLE 11 Convert $8\frac{1}{3}\%$ to a fraction.

SOLUTION

$$8\frac{1}{3}\% = 8\frac{1}{3} \div 100$$
Drop the percent symbol and divide by 100.

$$= \frac{25}{3} \times \frac{1}{100}$$
Dividing by 100 is the same as multiplying by $\frac{1}{100}$.

$$= \frac{\overset{1}{25}}{3} \times \frac{1}{25 \times 4}$$

$$= \frac{1}{12} \blacksquare$$

 Try Problems 26 and 27.

EXAMPLE 12 Convert $66\frac{2}{3}\%$ to a fraction.

SOLUTION

$$66\frac{2}{3}\% = 66\frac{2}{3} \div 100$$
Drop the percent symbol and divide by 100.

$$= \frac{\overset{2}{200}}{3} \times \frac{1}{\underset{1}{100}}$$
Dividing by 100 is the same as multiplying by $\frac{1}{100}$.

$$= \frac{2}{3} \blacksquare$$

Each of the percents in Examples 11 and 12 convert to a repeating decimal or to a decimal with fraction. That is, $8\frac{1}{3}\% = 0.08\overline{3}$ or $0.08\frac{1}{3}$ and $66\frac{2}{3}\% = 0.\overline{6}$ or $0.66\frac{2}{3}$. These percents can also be approximated as terminating decimals, $8\frac{1}{3}\% \approx 0.083$ and $66\frac{2}{3}\% \approx 0.66$ or 0.67. When you work with percents like $8\frac{1}{3}\%$ and $66\frac{2}{3}\%$ be sure to convert them to fractions if you want an exact answer. Using the decimal approximations will result in only an approximate answer. Also, do not try to calculate with a repeating decimal or a decimal with fraction because they are much harder to work with than fractions.

 Try Problems 28 and 29.

ch 9.1 pg 372-378 1-37 odd

1. Less

3. Less

5. $\frac{4}{100}$ = $100\overline{)4.00}$ $^{0.04}$ 0.04

7. $\frac{100}{100}$ = 1

9   0.0805

11   62.5 = 0.625

13 $\frac{1}{2}\% = \frac{50}{100} =$ 0.05 = 0.005

15 12.5 = 0.125 = 0.125

17. $66\frac{2}{3}\% =$ $3\overline{)12.09}$ $^{0.66}$ $66.\overline{6}\% = .\overline{6}$

$\underline{18}\downarrow$
120
$66.\overline{6}\%\underline{18}$
2

$66.\overline{6}\% = .66.\overline{6} \div 100$

$.66\overline{6} = .\overline{6}$

19. $\frac{1}{3}\% = \frac{1}{3} \div \frac{100}{1} = \frac{1}{3} \times \frac{1}{100} = \frac{1}{300}$

300
$\underline{\times 3}$ $^{0.0033}$
900 $300\overline{)1.0000} = 0.00\overline{3}$
$\underline{900}\downarrow$
1000
$\underline{1000}$
0

21   2% $\frac{2}{100} = \frac{2 \times 1}{50 \times 2} = \frac{1}{50}$

     420% =

23   $4 \frac{20}{100} = 4 \frac{2 \times 1}{2 \times 5} = 14 \frac{1}{5}$

25   $\frac{3}{10}$ %

Try These Problems

Convert each percent to a fraction

30. 2.5%

31. 5.6%

32. 87.5%

33. 0.6%

EXAMPLE 13   Convert 3.5% to a fraction.

SOLUTION

$$3.5\% = 3.5 \div 100$$ Drop the percent symbol and divide by 100.

$$= .035$$ Dividing a decimal by 100 moves the decimal point 2 places to the left.

$$= 0.035$$ This decimal is 35 thousandths.

$$= \frac{35}{1000}$$ Convert the decimal to a fraction.

$$= \frac{\not{5} \times 7}{\not{5} \times 200}$$ Reduce the fraction to lowest terms.

$$= \frac{7}{200} \;■$$

 Try Problems 30 and 31.

EXAMPLE 14   Convert 37.5% to a fraction.

SOLUTION

$$37.5\% = 37.5 \div 100$$ Drop the percent symbol and divide by 100.

$$= .375$$ Dividing a decimal by 100 moves the decimal point 2 places to the left.

$$-= 0.375$$ This decimal is 375 thousandths.

$$= \frac{375}{1000}$$ Convert the decimal to a fraction.

$$= \frac{\not{25} \times 15}{\not{25} \times 40}$$

$$= \frac{15}{40}$$

$$= \frac{3 \times \not{5}}{\not{5} \times 8}$$ Reduce the fraction to lowest terms.

$$= \frac{3}{8} \;■$$

Try Problems 32 and 33.

EXAMPLE 15   Convert 0.04% to a fraction.

SOLUTION   Be careful here. The percent, 0.04%, is not the same as the number 0.04.

$$0.04\% = 0.04 \div 100$$ Drop the percent symbol and divide by 100.

$$= .0004$$ Dividing a decimal by 100 moves the decimal point 2 places to the left.

$$= 0.0004$$ This decimal is 4 ten-thousandths.

Try These Problems

Convert each percent to a fraction.

34. 0.05%

35. 0.12%

36. 3.75%

37. 8.25%

$$= \frac{4}{10,000}$$

Convert the decimal to a fraction.

$$= \frac{\overset{1}{\cancel{4}}}{4 \times 2500}$$

Reduce the fraction to lowest terms.

$$= \frac{1}{2500} \; \blacksquare$$

 Try Problems 34 and 35.

EXAMPLE 16   Convert 6.25% to a fraction.

SOLUTION

$$6.25\% = 6.25 \div 100$$

Drop the percent symbol and divide by 100.

$$= .0625$$

Dividing a decimal by 100 moves the decimal point 2 places to the left.

$$= 0.0625$$

This decimal is 625 ten-thousandths.

$$= \frac{625}{10,000}$$

Convert the decimal to a fraction.

$$= \frac{25 \times 25}{25 \times 400}$$

$$= \frac{25}{400}$$

$$= \frac{\overset{1}{\cancel{25}}}{16 \times \cancel{25}}$$

Reduce the fraction to lowest term.

$$= \frac{1}{16} \; \blacksquare$$

 Try Problems 36 and 37.

  Answers to Try These Problems

1. less than 1   **2.** more than 1   **3.** less than 1   **4.** equal to 1
5. 0.04   **6.** 0.39   **7.** 1   **8.** 3.75   **9.** 0.0805   **10.** 0.0025
11. 0.625   **12.** 2.008   **13.** 0.005   **14.** 0.000625   **15.** 0.125
16. 0.04875   **17.** $0.\overline{6}$ or $0.66\frac{2}{3}$ **18.** $0.051\overline{6}$ or $0.05\frac{1}{6}$
19. $0.00\overline{3}$, $0.003\frac{1}{3}$ **20.** $0.04\overline{63}$, $0.04\frac{7}{11}$ **21.** $\frac{1}{50}$ **22.** $\frac{4}{5}$
23. $\frac{21}{5}$ or $4\frac{1}{5}$ **24.** $\frac{1}{400}$ **25.** $\frac{3}{1000}$ **26.** $\frac{4}{125}$ **27.** $\frac{1}{15}$ **28.** $\frac{1}{8}$ **29.** $\frac{8}{75}$
30. $\frac{1}{40}$ **31.** $\frac{7}{125}$ **32.** $\frac{7}{8}$ **33.** $\frac{3}{500}$ **34.** $\frac{1}{2000}$ **35.** $\frac{3}{2500}$ **36.** $\frac{3}{80}$
37. $\frac{33}{400}$

EXERCISES   9.1

Indicate whether each percent is less than, equal to, or more than the number 1.

1. 50%   **2.** 300%   **3.** 150%   **4.** 8%   **5.** 100%   **6.** 1%

Convert each percent to a decimal. If the decimal is repeating, express the answer as both a repeating decimal and as a decimal with fraction.

7. 6%   **8.** 5%   **9.** 10%   **10.** 25%   **11.** 100%

12. 125%   **13.** 350%   **14.** 275%   **15.** 4.2%   **16.** 8.7%

17. 15.32%   **18.** 9.02%   **19.** 0.9%   **20.** 0.75%   **21.** 0.145%

22. 0.025%   **23.** 100.5%   **24.** 230.6%   **25.** $\frac{1}{4}$%   **26.** $\frac{2}{5}$%

27. $2\frac{1}{2}$%   **28.** $6\frac{2}{5}$%   **29.** $37\frac{3}{4}$%   **30.** $50\frac{1}{4}$%   **31.** $\frac{1}{40}$%

32. $\frac{3}{100}$%   **33.** $\frac{5}{6}$%   **34.** $2\frac{2}{3}$%   **35.** $33\frac{1}{3}$%   **36.** $6\frac{1}{6}$%

Convert each percent to a fraction. Simplify.

37. 1%   **38.** 8%   **39.** 75%   **40.** 12%   **41.** 36%

42. 40%   **43.** 175%   **44.** 200%   **45.** 325%   **46.** 260%

47. $\frac{2}{5}$%   **48.** $\frac{2}{3}$%   **49.** $33\frac{1}{3}$%   **50.** $62\frac{1}{2}$%   **51.** $3\frac{1}{3}$%

52. $7\frac{1}{2}$%   **53.** $\frac{1}{2}$%   **54.** $\frac{2}{5}$%   **55.** $\frac{7}{10}$%   **56.** $\frac{1}{30}$%

57. $43\frac{3}{4}$%   **58.** $16\frac{2}{5}$%   **59.** $9\frac{2}{3}$%   **60.** $4\frac{3}{5}$%   **61.** $\frac{3}{400}$%

62. $\frac{9}{200}$%   **63.** 2.5%   **64.** 7.5%   **65.** 4.5%   **66.** 6.4%

67. 37.5%   **68.** 62.5%   **69.** 0.8%   **70.** 0.4%   **71.** 0.09%

72. 0.02%   **73.** 0.25%   **74.** 0.16%   **75.** 4.25%   **76.** 8.75%

9.2   FINDING A PERCENT OF A NUMBER

OBJECTIVES

- Find a percent of a number by using decimals.
- Find a percent of a number by using fractions.

1   Finding a Percent of a Number in Two Ways: Using Decimals and Using Fractions

Suppose your take-home pay for one month is $2000 and you pay 25% of the take-home pay in rent. How much do you pay in rent? We have the following.

$$\begin{matrix} \text{Amount paid} \\ \text{in rent} \end{matrix} \quad = \quad 25\% \quad \underset{\downarrow}{\text{of}} \quad \begin{matrix} \text{take-home} \\ \text{pay} \end{matrix}$$

$$= \quad 25\% \quad \times \quad \$2000$$

The word *of* used in this way translates to multiplication. To find 25% of $2000 we must multiply 25% by $2000. Before multiplying, convert 25% to a fraction or a decimal. Here we show the calculation done in both ways.

USING DECIMALS

$$\begin{aligned} \begin{matrix} \text{Amount paid} \\ \text{in rent (\$)} \end{matrix} &= 25\% \text{ of } 2000 \\ &= 0.25 \times 2000 \\ &= 500.00 \\ &= 500 \end{aligned}$$

USING FRACTIONS

$$\begin{aligned}\text{Amount paid}\atop\text{in rent (\$)} &= 25\% \text{ of } 2000\\[4pt] &= \frac{25}{100} \times 2000\\[8pt] &= \frac{25}{\cancel{100}_{\,1}} \times \frac{\cancel{2000}^{\,20}}{1}\\[8pt] &= 500\end{aligned}$$

Observe that 25% of 2000 is 500. Therefore, the amount paid in rent is $500.

In the above problem, it did not matter whether we chose to do the problem using fractions or decimals. One method was as easy as the other and both methods gave the precise answer. Sometimes, however, choosing decimals is easier, and at other times, choosing fractions is easier. Also, when the percent converts to a repeating decimal, you need to choose fractions in order to obtain an answer that is not an approximation. In this section we learn how to choose the most convenient method or the method that leads to a precise answer. First we look at more examples where one method is as easy as the other and both are precise.

EXAMPLE 1   Find 5% of 60.

SOLUTION
USING DECIMALS

$$5\% \text{ of } 60$$
$$\downarrow$$

$= 0.05 \times 60$ Convert 5% to a decimal.
                       5% = 5 ÷ 100 = 0.05

$= 3.00$ Multiply 0.05 by 60.

$$\begin{array}{r}0.05\\ \times \quad 60\\ \hline 3.00\end{array}$$

$= 3$

USING FRACTIONS

$$5\% \text{ of } 60$$
$$\downarrow$$

$= \dfrac{1}{20} \times \dfrac{60}{1}$ Convert 5% to a fraction.

$$5\% = 5 \div 100 = \frac{5}{100}$$

$$= \frac{\cancel{5}^{\,1}}{\cancel{5}\times 20} = \frac{1}{20}$$

$= \dfrac{1}{\cancel{20}_{\,1}} \times \dfrac{3 \times \cancel{20}}{1}$ Cancel common factors from the numerator and denominator before multiplying the fractions.

$= 3$

5% of 60 is 3.   ■

Try These Problems

Solve each problem in two ways, by using decimals *and by using* fractions.

1. 3% of 400
2. 50% of 36
3. $7\frac{1}{2}$% of 620
4. $37\frac{1}{2}$% of 20

In Example 1 note that the result 3 is less than 60 because 5% is less than 100% or 1.

 Try Problems 1 and 2.

EXAMPLE 2   Find $3\frac{1}{2}$% of 2600.

SOLUTION

USING DECIMALS

$$3\frac{1}{2}\% \text{ of } 2600$$
$$\downarrow$$
$$= 0.035 \times 2600$$

Convert $3\frac{1}{2}$% to a decimal.

$3\frac{1}{2}\% = 3.5\% = 3.5 \div 100$

$= 0.035$

$$= 91.000$$

Multiply 0.035 by 2600.

$$= 91$$

$$\begin{array}{r} 0.035 \\ \times \quad 2600 \\ \hline 21\ 0 \\ 70 \quad \\ \hline 91.000 \end{array}$$

USING FRACTIONS

$$3\frac{1}{2}\% \text{ of } 2600$$
$$\downarrow$$
$$= \frac{7}{200} \times \frac{2600}{1}$$

Convert $3\frac{1}{2}$% to a fraction.

$3\frac{1}{2}\% = 3\frac{1}{2} \div 100$

$$= \frac{7}{2} \times \frac{1}{100} = \frac{7}{200}$$

$$= \frac{7}{200} \times \frac{13 \times 200}{1}$$

$$= 91$$

$3\frac{1}{2}$% of 2600 is 91. ■

 Try Problems 3 and 4.

EXAMPLE 3   Find 125% of 86.

SOLUTION

USING DECIMALS

$$125\% \text{ of } 86$$
$$\downarrow$$
$$= 1.25 \times 86$$

Convert 125% to a decimal.
125% = 125 ÷ 100 = 1.25

$$= 107.50$$

Multiply 1.25 by 86.

$$= 107.5$$

Try These Problems

Solve each problem in two ways, by using decimals *and by using* fractions.

5. 175% of 1600

6. 250% of 47

7. $\frac{2}{5}$% of 2500

8. 0.03% of 5000

USING FRACTIONS

$$125\% \text{ of } 86$$
$$\downarrow$$
$$= \frac{5}{4} \times \frac{86}{1}$$

Convert 125% to a fraction.

$$125\% = \frac{125}{100} = \frac{5 \times 25}{4 \times 25} = \frac{5}{4}$$

$$= \frac{5}{2 \times 2} \times \frac{2 \times 43}{1}$$

$$= \frac{215}{2} \quad \text{or} \quad 107\frac{1}{2}$$

125% of 86 is 107.5 or $107\frac{1}{2}$.

In Example 3 note that the result 107.5 is more than 86, because 125% is more than 100% or 1.

Try Problems 5 and 6.

EXAMPLE 4   Find $\frac{1}{4}$% of 3200.

SOLUTION
USING DECIMALS

$$\frac{1}{4}\% \quad \text{of } 3200$$
$$\downarrow$$
$$= 0.0025 \times 3200$$

Convert $\frac{1}{4}$% to a decimal.

$$\frac{1}{4}\% = 0.25\%$$
$$= 0.25 \div 100 = 0.0025$$

$$= 8.0000$$
$$= 8$$

Multiply 0.0025 by 3200.

$$\begin{array}{r} 0.0025 \\ \times \quad 3200 \\ \hline 50 \\ 75 \\ \hline 8.0000 \end{array}$$

USING FRACTIONS

$$\frac{1}{4}\% \text{ of } 3200$$
$$\downarrow$$
$$= \frac{1}{400} \times \frac{3200}{1}$$

Convert $\frac{1}{4}$% to a fraction.

$$\frac{1}{4}\% = \frac{1}{4} \div 100$$

$$= \frac{1}{4 \times 100} \times \frac{32 \times 100}{1}$$

$$= \frac{1}{4} \times \frac{1}{100} = \frac{1}{400}$$

$$= \frac{32}{4}$$

$$= 8$$

$\frac{1}{4}$% of 3200 is 8.

In Example 4 we should expect $\frac{1}{4}$% of 3200 to be less than 1% of 3200, because $\frac{1}{4}$% is less than 1%. This means we should expect the result, 8, to be less than 1% of 3200 which is 32.

Try Problems 7 and 8.

◢ Try These Problems

Solve each of these problems by using decimals.

9. 9.3% of 780

10. 275% of 13.6

11. 0.7% of $59.30 (Round off to the nearest cent.)

2 Choosing Decimals over Fractions to Solve Problems

Now that you have seen that we can use decimals or fractions to find a percent of a number, we want to look at some situations where it is better to choose the decimal method.

EXAMPLE 5   Find 8% of 37.9.

SOLUTION   Because the number 37.9 is already written in decimal form, and it is easy to convert 8% to a decimal, we choose to use decimals to solve this problem.

$$8\% \text{ of } 37.9$$
$$\downarrow$$
$$= 0.08 \times 37.9 \qquad \text{Convert 8\% to a decimal.}$$
$$\qquad\qquad\qquad\quad 8\% = 8 \div 100 = 0.08$$
$$= 3.032 \qquad\quad \text{Multiply 0.08 by 37.9.}$$

8% of 37.9 is 3.032.   ■

EXAMPLE 6   Find 0.75% of $65.25. (Round off the answer to the nearest cent.)

SOLUTION   Because the number 65.25 is already written in decimal form, and the percent 0.75% is easy to convert to a decimal, we choose to use decimals to solve this problem.

$$0.75\% \text{ of } \$65.25$$
$$\downarrow$$
$$= 0.0075 \times \$65.25 \qquad \text{Convert 0.75\% to a decimal.}$$
$$\qquad\qquad\qquad\qquad 0.75\% = 0.75 \div 100 = 0.0075$$
$$= \$0.489375 \qquad\quad \text{Multiply 0.0075 by 65.25.}$$
$$\approx \$0.49$$

Multiply 0.0075 by 65.25.
$$\begin{array}{r} 65.25 \\ \times\ 0.0075 \\ \hline 32625 \\ 45675 \\ \hline .489375 \approx 0.49 \end{array}$$

0.75% of $65.25 is approximately $0.49.   ■

In Example 6 we expect the result to be less than 1% of $65.25 because 0.75% is less than 1%. This means the result $0.49 should be less than 1% of $65.25 which is approximately $0.65.

◢ Try Problems 9 through 11.

3 Choosing Fractions over Decimals to Solve Problems

Sometimes fractions convert to repeating decimals. Here are some examples.

$$\frac{1}{3} = 0.333\ldots \qquad \text{Divide 1 by 3.}$$
$$= 0.\overline{3}$$

$$\begin{array}{r} .333 \\ 3\overline{)1.000} \\ \underline{9} \\ 10 \\ \underline{9} \\ 10 \\ \underline{9} \\ 1 \end{array}$$

Try These Problems

Solve each of these problems by using fractions.

12. $66\frac{2}{3}\%$ of 900

13. $10\frac{5}{8}\%$ of 75

$$\frac{2}{3} = 0.666\ldots$$

$$= 0.\overline{6}$$

Divide 2 by 3.

```
   .666
3)2.000
   1 8
    20
    18
    20
    18
     2
```

$$\frac{5}{11} = 0.454545\ldots$$

$$= 0.\overline{45}$$

Divide 5 by 11.

```
    .4545
11)5.0000
   4 4
    60
    55
    50
    44
    60
    55
     5
```

If a fraction or percent converts to a repeating decimal, and you need to multiply or divide by this number, you should avoid using decimals. Using a decimal approximation for a repeating decimal will result in an answer that is not precise. *Use fractions when solving problems that involve repeating decimals.* Here are some examples.

EXAMPLE 7 Find $33\frac{1}{3}\%$ of 15.

SOLUTION Because $33\frac{1}{3}\%$ converts to the repeating decimal $0.\overline{3}$, we must use fractions to solve this problem.

$$33\frac{1}{3}\% \text{ of } 15$$

$$= \frac{1}{3} \times \frac{15}{1}$$

$$= \frac{15}{3} \text{ or } 5$$

Convert $33\frac{1}{3}\%$ to a fraction.

$$33\frac{1}{3}\% = 33\frac{1}{3} \div 100$$

$$= \frac{\overset{1}{\cancel{100}}}{3} \times \frac{1}{\underset{1}{\cancel{100}}} = \frac{1}{3}$$

$33\frac{1}{3}\%$ of 15 is 5. ■

In the previous example, let's look at what would happen if we used a decimal approximation for $33\frac{1}{3}\%$, instead of the fraction $\frac{1}{3}$, to calculate $33\frac{1}{3}\%$ of 15. Here we show the results when converting $33\frac{1}{3}\%$ to 0.3, 0.33, or 0.333 to compute $33\frac{1}{3}\%$ of 15.

$$0.3 \times 15 = 4.5$$
$$0.33 \times 15 = 4.95$$
$$0.333 \times 15 = 4.995$$

These three results—4.5, 4.95, and 4.995—are only approximations of the precise answer 5. When a percent converts to a repeating decimal, you must convert the percent to a fraction before calculating with it. Using the fraction will produce the precise answer, while using a decimal approximation will not produce the precise answer.

Try Problems 12 and 13.

Try These Problems

Solve each of these problems by using fractions.

14. $12\frac{1}{2}\%$ of $8\frac{1}{3}$

15. 125% of $\frac{5}{12}$

16. $\frac{2}{7}\%$ of 2100

17. $\frac{1}{4}\%$ of $66\frac{2}{3}$

EXAMPLE 8   Find 250% of $10\frac{2}{3}$.

SOLUTION   Because $10\frac{2}{3}$ converts to the repeating decimal $10.\overline{6}$, we must use fractions to solve this problem.

$$250\% \text{ of } 10\frac{2}{3}$$
$$\downarrow$$
$$= \frac{5}{\underset{1}{2}} \times \frac{\overset{16}{32}}{3}$$

Convert 250% to a fraction.
$$250\% = \frac{250}{100} = \frac{5 \times \cancel{50}}{2 \times \cancel{50}} = \frac{5}{2}$$

$$= \frac{80}{3} \quad \text{or} \quad 26\frac{2}{3}$$

250% of $10\frac{2}{3}$ is $26\frac{2}{3}$. ▪

 Try Problems 14 and 15.

EXAMPLE 9   Find $\frac{3}{5}\%$ of $4\frac{1}{6}$.

SOLUTION   Because $4\frac{1}{6}$ converts to the repeating decimal $4.1\overline{6}$, we must use fractions to solve this problem.

$$\frac{3}{5}\% \text{ of } 4\frac{1}{6}$$
$$\downarrow$$
$$= \frac{3}{500} \times \frac{25}{6}$$

Convert $\frac{3}{5}\%$ to a fraction.
$$\frac{3}{5}\% = \frac{3}{5} \div 100 = \frac{3}{5} \times \frac{1}{100} = \frac{3}{500}$$

$$= \frac{\overset{1}{3}}{25 \times 20} \times \frac{\overset{1}{25}}{\underset{2}{6}}$$

$$= \frac{1}{40}$$

$\frac{3}{5}\%$ of $4\frac{1}{6}$ is $\frac{1}{40}$. ▪

 Try Problems 16 and 17.

At this time we summarize the procedure for finding the percent of a number.

Finding a Percent of a Number

1. Convert the percent to a fraction or decimal. Use fractions if repeating decimals are involved. Otherwise, choose whichever seems more convenient.

2. Translate the word *of* to *multiply*.

3. Follow the rules for multiplying decimals or fractions when carrying out the multiplication.

 Answers to Try These Problems.

1. 12   **2.** 18   **3.** 46.5 or $46\frac{1}{2}$ or $\frac{93}{2}$ **4.** 7.5 or $7\frac{1}{2}$ or $\frac{15}{2}$
5. 2800   **6.** 117.5 or $117\frac{1}{2}$ or $\frac{235}{2}$ **7.** 10
8. 1.5 or $1\frac{1}{2}$ or $\frac{3}{2}$ **9.** 72.54   **10.** 37.4   **11.** \$0.42   **12.** 600
13. $\frac{65}{8}$ or $8\frac{1}{8}$ **14.** $\frac{25}{24}$ or $1\frac{1}{24}$ **15.** $\frac{25}{48}$ **16.** 6   **17.** $\frac{1}{6}$

EXERCISES 9.2

Solve these problems in two ways, by using decimals and by using fractions.

1. 1% of 3000 **2.** 10% of 250 **3.** 25% of 72 **4.** 50% of 700

5. 350% of 40 **6.** 275% of 64 **7.** $6\frac{1}{4}$% of 200

8. $12\frac{1}{2}$% of 680 **9.** 0.2% of 1500 **10.** $\frac{3}{4}$% of 2400

Use decimals to solve these problems.

11. 8.7% of 162 **12.** 36.4% of 95 **13.** 42% of 17.8

14. 9% of 3.14 **15.** 100% of 12.3 **16.** 100% of 7.98

17. 120% of 130.7 **18.** 250% of 9400 **19.** 162% of 8

20. 215% of 0.6 **21.** 0.6% of 42.5 **22.** 0.45% of 906

23. 0.064% of 5600 **24.** 0.03% of 8000

25. $\frac{1}{2}$% of 15.60 **26.** $5\frac{1}{4}$% of 76.8

Use fractions to solve these problems.

27. $33\frac{1}{3}$% of 450 **28.** $6\frac{2}{3}$% of 1800 **29.** $7\frac{1}{2}$% of $22\frac{2}{9}$

30. $87\frac{1}{2}$% of $13\frac{1}{3}$ **31.** 100% of $\frac{7}{12}$ **32.** 100% of $9\frac{5}{6}$

33. 240% of $14\frac{1}{6}$ **34.** 350% of $2\frac{2}{7}$ **35.** $\frac{2}{5}$% of $10\frac{5}{12}$

36. $\frac{1}{6}$% of 540 **37.** 1.5% of $16\frac{2}{3}$ **38.** 0.3% of $18\frac{1}{3}$

Solve.

39. Gloria pays 35% of her annual income in taxes. If her annual income is $56,000, how much does she pay in taxes?

40. Sales tax in a certain state is 5.2% of the marked price. How much tax is paid on a stereo that is marked $580?

A used-car dealer has a total of 460 automobiles on his lot to sell. The circle graph gives the percent of the total that are trucks, 4-door sedans, and 2-door sedans, respectively. Use the graph to answer Exercises 41 and 42.

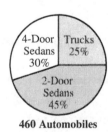

460 Automobiles

41. How many trucks are on the lot?
42. How many 2-door sedans are on the lot?

9.3 CONVERTING DECIMALS AND FRACTIONS TO PERCENT

OBJECTIVES ▌ Convert a decimal to a percent.
▌ Convert a fraction to a percent.
▌ Given a fraction, decimal, or percent, find the other two forms of the number.

1 Converting Decimals to Percents

In Section 9.1 you learned how to convert a percent to a decimal. For example,

Percent $\rightarrow$ Decimal

| 50% | = | 0.50 | Drop the percent symbol and divide by 100. |

Now we want to reverse this process. We want to be able to convert a decimal to a percent. For example,

Decimal $\rightarrow$ Percent

| 0.50 | = | 50% | Multiply by 100 and attach the percent symbol, %. |

Observe that if we multiply 0.50 by 100, then attach the percent symbol, we get 50% which we know to be the correct result. Here we show the procedure carefully.

$0.50 = 0.50 \times 100\%$	Multiply by 100 and attach the percent symbol, %.
$= 050. \quad \%$	Multiplying a decimal by 100 moves the decimal point 2 places to the right.
$= 50\%$	

Here we have really multiplied 0.50 by 100% to obtain 50%. Recall that 100% is equal to 1. Multiplying a number by 1 does not change that number, so multiplying a number by 100% does not alter the value of that number. Therefore, 0.50 is equal to 50%.

The above discussion suggests the following rule.

Converting a Decimal to a Percent

To convert a decimal to a percent, multiply by 100 and attach the percent symbol, %.

Here are some examples that illustrate how to use this rule to convert decimals to percents.

EXAMPLE 1 Convert 0.3 to a percent.

SOLUTION

$0.3 = 0.3 \times 100\%$	Multiply by 100 and attach the percent symbol, %.
$= 030. \quad \%$	Multiplying a decimal by 100 moves the decimal point 2 places to the right. ■
$= 30\%$	

EXAMPLE 2 Convert 0.065 to a percent.

SOLUTION

$0.065 = 0.065 \times 100\%$	Multiply by 100 and attach the percent symbol, %.
$= 006.5 \quad \%$	Multiplying a decimal by 100 moves the decimal point 2 places to the right.
$= 6.5\%$	

Try These Problems

Convert each decimal to a percent.
1. 0.68
2. 0.8
3. 0.075
4. 7
5. 1.6
6. 0.0004

EXAMPLE 3   Convert 2 to a percent.

SOLUTION

$$2 = 2 \times 100\%$$ Multiply by 100 and attach the percent symbol, %.

$$= 200\%$$ ■

EXAMPLE 4   Convert 0.0054 to a percent.

SOLUTION

$$0.0054 = 0.0054 \times 100\ \%$$ Multiply by 100 and attach the percent symbol, %.

$$=\ \ \ \ 000.54\ \%$$ Multiplying a decimal by 100 moves the decimal point 2 places to the right. ■

$$= 0.54\%$$

 Try Problems 1 through 6.

---

2   Converting Fractions to Percents

You have just learned how to convert a decimal to a percent. For example,

Decimal   →   Percent

0.04   =   4%   Multiply by 100 and attach the percent symbol, %.

The same rule should work for fractions. For example,

Fraction   →   Percent

$$\frac{4}{100}$$ =   4%   Multiply by 100 and attach the percent symbol, %.

Observe that if we multiply the fraction $\frac{4}{100}$ by 100, then attach the percent symbol, we get 4% which we know to be the correct result. Here we show the procedure.

$$\frac{4}{100} = \frac{4}{100} \times 100\ \%$$ Multiply by 100 and attach the percent symbol, %.

$$= \frac{4}{\overset{}{\underset{1}{100}}} \times \frac{\overset{1}{\cancel{100}}}{1}\ \%$$ Cancel the common factor 100.

$$= 4\%$$

Here we have really multiplied $\frac{4}{100}$ by 100% to obtain 4%. Recall that 100% equals 1. Multiplying a number by 1 does not change the value of the number, so multiplying a number by 100% does not change the value of that number. Therefore, the fraction $\frac{4}{100}$ is equal to 4%.

The above discussion suggests the following rule.

Converting a Fraction to a Percent

To convert a fraction to a percent, multiply by 100 and attach the percent symbol, %.

Try These Problems

Convert each fraction to a percent.

7. $\frac{2}{5}$

8. $\frac{3}{20}$

Here are some examples that illustrate how to use this rule to convert fractions to percents.

EXAMPLE 5 Convert $\frac{3}{4}$ to a percent.

SOLUTION
METHOD 1

$$\frac{3}{4} = \frac{3}{4} \times 100 \ \%$$ Multiply by 100 and attach the percent symbol, %.

$$= \frac{3}{4} \times \frac{100}{1} \%$$

$$= \frac{3}{\cancel{4}} \times \frac{\cancel{4} \times 25}{1} \%$$ Cancel the common factor 4.

$$= 75\%$$

METHOD 2 It is also possible to convert the fraction to a decimal, then multiply by 100 and attach the percent symbol, %.

$$\frac{3}{4} = 0.75$$ Convert $\frac{3}{4}$ to a decimal.

$$\begin{array}{r} .75 \\ 4\overline{)3.00} \\ \underline{2\ 8} \\ 20 \\ \underline{20} \end{array}$$

$$= 0.75 \times 100 \ \%$$ Multiply by 100 and attach the percent symbol, %.

$$= 075. \ \%$$ Multiplying a decimal by 100 moves the decimal point 2 places to the right. ■

$$= 75\%$$

 Try Problems 7 and 8.

EXAMPLE 6 Convert $3\frac{1}{2}$ to a percent.

SOLUTION
METHOD 1

$$3\frac{1}{2} = 3\frac{1}{2} \times 100 \ \%$$ Multiply by 100 and attach the percent symbol, %.

$$= \frac{7}{2} \times \frac{100}{1} \%$$ Convert $3\frac{1}{2}$ to an improper fraction. $3\frac{1}{2} = \frac{7}{2}$

$$= \frac{7}{\cancel{2}} \times \frac{\cancel{2} \times 50}{1} \%$$ Cancel the common factor 2.

$$= 350\%$$

METHOD 2 Here we convert $3\frac{1}{2}$ to a decimal, then multiply by 100 and attach the percent symbol, %.

$$3\frac{1}{2} = 3.5$$ Convert $3\frac{1}{2}$ to a decimal.

$$= 3.5 \times 100 \ \%$$ Multiply by 100 and attach the percent symbol, %.

$$= 350. \ \%$$ Multiplying a decimal by 100 moves the decimal point 2 places to the right. ■

$$= 350\%$$

Try These Problems

Convert each fraction to a percent.

9. $2\frac{1}{4}$

10. $1\frac{3}{5}$

11. $\frac{7}{8}$

12. $\frac{3}{40}$

 Try Problems 9 and 10.

EXAMPLE 7 Convert $\frac{7}{40}$ to a percent.

SOLUTION
METHOD 1

$$\frac{7}{40} = \frac{7}{40} \times 100 \%$$ Multiply by 100 and attach the percent symbol, %.

$$= \frac{7}{40} \times \frac{100}{1} \%$$

$$= \frac{7}{2 \times 20} \times \frac{5 \times 20}{1} \%$$ Cancel the common factor 20.

$$= \frac{35}{2} \%$$ Convert $\frac{35}{2}$ to a mixed numeral or a decimal.

$$= 17\frac{1}{2} \%$$

$$\text{or } 17.5\%$$

METHOD 2   Here we convert $\frac{7}{40}$ to a decimal, then multiply by 100 and attach the percent symbol, %.

$$\frac{7}{40} = 0.175$$ Convert $\frac{7}{40}$ to a decimal.

$$\begin{array}{r} .175 \\ 40\overline{)7.000} \\ \underline{4\,0} \\ 3\,00 \\ \underline{2\,80} \\ 200 \\ \underline{200} \end{array}$$

$$= 0.175 \times 100 \%$$ Multiply by 100 and attach the percent symbol, %.

$$= 0\underset{\smile}{17}.5 \%$$ Multiplying a decimal by 100 moves the decimal point 2 places to the right. ■

$$= 17.5\%$$

 Try Problems 11 and 12.

EXAMPLE 8 Convert $\frac{1}{3}$ to a percent.

SOLUTION
METHOD 1

$$\frac{1}{3} = \frac{1}{3} \times 100 \%$$ Multiply by 100 and attach the percent symbol, %.

$$= \frac{1}{3} \times \frac{100}{1} \%$$

$$= \frac{100}{3} \%$$ Convert $\frac{100}{3}$ to a mixed numeral.

$$= 33\frac{1}{3} \%$$ $\dfrac{100}{3} \rightarrow 3\overline{)100} \rightarrow \dfrac{100}{3} = 33\frac{1}{3}$

$$\begin{array}{r} 33 \\ 3\overline{)100} \\ \underline{9} \\ 10 \\ \underline{9} \\ 1 \end{array}$$

METHOD 2   Here we convert $\frac{1}{3}$ to a decimal, then multiply by 100 and attach the percent symbol, %.

$$\frac{1}{3} = 0.33\frac{1}{3}$$

Convert $\frac{1}{3}$ to a decimal. Because the division does not come out evenly, divide two places past the decimal point and write the remainder in fractional form.

$$\frac{1}{3} \rightarrow 3\overline{)1.00} \rightarrow \frac{1}{3} = 0.33\frac{1}{3}$$
$$\begin{array}{r} .33\frac{1}{3} \\ \underline{9} \\ 10 \\ \underline{9} \\ 1 \end{array}$$

$$= 0.33\frac{1}{3} \times 100 \ \%$$

Multiply by 100 and attach the percent symbol, %.

$$= 033.\frac{1}{3}\%$$

Multiplying a decimal by 100 moves the decimal point 2 places to the right.

$$= 33\frac{1}{3}\% \ \blacksquare$$

EXAMPLE 9   Convert $\frac{5}{7}$ to a percent.

SOLUTION
METHOD 1

$$\frac{5}{7} = \frac{5}{7} \times 100 \ \%$$

Multiply by 100 and attach the percent symbol, %.

$$= \frac{5}{7} \times \frac{100}{1} \%$$

$$= \frac{500}{7}\%$$

Convert $\frac{500}{7}$ to a mixed numeral.

$$= 71\frac{3}{7}\%$$

$$\frac{500}{7} \rightarrow 7\overline{)500} \rightarrow \frac{500}{7} = 71\frac{3}{7}$$
$$\begin{array}{r} 71 \\ \underline{49} \\ 10 \\ \underline{7} \\ 3 \end{array}$$

METHOD 2   Here we convert $\frac{5}{7}$ to a decimal, then multiply by 100 and attach the percent symbol, %.

$$\frac{5}{7} = 0.71\frac{3}{7}$$

Convert $\frac{5}{7}$ to a decimal. Because the division does not come out evenly, divide two places past the decimal point and write the remainder in fractional form.

$$\frac{5}{7} \rightarrow 7\overline{)5.00} \rightarrow \frac{5}{7} = 0.71\frac{3}{7}$$
$$\begin{array}{r} .71\frac{3}{7} \\ \underline{4\ 9} \\ 10 \\ \underline{7} \\ 3 \end{array}$$

Try These Problems

Convert each fraction to a percent.

13. $\frac{2}{3}$

14. $\frac{5}{6}$

15. $\frac{5}{18}$

16. $\frac{7}{6}$

17. $\frac{1}{200}$

18. $\frac{7}{4000}$

$$= 0.71\frac{3}{7} \times 100 \ \%$$ Multiply by 100 and attach the percent symbol, %.

$$= 071.\frac{3}{7}\% $$ Multiplying a decimal by 100 moves the decimal point 2 places to the right.

$$= 71\frac{3}{7}\% \ \blacksquare$$

 Try Problems 13 through 16.

EXAMPLE 9   Convert $\frac{3}{800}$ to a percent.

SOLUTION
METHOD 1

$$\frac{3}{800} = \frac{3}{800} \times 100 \ \%$$ Multiply by 100 and attach the percent symbol, %.

$$= \frac{3}{800} \times \frac{100}{1}\%$$

$$= \frac{3}{8 \times \cancel{100}} \times \frac{\overset{1}{\cancel{100}}}{1}\%$$ Cancel the common factor 100.

$$= \frac{3}{8}\%$$ The number in front of the percent symbol may be written as a fraction or a decimal.

or 0.375%

$$\frac{3}{8} \rightarrow 8\overline{)3.000} \rightarrow \frac{3}{8} = 0.375$$
$$\begin{array}{r} .375 \\ \underline{2\ 4} \\ 60 \\ \underline{56} \\ 40 \\ \underline{40} \end{array}$$

METHOD 2   Here we convert $\frac{3}{800}$ to a decimal, then multiply by 100 and attach the percent symbol, %.

$$\frac{3}{800} = 0.00375$$ Convert $\frac{3}{800}$ to a decimal.

$$\frac{3}{800} \rightarrow 800\overline{)3.00000} \rightarrow \frac{3}{800} = 0.00375$$
$$\begin{array}{r} .00375 \\ \underline{2\ 400} \\ 6000 \\ \underline{5600} \\ 4000 \\ \underline{4000} \end{array}$$

$$= 0.00375 \times 100 \ \%$$ Multiply by 100 and attach the percent symbol, %.

$$= 000.375 \ \%$$ Multiplying a decimal by 100 moves the decimal point 2 places to the right.

$$= 0.375\%$$ $\blacksquare$

 Try Problems 17 and 18.

3 │ Three Ways to Write a Number

In Section 9.1 we converted percents to fractions and decimals, and in this section we converted fractions and decimals to percents. In Section 6.1 we converted decimals to fractions, and in Section 7.2 we converted fractions to decimals. Now it should be clear to you that each number can be written in three ways: fraction, decimal, and percent. You want to be good at converting a number from one form to the other. Here we summarize the procedures.

CONVERTING NUMBERS FROM ONE FORM TO ANOTHER

Percent → Fraction or Decimal
To convert a percent to a fraction or decimal, drop the percent symbol, %, and divide by 100.

Example: $5\% = 5 \div 100 = 0.05$

$$5\% = 5 \div 100 = \frac{5}{100} = \frac{\overset{1}{\cancel{5}}}{\cancel{5} \times 20} = \frac{1}{20}$$

Fraction or Decimal → Percent
To convert a fraction or decimal to a percent, multiply by 100 and attach the percent symbol, %.

Example: $0.6 = 0.6 \times 100\% = 60\%$

$$\frac{3}{5} = \frac{3}{5} \times 100\% = \frac{3}{\underset{1}{\cancel{5}}} \times \frac{\cancel{5} \times 20}{1}\% = 60\%$$

Fraction → Decimal
To convert a fraction to a decimal, divide the numerator by the denominator.

$$\text{\textit{Example}: } \frac{3}{8} \rightarrow 8\overline{)3.000} \rightarrow \frac{3}{8} = 0.375$$

$$\begin{array}{r} .375 \\ 8\overline{)3.000} \\ \underline{2\,4} \\ 60 \\ \underline{56} \\ 40 \\ \underline{40} \end{array}$$

Decimal → Fraction
To convert a *terminating* decimal to a fraction, think of the formal English name for the decimal using tenths, hundredths, thousandths, and so on, then write the fraction with the same English name.

$$\textit{Example}: 0.004 = \frac{4}{1000} \qquad \text{Four thousandths}$$

$$= \frac{\overset{1}{\cancel{4}}}{\cancel{4} \times 250}$$

$$= \frac{1}{250}$$

Converting a *repeating* decimal to a fraction requires algebra, so we do not discuss this procedure in this text.

Try These Problems

19. Convert 35% to **a.** a decimal and **b.** a fraction.
20. Convert 0.025 to **a.** a fraction and **b.** a percent.
21. Convert $\frac{7}{2}$ to **a.** a decimal and **b.** a percent.

 Try Problems 19 through 21.

 Answers to Try These Problems

1. 68%   2. 80%   3. 7.5%   4. 700%   5. 160%   6. 0.04%
7. 40%   8. 15%   9. 225%   10. 160%   11. $87\frac{1}{2}$% or 87.5%
12. $7\frac{1}{2}$% or 7.5%   13. $66\frac{2}{3}$%   14. $83\frac{1}{3}$%   15. $27\frac{7}{9}$%
16. $116\frac{2}{3}$%   17. $\frac{1}{2}$% or 0.5%   18. $\frac{7}{40}$% or 0.175%
19. a. 0.35 b. $\frac{7}{20}$ 20. a. $\frac{1}{40}$ b. 2.5% or $2\frac{1}{2}$%
21. a. 3.5 b. 350%

EXERCISES 9.3

Convert each decimal to a percent.

1. 0.45	**2.** 0.62	**3.** 0.9	**4.** 0.3	**5.** 0.053
6. 0.015	**7.** 1	**8.** 3	**9.** 2.4	**10.** 1.7
11. 1.08	**12.** 3.24	**13.** 0.005	**14.** 0.0072	**15.** 0.00038
16. 0.0009	**17.** 0.672	**18.** 1.456	**19.** 0.0746	**20.** 0.0805

Convert each fraction to a percent.

21. $\frac{1}{2}$	**22.** $\frac{3}{5}$	**23.** $\frac{7}{20}$	**24.** $\frac{3}{25}$	**25.** $1\frac{4}{5}$
26. $3\frac{1}{4}$	**27.** $\frac{13}{10}$	**28.** $\frac{69}{50}$	**29.** $\frac{3}{8}$	**30.** $\frac{11}{80}$
31. $\frac{5}{16}$	**32.** $\frac{1}{40}$	**33.** $\frac{1}{3}$	**34.** $\frac{5}{12}$	**35.** $\frac{4}{15}$
36. $\frac{7}{300}$	**37.** $\frac{5}{3}$	**38.** $\frac{11}{6}$	**39.** $3\frac{1}{6}$	**40.** $2\frac{2}{3}$
41. $\frac{3}{500}$	**42.** $\frac{7}{200}$	**43.** $\frac{3}{1600}$	**44.** $\frac{1}{800}$	

Complete the following chart. Simplify the fractions when possible.

	Fraction	Decimal	Percent
45.	$\frac{3}{100}$		
46.		0.25	
47.			80%
48.	$1\frac{1}{5}$		
49.		2.06	
50.			375%
51.	$\frac{5}{8}$		
52.		0.125	
53.			$37\frac{1}{2}$% or 37.5%
54.	$\frac{1}{200}$		
55.		0.006	
56.			$\frac{3}{4}$% or 0.75%
57.	$\frac{1}{6}$		
58.		$0.83\frac{1}{3}$	
59.			$66\frac{2}{3}$%
60.	$\frac{4}{3}$		

9.4 THE MISSING NUMBER IN A PERCENT STATEMENT

OBJECTIVES
▌ Find the missing number in a basic percent statement by using decimals.
▌ Find the missing number in a basic percent statement by using fractions.

1 Using Fractions or Decimals

The statement *60 is 50% of 120* is a percent statement. Observe that the statement translates to a multiplication statement.

$$60 \text{ is } 50\% \text{ of } 120$$
$$\downarrow \qquad \downarrow$$
$$60 = 0.5 \times 120$$

Three types of percent problems can be obtained by omitting any one of the three numbers involved in the basic percent statement. For example, from the statement *60 is 50% of 120*, three questions can arise.

1. What number is 50% of 120?

$$\boxed{} = 0.5 \times 120$$

Here we are missing the answer to a multiplication problem, so we multiply to find the missing number 60.

2. 60 is 50% of what number?

$$60 = 0.5 \times \boxed{}$$

Here we are missing a multiplier, so we divide 60 by 0.5 to find the missing multiplier 120.

3. 60 is what percent of 120?

$$60 = \boxed{\%} \times 120$$

Here we are missing a multiplier, so we divide 60 by 120 to find the missing multiplier 0.5. Finally, we convert the decimal 0.5 to the percent 50%.

When solving these problems without a calculator, you will have to decide whether to use fractions or decimals. In some cases the problems can be done either way, with one method as convenient as the other. The first examples shown here are of this type.

EXAMPLE 1   150 is 25% of what number?

SOLUTION   This problem can be solved by using either decimals or fractions. We show the problems done both ways.
USING DECIMALS

$$150 \text{ is } 25\% \text{ of what number?}$$
$$\downarrow \qquad \downarrow$$
$$150 = 0.25 \times \boxed{}$$

Translate to a multiplication statement and convert the percent to a decimal.

$$25\% = 25.\% = 25. \div 100$$
$$= 0.25$$

Try These Problems

Solve these problems in two ways **a.** *by using decimals, and* **b.** *by using fractions.* Translate first.
1. 720 is 75% of what number?
2. 40% of what number is 80?

A multiplier is missing, so divide 150 by 0.25 to find the missing multiplier.

$$
0.2\,5\overline{)1\,5\,0.0\,0} \quad \underset{\underline{1\,5\,0}}{6\;0\;0.} = 600
$$

The answer to the multiplication statement goes inside the division symbol.

USING FRACTIONS

150 is 25% of what number?

$$150 = \frac{1}{4} \times \boxed{}$$

Translate to a multiplication statement and convert the percent to a fraction.

$$25\% = \frac{25}{100}$$

$$= \frac{\overset{1}{\cancel{25}}}{\cancel{25} \times 4} = \frac{1}{4}$$

A multiplier is missing, so divide 150 by $\frac{1}{4}$ to find the missing multiplier.

$$150 \div \frac{1}{4}$$

The answer to the multiplication statement is written first.

$$= \frac{150}{1} \times \frac{4}{1}$$

Dividing by $\frac{1}{4}$ is the same as multiplying by 4.

$$= 600$$

The answer is 600.

Try Problems 1 and 2.

EXAMPLE 2   4% of 200 is what number?

SOLUTION   This problem can be solved by using either decimals or fractions. We show the problems done both ways.

USING DECIMALS

4% of 200 is what number?

$$0.04 \times 200 = \boxed{}$$

Translate to a multiplication statement and convert the percent to a decimal.

$$4\% = 4.\% = 4. \div 100$$
$$= 0.04$$

We are missing the answer to the multiplication statement, so multiply 0.04 by 200 to find the missing number.

$$
\begin{array}{r}
2\,00 \\
\times\ 0.04 \\
\hline
8.00 = 8
\end{array}
$$

Try These Problems

Solve these problems in two ways
a. *by using* decimals, *and* **b.** *by using* fractions. **Translate first.**
3. 250% of 16 is what number?
4. What number is 8% of 650?

USING FRACTIONS

4% of 200 is what number?

$$\frac{4}{100} \times 200 = \boxed{}$$

Translate to a multiplication statement and convert the percent to a fraction.

$$4\% = 4 \div 100 = \frac{4}{100}$$

We are missing the answer to a multiplication statement, so multiply $\frac{4}{100}$ by 200 to find the missing number.

$$\frac{4}{100} \times 200$$

$$= \frac{4}{\cancel{100}_{1}} \times \frac{\cancel{200}^{2}}{1}$$

$$= 8$$

This answer is 8. ■

 Try Problems 3 and 4.

EXAMPLE 3   520 is what percent of 650?

SOLUTION   This problem can be solved by using either decimals or fractions. We show the problems done both ways.

USING DECIMALS

520 is what percent of 650?

$$520 = \boxed{\%} \times 650$$

Translate to a multiplication statement.

A multiplier is missing, so divide 520 by 650 to find the missing multiplier.

$$650\overline{)520.0}^{.8}$$
$$\underline{520}$$

The answer to the multiplication statement goes inside the division symbol.

The missing multiplier is the decimal 0.8, but the question is *what percent,* so convert 0.8 to a percent.

$$0.8 = 0.8 \times 100\% = 80.\% = 80\%$$

USING FRACTIONS

520 is what percent of 650?

$$520 = \boxed{\%} \times 650$$

Translate to a multiplication statement.

A multiplier is missing, so divide 520 by 650 to find the missing multiplier.

$$520 \div 650 = \frac{520}{650}$$

The answer to the multiplication statement is written first.

$$= \frac{\cancel{10} \times 52}{\cancel{10} \times 65}$$

$$= \frac{52}{65}$$

$$= \frac{4 \times \cancel{13}}{5 \times \cancel{13}}$$

Reduce the fraction to lowest terms.

$$= \frac{4}{5}$$

The missing multiplier is the fraction $\frac{4}{5}$, but the question is *what percent,* so convert the fraction to a percent.

$$\frac{4}{5} = \frac{4}{5} \times 100\% = \frac{4}{\underset{1}{\cancel{5}}} \times \frac{\overset{20}{\cancel{100}}}{1}\% = 80\%$$

The answer is 80%.

▲ **Try Problems 5 and 6.**

2   Choosing Decimals over Fractions to Solve Problems

The problems we have solved so far were easy to solve by using either fractions or decimals. Sometimes one of the methods is a lot easier to use than the other. You want to learn to choose the more convenient method. Next we look at examples where it is more convenient to use decimals.

EXAMPLE 4   170% of what number is 81.6?

SOLUTION   We choose *decimals* to solve this problem because the number 81.6 is already in decimal form, and the percent 170% is easy to convert to a decimal.

170%	of	what number	is	81.6?
		↓		↓
1.7	×	☐	=	81.6

Translate to a multiplication statement and convert the percent to a decimal.
  170%
= 170. ÷ 100
= 1.70 = 1.7

➤ Try These Problems

Use decimals *to solve these problems.* **Translate first.**

7. What number is 8.9% of 46,000?

8. 33 is 0.6% of what number?

9. 34.2% of what number is 513?

10. 125% of 10.2 is what number?

A multiplier is missing, so divide 81.6 by 1.7 to find the missing multiplier.

$$
\begin{array}{r}
4\ 8.\ =48 \\
1.7\overline{)8\ 1.6} \\
6\ 8 \\
\hline
1\ 3\ 6 \\
1\ 3\ 6 \\
\end{array}
$$

The answer to the multiplication statement goes inside the division symbol.

The answer is 48. ■

EXAMPLE 5 What number is 0.8% of 4.5?

SOLUTION We choose *decimals* to solve this problem because 0.8% is easy to convert to a decimal, and the number 4.5 is already written in decimal form.

What number is 0.8% of 4.5?
              ↓   ↓
$$
[\quad] = 0.008 \times 4.5
$$

Translate to a multiplication statement and convert the percent to a decimal.
0.8%
= 0.8 ÷ 100
= 0.008

The answer to the multiplication problem is missing, so multiply 0.008 by 4.5 to find the missing number.

$$
\begin{array}{r}
4.5 \\
\times\ 0.00\ 8 \\
\hline
.0\ 36\ 0 = 0.036 \\
\end{array}
$$

The answer is 0.036. ■

➤ Try Problems 7 through 10.

EXAMPLE 6 42.9 is what percent of 520?

SOLUTION We choose *decimals* to solve this problem because 42.9 is already in decimal form, and 520 can easily be converted to a decimal.

42.9 is what percent of 520?
      ↓   ↓
$$
42.9 = [\quad]\% \times 520
$$

Translate to a multiplication statement.

A multiplier is missing, so divide 42.9 by 520 to find the missing multiplier.

$$
\begin{array}{r}
.0825 \\
520\overline{)42.9000} \\
4160 \\
\hline
1300 \\
1040 \\
\hline
2600 \\
2600 \\
\end{array}
$$

The answer to the multiplication problem goes inside the division symbol.

Try These Problems

Use decimals to solve these problems. **Translate first.**

11. What percent of 200 is 3.2?

12. 45.3 is what percent of 75?

The missing multiplier is the decimal 0.0825. The question is *what percent*, so we must convert the decimal to percent form.

$$0.0825 = 0.0825 \times 100\%$$
$$= 008.25\%$$
$$= 8.25\%$$

The answer is 8.25%. ■

 Try Problems 11 and 12.

3 Choosing Fractions over Decimals to Solve Problems

Whenever the number you are trying to work with is a repeating decimal, you must choose fractions to solve the probem. Also, if the numbers are already in fractional form, you may want to choose fractions to do the problem. Here we show some examples.

EXAMPLE 7   Find $3\frac{1}{2}\%$ of $8\frac{1}{3}$.

SOLUTION   We must use *fractions* to solve this problem because $8\frac{1}{3}$ is the repeating decimal $8.\overline{3}$.

$$\text{Find} \qquad 3\frac{1}{2}\% \quad \text{of} \quad 8\frac{1}{3}.$$

$$\text{What} \quad \text{is} \quad 3\frac{1}{2}\% \quad \text{of} \quad 8\frac{1}{3}?$$

$$\downarrow \qquad\qquad \downarrow$$

$$\boxed{} \quad = \quad \frac{7}{200} \quad \times \quad 8\frac{1}{3}$$

Translate to a multiplication statement, and convert $3\frac{1}{2}\%$ to a fraction.

$$3\frac{1}{2}\% = 3\frac{1}{2} \div 100$$
$$= \frac{7}{2} \div \frac{100}{1}$$
$$= \frac{7}{2} \times \frac{1}{100} = \frac{7}{200}$$

The answer to the multiplication statement is missing, so multiply $\frac{7}{200}$ by $8\frac{1}{3}$ to find the missing number.

$$\frac{7}{200} \times 8\frac{1}{3}$$
$$= \frac{7}{200} \times \frac{25}{3}$$
$$= \frac{7}{25 \times 8} \times \frac{\overset{1}{\cancel{25}}}{3}$$
$$= \frac{7}{24}$$

The answer is $\frac{7}{24}$. ■

EXAMPLE 8 $66\frac{2}{3}\%$ of what number is 7?

SOLUTION   We must use *fractions* to solve this problem because $66\frac{2}{3}\%$ converts to the repeating decimal $0.\overline{6}$.

$$66\frac{2}{3}\% \text{ of what number is 7?}$$

$$\downarrow \qquad\qquad\qquad \downarrow$$

$$\frac{2}{3} \quad \times \quad \boxed{} \quad = 7$$

Translate to a multiplication statement, and convert $66\frac{2}{3}\%$ to a fraction.

$$66\frac{2}{3}\% = 66\frac{2}{3} \div 100$$

$$= \frac{\overset{2}{\cancel{200}}}{3} \times \frac{1}{\underset{1}{\cancel{100}}}$$

$$= \frac{2}{3}$$

A multiplier is missing, so divide 7 by $\frac{2}{3}$ to find the missing multiplier.

$$7 \div \frac{2}{3}$$

The answer to the multiplication problem is written first.

$$= \frac{7}{1} \div \frac{2}{3}$$

$$= \frac{7}{1} \times \frac{3}{2}$$

Dividing by $\frac{2}{3}$ is equivalent to multiplying by $\frac{3}{2}$.

$$= \frac{21}{2}$$

$$= 10\frac{1}{2} \text{ or } 10.5$$

The answer is $10\frac{1}{2}$ or 10.5. ■

EXAMPLE 9 $83\frac{1}{3}$ is what percent of 250?

SOLUTION   We must use *fractions* to solve this problem because $83\frac{1}{3}$ converts to the repeating decimal $83.\overline{3}$.

$$83\frac{1}{3} = \text{what percent of 250?}$$

$$\downarrow \qquad\qquad\qquad \downarrow$$

$$83\frac{1}{3} = \quad \boxed{\quad\% \quad} \quad \times 250$$

Translate to a multiplication statement.

A multiplier is missing, so divide $83\frac{1}{3}$ by 250 to find the missing multiplier.

Use fractions *to solve these problems.* Translate first.

13. Find $33\frac{1}{3}$ % of 120.

14. $\frac{5}{6}$ is what percent of $3\frac{1}{3}$?

15. $16\frac{2}{3}$ % of what number is 400?

16. $10\frac{1}{6}$ is 200% of what number?

17. What percent of 350 is $23\frac{1}{3}$?

18. $\frac{2}{3}$ % of 400 is what number?

$$83\frac{1}{3} \div 250$$

The answer to the multiplication problem is written first.

$$= \frac{\overset{1}{250}}{3} \times \frac{1}{\underset{1}{250}}$$

$$= \frac{1}{3}$$

The missing multiplier is the fraction $\frac{1}{3}$. The question is *what percent,* so we must convert $\frac{1}{3}$ to percent form.

$$\frac{1}{3} = \frac{1}{3} \times 100\% = \frac{100}{3}\% = 33\frac{1}{3}\%$$

The answer is $33\frac{1}{3}$ %. ▪

EXAMPLE 10   What percent of 50 is $\frac{1}{8}$?

SOLUTION   We choose *fractions* to solve this problem because the number $\frac{1}{8}$ is already written in fractional form.

$$\text{What percent of } 50 \text{ is } \frac{1}{8}?$$

$$\downarrow \qquad \downarrow$$

$$\boxed{}\% \quad \times 50 = \frac{1}{8}$$ Translate to a multiplication statement.

A multiplier is missing, so divide $\frac{1}{8}$ by 50 to find the missing multiplier.

$$\frac{1}{8} \div 50$$

The answer to the multiplication problem is written first.

$$= \frac{1}{8} \times \frac{1}{50}$$

$$= \frac{1}{400}$$

The missing multiplier is the fraction $\frac{1}{400}$. The question is *what percent,* so we must convert $\frac{1}{400}$ to a percent.

$$\frac{1}{400} = \frac{1}{400} \times 100\%$$

$$= \frac{1}{\underset{4}{400}} \times \frac{\overset{1}{100}}{1}\%$$

$$= \frac{1}{4}\% \text{ or } 0.25\%$$

The answer is $\frac{1}{4}$ % or 0.25%. ▪

▲ Try Problems 13 through 18.

Now we summarize the material presented in this section by giving a procedure for finding the missing number in a percent statement.

Finding the Missing Number in a Percent Statement

1. If you are given the percent, convert it to a decimal or a fraction. Use fractions if repeating decimals are involved.
2. Translate the percent statement to a multiplication statement.
3. If you are missing the answer to the multiplication problem, multiply.
4. If you are missing one of the multipliers, divide. Be careful to divide in the correct order. Here is how it is done:

$$\text{known multiplier} \overline{\smash{\big)}\ \text{answer to the multiplication problem}}$$

$$\text{or} \quad \text{answer to the multiplication problem} \div \text{known multiplier}$$

5. If the question asks *what percent*, convert the missing multiplier to percent form.

▲ Answers to Try These Problems

1. 960   2. 200   3. 40   4. 52   5. 6%   6. 125%
7. 4094   8. 5500   9. 1500   10. 12.75   11. 1.6%
12. 60.4%   13. 40   14. 25%   15. 2400   16. $\frac{61}{12}$ or $5\frac{1}{12}$
17. $6\frac{2}{3}$%   18. $\frac{8}{3}$ or $2\frac{2}{3}$

EXERCISES 9.4

Solve these problems in two ways, by using decimals and by using fractions. Translate first.

1. What number is 40% of 300?   **2.** 25% of 64 is what number?

3. 15 is what percent of 75?   **4.** What percent of 50 is 3?

5. 5% of what number is 8300?   **6.** 18 is 150% of what number?

7. What percent of 5000 is 5?   **8.** 2 is $\frac{1}{4}$% of what number?

Use decimals to solve these problems. Translate to an equation first.

9. 228 is 240% of what number?   **10.** 3.2% of what number is 40?

11. What percent of 650 is 5.2?   **12.** 3600 is what percent of 2400?

13. 6.5% of 82.90 is what number?   **14.** What number is 0.3% of 97.8?

15. 0.5% of what number is 2.04?   **16.** 27.3 is what percent of 32.5?

Use fractions to solve these problems. Translate to an equation first.

17. Find $16\frac{2}{3}$% of 126.   **18.** Find $33\frac{1}{3}$% of 1920.

19. $\frac{1}{3}$% of what number is 12?   **20.** $4\frac{1}{4}$ is 25% of what number?

21. $12\frac{2}{7}$ is what percent of $12\frac{2}{7}$?   **22.** $4\frac{5}{6}$ is what percent of $9\frac{2}{3}$?

23. What percent of 45 is 30?   **24.** What percent of 400 is $1\frac{1}{3}$?

25. $3\frac{1}{9}$% of $17\frac{1}{7}$ is what number?   **26.** 10 is 120% of what number?

You decide whether to use decimals or fractions to solve these problems. Translate first.

27. $12\frac{1}{2}\%$ of 1244 is what number?   **28.** 105 is what percent of 30?

29. 0.2% of what number is 18?   **30.** What number is $66\frac{2}{3}\%$ of 630?

31. 5 is what percent of 15?   **32.** 100% of 45.96 is what number?

33. $17\frac{1}{3}$ is 80% of what number?   **34.** 0.21 is what percent of 1050?

9.5	SOLVING PERCENT APPLICATIONS BY TRANSLATING

OBJECTIVES   ▌ Solve percent applications that contain the basic percent statement.

▌ Solve percent applications that contain the basic percent statement in an unclear form.

There are many situations in your everyday life where percents are used. At this time we introduce you to some of these situations, illustrating how you can use your knowledge of percents to solve problems related to these real-life situations. First we look at problems that contain the basic percent statement.

1 Problems Containing the Basic Percent Statement

If the problem contains a basic percent statement, you must recognize which sentence in the problem is the basic percent statement, then translate it to a multiplication statement. From this point you should know how to complete the problem by using what you have learned in the previous sections. Here we show some examples.

EXAMPLE 1   Two hundred fifty persons attended a convention. There were 100 women. What percent of those attending were women?

SOLUTION   First, notice that the last sentence in this problem translates to a multiplication statement. The word *of* in this sentence translates to $\times$ and the word *were* translates to $=$.

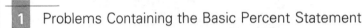

What percent of those attending were women?

$$\boxed{\%} \quad \times \quad 250 \quad = \quad 100$$

After filling in the given information that 250 persons attended and 100 were women, we see that a multiplier is missing, so we divide 100 by 250 to find the missing multiplier.

$$\begin{array}{r} .4 = 0.4 \\ 250\overline{)100.0} \\ \underline{100\ 0} \end{array}$$

The answer to the multiplication statement goes inside the division symbol.

The missing multiplier is 0.4, but because the question is *what percent*, we convert the decimal to percent form.

$$0.4 = 0.4 \times 100\% = 040.\% = 40\%$$

40% of those attending were women.   ▉

▲ Try These Problems

Solve. **Translate first,**

1. Sales tax in a certain city is 6.5% of the marked price. How much sales tax will Barbara pay when buying a dress marked $54?

2. A salesperson makes a $2100 bonus. The bonus is 14% of the base salary. What is the base salary?

3. A math teacher gave a test to 40 students. Five students received an A grade on the test. What percent of the class received an A grade?

4. The market value of a house in San Francisco is $400,000, while the replacement value is only $160,000. The market value is what percent of the replacement value?

5. Only 5% of the American troops serving in the Persian Gulf were women. If there were 26,500 women, how many American troops were there?

EXAMPLE 2   Ten years ago, Sally was a sales clerk in a major department store earning $15,000 per year. After completing her college degree and working for a few years, she now is a marketing manager for a major publisher. Her present annual salary is 420% of her salary ten years ago. What is her present annual salary?

SOLUTION   The next to the last sentence in this problem is a basic percent statement, thus translates to a multiplication statement. The word *of* in this sentence translates to $\times$ and the word *is* translates to =.

Her present annual salary ($)	is	420%	of	her salary ten years ago ($)
	↓			↓
☐	=	420%	×	15,000
☐	=	4.2	×	15,000

Convert 420% to a decimal.
420% = 420. ÷ 100 = 4.2

The problem states that her salary 10 years ago was $15,000. After filling in this information, we see that her present salary can be obtained by finding the answer to the multiplication problem. After converting 420% to the decimal 4.2, we multiply 4.2 by 15,000 to obtain her present annual salary.

$$15,000 \times 4.2 = 63,000$$

Her present annual salary is $63,000. ▪

EXAMPLE 3   A football team won 9 games, which were 60% of the total number of games played. How many games did the team play?

SOLUTION   The first sentence is a basic percent statement, thus translates to a multiplication statement. The word *of* in the phrase *60% of the total* translates to $\times$, and the word *were* translates to =.

The 9 games won	were	60%	of	the total games played
	↓			↓
9	=	60%	×	☐
9	=	0.6	×	☐

Convert 60% to a decimal.
60% = 60 ÷ 100
= .60 = 0.6

A multiplier is missing, so divide 9 by 0.6 to find the missing multiplier. This missing multiplier is the total number of games played.

$$\begin{array}{r} 1\,5. = 15 \\ 0.6\overline{)9.0} \\ 6 \\ \hline 3\,0 \\ 3\,0 \end{array}$$

The answer to the multiplication statement goes inside the division symbol.

The team played a total of 15 games. ▪

▲ Try Problems 1 through 5.

▲ **Try These Problems**

Solve. **Translate first.**

6. The population of a small town decreased from 750 to 732. What percent of the original population was the decrease?

7. Mr. Ortez's hourly wage increased from $15 per hour to $20 per hour. The increase is what percent of the original?

EXAMPLE 4 The enrollment of a college in Pennsylvania increased from 25,000 to 28,000 students. The increase in enrollment is what percent of the original enrollment?

SOLUTION The last sentence is a basic percent statement, thus translates to a multiplication statement. The word *of* in the phrase *what percent of the original* translates to ×, and the word *is* translates to =.

$$
\begin{array}{ccccc}
\text{The} & \text{is} & \text{what} & \text{of} & \text{the original} \\
\text{increase} & \downarrow & \text{percent} & \downarrow & \text{enrollment} \\
\end{array}
$$

$$
\begin{array}{ccccc}
\text{The} \\
\text{increase} & = & \boxed{\quad\%} & \times & 25{,}000
\end{array}
$$

The increase in enrollment is not given in the problem, but we can find it by subtracting 25,000 from 28,000.

$$
\begin{array}{ccccc}
\text{Increase} & = & \text{larger} & - & \text{smaller} \\
\text{in enrollment} & & \text{enrollment} & & \text{enrollment}
\end{array}
$$

$$
\text{Increase} = 28{,}000 - 25{,}000
$$

$$
\text{Increase} = 3000
$$

The increase in enrollment is 3000 students. Now we have the following.

$$
\begin{array}{ccccc}
\text{The} & \text{is} & \text{what} & \text{of} & \text{the original} \\
\text{increase} & \downarrow & \text{percent} & \downarrow & \text{enrollment} \\
\end{array}
$$

$$
3000 = \boxed{\quad\%} \times 25{,}000
$$

A multiplier is missing, so divide 3000 by 25,000 to find the missing multiplier.

$$
3000 \div 25{,}000 = \frac{3000}{25{,}000}
$$

$$
= \frac{3 \times 1000}{25 \times 1000}
$$

$$
= \frac{3}{25}
$$

The answer to the multiplication problem is written first.

The missing multiplier is the fraction $\frac{3}{25}$, but the question is *what percent,* so we convert the fraction to a percent.

$$
\frac{3}{25} = \frac{3}{25} \times 100\%
$$

$$
= \frac{3}{25} \times \frac{\overset{4}{100}}{1}\% \\
{\scriptstyle 1}
$$

$$
= 12\%
$$

The increase is 12% of the original enrollment. ■

▲ **Try Problems 6 and 7.**

2 Problems Containing Unclear Language

Suppose a truck contains 200 pieces of fruit, including 40 apples, 100 peaches, and 60 nectarines. It is easy to verify that 20% of the total are apples, 50% of the total are peaches, and 30% of the total are nectarines. In a situation like this, it is assumed that the parts are some percent *of the total,* so we often use language that is not as precise as the basic percent statement you are familiar with. Here are some examples of what might be said and what it really means.

Unclear Language	*Precise Translation*
20% are apples.	20% of the total are apples.
What percent are nectarines?	What percent of the total are nectarines?
The load is 50% peaches.	50% of the load is peaches.
The solution is 6% acid.	6% of the total solution is acid.

Observe that the unclear statements on the left do not contain the word *of* that translates to multiplication, so you must rephrase the statement into the precise form before translating it to a multiplication statement. It is important to remember that when language is used in this way, *the part is some percent of the total.*

EXAMPLE 5   Robyn took the percent test. She got 18 out of 20 questions correct. What percent did she get correct?

SOLUTION   The question *what percent did she get correct* is really asking what percent *of the total* is the number she got correct? Now we translate this basic percent statement to a multiplication statement.

$$
\begin{array}{ccccc}
\text{What} & \text{of} & \text{the} & \text{is} & \text{the number} \\
\text{percent} & & \text{total} & & \text{she got correct?} \\
\downarrow & & & & \downarrow \\
\boxed{\%} & \times & 20 & = & 18
\end{array}
$$

A multiplier is missing, so divide 18 by 20 to find the missing multiplier.

$$18 \div 20 = \frac{18}{20}$$
The answer to the multiplication probem is written first.

$$= \frac{18}{20} \times 100\%$$
Convert the fraction to a percent.

$$= \frac{18}{\underset{1}{\cancel{20}}} \times \frac{\overset{5}{\cancel{100}}}{1}\%$$

$$= 90\%$$

Robyn got 90% correct.   ■

EXAMPLE 6   A parking lot contains $66\frac{2}{3}\%$ cars and the rest are trucks. If there are 480 cars, what is the total number of automobiles?

SOLUTION   The unclear phrase *a parking lot contains $66\frac{2}{3}\%$ cars* means that $66\frac{2}{3}\%$ *of the total* are cars. We have the following:

$$66\frac{2}{3}\% \quad \text{of} \quad \begin{array}{c}\text{the}\\\text{total}\end{array} \quad \text{are} \quad \text{cars}$$

$$\qquad\qquad\qquad \downarrow \qquad\qquad \downarrow$$

$$\frac{2}{3} \quad \times \quad \boxed{} \quad = \quad 480$$

Convert the percent to a fraction.

$$66\frac{2}{3}\% = \frac{200}{3} \div \frac{100}{1}$$

$$= \frac{\overset{2}{\cancel{200}}}{3} \times \frac{1}{\underset{1}{\cancel{100}}}$$

$$= \frac{2}{3}$$

A multiplier is missing so divide 480 by $\frac{2}{3}$ to find the missing multiplier.

$$480 \div \frac{2}{3} = \frac{\overset{240}{\cancel{480}}}{1} \times \frac{3}{\underset{1}{\cancel{2}}}$$

The answer to the multiplication problem is written first.

$$= 720$$

There are 720 automobiles. ■

EXAMPLE 7   A punch was made by mixing orange juice and champagne. The punch is 70% orange juice and 30% champagne. If the total amount of punch is 140 ounces, how many ounces of champagne are in the punch?

SOLUTION   The phrase *the punch is 30% champagne* means that 30% *of the total* is champagne. We have the following:

$$30\% \quad \text{of the total} \quad \text{is} \quad \text{champagne.}$$

$$\downarrow \quad\;\; \text{(oz)} \qquad \downarrow \qquad \text{(oz)}$$

$$0.3 \quad \times \quad 140 \quad = \quad \boxed{}$$

Convert 30% to a decimal.
$$30\% = 30 \div 100 = 0.3$$

The answer to the multiplication problem is missing, so multiply 0.3 by 140 to find the missing number.

$$0.3 \times 140 = 42$$

There are 42 ounces of champagne in the punch. ■

Try These Problems

8. A town in New Jersey has a population of 63,000. After a week of cold damp weather, 210 people in the town caught a virus. What percent caught the virus?

9. A box contains a total of 40 balls, including 20% red balls, 50% black balls, and 30% blue balls. How many blue balls are there?

10. As an inspector, you reject 7 out of 2000 products tested. What percent did you reject?

11. Chitat prepares a solution by mixing acid and water. The total volume of the solution is 390 milliliters. If the solution is $6\frac{2}{3}$% acid, what is the volume of acid in the solution?

12. A bottle of wine is 12% alcohol. If the alcohol volume is 90 milliliters, what is the volume of all the wine in the bottle?

EXAMPLE 8   A pharmacist mixes an alcohol solution that is 15% alcohol. If the solution contains 60 milliliters of alcohol, what is the total volume of the solution?

SOLUTION   The phrase *alcohol solution that is 15% alcohol* means that 15% *of all the solution* is alcohol. We have the following:

$$0.15 \quad \times \quad \boxed{} \quad = \quad 60$$

Convert 15% to a decimal.
15% = 15 ÷ 100 = 0.15

A multiplier is missing, so divide 60 by 0.15 to find the missing multiplier.

$$\begin{array}{r} 4\ 0\ 0. = 400 \\ 0.1\ 5)\overline{6\ 0.0\ 0} \\ \underline{6\ 0} \end{array}$$

The total volume of the alcohol solution is 400 milliliters.   ■

Try Problems 8 through 12.

Answers to Try These Problems

1. $3.51   2. $15,000   3. 12.5% or $12\frac{1}{2}$%   4. 250%
5. 530,000 troops   6. 2.4% or $2\frac{2}{5}$%   7. $33\frac{1}{3}$%   8. $\frac{1}{3}$%
9. 12 blue balls   10. 0.35% or $\frac{7}{20}$%   11. 26 mℓ
12. 750 mℓ

EXERCISES 9.5

Solve. Show set up steps.

1. In a chemistry class, 9 students received grades of D or F. This represents 20% of the class. How many students are in the class?

2. Karl's regular salary is $12 per hour. His overtime pay is 150% of his regular pay. How much does Karl earn each hour when working overtime?

3. As an inspector in a factory, you reject 3 products in a sample of 1500 products. The number you rejected is what percent of the total sample?

4. The price of a portable radio decreased from $250 to $135. The lower price is what percent of the original price?

5. Sales tax in a town in Kentucky is 5.4% of the marked price. How much sales tax will George pay on a bedroom set marked $2800?

6. A basketball team won $66\frac{2}{3}$% of the total games played. If they played 126 games, how many games did they win?

7. Tom earns $32,000 per year as an auto mechanic and his girlfriend Gloria earns $48,000 per year as a teacher. Gloria's salary is what percent of Tom's salary?

8. A bowl of punch contains 6.6 ounces of pure alcohol, which is 2.4% of the total volume of the punch. What is the total volume?

9. The number of homeless people in a certain city increased from 2400 to 3600 in one year. The increase is what percent of the original number of homeless people?

10. The price of coffee decreased from $6.25 per pound to $4.25 per pound. What percent of the original price is the decrease in price?

11. A shipment of grapefruit consists of 100 crates of pink seedless grapefruit and 150 crates of white seedless grapefruit. What percent of the total are the white seedless grapefruit?

12. Joel sells men's colognes in a large department store. In addition to his regular monthly salary of $1500, he earns a commission that is $\frac{8}{10}$% of his total sales. If his total sales were $24,000 for the month of April, what were his total earnings for that month?

13. A can of concentrated soup contains 15% water. If the can contains 3 ounces of water, what is the total weight of the soup?

14. A bottle of gin contains 40% alcohol. What is the volume of alcohol in a 1000-milliliter bottle of gin?

15. A parking lot contains 720 automobiles. The lot includes 40% Hondas, 35% Toyotas, and 25% Buicks. How many Toyotas are there?

16. From 375 prospective jurors, only 15 were selected to serve on the jury. What percent were selected?

17. A biology class consists of 18 men and 12 women. What percent are women?

18. Manuel prepares a solution by mixing acid and water. If the solution is $7\frac{1}{3}$% acid and the volume of acid is 22 milliliters, what is the total volume of the solution?

19. You make a punch by mixing 16 ounces of orange juice, 14 ounces of lemon-lime soda, and 10 ounces of ginger ale. What percent is ginger ale?

20. A shipment of 700 crates of lettuce contains 15% romaine lettuce, 60% iceberg lettuce, and 25% butter lettuce. How many crates of romaine lettuce are there?

A statistician surveyed 1500 persons. She asked them to give their favorite color. She organized the results by making the circle graph shown here. Use the graph to answer Exercises 21 and 22.

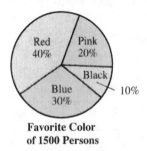

**Favorite Color
of 1500 Persons**

21. How many persons chose red?

22. How many persons chose black?

OBJECTIVES

▌ Solve a percent application that involves sales tax.

▌ Solve a percent application that involves commission.

▌ Solve a percent application that involves simple interest earned.

▌ Solve a percent application that involves monthly interest paid on a charge card or account.

▌ Solve a percent application that involves restaurant tips.

In this section we look carefully at some particular situations where percents are used.

1   Problems Involving Sales Tax

Suppose you purchase a TV that is marked $350. You really pay more than $350 for this TV, because you are charged a sales tax in addition to the marked price. The **sales tax** is computed by taking a certain percent of the marked price. This percent varies depending on where you purchase the TV. Suppose you are in a city that computes the sales tax by taking 6% of the marked price.

$$\text{Sales tax} = 6\% \text{ of } \text{the marked price}$$
$$\text{(\$)} \qquad \downarrow \qquad \text{(\$)}$$
$$= 0.06 \times \qquad 350$$
$$= 21$$

The tax charged for this TV is $21. The percent, 6%, is called the **sales tax rate.** Observe that the rate is multiplied by the marked price to obtain the tax. If you want to know the total cost of this TV, you must now add the $21 tax to the $350 marked price.

$$\text{Total cost} = \text{marked price} + \text{tax}$$
$$\text{(\$)} \qquad \text{(\$)} \qquad \text{(\$)}$$
$$= \qquad 350 \quad + 21$$
$$= \qquad 371$$

The total cost of the TV is $371.

The sales tax rate is always multiplied by the marked price to obtain the tax, and the tax is alway added to the marked price to obtain the total cost. You want to be familiar with these relationships since we encounter sales tax in our daily lives. Here we summarize the facts.

> *Rules Involving Sales Tax*
>
> Sales tax = sales tax rate (%) × marked price
>
> Total cost = marked price + sales tax

Now we look at some examples where we use these rules.

Try These Problems

Solve. **Show Set ups.**

1. The sales tax rate for a certain town in Texas is 5.8%. How much sales tax is paid on a $490 purchase?

2. The marked price of a car is $12,500. The sales tax amounts to $775. What is the sales tax rate? (Express the answer as a percent.)

3. Mr. Signorile buys a new pair of skis with bindings. If the sales tax is $37.80 and the tax rate is 7.5%, find the marked price of the skis.

4. Toni purchases some construction materials that are marked $6800. If the sales tax rate is 8.4%, what is the total cost of the materials?

5. Andrea buys 4 turtlenecks marked $12.50 each and 3 pairs of socks marked $2.80 each. If the sales tax rate is 7%, what is the total amount she pays? (Round off to the nearest cent.)

EXAMPLE 1   The marked price of a refrigerator was $760. A sales tax of $41.80 was added. What is the sales tax rate? Express the answer as a percent.

SOLUTION   We have the following.

$$\begin{array}{ccccc} \text{Sales} & = & \text{sales tax} & \times & \text{marked} \\ \text{tax} & & \text{rate} & & \text{price} \\ 41.80 & = & \boxed{\quad \%} & \times & 760 \end{array}$$

A multiplier is missing, so divide 41.80 by 760 to find the missing multiplier.

$$\begin{array}{r} .055 = 5.5\% \\ 760\overline{)41.800} \\ \underline{38\ 00} \\ 3\ 800 \\ \underline{3\ 800} \end{array}$$

Convert the decimal to percent.

The sales tax rate is 5.5%. ■

 Try Problems 1 through 3.

EXAMPLE 2   Mr. Washington buys 3 pairs of shoes marked $140 each. If the sales tax rate is 7.2%, what is the total amount he pays?

SOLUTION   First we find the total cost before the tax is added.

$$\begin{array}{cc} \text{Total cost} \\ \text{before tax} & = 3 \times 140 \\ (\$) \\ & = 420 \end{array}$$

The marked price of the 3 pairs of shoes is $420. Next we compute the sales tax.

$$\begin{array}{ccccc} \text{Sales} & = & \text{sales tax} & \times & \text{marked} \\ \text{tax} & & \text{rate} & & \text{price} \\ (\$) & & & & (\$) \\ \boxed{\quad} & = & 7.2\% & \times & 420 \\ \boxed{\quad} & = & 0.072 & \times & 420 \end{array}$$

Convert the percent to a decimal

The answer to the multiplication problem is missing so multiply 0.072 by 420.

$$0.072 \times 420 = 30.24$$

The sales tax is $30.24. The question was to find the *total* amount he pays, so finally we add the tax to the marked price.

$$\begin{array}{ccccc} \text{Total cost} & = & \text{marked} & + & \text{sales} \\ \text{after tax} & & \text{price} & & \text{tax} \\ & = & 420 & + & 30.24 \\ & = & 450.24 \end{array}$$

He pays a total of $450.24 for the 3 pairs of shoes. ■

 Try Problems 4 and 5.

2 Problems Involving Commission

Suppose you sell electronic goods for a large retail outlet. You earn $1500 per month, plus 1.2% of your total sales. Also assume that in July you sold $250,000 worth of merchandise. The $1500 is called your **base salary.** The additional amount earned that depends on your total sales is called the **commission.** The commission is computed by taking 1.2% of your total sales.

$$\begin{aligned} \text{Commission (\$)} &= 1.2\% \quad \text{of} \quad \text{the total sales (\$)} \\ &= 0.012 \times 250{,}000 \\ &= 3000 \end{aligned}$$

The commission earned for the month of July is $3000. The percent 1.2% is called the **commission rate.** The commission rate varies widely depending on the particular situation. If you want to know the total salary for the month of July, you must add the commission to the base salary.

$$\begin{aligned} \text{Total salary (\$)} &= \text{base salary (\$)} + \text{commission (\$)} \\ &= 1500 + 3000 \\ &= 4500 \end{aligned}$$

You earned $4500 in July.

Often the commission is based on the total sales. When this is the case we have the following rules.

Rules Involving Commission Based on Total Sales

Commission = commission rate (%) × total sales

Total salary = base salary + commission

Now we look at some examples where we use these rules.

EXAMPLE 3   Mr. Nguyen is paid a commission for selling rugs at the Emporium that is $7\frac{1}{2}\%$ of his total sales. Last week he received a commission of $156. What were his total sales for the week?

SOLUTION   We have the following:

$$\begin{aligned} \text{Commission (\$)} &= 7\frac{1}{2}\% \times \text{total sales (\$)} \\ 156 &= 0.075 \times \boxed{} \quad \text{Convert the percent to a decimal.} \end{aligned}$$

A multiplier is missing, so divide 156 by 0.075 to find the missing multiplier.

$$\begin{array}{r} 2080. = 2080 \\ 0.075{\overline{)156.000}} \\ 150 \\ \hline 600 \\ 600 \\ \hline \end{array}$$

He sold $2080 worth of rugs for the week. ■

Try These Problems

Solve. **Show setups,**

6. When Ms. Leong sells a refrigerator for $560, she receives a $21 commission. If her commission is based on the total sales, what is her commission rate? (Express the answer as a percent.)

7. Mr. Praxmarer sells ski equipment and clothing to retail stores across the United States and Canada. He is paid a commission that is $\frac{2}{3}$% of the total sales. If he sells $75,000 worth of ski equipment to the Truckee Sport Shop, how much commission does he earn on this sale?

8. Don sells men's clothing in a large department store. In addition to his regular salary, he earns a commission that is 0.8% of his total sales. Last month he earned a $75 commission. What were his total sales for that month?

9. Ms. Alvarez sells appliances to department stores. She receives a base salary of $1850 per month, plus a commission that is 0.75% of her total sales. Last month she sold $95,800 worth of appliances. What were her total earnings for the month?

 Try Problems 6 through 8.

EXAMPLE 4   Ms. Lane sells computer software. She earns a base salary of $2700 per month, plus a commission that is 1.5% of her total sales. One month she sold $82,400 worth of software. What were her total earnings for that month?

SOLUTION   First find her commission.

$$\begin{aligned} \text{Commission} &= 1.5\% \quad \text{of} \quad \text{total sales} \\ (\$) & \qquad\qquad\qquad (\$) \\ \boxed{} &= 0.015 \quad \times \quad 82{,}400 \end{aligned}$$

The answer to the multiplication problem is missing, so multiply 0.015 by 82,400 to find the commission.

$$0.015 \times 82{,}400 = 1236$$

The commission is $1236. Now we add the commission to the base salary to find the total earnings.

$$\begin{aligned} \text{Total} \\ \text{earnings} &= \text{base salary} + \text{commission} \\ (\$) & \qquad (\$) \qquad\qquad (\$) \\ &= 2700 \quad + \quad 1236 \\ &= 3936 \end{aligned}$$

She earned $3936 that month. ■

 Try Problem 9.

3 Problems Involving Interest Earned

Suppose you put $5000 in a savings account that pays an annual yield of 4%. If you make no further deposits and no withdrawals, at the end of one year you will have more than $5000 in that account, because the bank pays you additional money for leaving your money in the account. The amount of money that the account earns is called the **interest** or the **yield.** To compute the amount of interest earned, we take 4% of the **amount invested.**

$$\begin{aligned} \text{Interest} &= 4\% \quad \times \quad \text{amount invested} \\ (\$) & \qquad\qquad\qquad\qquad (\$) \\ &= 0.04 \quad \times \quad 5000 \\ &= 200 \end{aligned}$$

This account earns $200 in one year. The 4% is called the **interest rate** or the **rate of return.** The interest rate varies depending on the bank and the type of account. To find out how much money is in the account at the end of one year, we add the interest to the original amount invested.

$$\begin{aligned} \text{Final} \\ \text{amount} &= \text{amount} \\ (\$) & \quad \text{invested} + \text{interest} \\ & \qquad (\$) \qquad\qquad (\$) \\ &= 5000 \quad + \quad 200 \\ &= 5200 \end{aligned}$$

At the end of one year, the account contains $5200.

Try These Problems

Solve. **Show set ups,**

10. Melissa inherited some money from her grandmother. She invested all of it in an account that pays 12% interest. If she earned $1560 interest in one year, what was her inheritance?

11. Chuck invested $40,000 in an account and earned $3000 interest in one year. Find the interest rate. (Express the answer as a percent.)

12. Britt-Marie invested $12,900 in an account that earns $6\frac{2}{3}$% interest. How much interest did she earn in one year?

There is more than one type of interest that can be earned on an account. **Simple interest** is interest earned only on the amount invested, while **compound interest** is interest earned on both the amount invested and on the interest previously earned. In this text we assume that the interest earned is simple interest.

We also use the word *interest* to mean the earnings on any type of account, including savings accounts, money market funds, mutual fund accounts, and stock accounts. We use the phrase *interest rate* for the average annual rate of return on these accounts.

In general, if you invest a certain amount of money that earns simple interest, make no further deposits or withdrawals, and leave the money for one year, then the following rules apply.

Rules Involving Interest Earned

Interest (or yield) = interest rate (or rate of return) $\times$ amount invested

Final amount = amount invested + interest

Here are some examples where we use these rules.

EXAMPLE 5   Amy put $620 in a mutual fund account that earned a $58.90 yield in a year. Find the rate of return. (Express the answer as a percent.)

SOLUTION   We have the following.

$$\text{Yield} = \text{rate of return} \times \text{amount invested}$$

$$58.90 = \boxed{\%} \times 620$$

A multiplier is missing, so we divide 58.90 by 620 to find the missing multiplier.

$$
\begin{array}{r}
.095 = 9.5\% \\
620\overline{)58.90} \\
55\ 80 \\
\hline
3\ 100 \\
3\ 100 \\
\hline
\end{array}
$$

The rate of return is 9.5%. ■

 Try Problems 10 through 12.

EXAMPLE 6   Mr. Kung made an investment of $7800 in a stock account that paid $8\frac{1}{3}$% interest for one year. How much money was in the account at the end of one year?

SOLUTION   First find the amount of interest that the account earned.

$$\underset{(\$)}{\text{Interest}} = \underset{\text{rate}}{\overset{\text{interest}}{}} \times \underset{(\$)}{\overset{\text{amount}}{\text{invested}}}$$

$$= 8\frac{1}{3}\% \times 7800$$

Solve. Show setup.

13. Ms. Allen put $860 in an account that earns interest at an annual rate of $5\frac{3}{4}$%. How much money is in the account at the end of one year?

$$= \frac{1}{12} \times \frac{7800}{1}_{25}$$

$$= \frac{1}{3 \times \cancel{4}} \times \frac{78 \times \cancel{100}}{1}$$

$$= \frac{78 \times 25}{3}$$

$$= \frac{\cancel{3} \times 26 \times 25}{\cancel{3}}$$

$$= 650$$

Convert $8\frac{1}{3}$% to a fraction.

$$8\frac{1}{3}\% = \frac{25}{3} \div 100$$

$$= \frac{\cancel{25}^{1}}{3} \times \frac{1}{\cancel{100}_{4}}$$

$$= \frac{1}{12}$$

The interest is $650. Now we add the interest to the amount invested to find the final amount in the account at the end of one year.

$$\begin{array}{c} \text{Final} \\ \text{amount} \\ (\$) \end{array} = \begin{array}{c} \text{amount} \\ \text{invested} \\ (\$) \end{array} + \begin{array}{c} \text{interest} \\ (\$) \end{array}$$

$$= 7800 + 650$$

$$= 8450$$

The amount in the account at the end of one year is $8450. ■

◣ **Try Problem 13.**

4 Problems Involving Interest Paid

Suppose you purchase a sofa that costs $1500 by charging it on your credit card. When you receive your bill at the end of the month, assume you pay only $300 toward the $1500 bill. The amount that you did not pay, $1200, is called your **unpaid balance.** The next month when you receive your bill, the balance will be more than $1200, because the credit card company charges you **interest** for not paying the full bill by the end of last month. Assume your credit card charges 1.8% of the unpaid balance. The interest charged for one month is computed as follows.

$$\begin{array}{c} \text{Interest} \\ (\$) \end{array} = 1.8\% \text{ of } \begin{array}{c} \text{unpaid} \\ \text{balance} \\ \downarrow \quad (\$) \end{array}$$

$$= 0.018 \times 1200$$

$$= 21.60$$

The interest charged for the month is $21.60. Sometimes this interest is called a **service charge** or **finance charge**. The percent 1.8% is called the **monthly interest rate.** To compute the amount of the bill, we add the interest to the unpaid balance.

$$\begin{array}{c} \text{Total} \\ \text{bill} \\ (\$) \end{array} = \begin{array}{c} \text{unpaid} \\ \text{balance} \\ (\$) \end{array} + \begin{array}{c} \text{interest} \\ (\$) \end{array}$$

$$= 1200 + 21.60$$

$$= 1221.60$$

The balance is now $1221.60.

Try These Problems

Solve. Show setups.

14. Mr. Hummer has a credit card that charges 1.9% interest on the unpaid balance each month. Last month Mr. Hummer's unpaid balance was $3700. How much interest did he pay for the month?

15. Pablo received his credit card bill. It showed an unpaid balance from the last month of $540 and a finance charge of $11.34. Find the monthly interest rate.

16. Sharon charged a grand piano on an account that charges a monthly finance charge that is $1\frac{2}{3}$% of the unpaid balance. If her unpaid balance last month was $4800, how much is her bill this month?

Here we summarize the facts discussed in the previous paragraph.

Rules Involving Interest Paid on an Unpaid Balance

Interest = monthly interest rate × unpaid balance

Total bill = unpaid balance + interest

Now we look at some examples where we use these rules.

EXAMPLE 7   Asher has a charge account at a department store that adds a 1.5% service charge to the unpaid balance at the end of each month. Last month his unpaid balance was $76.32. How much service charge did he pay? (Round off to the nearest cent.)

SOLUTION   We have the following.

$$
\begin{array}{ccc}
\text{Service} & \text{interest} & \text{unpaid} \\
\text{charge} = & \text{rate} \times & \text{balance} \\
(\$) & & (\$)
\end{array}
$$

$$= 1.5\% \times 76.32$$
$$= 0.015 \times 76.32$$
$$= 1.1448$$
$$\approx 1.14$$

Asher is charged a service charge of $1.14. ■

 Try Problems 14 and 15.

EXAMPLE 8   Grace has a credit card that charges interest that is 2% of the unpaid balance. If her unpaid balance from last month was $640, and she makes no further pruchases, how much is her bill this month?

SOLUTION   First we find the interest she was charged for leaving an unpaid balance of $640.

$$
\begin{array}{ccc}
\text{Interest} = & \text{interest} & \text{unpaid} \\
(\$) & \text{rate} \times & \text{balance} \\
& & (\$)
\end{array}
$$

$$= 2\% \times 640$$
$$= 0.02 \times 640$$
$$= 12.80$$

Grace is charged $12.80 interest. Next we add the interest to the unpaid balance to find her total bill.

$$
\begin{array}{ccc}
\text{Total} & \text{unpaid} & \\
\text{bill} = & \text{balance} + & \text{interest} \\
(\$) & (\$) & (\$)
\end{array}
$$

$$= 640 + 12.80$$
$$= 652.80$$

Her bill this month is $652.80. ■

 **Try Problem 16.**

5   Solving Problems Involving Tips

Suppose you go out to eat at a restaurant where a person serves your table. It is customary to leave the server some money in addition to the dinner bill. This additional amount is called a **tip** or **gratuity.** If you were pleased with the service, it is common to leave a tip that is at least 15% of the dinner bill. The percent 15% is called the **rate.** Sometimes we take the percent of the dinner bill before tax is added. At other times we take the percent of the dinner bill after the tax is added. At the restaurant you get to choose how much money you want to leave for the tip. Here we summarize the rules about tips.

Rules Involving Tips

Tip = rate × dinner bill

Total bill = dinner bill + tip

Here are some examples where we use these rules.

EXAMPLE 9   Mr. Castro was not pleased with the service at the seafood restaurant. In order to express his dissatisfaction, he left a $3.50 tip which was only 10% of the dinner bill. What was the dinner bill?

SOLUTION   We have the following.

$$\text{Tip} = \text{rate} \times \text{dinner bill}$$
$$(\$) \qquad\qquad (\$)$$
$$3.50 = 10\% \times \boxed{}$$
$$3.50 = 0.10 \times \boxed{}$$

A multiplier is missing, so divide 3.50 by 0.10 to find the dinner bill.

$$\begin{array}{r} 3\ 5.\ = 35 \\ 0.1\overline{)3.5} \\ \underline{3} \\ 5 \\ \underline{5} \end{array}$$

Note that we can divide by 0.1 instead of 0.10 because these decimals are equal.

The dinner bill was $35. ■

EXAMPLE 10   A dinner bill for three persons was $60. A $5 gratuity was left. The gratuity is what percent of the dinner bill? Is this an appropriate amount?

SOLUTION   We have the following.

Gratuity	is	what percent	of	the dinner bill
5	=	$\boxed{}$ %	×	60

A multiplier is missing, so divide 5 by 60 to find the missing multiplier.

Try These Problems

Solve. **Show set ups.**

17. Sharmon took Ted out to eat at an exclusive French restaurant in New Orleans. She left a 15% tip that amounted to $9.30. What was the dinner bill?

18. Karla is pleased with the service at the Chinese restaurant. She wants to leave an 18% tip. If the dinner bill is $45, how much tip should she leave?

19. The dinner bill for a group of persons is $230. A $46 gratuity is left. The gratuity is what percent of the dinner bill?

$$5 \div 60 = \frac{5}{60}$$

$$= \frac{5}{60} \times \frac{100}{1}\%$$ Convert the fraction to a percent.

$$= \frac{5}{6 \times \cancel{10}} = \frac{\cancel{10} \times 10}{1}\%$$

$$= \frac{50}{6}\%$$

$$= \frac{25}{3}\%$$

$$= 8\frac{1}{3}\%$$

The gratuity is only $8\frac{1}{3}\%$ of the dinner bill. This is not an appropriate amount unless the server did a poor job. ■

Try Problems 17 through 19.

Here we summarize the information presented in this section.

Sales Tax

The sales tax is some percent of the marked price. The percent is called the sales tax rate.

Sales tax = sales tax rate (%) × marked price

Total cost = marked price + sales tax

Commission Based on Total Sales

The commission earned by a sales person is some percent of the total sales. The percent is called the commission rate.

Commission = commission rate (%) × total sales

Total salary = base salary + commission

Interest Earned

The interest earned on an investment is some percent of the original investment. The percent is called the monthly interest rate.

Interest = monthly interest rate (%) × amount invested

Final amount = amount invested + interest

Interest Paid

The interest paid on an unpaid balance is some percent of the unpaid balance. The percent is called the monthly interest rate.

Interest = monthly interest rate (%) × unpaid balance

Total bill = unpaid balance + interest

Tips

The tip (or gratuity) paid to a restaurant server is some percent of the dinner bill. The percent is usually about 15%.

Tip = rate (%) × dinner bill

Total bill = dinner bill + tip

EXERCISES 9.6

Solve. Show setups and calculation steps.

1. Gloria buys a bed that is marked $430. If the sales tax rate is 7.8%, how much sales tax does she pay?

2. The marked price of a radio is $135. A sales tax of $9.18 was added. What is the sales tax rate? (Express the answer as a percent.)

3. Larry bought a tool box and he was charged a sales tax of $1.88. If the tax rate is 8%, find the marked price of the tool box.

4. Leslie bought 4 sweaters at $42 each and 3 skirts at $69 each. If the sales tax rate is 5.4%, what is the total amount she paid for these items?

5. When Ms. Goldman sells a computer for $4000, she receives a $100 commission. If her commission is based on the total sales, what is her commission rate? (Express the answer as a percent.)

6. Mr. Lemus sells used cars. He is paid a commission that is 0.72% of the total sales. If he sells a car for $38,000, how much commission does he earn on this sale?

7. Paul sells commercial real estate. In addition to his base salary of $2000 per month, he receives a commission that is 0.38% of the total sales. Last month he sold $1,800,000 worth of real estate. What were his total earnings for that month?

8. Le Ha's commission rate for selling clothes at an exclusive boutique is 24%. For a three-day weekend, she earned a $480 commission. How many dollars worth of clothing did she sell during the three days?

9. Mr. Schectman invested some money in a stock account that earned $33\frac{1}{3}$% interest. If he earned $6400 interest after one year, how much did he invest?

10. Melissa earned $329 interest on an investment of $3500 in one year. Find the interest rate. (Express the answer as a percent.)

11. Ms. Jones invested $860 in an account that earns 7.6% annual interest. How much interest did she earn in one year?

12. Mr. DiGangi invested $20,000 in a growth stock account that earned 14% interest in one year. What was the total amount of money in this account at the end of one year?

13. Roberta received her credit card bill. It showed an unpaid balance from the last month of $630 and a finance charge of $11.97. Find the monthly interest rate. (Express the answer as a percent.)

14. Nell charged some vertical blinds on an account that charges a monthly finance charge that is $1\frac{5}{6}\%$ of the unpaid balance. If her unpaid balance last month was $714, how much interest is she charged on this month's bill?

15. Mr. Garcia charged a suit on an account that charges a monthly finance charge that is 1.88% of the unpaid balance. If his unpaid balance last month was $250, and he made no further charges, how much is his bill this month?

16. Susie charged a rug on an account that charges a monthly finance charge that is $1\frac{3}{4}\%$ of the unpaid balance. If her unpaid balance last month was $354 and she makes no additional purchases, how much is her bill this month? (Round up to the nearest cent.)

17. Edna, a lawyer, takes a client to lunch. She is very pleased with the service and food so she wants to leave a 20% tip. If the lunch bill is $38, how much tip should she leave?

18. Mr. Coyle is very displeased with the service he receives at a coffee shop. He left only a $0.75 tip for a bill that was $15. What percent tip did he leave?

19. Richard took his girlfriend Patricia out to eat at an expensive Italian restaurant in San Francisco. He left a $13.50 gratuity that was 15% of the dinner bill. What was the dinner bill?

20. Your dinner bill, not including tax, is $78.50. If the sales tax rate is 6%, and you leave a tip that is 15% of the dinner bill after the tax is added, what is your total bill? (Round off to the nearest cent.)

21. A student purchases 3 pens at $1.29 each and 5 notebooks at $4.69 each. If the sales tax rate is 5.2%, what is the total cost of these items? (Round off to the nearest cent.)

22. Delicia sells women's clothing for a department store. She makes a base salary of $1400 per month plus a commission that is $\frac{2}{3}\%$ of her total sales. If she sold $45,900 worth of clothing last month, what were her total earnings for the month?

23. Ms. Yee put $8000 of her royalty advances in a money market fund earning 8.8% interest annually. How much money is in the account at the end of one year?

24. David charged a television set on an account that charges a monthly service charge that is 1.5% of the unpaid balance. If his unpaid balance last month was $138 and he made no further purchases, how much is his bill this month?

25. Henry earns a weekly base salary of $420, plus 3.2% of all sales over $5000. If his total sales for one week were $6400, how much did he earn that week?

26. You plan to build a fence around a rectangular lot that is 15 yards wide and 20 yards long. If the fencing material costs $8.25 per yard and the sales tax rate is 5.6%, find the total cost of the fencing material.

A city contains 500,000 people. The bar graph below gives the age distribution of the population. Use the graph to answer Exercises 27 through 30.

27. What percent of the population is from 31 to 50 years old?

28. What percent of the population is 75 years old or older?

29. How many people in the city are 16 years old or younger?

30. How many people in the city are from 17 to 30 years old?

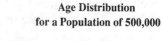

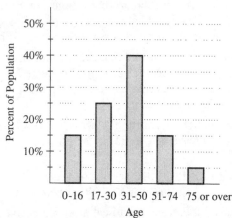

FIGURING THE RESTAURANT TIP MENTALLY

Suppose you are at a restaurant and you want to leave the server a 15% tip. How can you quickly compute the tip without using paper and pencil or a calculator? There is more than one way to do this. We will discuss one method which involves finding 10% of the dinner bill, halving that amount to obtain 5% of the dinner bill, then adding those two quantities together. Here we look at an example.

Computing the tip for a $40 dinner bill.

10% of $40 = $4	The decimal point in 40 shifts 1 place to the left
$4 ÷ 2 = $2	Dividing $4 in half is an easy way to obtain 5% of 40.
Tip = $4 + $2 = $6	Add the 10% of 40 to 5% of 40 to obtain 15% of 40.

Finally, add $6 to $40 to obtain the total amount, $46.

Of course the dinner bill is not always going to be a nice number like 40. You can round off the bill to the nearest dollar before trying to do the mental work. Here is an example.

Computing the tip for a $24.27 dinner bill.

10% of $24 = $2.40

Round off the dinner bill to $24, then take 10% of 24. The decimal point in 24 shifts 1 place to the left.

$2.40 ÷ 2 = $1.20	Divide $2.40 by 2 to obtain 5% of $24.
Tip = $2.40 + $1.20 = $3.60	Add to obtain the tip.

Finally, add $3.60 to $24 to find the total amount, $27.60. (Of course you can also add the tip to the original dinner bill, $24.27, to obtain $27.87 for the total amount.)

Here we look at one more example.

Computing the tip for a $12.87 dinner bill.

10% of $13 = $1.30

Round off the dinner bill to $13, then take 10% of $13. The decimal point in 13 shifts 1 place to the left.

$1.30 ÷ 2 ≈ $0.70	Divide $1.30 by 2 and round off to the nearest dime.
Tip = $1.30 + $0.70 = $2.00	Add to obtain the tip

Finally, add the $2 tip to $13 to obtain $15 for the total amount. (Of course you can also add the tip to the original dinner bill $12.87 to obtain $14.87 for the total amount.)

Number Sense Problems

Mentally round off each to the nearest dollar and then take 10% of the result.

1. $8.67   **2.** $14.12   **3.** $25.06   **4.** $67.89

Mentally round off each to the nearest dollar, take 10% of the result, then divide that amount by 2. (Here we are obtaining an approximation for 5% of the given amount.)

5. $9.13   **6.** $18.64   **7.** $38.79   **8.** $66.34

Mentally compute a 15% tip for the following dinner bills. No rounding is necessary.

9. $10   **10.** $26   **11.** $60   **12.** $150

Mentally compute an approximate 15% tip for the following dinner bills. Begin by rounding off the dinner bill to the nearest dollar, then round off all other amounts to the nearest dime.

13. $6.78   **14.** $26.25   **15.** $48.33   **16.** $103.76

Mentally compute the total dinner bill after an approximate 15% tip has been added. Begin by rounding off the dinner bill to the nearest dollar (if necessary), then round off all other amounts to the nearest dime. Finally add the tip to the rounded dinner bill to find the total amount.

17. $16   **18.** $25   **19.** $27.78   **20.** $68.14

9.7 APPLICATIONS: PERCENT INCREASE, PERCENT DECREASE

OBJECTIVES

▌ Solve an application that involves percent increase.
▌ Solve an application that involves percent decrease.
▌ Solve an application that involves markup based on the cost.
▌ Solve an application that involves markup based on the selling price.

1 Problems Involving Percent Increase

Suppose you are earning $200 per week, and your boss informs you that you are to receive a 12% raise. The 12%, called the **percent increase,** is multiplied by the original salary to obtain the increase in salary.

$$\begin{array}{ccccc} \text{Increase} \\ \text{in salary} & = & \text{percent} & \times & \text{original} \\ \text{($)} & & \text{increase} & & \text{salary} \\ & & & & \text{($)} \\ & = & 12\% & \times & 200 \\ & = & 0.12 & \times & 200 \\ & = & 24 \end{array}$$

The increase or raise is $24. To compute the final salary, add the increase to the original salary.

Solve. **Show set up.**

1. In one year, the price of gasoline has increased $16\frac{2}{3}\%$. If the original price was $1.20 per gallon, what is the price after the increase?

Final salary ($)	=	original salary ($)	+	increase in salary ($)
	=	200	+	24
	=	224		

Your new salary will be $224 per week.

Also observe that the increase in salary is the difference between the final salary and the original salary.

Increase in salary ($)	=	final salary ($)	−	original salary ($)
	=	224	−	200
	=	24		

There are many situations where we use percent increase to show how much a quantity has increased over its original value. The percent increase is taken of the original amount to obtain the increase. Here we give the rules that are relevant.

Rules Involving Increase and Percent Increase

Increase = percent increase × original amount

Final amount = original amount + increase

Increase = final amount − original amount

Here are some examples where we use these rules.

EXAMPLE 1   In Soraya's first year as president of the company, profits have increased 18%. If the original profit was $700,000, what is the profit after one year?

SOLUTION   First we find the increase in the profit. We have the following:

Increase in profit ($)	=	percent increase	×	original profit ($)
	=	18%	×	700,000
	=	0.18	×	700,000
	=	126,000		

The increase in the profit is $126,000. To find the final profit, we add the increase to the original profit.

Final profit ($)	=	original profit	+	increase in profit ($)
	=	700,000	+	126,000
	=	826,000		

The profit after one year is $826,000. ■

 Try Problem 1.

Try These Problems

Solve. **Show setups,**

2. Dahlia receives a $1.44-per-hour raise, which is 4.5% over her original hourly wage. Find her original hourly wage.

3. The population of a small town in Wyoming increased by 20 persons. If the original population was 320, what is the percent increase?

4. A dog's weight increased from 10 pounds to 25 pounds. What percent increase is this?

EXAMPLE 2 Mr. Vetterli gained 9 pounds over the summer, which was a 6% increase. What was his original weight?

SOLUTION The percent increase is given as 6% and the increase in weight is given as 9 pounds. The percent increase is taken of the original weight to obtain the increase in weight, so we have the following.

$$\begin{array}{ccccc} \text{Increase} \\ \text{in weight} & = & \text{percent} \\ \text{increase} & \times & \text{original} \\ \text{weight} \\ \text{(lb)} & & & & \text{(lb)} \\ 9 & = & 6\% & \times & \boxed{} \\ 9 & = & 0.06 & \times & \boxed{} \end{array}$$

A multiplier is missing, so divide 9 by 0.06 to find the missing multiplier.

$$\begin{array}{r} 1\,5\,0. = 1\,5\,0 \\ 0.0\,6\,)\overline{9.0\,0} \\ 6 \\ \overline{3\,0} \\ \underline{3\,0} \end{array}$$

His original weight was 150 pounds. ■

 Try Problem 2.

EXAMPLE 3 Due to inflation, the price of a box of cereal increased from $2.50 to $3.00. What is the percent increase?

SOLUTION First we find the increase in price by subtracting the original price from the final price.

$$\begin{array}{ccccc} \text{Increase} \\ \text{in price} & = & \text{final} \\ \text{price} & - & \text{original} \\ \text{price} \\ \text{(\$)} & & \text{(\$)} & & \text{(\$)} \\ & = & 3.00 & - & 2.50 \\ & = & 0.50 \end{array}$$

The increase in price is $0.50. This increase is a certain percent of the original price, so we have the following.

$$\begin{array}{ccccc} \text{Increase} \\ \text{in price} & = & \text{percent} \\ \text{increase} & \times & \text{original} \\ \text{price} \\ \text{(\$)} & & & & \text{(\$)} \\ 0.50 & = & \boxed{\%} & \times & 2.50 \end{array}$$

A multiplier is missing, so divide 0.50 by 2.50 to find the missing multiplier.

$$\begin{array}{r} .2 = 20\% \\ 2.5\,)\overline{0.5\,0} \\ 5\,0 \end{array}$$

The percent increase is 20%. ■

 Try Problems 3 and 4.

2 Problems Involving Percent Decrease

Suppose that the price of a comforter was $180, and you read in the newspaper that the store is having a 40%-off sale. The 40%, called the **percent decrease,** is multiplied by the original price to obtain the **decrease** (or **discount** or **savings**).

$$\begin{array}{c} \text{Decrease} \\ \text{in price} \\ (\$) \end{array} = \begin{array}{c} \text{percent} \\ \text{decrease} \end{array} \times \begin{array}{c} \text{original} \\ \text{price} \\ (\$) \end{array}$$

$$= \quad 40\% \quad \times \quad \$180$$
$$= \quad 0.40 \quad \times \quad \$180$$
$$= \quad \$72$$

The decrease in price is $72. To compute the final price, subtract the decrease from the original price.

$$\begin{array}{ccc} \text{Final price} & = & \text{original price} & - & \text{decrease in price} \\ (\$) & & (\$) & & (\$) \end{array}$$

$$= \quad 180 \quad - \quad 72$$
$$= \quad 108$$

The final price without tax is $108.

There are many situations where we use percent decrease to show how much a quantity has decreased from its original value. The percent decrease is taken of the original amount to obtain the decrease. Here we give the rules that are relevant.

Rules Involving Decrease and Percent Decrease

Decrease = percent decrease × original amount

Final amount = original amount − decrease

Decrease = original amount − final amount

Here are some examples where we use these rules.

EXAMPLE 4   Due to financial problems, a company had to reduce the average hourly wage of its workers from $24 to $22.68. What percent decrease is this?

SOLUTION   First, find the decrease in wage by subtracting the final wage from the original wage.

$$\begin{array}{c} \text{Decrease} \\ \text{in wage} \\ (\$) \end{array} = \begin{array}{c} \text{original} \\ \text{wage} \\ (\$) \end{array} - \begin{array}{c} \text{final} \\ \text{wage} \\ (\$) \end{array}$$

$$= \quad 24 \quad - 22.68$$
$$= \quad 1.32$$

Try These Problems

Solve. **Show setups.**

5. A television that was marked $350 is now on sale for 30% off. Find the savings.

6. While you were sick, your weight dropped 14 pounds. If this was an 8% decrease, what was your original weight?

7. The price of a scientific hand-held calculator decreased from $20 to $12. What percent decrease is this?

8. Due to less demand, the price of beef has decreased by $12\frac{1}{2}$% over the past few months. If the original price was $3.60 per pound, what is the current price?

The decrease is $1.32. This decrease in wage is a certain percent of the original wage, so we have the following.

$$\begin{array}{ccc} \text{Decrease} & = & \text{percent} \\ \text{in wage} & & \text{decrease} \\ (\$) & & \end{array} \times \begin{array}{c} \text{original} \\ \text{wage} \\ (\$) \end{array}$$

$$1.32 = \boxed{\%} \times 24$$

A multiplier is missing, so divide 1.32 by 24 to find the missing multiplier.

$$\begin{array}{r} .055 = 5.5\% \\ 24\overline{)1.320} \\ \underline{1\ 20} \\ 120 \\ \underline{120} \end{array}$$

The percent decrease is 5.5%. ■

EXAMPLE 5   The population of a mining town in Virginia decreased by $33\frac{1}{3}$%. If the original population was 24,000, what is the current population?

SOLUTION   First we find the decrease in population. We have the following.

$$\begin{array}{ccc} \text{Decrease} & = & \text{percent} \\ \text{in population} & & \text{decrease} \end{array} \times \begin{array}{c} \text{original} \\ \text{population} \end{array}$$

$$= 33\frac{1}{3}\% \times 24{,}000$$

$$= \frac{1}{3} \times 24{,}000 \qquad \begin{array}{l}\text{Convert } 33\frac{1}{3}\% \text{ to a}\\ \text{fraction.}\end{array}$$

$$33\frac{1}{3}\% = 33\frac{1}{3} \div 100$$

$$= \frac{1}{\cancel{3}} \times \frac{\overset{8000}{\cancel{24{,}000}}}{1} \qquad = \frac{\overset{1}{\cancel{100}}}{3} \times \frac{1}{\cancel{100}}$$

$$= 8000 \qquad\qquad\qquad = \frac{1}{3}$$

The decrease in population is 8000. To compute the current population, subtract the decrease from the original population.

$$\begin{array}{ccc} \text{Final} & = & \text{original} \\ \text{population} & & \text{population} \end{array} - \begin{array}{c} \text{decrease} \\ \text{in population} \end{array}$$

$$= 24{,}000 - 8000$$

$$= 16{,}000$$

The current population is 16,000. ■

 Try Problems 5 through 8.

Percent Increase

The percent increase is taken of the original amount to obtain the increase.

Increase = percent increase (%) × original amount

Final amount = original amount + increase

Increase = final amount − original amount

Percent Decrease

The percent decrease is taken of the original amount to obtain the decrease.

Decrease = percent decrease (%) × original amount

Final amount = original amount − decrease

Decrease = original amount − final amount

 Answers to Try These Problems

1. $1.40   2. $32   3. $6\frac{1}{4}$% or 6.25%   4. 150%   5. $105
6. 175 lb   7. 40%   8. $3.15 per lb

EXERCISES 9.7

Solve. Show setups and calculation steps.

1. Ms. Garcia was earning $26.80 per hour. She received a 6.5% raise. What is her increase in salary? (Round off to the nearest cent.)

2. Your typing speed increased 8 words per minute, which was a $12\frac{1}{2}$% increase. What was your original typing speed?

3. The price of a stock increased from $35 per share to $41\frac{1}{8}$ per share. Find the percent increase.

4. A carpenter calculated that he needed 260 feet of lumber for a job. He wants to increase that amount by 12% to allow for waste. What is the total amount of lumber he should buy?

5. It is estimated that the value of a $5000 computer decreased by $1500 in the first year. What percent decrease is this?

6. By conserving water, the Jefferson family reduced their daily water usage from 450 gallons to 270 gallons. What percent decrease is this?

7. A hotel reduced the average amount of time a person spends waiting for the elevator by 1.8 minutes. If this represents a 72% decrease, what was the original average waiting time?

8. A bath towel that was selling for $14 is now on sale at 40% off. What is the sale price?

17. Over a ten-year period, the cost of fuel increased from $4 a barrel to $40 a barrel. What percent increase is this?

18. Linda lost 6 pounds over the summer, which was a 5% decrease.
    a. What was Linda's original weight?
    b. What was Linda's weight at the end of the summer?

CHAPTER 9 SUMMARY

KEY WORDS AND PHRASES

percent [9.1]
percent of a number [9.2]
marked price [9.6]
sales tax [9.6]
sales tax rate [9.6]
base salary [9.6]
commission [9.6]
commission rate [9.6]
interest (yield) [9.6]
amount invested [9.6]
interest rate (rate of return) [9.6]

simple interest [9.6]
compound interest [9.6]
service charge (finance charge) [9.6]
unpaid balance [9.6]
monthly interest rate [9.6]
tip (gratuity) [9.6]
percent increase [9.7]
percent decrease [9.7]
cost [9.7]
selling price [9.7]

markup [9.7]
markup based on cost [9.7]
percent markup (markup rate) [9.7]
markup based on selling price [9.7]
rate [9.6, 9.8]
base [9.8]
amount [9.8]
proportion [9.8]

SYMBOLS

$0.1\overline{6}$ means $0.16666666666\ldots$.
$\approx$ means *approximately equal to*
30% means $\frac{30}{100} = 0.30$

IMPORTANT RULES

Comparing a Percent to the Number 1 [9.1]

The percent, 100%, is equal to the number 1. A percent that is less than 100% represents a number that is less than 1. A percent that is more than 100% represents a number that is more than 1.

Converting a Percent to a Fraction or Decimal [9.1]

To convert a percent to a fraction or decimal, drop the percent symbol, %, and divide by 100.

Converting a Fraction or Decimal to a Percent [9.3]

To convert a fraction or decimal to a percent, multiply by 100 and attach the percent symbol, %.

Finding a Percent of a Number [9.2]

- Convert the percent to a fraction or decimal. Use fractions if repeating decimals are involved.
- Multiply the number by the converted percent.

Finding the Missing Number in a Basic Percent Statement [9.4, 9.8]

METHOD 1 [9.4]

- Translate the basic percent statement to a multiplication statement.
- Find the missing number in the multiplication statement.
- If the percent is given, be sure to convert it to a fraction or decimal before beginning. Use fractions if repeating decimals are involved.
- If the question is *what percent* be sure to convert the answer to percent form.

METHOD 2 [9.8]

- Identify the rate, base, and amount in the basic percent statement.
- Write the proportion that corresponds to the basic percent statement.

  Remember that $\text{Rate} = \dfrac{\text{amount}}{\text{base}}$.

- Solve the proportion for the missing number.
- If the rate is missing, and you have let the rate be a missing number followed by the percent symbol, be sure to attach the percent symbol to the missing number found.

Solving Problems Involving Sales Tax, Commission, Interest Earned, Interest Paid, and Tips [9.6, 9.8]
A summary of the information needed to solve these types of problems is on page 419.

Solving Problems Involving Percent Increase, Percent Decrease, and Markup [9.7, 9.8]
A summary of the information needed to solve these types of problems is on page 431.

CHAPTER 9 REVIEW EXERCISES

Indicate whether each percent is less than, equal to, or more than the number 1.

1. 100%   **2.** 85%   **3.** 4%   **4.** 230%

Convert each percent to a decimal.

5. 7%   **6.** 68%   **7.** 120%   **8.** 6.7%

9. 52.08%   **10.** 0.5%   **11.** 0.018%   **12.** $\frac{1}{4}$%

13. $7\frac{1}{2}$%   **14.** $13\frac{2}{5}$%   **15.** 300%   **16.** 460%

Convert each percent to a fraction.

17. 5%   **18.** 80%   **19.** 64%   **20.** 150%

21. 200%   **22.** $\frac{3}{10}$%   **23.** $\frac{5}{6}$%   **24.** $8\frac{3}{4}$%

25. $66\frac{2}{3}$%   **26.** $6\frac{1}{4}$%   **27.** 12.5%   **28.** 3.2%

29. 0.9%   **30.** 0.06%   **31.** 50.25%   **32.** 0.001%

Solve.

33. 7% of 120   **34.** 9.4% of 25.6   **35.** $\frac{1}{2}$% of 8000

36. $3\frac{1}{3}$% of 990   **37.** 45.2% of 8.5   **38.** 125% of $8\frac{4}{7}$

Convert each number to a percent.

39. 0.16   **40.** 0.046   **41.** 8.7   **42.** 0.001

43. 0.4   **44.** 4.18   **45.** 0.502   **46.** 0.0037

47. $\frac{67}{100}$ **48.** $\frac{3}{5}$ **49.** $\frac{7}{20}$ **50.** $\frac{1}{8}$

51. 8   **52.** $\frac{5}{2}$ **53.** $\frac{5}{6}$ **54.** $5\frac{1}{3}$

Complete the following chart. Simplify the fractions when possible.

	Fraction	Decimal	Percent
55.			125%
56.		0.75	
57.	$\frac{1}{3}$		
58.			2.5%
59.		0.002	
60.	$\frac{7}{8}$		

Translate to an equation. Then solve.

61. 30% of what number is 411?   **62.** What percent of 72 is 60?

63. Find 350% of 20.   **64.** 0.03% of what number is 5.1?

65. 4.2 is what percent of 175?

66. 0.5% of 80.6 is what number?

67. What number is $12\frac{1}{2}$% of $\frac{8}{25}$?

68. 7 is what percent of $2\frac{1}{3}$?

69. What percent of 600 is 20?

70. $\frac{1}{9}$ is $\frac{2}{3}$% of what number?

Solve. Show setups and calculation steps.

71. Frank works in the quality control department of a textbook bindery company. He rejected 3 textbooks, which was $2\frac{1}{2}$% of the sample he checked. How many textbooks did he check?

72. Only 15% of the population of a small town are smokers. If the town has 460 people, how many are smokers?

73. At a convention there were 208 men and 442 women. What percent were men?

74. In a chemistry lab, Pancho mixed a solution that contained salt and water. He put in 27.3 grams of salt and the rest was water. If the solution is 12% salt, what is the total weight of the solution?

75. A certain type of beer is 4% alcohol. If you drink 20 ounces of beer, how much alcohol have you consumed?

76. Three-fourths percent of the population of a town caught a certain virus. If the town has a population of 24,000, how many caught the virus?

77. Sharon purchased a new dress that was marked $140. If the sales tax rate is 5.8%, how much did she pay for the dress?

78. Mr. Bragg paid $9.61 in sales tax for tires that were marked $155. What is the sales tax rate? (Express the answer as a percent.)

79. A real estate agent receives 5.5% commission for selling property. If the agent earns an $11,440 commission that is based on the total sales, what was the total value of the sale?

80. Bill invests $4800 in an account that earns $13\frac{1}{3}$% interest. How much money does he have in the account at the end of one year?

81. Ms. Wong received her credit card bill. It showed an unpaid balance from last month of $840 and a finance charge of $14.70. Find the monthly interest rate. (Express the answer as a percent.)

82. You are pleased with the service and food at an Italian restaurant, so you want to leave a 15% tip. How much tip do you leave if the dinner bill is $38?

83. Chuck took his office staff out to eat at a seafood restaurant. He left an 18% tip which amounted to $54.90. What was the dinner bill?

84. Cynthia's monthly salary increased from $800 to $840. What percent increase in this?

85. Mr. Fredericks researches the stock market for his large corporate clients. The price of a stock he was observing decreased from $43 to $37\frac{5}{8}$ yesterday. What percent decrease is this?

86. Just prior to the wedding of a very famous couple, the London police were granted a 17% pay raise. A policewoman who was making the equivalent of $2400 a month is now making how much a month?

87. After Mr. Reid became vice-president in charge of finance, the company's profits decreased by 2.4 million dollars, which was a 12% decrease from last year. What were the profits last year?

90. Mr. Huynh plans to build a fence around his rectangular vegetable garden with fencing that costs $6.80 per foot. The garden is 64 feet long and 31 feet wide. If he increases the amount of fencing needed by 8% to allow for waste and the sales tax rate is 5%, what is the total amount he pays for the fencing? (Round off to the nearest cent.)

✎ In Your Own Words

Write complete sentences to discuss each of the following. Support your comments with examples or pictures, if appropriate.

91. Discuss the basic meaning of the percent symbol and why you think the symbol was introduced.

92. Discuss how you can decide whether a percent is less than 1, equal to 1, or more than 1.

93. Discuss how the following two problems differ.
 a. 2.5% of what number is 80?
 b. What number is 2.5% of 80?

94. A business student wants to compute $66\frac{2}{3}\%$ of 900. The student calculates 0.66 times 900. Discuss why the student's result is not exactly correct, and how the correct result would be obtained.

95. Discuss a real-life situation that involves a percent that is more than 100%.

CHAPTER 9 PRACTICE TEST

Convert each percent to a decimal
 1. 26.4%   **2.** 370%   **3.** 0.5%   **4.** $6\frac{1}{4}\%$

Convert each percent to a fraction. Simplify if possible.
 5. 45%   **6.** 350%   **7.** $\frac{4}{5}\%$ **8.** $6\frac{2}{3}\%$

Convert each number to a percent.
 9. 4   **10.** 0.057   **11.** $\frac{9}{10}$ **12.** $2\frac{1}{3}$

Solve. **Show setups and calculation steps,**

13. Find 2.8% of 75

14. What percent of 85 is 34?

15. 220% of what number is $8\frac{1}{4}$?

16. 4.7 is what percent of 9400?

17. What number is 7% of 33.5?

18. $66\frac{2}{3}\%$ of what number is 144?

19. Due to inflation the price of gasoline has increased from $0.50 per gallon to $1.40 per gallon over the past few years.
 a. The new price is what percent of the original price?
 b. What percent increase is this?

20. Last year the Giants baseball team won 21 out of 50 games. What percent did they win?

21. Jim and Nell bought a new dishwasher for their home in Little Rock. The marked price of the dishwasher was $330. If the sales tax rate is 4%, how much did they pay for the dishwasher?

22. Mr. Dittmer sells real estate in Boston. His commission rate based on the total sales is 5%. On a recent sale of an apartment building he earned an $18,000 commission. What was the selling price of the building?

23. Ms. Kim enjoyed her meal at the Japanese restaurant. She wants to leave an 18% tip. How much tip will she leave if the dinner bill is $35?

24. A company survey revealed that 20.6% of the employees preferred increased dental coverage to a pay increase. Five hundred fifteen employees wanted increased dental coverage. How many employees took part in the survey?

CUMULATIVE REVIEW EXERCISES: CHAPTERS 1-9

Evaluate. Answer with a fraction.

1. $\frac{5}{36} + \frac{11}{42}$ **2.** $12\frac{5}{12} - 8\frac{22}{27}$ **3.** $\frac{450}{100} \times \frac{86}{21}$ **4.** $5\frac{1}{4} \div 4\frac{9}{10}$

Evaluate. Answer with a decimal.

5. $34 - 7.89$ **6.** $67 + 5.6 + 18.56$ **7.** $0.078 \times 43,000$

8. $40 \div 0.125$ **9.** $5.46 \div 1500$ **10.** $4.275 \div 9.5$

Solve.

11. Convert 0.308 to a fraction reduced to lowest terms.

12. Convert $\frac{27}{1500}$ to a decimal.

13. Convert $\frac{7}{11}$ to a repeating decimal.

14. Find the ratio of 1.5 to 60. Express the answer as **a.** a fraction, **b.** a decimal, and **c.** a percent.

15. Find the average of $5\frac{1}{3}$, $6\frac{2}{3}$, and $7\frac{5}{6}$. Answer with a fraction.

16. A pharmacist divides 2.4 liters of solution into 8 equal parts. How much is in each part?

17. If 4.5 centigrams of medicine are given for each 40 pounds of body weight, how much of this medicine should be given for a person who weighs 175 pounds? (Round off the answer to the nearest tenth of a centigram.)

18. Leon completed $\frac{1}{8}$ of the job on Monday and Tom completed $\frac{1}{4}$ of the job on Tuesday.
   a. What fraction of the job has been completed?
   b. What fraction of the job has not been completed?
   c. If the job is to write a 200-page report, how many pages did Leon write on Monday?
   d. What percent of the job did Tom complete on Tuesday?

19. Sue's hourly wage went from $32.60 per hour to $33.93 per hour.
   a. What is her increase in pay per hour?
   b. What is the percent increase? (Round off to the nearest whole percent.)
   c. The new salary is what percent of the old salary? (Round off to the nearest whole percent.)
   d. How much more will she make now than before for working an 8-hour day?

20. Mr. Tsu purchased 6 items at $4.69 each, 4 items at $9.29 each, and 2 items at $13.49 each. The sales tax rate is 7.4% on all of the items.
   a. What is the total cost of these items? (Round up the answer to the nearest cent.)
   b. How much change does Mr. Tsu receive from a $100 bill?

APPENDIX TABLES

TABLE 1   MULTIPLICATION FACTS

×	0	1	2	3	4	5	6	7	8	9
0	0	0	0	0	0	0	0	0	0	0
1	0	1	2	3	4	5	6	7	8	9
2	0	2	4	6	8	10	12	14	16	18
3	0	3	6	9	12	15	18	21	24	27
4	0	4	8	12	16	20	24	28	32	36
5	0	5	10	15	20	25	30	35	40	45
6	0	6	12	18	24	30	36	42	48	54
7	0	7	14	21	28	35	42	49	56	63
8	0	8	16	24	32	40	48	56	64	72
9	0	9	18	27	36	45	54	63	72	81

TABLE 2 PRIMES LESS THAN 100

2	3	5	7	11
13	17	19	23	29
31	37	41	43	47
53	59	61	67	71
73	79	83	89	97

TABLE 3 COMMON CONVERSIONS: FRACTION-DECIMAL-PERCENT

Fraction	Decimal	Percent	Fraction	Decimal	Percent
$\frac{1}{100}$	0.01	1%	$\frac{3}{5}$	0.60	60%
$\frac{1}{20}$	0.05	5%	$\frac{5}{8}$	0.625	$62\frac{1}{2}\%$
$\frac{1}{16}$	0.0625	$6\frac{1}{4}\%$	$\frac{2}{3}$	$0.\overline{66}$	$66\frac{2}{3}\%$
$\frac{1}{12}$	$0.08\overline{3}$	$8\frac{1}{3}\%$	$\frac{7}{10}$	0.70	70%
$\frac{1}{10}$	0.10	10%	$\frac{3}{4}$	0.75	75%
$\frac{1}{8}$	0.125	$12\frac{1}{2}\%$	$\frac{4}{5}$	0.80	80%
$\frac{1}{6}$	$0.1\overline{6}$	$16\frac{2}{3}\%$	$\frac{5}{6}$	$0.8\overline{3}$	$83\frac{1}{3}\%$
$\frac{1}{5}$	0.20	20%	$\frac{7}{8}$	0.875	$87\frac{1}{2}\%$
$\frac{1}{4}$	0.25	25%	$\frac{9}{10}$	0.90	90%
$\frac{3}{10}$	0.30	30%	1	1.00	100%
$\frac{1}{3}$	$0.3\overline{3}$	$33\frac{1}{3}\%$	$1\frac{1}{4}$	1.25	125%
$\frac{3}{8}$	0.375	$37\frac{1}{2}\%$	$1\frac{1}{2}$	1.50	150%
$\frac{2}{5}$	0.40	40%	$1\frac{3}{4}$	1.75	175%
$\frac{1}{2}$	0.50	50%	2	2.00	200%

TABLE 4 PERFECT SQUARES

$1^2 = 1$	$6^2 = 36$	$11^2 = 121$	$16^2 = 256$	$21^2 = 441$
$2^2 = 4$	$7^2 = 49$	$12^2 = 144$	$17^2 = 289$	$22^2 = 484$
$3^2 = 9$	$8^2 = 64$	$13^2 = 169$	$18^2 = 324$	$23^2 = 529$
$4^2 = 16$	$9^2 = 81$	$14^2 = 196$	$19^2 = 361$	$24^2 = 576$
$5^2 = 25$	$10^2 = 100$	$15^2 = 225$	$20^2 = 400$	$25^2 = 625$

TABLE 5   CHOOSING THE CORRECT OPERATION

Operation	Situation
Addition +	1. You are looking for the total or whole. 2. You are looking for the result when a quantity has been increased. 3. You are looking for the perimeter of a figure.
Subtraction −	1. You are looking for one of the parts in a total or whole. 2. You are looking for the result when a quantity has been decreased. 3. You are looking for how much larger one quantity is than another. 4. You are looking for how much smaller one quantity is than another.
Multiplication ×	1. You are looking for a total quantity. $$\frac{\text{Total}}{\text{quantity}} = \frac{\text{number of}}{\text{equal parts}} \times \frac{\text{size of}}{\text{each part}}$$ 2. You are looking for a total as in the following example. $$\text{Total miles} = \text{miles per hour} \times \frac{\text{number}}{\text{of hours}}$$ $$= \frac{\text{miles}}{\text{hour}} \times \text{hours}$$ 3. You are looking for a number that is a certain amount times as large as another number. 4. You are looking for the area of a rectangle. $$\text{Area} = \text{length} \times \text{width}$$ 5. You are looking for a fraction of a number.
Division ÷	1. A total quantity is being separated into a number of equal parts. $$\frac{\text{Size of}}{\text{each part}} = \text{total quantity} \div \frac{\text{number of}}{\text{equal parts}} = \frac{\text{total quantity}}{\text{number of equal parts}}$$ $$\frac{\text{Number of}}{\text{equal parts}} = \text{total quantity} \div \frac{\text{size of}}{\text{each part}} = \frac{\text{total quantity}}{\text{size of each part}}$$ 2. You are looking for a missing multiplier in a multiplication statement. $$\frac{\text{Missing}}{\text{multiplier}} = \frac{\text{answer to the}}{\text{multiplication problem}} \div \frac{\text{given}}{\text{multiplier}}$$ 3. You are looking for the average of a collection of numbers. $$\frac{\text{Average of a}}{\text{collection of numbers}} = \frac{\text{sum of}}{\text{the numbers}} \div \frac{\text{how many}}{\text{numbers}}$$ 4. You are looking for an average rate as in the following example. $$\frac{\text{average rate}}{\text{in miles per hour}} = \frac{\text{number of miles}}{\text{number of hours}}$$ 5. You are looking for what ratio one number is to another number.

TABLE 6 PERCENT FORMULAS

Converting a Percent to a Decimal or Fraction	Drop the percent symbol and divide by 100.
Converting Decimals and Fractions to Percent Form	Multiply by 100 and attach the percent symbol.
Percent of a Number	Percent of a number = percent (%) $\times$ the number Amount = rate (%) $\times$ base
Percent as a Rate	Rate (%) = $\dfrac{\text{amount}}{\text{base}}$
What Percent of B is A?	Percent (%) = $\dfrac{A}{B}$
Sales Tax	Sales tax = sales tax rate (%) $\times$ marked price
Commission Based on Total Sales	Commission = commission rate (%) $\times$ total sales
Simple Interest Earned in One Year (Yield)	Yield = rate of return (%) $\times$ amount invested
Interest (Finance Charge) Paid on an Unpaid Balance	Interest = interest rate (%) $\times$ unpaid balance
Tip (Gratuity)	Tip = rate (%) $\times$ dinner bill
Percent Increase	Increase = percent increase (%) $\times$ original amount
Percent Decrease	Decrease = percent decrease (%) $\times$ original amount
Markup Based on Cost	Markup = markup rate (%) $\times$ cost
Markup Based on Selling Price	Markup = markup rate (%) $\times$ selling price

TABLE 7 UNITS OF TIME

1 calendar year (yr) = 365 days (da)

1 year = 12 months (mo)

1 year $\approx$ 52 weeks (wk)

1 week = 7 days

1 day = 24 hours (hr)

1 hour = 60 minutes (min)

1 minute = 60 seconds (sec)

TABLE 8   UNITS OF MEASUREMENT: ENGLISH SYSTEM

LENGTH

1 mile (mi) = 5280 feet (ft)

1 yard (yd) = 3 feet

1 yard = 36 inches (in)

1 foot (ft) = 12 inches

AREA

1 square mile (sq mi) = 640 acres

1 acre = 4840 square yards (sq yd)

1 square yard = 9 square feet (sq ft)

1 square yard = 1296 square inches (sq in)

1 square foot = 144 square inches

VOLUME

1 cubic yard (cu yd) = 27 cubic feet (cu ft)

1 cubic foot = 1728 cubic inches (cu in)

1 cubic foot = 7.48 gallons (gal)

1 gallon = 231 cubic inches

1 gallon = 4 quarts (qt)

1 quart = 2 pints (pt)

1 pint = 2 cups (c)

1 cup = 8 fluid ounces (fl oz)

1 fluid ounce = 2 tablespoons (T)

1 tablespoon = 3 teaspoons (t)

WEIGHT

1 ton = 2000 pounds (lb)

1 pound = 16 ounces (oz)

1 pound = 7000 grains (gr)

1 ounce = 437.5 grains

TABLE 9   METRIC PREFIXES

Prefix	Meaning
kilo-	1000 ×
hecto-	100 ×
deka-	10 ×
deci-	0.1 ×
centi-	0.01 ×
milli-	0.001 ×

TABLE 10 UNITS OF MEASUREMENT: METRIC SYSTEM

LENGTH

1 kilometer (km) = 1000 meters (m)

1 hectometer (hm) = 100 meters

1 dekameter (dam) = 10 meters

1 meter = 10 decimeters (dm)

1 meter = 100 centimeters (cm)

1 meter = 1000 millimeters (mm)

AREA

1 square kilometer (sq km) = 1,000,000 square meters (sq m)

1 hectare (ha) = 1 square hectometer (sq hm)

1 hectare = 10,000 square meters

1 are = 1 square dekameter (sq dam)

1 are = 100 square meters

1 square meter = 100 square decimeters (sq dm)

1 square meter = 10,000 square centimeters (sq cm)

1 square meter = 1,000,000 square millimeters (sq mm)

VOLUME

1 liter (ℓ) = 1 cubic decimeter (cu dm)

1 liter = 1000 cubic centimeters (cu cm)

1 liter = 1000 milliliters (mℓ)

1 milliliter = 1 cubic centimeter

1 milliliter = 1000 cubic millimeters (cu mm)

WEIGHT

1 kilogram (kg) = 1000 grams (g)

1 hectogram (hg) = 100 grams

1 dekagram (dag) = 10 grams

1 gram = 10 decigrams (dg)

1 gram = 100 centigrams (cg)

1 gram = 1000 milligrams (mg)

TABLE 11 ENGLISH-METRIC CONVERSIONS

LENGTH

1 mi ≈ 1.6 km

0.62 mi ≈ 1 km

39.37 in ≈ 1 m

1 in ≈ 2.54 cm

VOLUME

1.06 qt ≈ 1 ℓ

33.9 fl oz ≈ 1 ℓ

WEIGHT

2.2 lb ≈ 1 kg

1 lb ≈ 454 g

ANSWERS TO SELECTED EXERCISES

CHAPTER 1

Exercises 1.1 (page 6)

1. 5 **3.** 10 (ten) **5.** 5 **7.** 100,000,000 (one hundred million) **9.** 10,000 **11.** Aron **13.** Yes
15. 14 **17.** 280 **19.** 2600 **21.** 15,500,000 **23.** 700,000 people
25. forty-seven **27.** eight hundred six
29. five thousand five hundred or fifty-five hundred
31. one hundred three thousand, eighty-five
33. five billion, seventy million **35.** thirty-five thousand dollars
37. 900 **39.** 6830 **41.** 5000 **43.** 5,090,000 **45.** 45,000,000

Exercises 1.2 (page 12)

1. 44 **3.** 20 **5.** 21 **7.** 847 **9.** 31,035 **11.** 411 **13.** 1,195,598 **15.** $32 **17.** $1012
19. 38 **21.** 592 **23.** 2533 **25.** 2324 **27.** 59,805 **29.** 48,575 **31.** 233 **33.** 4962
35. 69,700 **37.** 448,458 **39.** 329,707 **41.** 31,638 **43.** 609,318 **45.** $38 **47.** 2063 mi
49. 16 **51.** 19 **53.** 165 **55.** 697

Exercises 1.3 (page 17)

1. $18 + 17 = 35$ **3.** $54 = 63 - 9$ **5.** $50 + 360 = 410$ **7.** $1023 + 978 = 2101$ **9.** $3 = 7 - 4$
11. 325 **13.** 3802 **15.** 2094 **17.** 6026 **19.** 6936

Exercises 1.4 (page 22)

1. $210 **3.** 6997 **5.** 32,000 pages **7.** decrease; $102,000 **9.** Burton; $340 **11.** 39 cm
13. 154 ft **15.** $6500 **17.** $200,000 **19.** $80,000 **21.** increase; $40,000

Developing Number Sense #1 (page 13)

1. 1100 **2.** 800 **3.** 900 **4.** 1300 **5.** 16,000 **6.** 29,000 **7.** 4580 **8.** 856,000
9. 194,000

Using the Calculator #2 (page 14)

1. 12 **2.** 85 **3.** 9275 **4.** 591,968 **5.** 22 **6.** 258 **7.** 338 **8.** 5256 **9.** 54
10. 6463

Chapter 1 Review Exercises (page 25)

1. 3 **2.** 5 **3.** 1 (one) **4.** 10,000 (ten thousand) **5.** 0 **6.** 10,000,000 (ten million)
7. 2099; 2200; 3000 **8.** 720 **9.** 1100 **10.** 18,000 **11.** 803,000 **12.** 12 **13.** 308
14. 57,024 **15.** 2,080,911 **16.** 65,000,000,000 **17.** eighteen **18.** four hundred eighty-nine
19. two hundred six thousand, eight hundred one **20.** three billion, eight hundred thousand, five **21.** 665 mi
22. 227 **23.** 750 **24.** 9239 **25.** 110,152 **26.** 177,289 **27.** 2577 **28.** 20,265
29. 12,021,626,700 **30.** 708 **31.** 7308 **32.** 6797 **33.** 70,068 **34.** 209,363 **35.** 319
36. 2906 **37.** 4935 **38.** 5297 **39.** 32,964 **40.** 149,000 **41.** 1,926,681 **42.** 9,015,513
43. 203,463 **44.** 428 **45.** 24,114 **46.** 683 **47.** 593,097 **48.** 92,800 **49.** 202,968,274
50. 174 **51.** 19,785 **52.** 328 **53.** 5090 **54.** 185,438 **55.** 10,503 **56.** $1000 - 72 = 928$
57. $4300 + 486 = 4786$ **58.** $26 + 193 = 219$ **59.** $800 - 108 = 692$ **60.** 13 **61.** 1702
62. 2048 **63.** 3804 **64.** 14 mi **65.** 245,222 **66.** $2020 **67.** 96 sq mi **68.** 190 ft
69. $825 **70.** 39°F **71.** 46 ft **72.** 555 ft **73.** $192 **74.** $173 **75.** 363 mi
76. Nancy; $4120

Chapter 1 Practice Test (page 28)

1. 6   **2.** 3   **3.** 100 (hundred)   **4.** 10,000,000 (ten million)   **5.** 746   **6.** ninety thousand
7. 98; 799; 801; 1002   **8.** 700   **9.** 98,000   **10.** 8123   **11.** 82,717   **12.** 175,469   **13.** 7087
14. 490   **15.** 415   **16.** 1596   **17.** 5826   **18.** 49,654   **19.** 39,180   **20.** 1171   **21.** 182
22. 1331   **23.** 452   **24.** 4908   **25.** $619   **26.** 21 ft   **27.** $27,800   **28.** 319 workers

CHAPTER 2

Exercises 2.1 (page 35)

1. 438   **3.** 924   **5.** 5400   **7.** 38,815   **9.** 2752   **11.** 8525   **13.** 201,344   **15.** 376,272
17. 280,232   **19.** 7,940,184   **21.** 1200   **23.** 72,000,000   **25.** 192,000   **27.** 170,000,000
29. 23,220   **31.** 12,587,146   **33.** 186,215,960   **35.** 195,156,000   **37.** 60   **39.** 432   **41.** 648
43. 14,250   **45.** $2844   **47.** $3990

Exercises 2.2 (page 45)

1. 9 R3   **3.** 65 R6   **5.** 874 R4   **7.** 1031 R1   **9.** 9 R20   **11.** 662 R60   **13.** 218 R15
15. 8893 R16   **17.** 32 R400   **19.** 62 R100   **21.** 235   **23.** 42,240   **25.** 600 R4   **27.** 6007 R68
29. 50,040   **31.** 8002 R20   **33.** $252   **35.** 40 chandeliers; 10 bulbs left over   **37.** 40 hr

Exercises 2.3 (page 56)

1. 12   **3.** 11   **5.** 300   **7.** 4,048,000   **9. a.** yes   **b.** yes   **c.** no   **d.** yes
11. a. yes   **b.** no   **c.** yes   **d.** yes   **13. a.** yes   **b.** yes   **c.** yes   **d.** yes
15. a. yes   **b.** yes   **c.** yes   **d.** no   **17. a.** yes   **b.** yes   **c.** yes   **d.** no
19. a. no   **b.** yes   **c.** yes   **d.** yes   **21. a.** no   **b.** yes   **c.** yes   **d.** yes
23. 3×3 **25.** $2 \times 2 \times 3$ **27.** $3 \times 3 \times 5$ **29.** 5×11 **31.** 2×13 **33.** 3×19
35. $2 \times 3 \times 19$ **37.** $5 \times 7 \times 7$ **39.** $2 \times 3 \times 5 \times 5$ **41.** $2 \times 2 \times 2 \times 2 \times 3 \times 5 \times 5$
43. $3 \times 3 \times 3 \times 11$ **45.** 3×29 **47.** $2 \times 2 \times 2 \times 3 \times 3 \times 7$

Exercises 2.4 (page 61)

1. $9\overline{)54}$ (6)   **3.** $30\overline{)1350}$ (45)   **5.** $15\overline{)75}$ (5)   **7.** $16 \div 8 = 2$ **9.** $600 \div 50 = 12$ **11.** $621 \div 3 = 207$
13. into   **15.** by   **17.** by   **19.** into   **21.** $17 \times 38 = 646$ **23.** $3 \times 11 = 33$ **25.** $2 \times 230 = 460$
27. 12   **29.** 162   **31.** 78,000   **33.** 19,000

Exercises 2.5 (page 75)

1. 120 min   **3.** 17 lb   **5.** 205 chandeliers; 10 bulbs   **7.** 32 mi   **9.** $530   **11.** 40 yd   **13.** $50,400
15. 55 mi   **17.** 32 hr   **19.** 105 hr   **21.** 1425 sq in   **23.** 45 in   **25.** 1620 sq in   **27.** $760
29. 180 sq ft   **31.** $896   **33.** 110 mm   **35.** $37,500   **37.** $2550   **39.** 31 in   **41.** 73   **43.** 24 mi
45. $45,800   **47.** $28,627   **49.** 260 lb   **51.** 120 lb   **53.** 160 lb

Developing Number Sense #2 (page 46)

1. 560   **2.** 600   **3.** 1800   **4.** 48,000   **5.** 150,000   **6.** 21,000   **7.** 160,000   **8.** 14,000,000
9. 40   **10.** 20   **11.** 50   **12.** 225

Using the Calculator #3 (page 47)

1. 72   **2.** 3,900,000   **3.** 5278   **4.** 673,644   **5.** 2   **6.** 906   **7.** 887   **8.** 264   **9.** 4
10. 6080

Using the Calculator #4 (page 57)

4. 20   **5.** 6843   **6.** 135,000   **7.** 625   **8.** 23   **9.** 13×17 **10.** 7×23 **11.** 19×111
12. $13 \times 17 \times 19$

Using the Calculator #5 (page 78)

1. 75   **2.** 42,942   **3.** 20   **4.** 5225   **5.** $1181   **6.** 184 sq ft

Chapter 2 Review Exercises (page 80)

1. 1148 **2.** 12,623 **3.** 11,178 **4.** 217,674 **5.** 7,468,606 **6.** 2,625,104 **7.** 154,080
8. 6,717,512 **9.** 425,000 **10.** 5,760,000 **11.** 63,856 **12.** 15,460,242 **13.** 48 **14.** 126
15. 60 **16.** 980 **17.** 7 R3 **18.** 30 **19.** 839 **20.** 5415 R4 **21.** 2 R20 **22.** 600 R22
23. 555 **24.** 2003 R16 **25.** 1056 R8 **26.** 16 R346 **27.** 82 R220 **28.** 860 R400
29. 1751 R347 **30.** 5060 **31.** 25 **32.** 7 **33.** 384 **34.** 15 **35.** 436 **36.** 36,000
37. a. no **b.** yes **c.** yes **d.** no **38. a.** no **b.** no **c.** yes **d.** yes
39. a. yes **b.** yes **c.** yes **d.** no **40. a.** yes **b.** yes **c.** no **d.** yes
41. a. yes **b.** yes **c.** no **d.** yes **42. a.** yes **b.** yes **b.** yes **d.** yes
43. a. no **b.** no **c.** yes **d.** yes **44. a.** no **b.** no **c.** yes **d.** yes
45. $2 \times 3 \times 3$ **46.** $2 \times 3 \times 3 \times 3$ **47.** $2 \times 2 \times 2 \times 3 \times 7$ **48.** $3 \times 3 \times 7 \times 7$
49. $2 \times 3 \times 5 \times 5 \times 5$ **50.** $2 \times 2 \times 5 \times 7$ **51.** $2 \times 2 \times 3 \times 3 \times 3 \times 5 \times 5$
52. $2 \times 2 \times 2 \times 2 \times 2 \times 2 \times 3 \times 5 \times 5 \times 5$ **53.** $3 \times 3 \times 3 \times 13$ **54.** $3 \times 5 \times 17$
55. $4\overline{)12}$ $^{3}$ **56.** $5\overline{)100}$ $^{20}$ **57.** $72 \div 8 = 9$ **58.** $325 \div 25 = 13$ **59.** into **60.** by **61.** by
62. into **63.** $3 \times 16 = 48$ **64.** $2 \times 400 = 800$ **65.** $174 \div 6 = 29$ **66.** $585 \div 13 = 45$
67. $4 \times 17 = 68$ **68.** $60 \times 400 = 24,000$ **69.** $9 \times 9 = 81$ **70.** $8080 \div 16 = 505$ **71.** 201
72. 6,000,000 **73.** 34 **74.** 3 **75.** 1900 **76.** 44 **77.** 8, 16, 24, 32, 40 **78.** yes; $17 \times 4 = 68$
79. $2250 **80.** $105 **81.** 122 **82.** 1080 assistants **83.** 42 hr **84.** $13,500 **85.** 112 sq ft
86. 7203 sq ft **87.** 15 min **88.** 194 m **89.** $130,000 **90.** $11

Chapter 2 Practice Test (page 82)

1. 73,896 **2.** 538,479 **3.** 221,844 **4.** 4,800,000 **5.** 949,000 **6.** 63,856 **7.** 16,495,338
8. 42 **9.** 525 **10.** 839 **11.** 6082 R2 **12.** 555 **13.** 2003 R16 **14.** 860 R400 **15.** 5060
16. 1230 **17.** 405,000 **18.** yes **19.** yes **20.** $2 \times 3 \times 7$ **21.** $2 \times 5 \times 5 \times 17$ **22.** by
23. into **24.** 454 **25.** 833 **26.** $325 **27.** 250 packages; no ears left over
28. 42 in **29.** 29 oz **30.** 25 cm **31.** $2520 **32.** 1280 mi **33.** 15 min

Cumulative Review Exercises: Chapters 1–2 (page 84)

1. sixty-four thousand, ninety-eight **2.** 2,013,500 **3.** 150,000 **4.** 386,000 **5.** 7248
6. 238,000,000 **7.** 9060 **8.** 256 R 26 **9.** 4004 R 100 **10.** 98 R 228 **11.** $2 \times 2 \times 3 \times 3$
12. $5 \times 5 \times 11$ **13.** $2 \times 2 \times 2 \times 3 \times 3 \times 5 \times 5 \times 5$ **14.** $7 \times 7 \times 13$ **15.** 6 **16.** 512
17. 4661 **18.** 1,410,640 **19.** 1461 **20.** 80 **21.** 135 **22.** 18
23. a. 98,000 sq ft **b.** 1260 ft **24.** $165 **25.** $109 **26.** $275 **27.** 150 mi **28.** 75 hr
29. a. 435 **b.** 87 **c.** 19 **30.** 142 customers **31.** under, $34

CHAPTER 3

Exercises 3.1 (page 89)

1. $\dfrac{1}{4}$ **3.** $\dfrac{1}{5}$ **5.** $\dfrac{5}{6}$ **7.** $\dfrac{3}{8}$ **9.** $\dfrac{5}{5}$ or 1 **11.** $\dfrac{4}{3}, 1\dfrac{1}{3}$ **13.** $\dfrac{13}{9}, 1\dfrac{4}{9}$ **15.** $\dfrac{23}{6}, 3\dfrac{5}{6}$ **17.** $\dfrac{8}{4}, 2$

19. $\dfrac{7}{5}, \dfrac{8}{3}, \dfrac{30}{13}$ **21.** $\dfrac{8}{8}, \dfrac{4}{4}, \dfrac{13}{13}$ **23.** $\dfrac{2}{5}, \dfrac{7}{12}$

Exercises 3.2 (page 93)

1. $\dfrac{1}{2}$ **3.** $\dfrac{12}{5}$ **5.** $\dfrac{2}{13}$ **7.** $\dfrac{11}{30}$ **9.** $\dfrac{5}{10}$ **11.** $\dfrac{36}{1000}$ **13.** seven-halves **15.** six-elevenths

17. one hundredth **19.** $6\dfrac{2}{5}$ **21.** $60\dfrac{3}{100}$ **22.** $5\dfrac{13}{1000}$ **23.** nine and three-tenths

24. eighty and one-half **25.** fourteen and seventeen-hundredths

Exercises 3.3 (page 98)

1. $\frac{2}{8}, \frac{1}{4}$ **3.** $\frac{6}{10}, \frac{3}{5}$ **5.** $\frac{6}{9}, \frac{2}{3}$ **7.** $\frac{10}{12}, \frac{5}{6}$ **9.** 15 **11.** 40 **13.** 143 **15.** 28 **17.** 8 **19.** 6

21. 35 **23.** 126 **25.** $\frac{8}{24}$ **27.** $\frac{30}{42}$ **29.** $\frac{60}{15}$

Exercises 3.4 (page 102)

1. 5 **3.** $7\frac{1}{5}$ **5.** $40\frac{5}{6}$ **7.** 25 **9.** $10\frac{11}{20}$ **11.** 301 **13.** $\frac{13}{4}$ **15.** $\frac{37}{5}$ **17.** $\frac{55}{4}$ **19.** $\frac{174}{5}$

21. $\frac{41}{11}$ **23.** $\frac{159}{10}$ **25.** not possible **27.** 3 **29.** 2 **31.** 1 **33.** not possible **35.** $2\frac{1}{13}$

Exercises 3.5 (page 108)

1. $\frac{2}{3}$ **3.** $\frac{3}{2}$ or $1\frac{1}{2}$ **5.** $\frac{3}{5}$ **7.** $\frac{3}{4}$ **9.** not possible **11.** $\frac{3}{10}$ **13.** $\frac{9}{2}$ or $4\frac{1}{2}$

15. $\frac{8}{7}$ or $1\frac{1}{7}$ **17.** not possible **19.** $\frac{3}{5}$ **21.** $\frac{7}{11}$ **23.** $\frac{3}{17}$ **25.** $\frac{13}{2}$ or $6\frac{1}{2}$ **27.** $\frac{11}{20}$

29. $\frac{11}{3}$ or $3\frac{2}{3}$ **31.** $\frac{2}{7}$ **33.** $\frac{5}{12}$ **35.** $\frac{3}{8}$ **37.** $\frac{3}{2}$ or $1\frac{1}{2}$ **39.** $\frac{5}{4}$ or $1\frac{1}{4}$ **41.** $\frac{1}{2}$ **43.** $\frac{7}{9}$

45. $\frac{4}{5}$ **47.** $\frac{35}{26}$ or $1\frac{9}{26}$ **49.** $\frac{13}{15}$ **51.** $\frac{7}{8}$ **53.** $\frac{20}{7}$ or $2\frac{6}{7}$ **55.** $\frac{9}{50}$ **57.** $\frac{3}{20}$ **59.** $\frac{23}{710}$

Exercises 3.6 (page 118)

1. 4 gal **3.** $1\frac{1}{2}$ lb **5.** $\frac{1}{5}$ ft **7.** $\frac{1}{3}$ qt **9.** $\frac{100}{3}$ or $33\frac{1}{3}$ km **11.** $\frac{2}{7}$ **13.** $\frac{2}{5}$ **15.** $\frac{7}{3}$ or $2\frac{1}{3}$

17. $\frac{3}{5}$ **19.** $1 \div 8$ **21.** $19 \div 5$ **23.** $3 \div 4$ **25.** $4 \div 15$ **27.** $12\overline{)1}$ **29.** $5\overline{)12}$

31. $13\overline{)8}$ **33.** $6\overline{)1}$ **35.** $\frac{2}{3}$ **37.** $\frac{4}{5}$ **39.** $\frac{1}{5}$ **41.** $\frac{1}{4}$ **43.** $\frac{3}{11}$ **45.** $3\frac{2}{5}$ **47.** $\frac{7}{10}$ **49.** $\frac{1}{200}$

51. $\frac{2}{3}$ **53.** $\frac{3}{2}$ **55.** $\frac{3}{4}$ **57.** $\frac{8}{21}$ **59.** $\frac{23}{50}$ **61.** $\frac{7}{15}$ **63.** $\frac{7}{20}$ **65.** $\frac{34}{5}$ **67.** $\frac{1}{9}$ **69.** $\frac{1}{6}$ **71.** $\frac{1}{5}$

73. $\frac{3}{8}$ **75.** $\frac{1}{4}$

Using the Calculator #6 (page 109)

2. $\frac{7}{3}$ **3.** $\frac{113}{6}$ **4.** $\frac{971}{79}$ **5.** $\frac{83}{4}$ **6.** $3\frac{1}{9}$ **7.** $23\frac{2}{15}$ **8.** $28\frac{1}{4}$ **9.** $3\frac{5}{6}$ **10.** $\frac{2}{3}$

11. $\frac{50}{17}$ or $2\frac{16}{17}$ **12.** $\frac{2}{5}$ **13.** $\frac{69}{8}$ or $8\frac{5}{8}$ **15.** $\frac{5,567,076}{6255}$ **17.** $\frac{77}{221}$

Chapter 3 Review Exercises (page 122)

1. one-half **2.** two-thirds **3.** six-thirteenths **4.** three and one-fourth
5. fourteen and two-fifths **6.** twenty and thirteen one-hundredths
7. $\frac{2}{5}$ **8.** $\frac{5}{9}$ **9.** $\frac{9}{2}, 4\frac{1}{2}$ **10.** $\frac{17}{6}, 2\frac{5}{6}$ **11.** $\frac{8}{4}, 2$ **12.** $\frac{15}{3}, 5$ **13.** $\frac{21}{5}, \frac{11}{2}$ **14.** $\frac{130}{21}, \frac{19}{4}$

15. $\frac{4}{4}, \frac{30}{30}$ **16.** $\frac{15}{15}, \frac{1}{1}, \frac{7}{7}$ **17.** $\frac{6}{9}, \frac{2}{3}$ **18.** $\frac{8}{10}, \frac{4}{5}$ **19.** $\frac{2}{6}, \frac{1}{3}$ **20.** $\frac{6}{9}, \frac{2}{3}$ **21.** 28 **22.** 156 **23.** 12

24. 180 **25.** $\frac{16}{56}$ **26.** $\frac{32}{4}$ **27.** $5\frac{7}{8}$ **28.** 20 **29.** 19 **30.** $20\frac{3}{4}$ **31.** $\frac{37}{7}$ **32.** $\frac{141}{4}$

33. $\frac{77}{6}$ **34.** $\frac{167}{23}$ **35.** $5\frac{1}{3}$ **36.** not possible **37.** 1 **38.** not possible **39.** 4 **40.** $20\frac{5}{6}$

41. $\frac{3}{10}$ **42.** $\frac{3}{2}$ or $1\frac{1}{2}$ **43.** not possible **44.** $\frac{4}{7}$ **45.** $\frac{9}{7}$ or $1\frac{2}{7}$ **46.** not possible **47.** $\frac{8}{15}$

48. $\dfrac{10}{27}$ **49.** $\dfrac{9}{10}$ **50.** $\dfrac{49}{6}$ or $8\dfrac{1}{6}$ **51.** $\dfrac{11}{5}$ or $2\dfrac{1}{5}$ **52.** $\dfrac{18}{35}$ **53.** not possible   **54.** $\dfrac{2}{3}$ **55.** 5

56. $\dfrac{3}{20}$ **57.** $\dfrac{13}{3}$ or $4\dfrac{1}{3}$ **58.** $\dfrac{3}{13}$ **59.** $\dfrac{5}{6}$ **60.** $\dfrac{6}{5} = 1\dfrac{1}{5}$ **61.** $\dfrac{3}{5}$ **62.** $\dfrac{5}{3} = 1\dfrac{2}{3}$ **63.** $\dfrac{5}{3}$ or $1\dfrac{2}{3}$

64. $\dfrac{13}{2}$ or $6\dfrac{1}{2}$ **65.** $\dfrac{7}{5}$ or $1\dfrac{2}{5}$ **66.** $\dfrac{1}{3}$ **67.** $\dfrac{1}{3}$ **68.** $\dfrac{1}{20}$ **69.** $\dfrac{1}{5}$ **70.** 4   **71.** $\dfrac{3}{10}$ **72.** $\dfrac{5}{12}$

73. $\dfrac{3}{4}$ **74.** $\dfrac{4}{7}$ **75.** $\dfrac{5}{3}$ or $1\dfrac{2}{3}$ lb   **76.** $\dfrac{1}{4}$ m   **77.** $\dfrac{7}{12}$ gal   **78.** $\dfrac{25}{8}$ or $3\dfrac{1}{8}$ gal   **79.** $\dfrac{4}{5}$ **80.** $\dfrac{13}{50}$

81. $\dfrac{3}{7}$ **82.** $\dfrac{1}{5}$

Chapter 3 Practice Test (page 125)

1. $\dfrac{4}{7}$ **2.** $\dfrac{3}{8}$ **3.** $\dfrac{13}{4}, 3\dfrac{1}{4}$ **4.** $\dfrac{10}{12}, \dfrac{5}{6}$ **5.** $\dfrac{5}{8}, \dfrac{6}{7}, \dfrac{1}{8}$ **6.** 30   **7.** 18   **8.** 24   **9.** $\dfrac{2}{7}$

10. $\dfrac{5}{4}$ or $1\dfrac{1}{4}$ **11.** $\dfrac{4}{5}$ **12.** $\dfrac{2}{3}$ **13.** $5\overline{)2}$ **14.** seven-elevenths   **15.** four and three-fifths

16. $2\dfrac{3}{5}$ **17.** $24\dfrac{17}{18}$ **18.** 70   **19.** $\dfrac{99}{8}$ **20.** $\dfrac{197}{20}$ **21.** $\dfrac{5}{7}$ **22.** $\dfrac{20}{7}$ or $2\dfrac{6}{7}$ **23.** $\dfrac{6}{29}$ **24.** $\dfrac{2}{7}$

25. $\dfrac{83}{150}$ **26.** $\dfrac{2}{5}$ **27.** $\dfrac{1}{5}$ **28.** $\dfrac{27}{20}$ or $1\dfrac{7}{20}$ cm   **29.** $\dfrac{3}{8}\ell$ **30.** $\dfrac{39}{80}$

CHAPTER 4

Exercises 4.1 (page 133)

1. $\dfrac{10}{3}$ or $3\dfrac{1}{3}$ **3.** $\dfrac{6}{77}$ **5.** $\dfrac{310}{243}$ or $1\dfrac{67}{243}$ **7.** $\dfrac{130}{9}$ or $14\dfrac{4}{9}$ **9.** $\dfrac{7}{19}$ **11.** 32   **13.** $\dfrac{12}{7}$ or $1\dfrac{5}{7}$

15. $\dfrac{8}{15}$ **17.** $\dfrac{9}{8}$ or $1\dfrac{1}{8}$ **19.** $\dfrac{459}{5}$ or $91\dfrac{4}{5}$ **21.** $\dfrac{1}{3}$ **23.** $\dfrac{9}{4}$ or $2\dfrac{1}{4}$ **25.** 200   **27.** $\dfrac{13}{6}$ or $2\dfrac{1}{6}$

29. $\dfrac{11}{36}$ **31.** $\dfrac{21}{16}$ or $1\dfrac{5}{16}$ **33.** $\dfrac{44}{49}$ **35.** $\dfrac{57}{25}$ or $2\dfrac{7}{25}$ **37.** $\dfrac{15}{7}$ or $2\dfrac{1}{7}$ **39.** $\dfrac{39}{8}$ or $4\dfrac{7}{8}$ **41.** $\dfrac{2}{5}$

43. \$15   **45.** \$42

Exercises 4.2 (page 138)

1. $\dfrac{6}{5}$ or $1\dfrac{1}{5}$ **3.** $\dfrac{27}{20}$ or $1\dfrac{7}{20}$ **5.** $\dfrac{9}{58}$ **7.** 15   **9.** 2625   **11.** $\dfrac{1}{24}$ **13.** $\dfrac{9}{10}$ **15.** $\dfrac{3}{7}$ **17.** $\dfrac{3}{5}$

19. 14   **21.** $\dfrac{35}{2}$ or $17\dfrac{1}{2}$ **23.** 5   **25.** $\dfrac{125}{39}$ or $3\dfrac{8}{39}$ **27.** 1   **29.** $\dfrac{3}{40}$

31. $\dfrac{27}{2}$ or $13\dfrac{1}{2}$ **33.** $\dfrac{75}{38}$ or $1\dfrac{37}{38}$ **35.** $\dfrac{1}{25}$ **37.** $\dfrac{20,000}{7}$ or $2857\dfrac{1}{7}$ **39.** $\dfrac{5}{3}$ or $1\dfrac{2}{3}$ ft

41. $\dfrac{7}{40}\ell$ **43.** 50 bows

Exercises 4.3 (page 141)

1. 3   **3.** $\dfrac{42}{5}$ or $8\dfrac{2}{5}$ **5.** $\dfrac{1}{4}$ **7.** $\dfrac{1}{7}$ **9.** $\dfrac{1}{6}$ **11.** 72   **13.** 12   **15.** $\dfrac{800}{7}$ or $114\dfrac{2}{7}$ **17.** $\dfrac{2}{7}$

19. $\dfrac{4}{5}$ **21.** $\dfrac{3}{20}$ **23.** 720   **25.** $\dfrac{500,000}{43}$ or $11,627\dfrac{39}{43}$

Exercises 4.4 (page 149)

1. $\dfrac{2}{5} \times 25 = 10$ **3.** $\dfrac{3}{5} \times \dfrac{5}{6} = \dfrac{1}{2}$ **5.** $\dfrac{3}{\frac{1}{4}} = 12$ **7.** $\dfrac{40}{100} \times 200 = 80$ **9.** $4 \div 2\dfrac{2}{3} = 1\dfrac{1}{2}$

11. $4\frac{1}{2} = \frac{1}{2} \times 9$ **13.** $\frac{7}{8} = 2 \times \frac{7}{16}$ **15.** 360 **17.** 105 **19.** 72 **21.** 4 **23.** $\frac{37}{10}$ or $3\frac{7}{10}$

25. 150 **27.** $\frac{17}{2}$ or $8\frac{1}{2}$ **29.** $\frac{203}{8}$ or $25\frac{3}{8}$ **31.** 90 **33.** 240 **35.** $\frac{1}{32}$ **37.** $\frac{1000}{7}$ or $142\frac{6}{7}$

39. $\frac{3}{100}$ **41.** 5400 **43.** 800 **45.** $\frac{5}{2}$ or $2\frac{1}{2}$

Exercises 4.5 (page 167)

1. $\frac{3}{2}$ or $1\frac{1}{2}$ gal **3.** 28 slices **5.** $\frac{1}{8}$ lb **7.** 975 oz **9.** $1512 **11.** $\frac{50}{7}$ or $7\frac{1}{7}$ min

13. $\frac{215}{32}$ or $6\frac{23}{32}$ gal **15.** 6 ft per sec **17.** $\frac{6}{25}$ gal per person **19.** $\frac{40}{3}$ or $13\frac{1}{3}$ persons per sq mi

21. 70 words per min **23.** 42 min **25.** $\frac{13}{4}$ or $3\frac{1}{4}$ lb **27.** $\frac{1}{30}$ lb **29.** $\frac{40}{3}$ or $13\frac{1}{3}$ sq ft

31. 15 ft **33.** 81 games **35.** $\frac{3}{10}$ **37.** $\frac{1}{5}$ **39.** $18 per hr **41.** 40¢ per ℓ **43.** $\frac{1}{3}$

45. 10,800 Asians

Developing Number Sense #3 (page 134)

1. more than 84 **2.** more than 84 **3.** less than 84 **4.** equal to 84 **5.** less than 84

6. more than 84 **7.** less than 682 **8.** more than 682 **9.** more than 682 **10.** more than 682

11. equal to 682 **12.** less than 682 **13.** less than $25\frac{1}{2}$ **14.** more than $25\frac{1}{2}$ **15.** more than $25\frac{1}{2}$

16. equal to $25\frac{1}{2}$

Chapter 4 Review Exercises (page 170)

1. 18 **2.** $\frac{61}{3}$ or $20\frac{1}{3}$ **3.** 18 **4.** $\frac{15}{2}$ or $7\frac{1}{2}$ **5.** $\frac{2}{15}$ **6.** $\frac{5}{14}$ **7.** $\frac{13}{14}$ **8.** 3

9. $\frac{21}{4}$ or $5\frac{1}{4}$ **10.** 10 **11.** $\frac{27}{10}$ or $2\frac{7}{10}$ **12.** $\frac{2}{7}$ **13.** 18 **14.** $\frac{3}{26}$ **15.** 208,000

16. $\frac{497}{12}$ or $41\frac{5}{12}$ **17.** $\frac{11}{2}$ or $5\frac{1}{2}$ **18.** 9 **19.** $69 **20.** $\frac{25}{8}$ or $3\frac{1}{8}$ **21.** $\frac{5}{9}$ **22.** $\frac{9}{5}$ or $1\frac{4}{5}$

23. $\frac{4}{15}$ **24.** $\frac{42}{25}$ or $1\frac{17}{25}$ **25.** $\frac{2}{9}$ **26.** $\frac{2}{5}$ **27.** $\frac{22}{3}$ or $7\frac{1}{3}$ **28.** $\frac{25}{24}$ or $1\frac{1}{24}$ **29.** 49

30. 480 **31.** 36 **32.** $\frac{125}{7}$ or $17\frac{6}{7}$ **33.** $\frac{9}{4}$ or $2\frac{1}{4}$ **34.** $\frac{9}{160}$ **35.** $\frac{625}{2}$ or $312\frac{1}{2}$ **36.** 30

37. $\frac{2}{3}$ ft **38.** 9 doses **39.** 410 **40.** 32 **41.** $\frac{3}{8}$ **42.** $\frac{14}{3}$ or $4\frac{2}{3}$ **43.** $\frac{9}{4}$ or $2\frac{1}{4}$ **44.** 440

45. 150 **46.** 320 **47.** $\frac{1}{4}$ **48.** $\frac{1}{4}$ **49.** $\frac{7}{16}$ **50.** 10 **51.** $\frac{125}{2}$ or $62\frac{1}{2}$ **52.** $\frac{1}{15}$

53. 36 workers **54.** $30,000 **55.** $\frac{7}{4}$ or $1\frac{3}{4}$ lb **56.** 24¢ **57.** $\frac{135}{4}$ or $33\frac{3}{4}$ sq yd

58. $\frac{3}{2}$ or $1\frac{1}{2}$ gal **59.** $\frac{145}{14}$ or $10\frac{5}{14}$ lb **60.** $\frac{169}{8}$ or $21\frac{1}{8}$ sq ft **61.** $\frac{7}{2}$ or $3\frac{1}{2}$ hr

62. $189 **63.** $\frac{19}{4}$ or $4\frac{3}{4}$ ft **64.** $\frac{1}{4}$

Chapter 4 Practice Test (page 172)

1. $\frac{6}{35}$ **2.** 2 **3.** 5100 **4.** $\frac{115}{2}$ or $57\frac{1}{2}$ **5.** $\frac{1}{12}$ **6.** $\frac{2}{5}$ **7.** $\frac{1}{108}$ **8.** $\frac{4}{9}$ **9.** $\frac{45}{22}$ or $2\frac{1}{22}$

10. $\frac{15}{7}$ or $2\frac{1}{7}$ **11.** 9 **12.** 9225 **13.** $\frac{8}{7}$ or $1\frac{1}{7}$ **14.** 27 **15.** 35 **16.** $\frac{7}{6}$ or $1\frac{1}{6}$

17. $37\frac{1}{2}$ servings **18.** $80 **19.** $\frac{22}{3}$ or $7\frac{1}{3}$ min **20.** $84 **21.** $\frac{2}{3}$ ft **22.** $\frac{9}{2}$ or $4\frac{1}{2}$ yd

23. $\frac{4}{5}$ **24.** $3\frac{3}{5}$ hr

CHAPTER 5

Exercises 5.1 (page 177)

1. $\frac{5}{8}$ **3.** $\frac{2}{3}$ **5.** 1 **7.** $\frac{25}{18}$ or $1\frac{7}{18}$ **9.** $\frac{16}{3}$ or $5\frac{1}{3}$ **11.** $9\frac{3}{4}$ or $\frac{39}{4}$ **13.** 3 **15.** $8\frac{5}{6}$

17. $34\frac{5}{32}$ **19.** $22\frac{2}{5}$ **21.** 34 **23.** $157\frac{2}{3}$ **25.** 9 lb **27.** $28\frac{1}{4}$ in

Exercises 5.2 (page 182)

1. 2, 7 **3.** 31, 13, 17 **5.** 3×3 **7.** $2 \times 2 \times 3$ **9.** 11 is prime **11.** $2 \times 3 \times 2 \times 2 \times 2$
13. $2 \times 2 \times 2 \times 2 \times 2 \times 2$ **15.** $5 \times 5 \times 5$ **17.** 97 is prime **19.** 7×13 **21.** $5 \times 7 \times 7$
23. 18 **25.** 120 **27.** 84 **29.** 154 **31.** 36 **33.** 44 **35.** 225 **37.** 325 **39.** 884

Exercises 5.3 (page 189)

1. $\frac{31}{18}$ or $1\frac{13}{18}$ **3.** $\frac{11}{8}$ or $1\frac{3}{8}$ **5.** $\frac{4}{5}$ **7.** $\frac{81}{22}$ or $3\frac{15}{22}$ **9.** $\frac{5}{4}$ or $1\frac{1}{4}$ **11.** $\frac{131}{210}$ **13.** $35\frac{8}{21}$

15. $104\frac{49}{64}$ **17.** $64\frac{29}{102}$ **19.** $\frac{7}{5}$ or $1\frac{2}{5}$ **21.** $\frac{433}{210}$ or $2\frac{13}{210}$ **23.** $14\frac{10}{99}$ **25.** $113\frac{94}{105}$

27. $20\frac{1}{40}$ **29.** $32\frac{123}{260}$ **31.** $15\frac{11}{15}$ hr **33.** $22\frac{1}{12}$ ft

Exercises 5.4 (page 193)

1. $\frac{2}{3}$ **3.** $\frac{7}{9}$ **5.** $\frac{2}{5}$ **7.** $\frac{7}{20}$ **9.** $\frac{10}{12}$ **11.** $\frac{1}{4}$ **13.** $\frac{6}{6}$ **15.** $\frac{2}{5}$ **17.** $\frac{1}{4}, \frac{3}{4}, \frac{5}{4}, \frac{11}{4}$ **19.** $\frac{1}{2}, \frac{3}{5}, \frac{13}{20}$

21. $\frac{11}{24}, \frac{24}{11}, 3$ **23.** $<$ **25.** $>$ **27.** $=$ **29.** $<$ **31.** $>$ **33.** $\frac{7}{8}$ in **35.** Paul

Exercises 5.5 (page 199)

1. $\frac{2}{3}$ **3.** $\frac{5}{8}$ **5.** $\frac{13}{36}$ **7.** $11\frac{1}{2}$ **9.** $5\frac{3}{8}$ **11.** $3\frac{5}{8}$ **13.** $23\frac{17}{36}$ **15.** $4\frac{1}{5}$ **17.** $9\frac{5}{12}$ **19.** $\frac{7}{18}$

21. $4\frac{2}{3}$ **23.** $5\frac{1}{2}$ **25.** $3\frac{29}{75}$ **27.** $49\frac{37}{39}$ **29.** $5\frac{13}{40}$ **31.** $7\frac{1}{4}$ ft **33.** $1\frac{7}{8}$ in **35.** $\frac{5}{6}$ of the job

37. $\frac{13}{24}$ of the pizza **39.** $\frac{1}{3}$ **41.** $\frac{16}{15}$ or $1\frac{1}{15}$ **43.** $1\frac{7}{12}$ **45.** $\frac{3}{13}$

Exercises 5.6 (page 204)

1. $2\frac{1}{3} + \frac{2}{3} = 3$ **3.** $7 - 6\frac{1}{4} = \frac{3}{4}$ **5.** $\frac{7}{8} + \frac{1}{8} = 1$ **7.** $\frac{1}{2} + \frac{3}{2} = 2$ **9.** $\frac{3}{10} = \frac{1}{2} - \frac{1}{5}$ **11.** $5\frac{1}{5}$

13. $\frac{1}{27}$ **15.** l **17.** $2\frac{1}{4}$ **19.** $\frac{1}{40}$ **21.** $\frac{22}{15}$ or $1\frac{7}{15}$

Exercises 5.7 (page 214)

1. $\frac{5}{6}$ **3.** $\frac{7}{12}$ cup **5.** $\frac{3}{4}$ of her income **7.** $1\frac{3}{4}$ mi **9.** 3 c **11.** $3\frac{5}{16}$ lb **13.** $1\frac{3}{4}$ hr **15.** $6\frac{3}{16}$ in

17. too large by $\frac{1}{16}$ in **19.** $5\frac{7}{12}$ hr **21.** $\frac{29}{48}$ **23.** $\frac{41}{12}$ or $3\frac{5}{12}$ mi per hr **25.** $\frac{41}{16}$ or $2\frac{9}{16}$ lb

27. $300 **29.** Nancy, $\frac{1}{48}$ **31.** $41\frac{1}{4}$ ft **33.** $\frac{1}{3} + \frac{1}{4} + \frac{1}{8} + \frac{7}{24} = \frac{8}{24} + \frac{6}{24} + \frac{3}{24} + \frac{7}{24} = \frac{24}{24} = 1$

35. $9000 **37.** 11 in **39.** $\frac{11}{5}$ or $2\frac{1}{5}$ in

Developing Number Sense #4 (page 194)

1. b. $\frac{10}{20}$ **c.** $\frac{24}{48}$ **g.** $\frac{43}{86}$ **2. a.** $\frac{8}{17}$ **d.** $\frac{99}{202}$ **e.** $\frac{87}{180}$ **3. a.** $\frac{9}{17}$ **b.** $\frac{17}{30}$ **f.** $\frac{76}{150}$

4. $\frac{1}{4} < \frac{1}{2}$ **5.** $\frac{5}{8} > \frac{1}{2}$ **6.** $\frac{10}{18} > \frac{1}{2}$ **7.** $\frac{18}{36} = \frac{1}{2}$ **8.** $\frac{34}{70} < \frac{1}{2}$ **9.** $\frac{42}{87} < \frac{1}{2}$

Developing Number Sense #5 (page 201)

1. 5   **2.** 8   **3.** 12   **4.** 46   **5.** 0   **6.** 1   **7.** 70   **8.** 150   **9.** 20   **10.** 10   **11.** 50
12. 180   **13.** 15   **14.** 6   **15.** 51   **16.** 16   **17.** 864   **18.** 280   **19.** 170   **20.** 140
21. 6600   **22.** 23

Using the Calculator #7 (page 217)

1. $\frac{7}{10}$ **2.** $\frac{24}{203}$ **3.** $3\frac{3}{4}$ **4.** $\frac{11}{45}$ **5.** $71\frac{13}{35}$ **6.** $\frac{8}{19}$

Chapter 5 Review Exercises (page 218)

1. 13, 23   **2.** 2, 7, 17, 37   **3.** 5×7 **4.** $2 \times 2 \times 2 \times 3 \times 3$ **5.** $2 \times 3 \times 13$ **6.** $3 \times 3 \times 19$

7. 30   **8.** 42   **9.** 45   **10.** 132   **11.** 136   **12.** 180   **13.** $\frac{5}{4}$ or $1\frac{1}{4}$ **14.** 12   **15.** $\frac{3}{5}$

16. $\frac{7}{9}$ **17.** $16\frac{1}{6}$ **18.** $\frac{17}{21}$ **19.** $14\frac{13}{36}$ **20.** $\frac{26}{33}$ **21.** $35\frac{19}{42}$ **22.** $\frac{67}{80}$ **23.** $\frac{77}{52}$ or $1\frac{25}{52}$

24. $57\frac{8}{25}$ **25.** $\frac{10}{9}$ **26.** $\frac{3}{11}$ **27.** $\frac{3}{4}$ **28.** $\frac{8}{27}, \frac{1}{3}, \frac{4}{9}$ **29.** $\frac{2}{7}, \frac{2}{5}, \frac{2}{3}$ **30.** $\frac{47}{50}, \frac{19}{20}, 1$ **31.** $>$

32. $<$ **33.** $>$ **34.** $>$ **35.** $>$ **36.** $\frac{1}{3}$ **37.** $2\frac{3}{4}$ **38.** $7\frac{2}{5}$ **39.** $11\frac{4}{7}$ **40.** $\frac{11}{24}$ **41.** $9\frac{5}{9}$

42. $3\frac{17}{20}$ **43.** $7\frac{1}{20}$ **44.** $19\frac{87}{98}$ **45.** $2\frac{1}{3} - 2 = \frac{1}{3}$ **46.** $\frac{3}{5} + \frac{4}{5} = \frac{7}{5}$ **47.** $\frac{2}{3} + \frac{5}{3} = \frac{7}{3}$

48. $5 - 2\frac{1}{3} = 2\frac{2}{3}$ **49.** $\frac{3}{10} + \frac{2}{10} = \frac{1}{2}$ **50.** $2\frac{4}{7}$ **51.** $5\frac{1}{5}$ **52.** $\frac{3}{8}$ **53.** 6   **54.** Shirley

55. $8\frac{1}{8}$ ft   **56.** $66\frac{1}{6}$ ft   **57.** $5\frac{1}{2}$ ft   **58.** $12\frac{1}{4}$ hr   **59.** $3\frac{1}{4}$ ft   **60.** $1\frac{1}{2}$ lb   **61.** $9\frac{1}{2}$ lb   **62.** no

63. $\frac{23}{7}$ or $3\frac{2}{7}$ mi   **64.** $\frac{7}{20}$ of the voters   **65.** $\frac{1}{12}$ of the job   **66.** 1980 students   **67.** $18\frac{1}{6}$ mi per hr

68. $\frac{1545}{16}$ or $96\frac{9}{16}$ sq ft   **69.** 600 students   **70.** $\frac{1}{24}$

Chapter 5 Practice Test (page 221)

1. 17, 23   **2.** $2 \times 3 \times 7$ **3.** $2 \times 5 \times 11$ **4.** 60   **5.** 216   **6.** $\frac{4}{3}$ or $1\frac{1}{3}$ **7.** $\frac{13}{18}$ **8.** $15\frac{4}{75}$

9. $2\frac{5}{36}$ **10.** $18\frac{13}{14}$ **11.** $\frac{1}{2}$ **12.** $\frac{7}{12}, \frac{2}{3}, \frac{3}{4}$ **13.** $\frac{17}{24} < \frac{3}{4}$ **14.** $\frac{1}{8}$ **15.** $5\frac{37}{45}$ **16.** $4\frac{1}{2}$ or $\frac{9}{2}$

17. $6\frac{7}{24}$ **18.** $5\frac{1}{3}$ or $\frac{16}{3}$ **19.** $\frac{1}{3} + \frac{2}{3} = 1$ **20.** $9 - 1\frac{3}{4} = 7\frac{1}{4}$ **21.** $\frac{1}{2}$ **22.** $\frac{7}{5}$ or $1\frac{2}{5}$

23. $18\frac{1}{16}$ or $\frac{289}{16}$ **24.** $1\frac{1}{8}$ in   **25.** $25\frac{1}{2}$ ft   **26.** $6\frac{1}{4}$ ft   **27.** $\frac{3}{4}$ cup   **28.** $7\frac{1}{4}$ or $\frac{29}{4}$ gal per min

29. $\frac{3}{5}$ of the soft drinks   **30.** $\frac{2349}{32}$ or $73\frac{13}{32}$ sq in

Cumulative Review Exercises: Chapters 1–5 (page 222)

1. thirteen hundredths   **2.** $\frac{67}{12}$ **3.** $10\frac{2}{3}$ **4.** $\frac{60}{7}$ or $8\frac{4}{7}$ **5.** $\frac{17}{30}, \frac{3}{5}, \frac{2}{3}$ **6.** $\frac{63}{9}$

7. $2 \times 3 \times 5 \times 23$ **8.** $3 \times 7 \times 11$ **9.** $2 \times 2 \times 2 \times 2 \times 3 \times 5 \times 5$ **10.** $2 \times 2 \times 2 \times 5 \times 5 \times 17$

$\frac{1.50}{1}$

1.56 First H

11. 315   **12.** 560   **13.** 480   **14.** $\frac{121}{15}$ or $8\frac{1}{15}$ **15.** $\frac{2}{5}$ **16.** $\frac{5}{2}$ or $2\frac{1}{2}$ **17.** $12\frac{1}{8}$ or $\frac{97}{8}$

18. $16\frac{5}{12}$ **19.** $\frac{10}{27}$ **20.** $\frac{1}{6}$ **21.** $12\frac{7}{8}$ **22.** $\frac{81}{112}$ **23.** $\frac{41}{36}$ or $1\frac{5}{36}$ **24.** 125 R 20   **25.** 66,038

26. 309,894   **27. a.** 4 in   **b.** $\frac{21}{5}$ or $4\frac{1}{5}$ in   **c.** $\frac{14}{15}$ in   **28. a.** 6800 lb   **b.** $\frac{3}{10}$ **c.** $\frac{25}{17}$

29. a. $\frac{75}{4}$ or $18\frac{3}{4}$ mi   **b.** $\frac{195}{8}$ or $24\frac{3}{8}$ mi   **c.** $\frac{4}{15}$ hr   **d.** $\frac{16}{15}$ or $1\frac{1}{15}$ hr

30. a. 40 tons   **b.** 460 tons   **c.** $\frac{23}{25}$

31. a. $\frac{255}{2}$ or $127\frac{1}{2}$ ft   **b.** 340 ft   **c.** $\frac{21675}{4}$ or $5418\frac{3}{4}$ sq ft   **d.** $21,675

CHAPTER 6

Exercises 6.1 (page 228)

1. 2   **3.** 7   **5.** 8   **7.** 1   **9.** $\frac{2}{10} + \frac{3}{100} + \frac{8}{1000}$ **11.** $70 + 6 + \frac{8}{1000}$ **13.** 0.57   **15.** 630.803

17. $\frac{3}{10}$ **19.** $\frac{58}{100}$ **21.** $\frac{6}{1000}$ **23.** 0.04   **25.** 14.032   **27.** 2.368   **29.** 0.9   **31.** 0.04

33. 12.3   **35.** 50.104   **37.** 50.3   **39.** thirty-four hundredths   **41.** eight thousandths

43. twenty-four and two hundredths   **45.** nine and one hundred five ten-thousandths

47. nine thousand

Exercises 6.2 (page 233)

1. a. 100¢   **b.** $1.00   **3. a.** 2000¢   **b.** $20.00   **5. a.** 25¢   **b.** $0.25   **7.** half dollar

9. dime   **11.** $0.17   **13.** $0.46   **15.** $25.83   **17.** $800.09

19. a. fifty-five cents   **b.** fifty-five hundredths dollars

21. a. eight dollars and three cents   **b.** eight and three hundredths dollars

23. a. sixty-seven dollars   **b.** sixty-seven dollars   **25.** 348.92   **27.** six hundred seventy-five and $\frac{80}{100}$

Exercises 6.3 (page 236)

1. a. .43   **c.** .430   **d.** 0.430   **3. c.** $30.00   **e.** $30.0   **5.** 2.8   **7.** 0.03   **9.** 132.113

11. 8.   **13.** .138   **15.** .5; .55; 5   **17.** .32; .327; .33   **19.** =   **21.** <

Exercises 6.4 (page 240)

1. 0.32   **3.** 732.014   **5.** $18   **7.** $0.44   **9.** 9.0140   **11.** 2304.20   **13.** 23   **15.** 0.236

17. 790.3   **19.** 75

Exercises 6.5 (page 245)

1. 49.33   **3.** 83.915   **5.** 738.85   **7.** $599.91   **9.** 388.443   **11.** 14.53   **13.** 8.069   **15.** 145.68

17. 301.547   **19.** $93.21   **21.** 1972.095   **23.** 3769.33   **25.** 4.7 m   **27.** 109.67   **29.** 44.834

31. 1198.18

Exercises 6.6 (page 248)

1. $0.8 + 0.4 = 1.2$ **3.** $18.7 - 7.3 = 11.4$ **5.** $72.8 + 0.6 = 73.4$ **7.** $8.2 = 8.6 - 0.4$ **9.** 7.63

11. 10.82   **13.** 20.17   **15.** 16.416   **17.** 6.6

Exercises 6.7 (page 254)

1. $16.75   **3.** 39.8 cm   **5.** 38.54 m   **7.** 44.1 gal   **9.** 1.8 mi   **11.** 2.9 in   **13.** $0.59   **15.** 4.8 ft

17. 70 in   **19.** 485 calories   **21.** 0.4 yd   **23.** $1.25   **25.** increased by $0.75

Chapter 6 Review Exercises (page 256)

1. 0   **2.** 7   **3.** 6   **4.** 1   **5.** 0.609   **6.** 804.037   **7.** $\dfrac{3}{1000}$ **8.** $7\dfrac{27}{100}$ or $\dfrac{727}{100}$ **9.** 0.0019

10. 14.15   **11.** 16,000   **12.** 0.016   **13.** 90.0203   **14.** 7.14
15. five hundredths   **16.** fifty and two ten-thousandths   **17.** three hundred four thousandths
18. three hundred four thousand   **19. a.** 5¢   **b.** $0.05   **20. a.** 25¢   **b.** $0.25
21. a. 100¢   **b.** $1.00   **22. a.** 500¢   **b.** $5.00   **23.** dime   **24.** penny   **25.** ten-dollar bill
26. half dollar   **27.** $0.47   **28.** $62.12   **29. a.** sixty-one cents   **b.** sixty-one hundredths dollar
30. a. two hundred dollars and seven cents   **b.** two hundred and seven hundredths dollars
31. a. .58   **d.** 0.58   **32. b.** $102   **c.** $102.
33. 0.39, 1, 3.9   **34.** .732323; 73.23222; 73.2323   **35.** >   **36.** =   **37.** >   **38.** >   **39.** 138.14
40. $43   **41.** 0.232   **42.** $204.84   **43.** 9.8176   **44.** 93.15   **45.** 86.382   **46.** 29.3407
47. 92.03   **48.** 1043.45   **49.** $726.11   **50.** $364.41   **51.** 71.42   **52.** $61.13   **53.** 427.46
54. 81.392   **55.** 5.4   **56.** 54.74   **57.** 2995.48   **58.** 79,748.6   **59.** 42.08   **60.** 112.4
61. $210.8 - 107 = 103.8$ **62.** $0.7 + 0.6 = 1.3$ **63.** $4.2 + 15.8 = 20$ **64.** $19.7 - 2 = 17.7$
65. 1.35   **66.** 2.99   **67.** 148.97   **68.** 11.02   **69.** 2.55 mi   **70.** 127.15 ft   **71.** $34.15
72. $1905.80   **73.** 81.5 in   **74.** 18.8 m

Chapter 6 Practice Test (page 259)

1. 93.4   **2.** 6.0019   **3.** 0.65   **4.** 48.007   **5.** thirteen ten-thousandths   **6.** seven and two-tenths
7. $0.25   **8.** 500¢   **9. b.** .900   **c.** 0.9   **d.** .9   **10.** 0.079; 0.701; 1.07   **11.** $0.007 > 0.00089$
12. 26.084   **13.** $79   **14.** 0.0134   **15.** 136.11   **16.** 876.556   **17.** 11.397   **18.** $774.34
19. 224.56   **20.** 4921.4   **21.** 183.42   **22.** 7.7   **23.** 230.24 ft   **24.** 9.6 lb.   **25.** $52.50
26. 3.5 mi

CHAPTER 7

Exercises 7.1 (page 267)

1. .09 or 0.09   **3.** 32.76   **5.** 3517.4   **7.** 152.75262   **9.** 4512.95   **11.** 3   **13.** 0.555
15. 1.17072   **17.** 54   **19.** 23,000   **21.** 781.3   **23.** 1.08252   **25.** $13,870,000   **27.** 12.9792
29. 271,606.8   **31.** $20.30   **33.** $9.49

Exercises 7.2 (page 278)

1. 1.4   **3.** 0.16   **5.** 1.3   **7.** 42   **9.** 350   **11.** 1990.4   **13.** 67,000   **15.** 1900   **17.** 3006.2
19. 0.0305   **21.** 608.004   **23.** 0.0026   **25.** 400   **27.** $8.9\overline{3}$ **29.** $138.\overline{8}$ **31.** $0.0\overline{1}$ **33.** 0.875
35. 0.0175   **37.** $1.041\overline{6}$ **39.** $0.\overline{27}$ **41.** 13.817   **43.** 7.606   **45.** 0.009   **47.** 0.0004   **49.** 15.64
51. $2.61\dfrac{3}{7}$ **53.** $71.66\dfrac{2}{3}$ **55.** $2.85\dfrac{5}{7}$ **57.** 0.0456   **59.** 8.976   **61.** 0.000075   **63.** 3.85 in
65. 6.5 m

Exercises 7.3 (page 282)

1. 23.2   **3.** 0.0205   **5.** 3.81   **7.** 0.0125   **9.** 360   **11.** 9.763   **13.** 13   **15.** 8.05   **17.** 1.03
19. 500

Exercises 7.4 (page 287)

1. $0.3 \times 0.2 = 0.06$ **3.** $45.2 = 5 \times 9.04$ **5.** $41.6 = 2 \times 20.8$ **7.** 940   **9.** 0.025   **11.** 15.25
13. 135   **15.** 6.5   **17.** 500   **19.** 36.18   **21.** 20   **23.** 0.08

Exercises 7.5 (page 302)

1. $425.50   **3.** 486 m   **5.** 18 pieces   **7.** $16.60   **9.** 49.6 mi   **11.** 9.2 min   **13.** $27.23
15. $1.06   **17.** 0.337   **19.** 9.3 ft   **21.** $430.20   **23.** 15 doses   **25.** 537 mi   **27.** 14.6 gal
29. 121.6 g   **31.** 120   **33.** $2.18   **35.** 0.15 m   **37.** 4104.18 sq ft   **39.** $4.37   **41.** 128 games
43. $1.75   **45.** $1.40

Developing Number Sense #6 (page 279)

1. 34   **2.** 7.84   **3.** 0.0659   **4.** 0.92   **5.** 0.84   **6.** 0.0875   **7.** 0.00006   **8.** 0.1245   **9.** 0.003
10. 0.057   **11.** 0.0457   **12.** 0.0005   **13.** 0.0367   **14.** 0.0786   **15.** 0.8   **16.** 120

Developing Number Sense #7 (page 283)

1. more than 850   **2.** less than 850   **3.** less than 850   **4.** more than 850   **5.** equal to 850
6. less than 850   **7.** more than 850   **8.** more than 850   **9.** more than 47.2   **10.** less than 47.2
11. more than 47.2   **12.** less than 47. 2

Chapter 7 Review Exercises (page 305)

1. 0.6   **2.** 0.0768   **3.** 220.5   **4.** 2578.8   **5.** 44.82   **6.** 64.68   **7.** 38.545   **8.** 98.4   **9.** 0.216
10. 63.45   **11.** 184,525   **12.** 6.2521   **13.** 2,375,000   **14.** 162   **15.** 100,800   **16.** 1080   **17.** 86
18. 78,000   **19.** 1575   **20.** 2374.152   **21.** 0.405   **22.** 0.0025   **23.** 3.4   **24.** 0.25   **25.** 0.056
26. 2.08   **27.** 20,780   **28.** 7300   **29.** 37,000   **30.** 28.125   **31.** 3.7   **32.** 0.0075   **33.** $0.\overline{5}$
34. $8.\overline{6}$ **35.** $1.1\overline{6}$ **36.** $573.\overline{3}$ **37.** $8.36\frac{1}{4}$ **38.** $103.33\frac{1}{3}$ **39.** $0.06\frac{2}{13}$ **40** $104.16\frac{2}{3}$ **41.** 30.643
42. 0.57   **43.** 0.2692   **44.** 0.254   **45.** 5.834   **46.** 18.64   **47.** 0.75   **48.** 26.25   **49.** 2.48
50. 0.175   **51.** $8.8\overline{3}$ **52.** $0.041\overline{6}$ **53.** $0.\overline{703}$ **54.** $8.\overline{45}$ **55.** 76.5   **56.** 25.125   **57.** 68.75
58. 4600   **59.** 0.0125   **60.** 9450   **61.** 9.75   **62.** 1.3   **63.** 0.0372   **64.** 0.06   **65.** 17.2
66. 8.865   **67.** 0.375   **68.** 1.53   **69.** 0.725 lb   **70.** 13 pieces   **71.** 33.75 min   **72.** $23.62
73. 0.015 ton   **74.** 80 hr   **75.** 16 gal per min   **76.** $32.30   **77.** $408   **78.** 0.02   **79.** $2.84
80. $147   **81.** 2148 sq cm   **82.** 21.1 ft   **83.** $16.51   **84.** 0.21   **85.** 7.2 min   **86.** 32 mi

Chapter 7 Practice Test (page 307)

1. 61.92   **2.** 125.6049   **3.** 450,000   **4.** 60.8   **5.** 0.0117   **6.** 136   **7.** 2.875   **8.** 0.401
9. 351,000   **10.** $0.\overline{6}$ **11.** $1.78\overline{3}$ **12.** $481.\overline{481}$ **13.** $26.06\frac{2}{3}$ **14.** $0.01\frac{7}{8}$ **15.** $23.33\frac{1}{3}$
16. 40.033   **17.** 1.8823   **18.** 3.195   **19.** 0.625   **20.** 1.72   **21.** $0.2\overline{7}$ **22.** $6.\overline{30}$ **23.** 0.5
24. 5   **25.** 29.05   **26.** 1600   **27.** 400   **28.** 3100   **29.** 0.003125   **30.** 0.0656   **31.** $3007.20
32. $750   **33.** 15 slices   **34.** 1384 sq ft   **35.** 47.6 mi per hr   **36.** 4743.6 mi   **37.** 25.4 in

Cumulative Review Exercises: Chapters 1–7 (page 308)

1. $\frac{18}{5}$ or $3\frac{3}{5}$ **2.** $\frac{17}{20}$ **3.** $\frac{1}{400}$ **4.** $2\frac{1}{8}$ or $\frac{17}{8}$ **5.** 0.375   **6.** 0.055   **7.** 75.5   **8.** 23.6
9. $19\frac{1}{3}$ **10.** 2000   **11.** $\frac{3}{2}$ or $1\frac{1}{2}$ **12.** $1\frac{27}{56}$ or $\frac{83}{56}$ **13.** 14.34   **14.** 7.7   **15.** $\frac{15}{4}$ or $3\frac{3}{4}$
16. $\frac{1}{8}$ or 0.125   **17.** 397,800   **18.** 0.00625   **19.** 160   **20.** $58.67   **21.** $6\frac{1}{2}$ hr
22. a. 2600 sq ft   **b.** 210 ft   **c.** 166.4 fl oz   **d.** $5197.50   **23.** $1500

CHAPTER 8

Exercises 8.1 (page 319)

1. A. 3   B. 5   **3.** A. 22   B. 25   **5.** A. 5   B. 25   **7.** A. 8   B. 22
9. A. $\frac{2}{8}$ or $\frac{1}{4}$ B. $\frac{7}{8}$ **11.** A. $4\frac{1}{3}$ B. $5\frac{2}{3}$ **13.** A. $\frac{1}{5}$ B. $\frac{3}{5}$
15. A. $2\frac{2}{6}$ or $2\frac{1}{3}$ B. $3\frac{1}{6}$ **17.** A. 2.9   B. 3.0 or 3   **19.** A. 8.25   B. 9.75
21. A. 13.2   B. 13.6   **23.** A. 3.875   B. 4.375   **25.** $\frac{1}{8}$ **27.** $\frac{3}{4}$

Exercises 8.2 (page 329)

1. $>$ **3.** $<$ **5.** $=$ **7.** $>$ **9.** $>$ **11. a.** $\dfrac{28}{100}$ **c.** $\dfrac{35}{125}$ **d.** 0.28

13. b. $\dfrac{3}{50}$ **c.** 0.0600 **d.** $\dfrac{60}{1000}$ **15. a.** $\dfrac{60}{5}$ **d.** 12.0 **17.** 8.1638109 **19.** $1\dfrac{13}{18}$ **21.** $8\dfrac{1}{12}$

23. 1.3 **25.** 2.1, 20.75, 21.5, 21.6 **27.** $\dfrac{3}{4}$, 1, $1\dfrac{1}{4}$, $\dfrac{4}{3}$ **29.** $\dfrac{23}{40}$, $\dfrac{3}{5}$, $0.63\overline{7}$, 0.64

31. 2.06, 20.6, $20\dfrac{11}{18}$, $20\dfrac{2}{3}$

Exercises 8.3 (page 334)

1. 1350 **3.** $1\dfrac{7}{12}$ **5.** 0.085 **7.** $13\dfrac{3}{8}$ **9.** 31.25 **11.** $4\dfrac{137}{180}$ **13.** 0.025 **15.** $\dfrac{1}{4}$ or 0.25

17. $8\dfrac{1}{6}$ **19.** $\dfrac{2}{125}$ or 0.016

Exercises 8.4 (page 345)

1. $\dfrac{3}{4}$ or 0.75 ft **3.** $\dfrac{1}{4}$ or 0.25 **5.** 550 boxes **7.** 30 servings

9. a. $93\dfrac{1}{2}$ or 93.5 sq in **b.** 39 in **11.** $17\dfrac{11}{12}$ in **13.** $2.54 **15.** 5.25 or $5\dfrac{1}{4}$ hr

17. $\dfrac{14}{15}$ or $0.9\overline{3}$ **19. a.** $\dfrac{1}{7}$ **b.** $\dfrac{8}{5}$ **21.** 52 words per min **23.** $7.12 **25.** 200 mi

Exercises 8.5 (page 355)

1. $1778.67 **3.** $3.61 **5.** $6\dfrac{1}{4}$ or 6.25 mi **7.** increased by $1.25 per share

9. a. 216.72 ft **b.** 2695.842 sq ft **11.** $\dfrac{9}{283}$ **13.** 375 acres **15.** $65\dfrac{1}{2}$ or 65.5 lb

17. 53.8 mi per hr **19.** $7.35 **21.** 3500 **23.** 2875

Using the Calculator #8 (page 334)

1. 0.875 **2.** 1.143 **3.** 2.692 **4.** 0.371 **5.** 0.042 **6.** 24 **7.** 0.625 **8.** 0.722 **9.** 353.581
10. 12.75 **11.** 1.111 **12.** 0.216 **13.** 1300.083 **14.** 0.006 **15.** 33.943 **16.** 2.281
17. 2146.912 **18.** 2.837

Using the Calculator #9 (page 346)

1. 0.775 **2.** 0.025 **3.** 0.542 **4.** 0.201 **5.** 348.208 **6.** 347.792 **7.** 59.304 **8.** 17.304
9. 7.867 **10.** 0.533 **11.** 26.037 **12.** 10.732

Chapter 8 Review Exercises (page 366)

1. A. 35 B. 40 **2.** A. 25 B. 75 **3.** A. $\dfrac{1}{4}$ B. 2 **4.** A. $4\dfrac{2}{3}$ B. 6

5. A. 7.5 B. 7.8 **6.** A. 0.53 B. 0.59 **7. b.** 0.18 **c.** 0.1800 **d.** $\dfrac{27}{150}$

8. b. $\dfrac{39}{5}$ **d.** $7\dfrac{32}{40}$ **9. b.** $\dfrac{75}{3}$ **c.** 25.00 **10.** $<$ **11.** $>$ **12.** $<$ **13.** $=$

14. $\frac{31}{36}, \frac{7}{8}, 0.8\overline{7}$ **15.** $0.044, \frac{4}{90}, 0.44, 4\frac{2}{5}$ **16.** $8\frac{2}{3}, 8\frac{3}{4}, 8\frac{5}{6}$ **17.** $0.5625, 0.58, \frac{5}{8}$ **18.** 27.2

19. $\frac{2}{5}$ or 0.4   **20.** $\frac{4}{27}$ **21.** $\frac{25}{4}$ or $6\frac{1}{4}$ or 6.25   **22.** 400   **23.** $27\frac{2}{3}$ **24.** 0.016

25. \$315,000   **26.** $\frac{5}{12}$ **27.** $10\frac{1}{4}$ gal   **28.** 20 slices   **29.** $\frac{1}{3}$ **30. a.** 129.4 in   **b.** 1029.3 sq in

31. 33.75 gal   **32.** 4.2 yd per sec   **33.** 9.2 ft   **34.** \$96.12   **35.** $\frac{1}{4}$ or 0.25

36. 62.4 sq ft   **37.** \$86.25   **38.** \$771.85   **39.** \$277.50   **40.** \$5   **41.** 31.2 sec

42. Natalie at 55.5 words per min   **43.** 12 hr   **44.** $31\frac{7}{15}$ yd   **45.** 0.8 in   **46.** 2.4 in   **47.** 8 in

48. 1.6 in   **49.** 0.075 or $\frac{3}{40}$ **50.** May

Chapter 8 Practice Test (page 369)

1. A. 680   **B.** 720   **2. A.** $\frac{1}{8}$ **B.** $\frac{7}{8}$ **3. A.** 10   **B.** 10.6   **4. c.** $\frac{232}{25}$ **d.** $8\frac{32}{25}$ **5.** =

6. <   **7.** $9.14, \frac{46}{5}, 9\frac{1}{4}$ **8.** $0.95, \frac{83}{10}, 7\frac{4}{3}, 9.2$ **9.** $7\frac{5}{6}$ **10.** $\frac{52}{125}$ or 0.416   **11.** \$26.10

12. 76 servings   **13.** 147.73 sq ft   **14.** $\frac{3}{5}$ **15.** $1\frac{1}{2}$ hr   **16.** \$2176.50   **17.** 8.6 lb   **18.** $6\frac{2}{3}$ sec

19. 57 m   **20.** $\frac{1}{5}$ or 0.2   **21.** \$17.18   **22.** \$598.56

CHAPTER 9

Exercises 9.1 (page 378)

1. less than 1   **3.** more than 1   **5.** equal to 1   **7.** 0.06   **9.** 0.1   **11.** 1   **13.** 3.5   **15.** 0.042
17. 0.1532   **19.** 0.009   **21.** 0.00145   **23.** 1.005   **25.** 0.0025   **27.** 0.025   **29.** 0.3775

31. 0.00025   **33.** $0.008\overline{3}, 0.008\frac{1}{3}$ **35.** $0.\overline{3}, 0.33\frac{1}{3}$ **37.** $\frac{1}{100}$ **39.** $\frac{3}{4}$ **41.** $\frac{9}{25}$ **43.** $1\frac{3}{4}$ or $\frac{7}{4}$

45. $3\frac{1}{4}$ or $\frac{13}{4}$ **47.** $\frac{1}{250}$ **49.** $\frac{1}{3}$ **51.** $\frac{1}{30}$ **53.** $\frac{1}{200}$ **55.** $\frac{7}{1000}$ **57.** $\frac{7}{16}$ **59.** $\frac{29}{300}$

61. $\frac{3}{40,000}$ **63.** $\frac{1}{40}$ **65.** $\frac{9}{200}$ **67.** $\frac{3}{8}$ **69.** $\frac{1}{125}$ **71.** $\frac{9}{10,000}$ **73.** $\frac{1}{400}$ **75.** $\frac{17}{400}$

Exercises 9.2 (page 386)

1. 30   **3.** 18   **5.** 140   **7.** 12.5 or $12\frac{1}{2}$ **9.** 3   **11.** 14.094   **13.** 7.476   **15.** 12.3

17. 156.84   **19.** 12.96   **21.** 0.255   **23.** 3.584   **25.** 0.078   **27.** 150   **29.** $\frac{5}{3}$ or $1\frac{2}{3}$ **31.** $\frac{7}{12}$

33. 34   **35.** $\frac{1}{24}$ **37.** $\frac{1}{4}$ or 0.25   **39.** \$19,600   **41.** 115 trucks

Exercises 9.3 (page 394)

1. 45%   **3.** 90%   **5.** 5.3%   **7.** 100%   **9.** 240%   **11.** 108%   **13.** 0.5%   **15.** 0.038%

17. 67.2%   **19.** 7.46%   **21.** 50%   **23.** 35%   **25.** 180%   **27.** 130%   **29.** $37\frac{1}{2}$% or 37.5%

31. $31\frac{1}{4}$% or 31.25%   **33.** $33\frac{1}{3}$%   **35.** $26\frac{2}{3}$%   **37.** $166\frac{2}{3}$%   **39.** $316\frac{2}{3}$%   **41.** 0.6% or $\frac{3}{5}$%

43. 0.1875% or $0.18\frac{3}{4}$%   **45.** 0.03, 3%   **47.** $\frac{4}{5}, 0.8$ **49.** $2\frac{3}{50}$ or $\frac{103}{50}, 206$%

51. 0.625, 62.5% or $62\frac{1}{2}$% **53.** $\frac{3}{8}$, 0.375 **55.** $\frac{3}{500}$, 0.6% or $\frac{3}{5}$% **57.** $0.1\overline{6}$ or $0.16\frac{2}{3}$, $16\frac{2}{3}$%

59. $\frac{2}{3}$, $0.\overline{6}$ or $0.66\frac{2}{3}$

Exercises 9.4 (page 403)

1. 120 **3.** 20% **5.** 166,000 **7.** 0.1% or $\frac{1}{10}$% **9.** 95 **11.** 0.8% **13.** 5.3885 **15.** 408

17. 21 **19.** 3600 **21.** 100% **23.** $66\frac{2}{3}$% **25.** $\frac{8}{15}$ **27.** 155.5 or $155\frac{1}{2}$ **29.** 9000

31. $33\frac{1}{3}$% **33.** $\frac{65}{3}$ or $21\frac{2}{3}$

Exercises 9.5 (page 409)

1. 45 students **3.** 0.2% or $\frac{1}{5}$% **5.** $151.20 **7.** 150% **9.** 50% **11.** 60% **13.** 20 oz

15. 252 Toyotas **17.** 40% **19.** 25% **21.** 600 persons

Exercises 9.6 (page 420)

1. $33.54 **3.** $23.50 **5.** 2.5% **7.** $8840 **9.** $19,200 **11.** $65.36 **13.** 1.9% **15.** $254.70
17. $7.60 **19.** $90 **21.** $28.74 **23.** $8704 **25.** $464.80 **27.** 40% **29.** 75,000

Exercises 9.7 (page 431)

1. $1.74 per hr **3.** 17.5% **5.** 30% **7.** 2.5 min *8. $8.40*

17. 900% *18. a. 120 lb b. 114 lb*

Developing Number Sense #8 (page 423)

1. $0.90 **2.** $1.40 **3.** $2.50 **4.** $6.80 **5.** $0.45 **6.** $0.95 **7.** $1.95 **8.** $3.30
9. $1.50 **10.** $3.90 **11.** $9 **12.** $22.50 **13.** $1.10 **14.** $3.90 **15.** $7.20 **16.** $15.60
17. $18.40 **18.** $28.80 **19.** $32.20 **20.** $78.20

Using the Calculator #10 (page 433)

1. 360 **2.** 2.7 **3.** 476 **4.** $12.25 **5.** 660 **6.** 540 **7.** $80.08 **8.** $11.44 **9.** 2125
10. 849.49 **11.** 500 or 500.000 **12.** 540 **13.** 93.3 or 93.300 **14.** 40 **15.** 31.25%
16. 6400

Chapter 9 Review Exercises (page 450)

1. equal to 1 **2.** less than 1 **3.** less than 1 **4.** more than 1 **5.** 0.07 **6.** 0.68 **7.** 1.2
8. 0.067 **9.** 0.5208 **10.** 0.005 **11.** 0.00018 **12.** 0.0025 **13.** 0.075 **14.** 0.134 **15.** 3

16. 4.6 **17.** $\frac{1}{20}$ **18.** $\frac{4}{5}$ **19.** $\frac{16}{25}$ **20.** $\frac{3}{2}$ or $1\frac{1}{2}$ **21.** 2 **22.** $\frac{3}{1000}$ **23.** $\frac{1}{120}$ **24.** $\frac{7}{80}$

25. $\frac{2}{3}$ **26.** $\frac{1}{16}$ **27.** $\frac{1}{8}$ **28.** $\frac{4}{125}$ **29.** $\frac{9}{1000}$ **30.** $\frac{3}{5000}$ **31.** $\frac{201}{400}$ **32.** $\frac{1}{100,000}$ **33.** 8.4

34. 2.4064 **35.** 40 **36.** 33 **37.** 3.842 **38.** $\frac{75}{7}$ or $10\frac{5}{7}$ **39.** 16% **40.** 4.6% **41.** 870%

42. 0.1% **43.** 40% **44.** 418% **45.** 50.2% **46.** 0.37% **47.** 67% **48.** 60% **49.** 35%

50. $12\frac{1}{2}$% or 12.5% **51.** 800% **52.** 250% **53.** $83\frac{1}{3}$% **54.** $533\frac{1}{3}$%

55. a. $\frac{5}{4}$ or $1\frac{1}{4}$ **b.** 1.25   **56. a.** $\frac{3}{4}$ **b.** 75%

57. a. $0.\overline{3}$ **b.** $33\frac{1}{3}$% or $33.\overline{3}$%   **58. a.** $\frac{1}{40}$ **b.** 0.025   **59. a.** $\frac{1}{500}$ **b.** 0.2%

60. a. 0.875   **b.** 87.5% or $87\frac{1}{2}$%   **61.** 1370   **62.** $83\frac{1}{3}$%   **63.** 70   **64.** 17,000   **65.** 2.4%

66. 0.403   **67.** $\frac{1}{25}$ or 0.04   **68.** 300%   **69.** $3\frac{1}{3}$%   **70.** $16\frac{2}{3}$ **71.** 120 textbooks

72. 69 smokers   **73.** 32%   **74.** 227.5 g   **75.** 0.8 oz   **76.** 180   **77.** $148.12   **78.** 6.2%

79. $208,000   **80.** $5440   **81.** 1.75%   **82.** $5.70   **83.** $305   **84.** 5%   **85.** $12\frac{1}{2}$% or 12.5%

86. $2808   **87.** $20 million   **90.** $1465.13

Chapter 9 Practice Test (page 452)

1. 0.264   **2.** 3.7   **3.** 0.005   **4.** 0.0625   **5.** $\frac{9}{20}$ **6.** $\frac{7}{2}$ or $3\frac{1}{2}$ **7.** $\frac{1}{125}$ **8.** $\frac{1}{15}$ **9.** 400%

10. 5.7%   **11.** 90%   **12.** $233\frac{1}{3}$%   **13.** 2.1   **14.** 40%   **15.** 3.75   **16.** 0.05%   **17.** 2.345

18. 216   **19. a.** 280%   **b.** 180%   **20.** 42%   **21.** $343.20   **22.** $360,000   **23.** $6.30
24. 2500

Cumulative Review Exercises: Chapters 1–9 (page 453)

1. $\frac{101}{252}$ **2.** $3\frac{65}{108}$ **3.** $\frac{129}{7}$ or $18\frac{3}{7}$ **4.** $\frac{15}{14}$ or $1\frac{1}{14}$ **5.** 26.11   **6.** 91.16   **7.** 3354   **8.** 320

9. 0.00364   **10.** 0.45   **11.** $\frac{77}{250}$ **12.** 0.018   **13.** $0.\overline{63}$ **14. a.** $\frac{1}{40}$ **b.** 0.025   **c.** 2.5%

15. $\frac{119}{18}$ or $6\frac{11}{18}$ **16.** 0.3 ℓ   **17.** 19.7 cg   **18. a.** $\frac{3}{8}$ **b.** $\frac{5}{8}$ **c.** 25   **d.** 25%
19. a. $1.33   **b.** 4%   **c.** 104%   **d.** $10.64   **20. a.** $99.11   **b.** $0.89

ANSWERS - Custom Enhancement

ANSWERS TO TRY THESE PROBLEMS – Chapter 2 Custom Enhancement

1. rate   2. distance   3. weight   4. rate   5. area   6. time

7. rate   8. time   9. weight   10. volume   11. rate   12. area

13. 120 kilometers, 500 miles   14. 240 square meters, 120 square miles

15. 8 inches per minute, $200 per week   16. 16 ounces   17. 36 days

18. 56 inches   19. 24¢   20. 18 weeks   21. 17 cartons   22. 4 hours

23. 20 years   24. 31 miles   25. 76 pints   26. 1845 years   27. 5585 gallons

28. 34 tons   29. 70 persons   30. $702   31. 10,952 hours   32. 2750 years

33. 50 miles   34. 50 square feet   35. 608,000 centiliters   36. 300 tons

37. 16 feet   38. 13 miles   39. 9 inches   40. 24 yards   41. 2 square miles

42. 200 square miles   43. 140 square meters   44. 80 meters   45. 19 miles

46. 560 square yards   47. 599 square feet   48. 54 square kilometers

49. $4 per 1 video   50. 12 games per 1 carton   51. 70 miles every 1 hour

52. 130 inches every 1 year   53. 40 students per 1 class

54. 12 gallons in 1 minute   55. 60¢ per hour   56. 4 bottles per carton

57. 6 feet per second   58. 20 pounds per case   59. 5 ounces per person

60. 2 liters per bottle   61. $63   62. $30   63. 180 bottles   64. 40 pints

65. 104 pounds   66. $560   67. $270   68. $1360   69. inches   70. $

71. persons   72. feet   73. seconds   74. envelopes per minute   75. feet

76. calories per meal

ANSWERS EXERCISES 3-A – Chapter 3 Custom Enhancement

1. $\frac{3}{2}$, three halves; $1\frac{1}{2}$, one and one half   2. $\frac{2}{2}$, two halves; 1, one

3. $\frac{4}{2}$, four halves; 2, two; $1\frac{2}{2}$, one and two halves

4. $1\frac{1}{2}$, one and one half; $\frac{3}{2}$, three halves

5. $1\frac{2}{2}$, one and two halves; 2, two

6. $1\frac{3}{2}$, one and three halves; $2\frac{1}{2}$, two and one half

7. $2\frac{2}{2}$, two and two halves; 3, three   8. $\frac{9}{2}$, nine halves; $4\frac{1}{2}$, four and one half

9. $1\frac{4}{2}$, one and four halves; 3, three   10. $\frac{7}{2}$, seven halves; $3\frac{1}{2}$, three and one half

11. $4\frac{1}{2}$, four and a half; $\frac{9}{2}$, nine halves

12. $2\frac{3}{2}$, two and three halves; $\frac{7}{2}$, seven halves

13. A) $\frac{1}{2},\frac{2}{2},\frac{3}{2},\frac{4}{2},\frac{5}{2},\frac{6}{2},\frac{7}{2},\frac{8}{2}$ **B)** $\frac{1}{2},1,1\frac{1}{2},2,2\frac{1}{2},3,3\frac{1}{2},4$

14. A) $\frac{1}{2},\frac{2}{2},\frac{3}{2},\frac{4}{2},\frac{5}{2},\frac{6}{2},\frac{7}{2},\frac{8}{2},\frac{9}{2},\frac{10}{2},\frac{11}{2},\frac{12}{2},\frac{13}{2}$

14. B) $\frac{1}{2},1,1\frac{1}{2},2,2\frac{1}{2},3,3\frac{1}{2},4,4\frac{1}{2},5,5\frac{1}{2},6,6\frac{1}{2}$

15. A) $\frac{1}{2},\frac{2}{2},\frac{3}{2},\frac{4}{2},\frac{5}{2},\frac{6}{2},\frac{7}{2},\frac{8}{2},\frac{9}{2},\frac{10}{2}$ **B)** $\frac{1}{2},1,1\frac{1}{2},2,2\frac{1}{2},3,3\frac{1}{2},4,4\frac{1}{2},5$

16. A) $\frac{1}{2},\frac{2}{2},\frac{3}{2},\frac{4}{2},\frac{5}{2},\frac{6}{2},\frac{7}{2},\frac{8}{2},\frac{9}{2}$ **B)** $\frac{1}{2},1,1\frac{1}{2},2,2\frac{1}{2},3,3\frac{1}{2},4,4\frac{1}{2}$

17. A) $\frac{3}{2},\frac{4}{2},\frac{5}{2},\frac{6}{2},\frac{7}{2},\frac{8}{2},\frac{9}{2},\frac{10}{2},\frac{11}{2},\frac{12}{2},\frac{13}{2},\frac{14}{2},\frac{15}{2}$

17. B) $1\frac{1}{2},2,2\frac{1}{2},3,3\frac{1}{2},4,4\frac{1}{2},5,5\frac{1}{2},6,6\frac{1}{2},7,7\frac{1}{2}$

18. A) $\frac{5}{2},\frac{6}{2},\frac{7}{2},\frac{8}{2},\frac{9}{2},\frac{10}{2},\frac{11}{2},\frac{12}{2},\frac{13}{2},\frac{14}{2},\frac{15}{2},\frac{16}{2},\frac{17}{2}$

18. B) $2\frac{1}{2},3,3\frac{1}{2},4,4\frac{1}{2},5,5\frac{1}{2},6,6\frac{1}{2},7,7\frac{1}{2},8,8\frac{1}{2}$

19. A) $\frac{7}{2},\frac{8}{2},\frac{9}{2},\frac{10}{2},\frac{11}{2},\frac{12}{2},\frac{13}{2},\frac{14}{2}$ **B)** $3\frac{1}{2},4,4\frac{1}{2},5,5\frac{1}{2},6,6\frac{1}{2},7$

20. A) $\frac{11}{2},\frac{12}{2},\frac{13}{2},\frac{14}{2},\frac{15}{2},\frac{16}{2},\frac{17}{2},\frac{18}{2},\frac{19}{2}$ **B)** $5\frac{1}{2},6,6\frac{1}{2},7,7\frac{1}{2},8,8\frac{1}{2},9,9\frac{1}{2}$

ANSWERS EXERCISES 3-B – Chapter 3 Custom Enhancement

1. $\frac{3}{4}$, three fourths   **2.** $1\frac{1}{4}$, one and one fourth or $\frac{5}{4}$, five fourths

3. $\frac{2}{4}$, two fourths or $\frac{1}{2}$, one half   **4.** $\frac{4}{4}$, four fourths or 1, one

5. $1\frac{2}{4}$, one and two fourths or $\frac{6}{4}$, six fourths   **6.** $\frac{5}{4}$, five fourths or $1\frac{1}{4}$, one and a fourth

7. $\frac{4}{4}$, four fourths; 1, one   **8.** $\frac{5}{4}$, five fourths; $1\frac{1}{4}$, one and a fourth

9. $\frac{7}{4}$, seven fourths; $1\frac{3}{4}$, one and three fourths   **10.** $\frac{6}{4}$, six fourths; $1\frac{1}{2}$, one and a half

11. $\frac{8}{4}$, eight fourths; 2, two   **12.** $\frac{6}{4}$, six fourths; $\frac{3}{2}$, three halves

13. $\frac{8}{4}$, eight fourths; $\frac{4}{2}$, four halves   **14.** $\frac{9}{4}$, nine fourths; $2\frac{1}{4}$, two and a fourth

15. $2\frac{2}{4}$, two and two fourths; $\frac{5}{2}$, five halves

16. A) $\frac{1}{4},\frac{2}{4},\frac{3}{4},\frac{4}{4},\frac{5}{4},\frac{6}{4},\frac{7}{4},\frac{8}{4}$ **B)** $\frac{1}{4},\frac{2}{4},\frac{3}{4},1,1\frac{1}{4},1\frac{2}{4},1\frac{3}{4},2$

17. A) $\frac{1}{4},\frac{2}{4},\frac{3}{4},\frac{4}{4},\frac{5}{4},\frac{6}{4},\frac{7}{4},\frac{8}{4},\frac{9}{4},\frac{10}{4},\frac{11}{4},\frac{12}{4},\frac{13}{4},\frac{14}{4},\frac{15}{4},\frac{16}{4}$

17. B) $\frac{1}{4},\frac{2}{4},\frac{3}{4},1,1\frac{1}{4},1\frac{2}{4},1\frac{3}{4},2,2\frac{1}{4},2\frac{2}{4},2\frac{3}{4},3,3\frac{1}{4},3\frac{2}{4},3\frac{3}{4},4$

18. A) $\frac{1}{4},\frac{2}{4},\frac{3}{4},\frac{4}{4},\frac{5}{4},\frac{6}{4},\frac{7}{4},\frac{8}{4},\frac{9}{4}$ **B)** $\frac{1}{4},\frac{2}{4},\frac{3}{4},1,1\frac{1}{4},1\frac{2}{4},1\frac{3}{4},2,2\frac{1}{4}$

19. A) $\frac{1}{4},\frac{2}{4},\frac{3}{4},\frac{4}{4},\frac{5}{4},\frac{6}{4},\frac{7}{4},\frac{8}{4},\frac{9}{4},\frac{10}{4},\frac{11}{4},\frac{12}{4},\frac{13}{4}$

19. B) $\frac{1}{4},\frac{2}{4},\frac{3}{4},1,1\frac{1}{4},1\frac{2}{4},1\frac{3}{4},2,2\frac{1}{4},2\frac{2}{4},2\frac{3}{4},3,3\frac{1}{4}$

20. A) $\frac{1}{4}$, $\frac{2}{4}$, $\frac{3}{4}$, $\frac{4}{4}$, $\frac{5}{4}$, $\frac{6}{4}$, $\frac{7}{4}$, $\frac{8}{4}$, $\frac{9}{4}$, $\frac{10}{4}$, $\frac{11}{4}$, $\frac{12}{4}$, $\frac{13}{4}$, $\frac{14}{4}$, $\frac{15}{4}$

20. B) $\frac{1}{4}$, $\frac{2}{4}$, $\frac{3}{4}$, 1, $1\frac{1}{4}$, $1\frac{2}{4}$, $1\frac{3}{4}$, 2, $2\frac{1}{4}$, $2\frac{2}{4}$, $2\frac{3}{4}$, 3, $3\frac{1}{4}$, $3\frac{2}{4}$, $3\frac{3}{4}$

21. A) $\frac{1}{4}$, $\frac{2}{4}$, $\frac{3}{4}$, $\frac{4}{4}$, $\frac{5}{4}$, $\frac{6}{4}$, $\frac{7}{4}$, $\frac{8}{4}$, $\frac{9}{4}$, $\frac{10}{4}$, $\frac{11}{4}$, $\frac{12}{4}$, $\frac{13}{4}$, $\frac{14}{4}$, $\frac{15}{4}$, $\frac{16}{4}$, $\frac{17}{4}$, $\frac{18}{4}$

21. B) $\frac{1}{4}$, $\frac{2}{4}$, $\frac{3}{4}$, 1, $1\frac{1}{4}$, $1\frac{2}{4}$, $1\frac{3}{4}$, 2, $2\frac{1}{4}$, $2\frac{2}{4}$, $2\frac{3}{4}$, 3, $3\frac{1}{4}$, $3\frac{2}{4}$, $3\frac{3}{4}$, 4, $4\frac{1}{4}$, $4\frac{2}{4}$

22. A) $\frac{5}{4}$, $\frac{6}{4}$, $\frac{7}{4}$, $\frac{8}{4}$, $\frac{9}{4}$, $\frac{10}{4}$, $\frac{11}{4}$, $\frac{12}{4}$, $\frac{13}{4}$, $\frac{14}{4}$, $\frac{15}{4}$, $\frac{16}{4}$, $\frac{17}{4}$, $\frac{18}{4}$, $\frac{19}{4}$

22. B) $1\frac{1}{4}$, $1\frac{2}{4}$, $1\frac{3}{4}$, 2, $2\frac{1}{4}$, $2\frac{2}{4}$, $2\frac{3}{4}$, 3, $3\frac{1}{4}$, $3\frac{2}{4}$, $3\frac{3}{4}$, 4, $4\frac{1}{4}$, $4\frac{2}{4}$, $4\frac{3}{4}$

23. A) $\frac{9}{4}$, $\frac{10}{4}$, $\frac{11}{4}$, $\frac{12}{4}$, $\frac{13}{4}$, $\frac{14}{4}$, $\frac{15}{4}$, $\frac{16}{4}$, $\frac{17}{4}$, $\frac{18}{4}$, $\frac{19}{4}$, $\frac{20}{4}$, $\frac{21}{4}$, $\frac{22}{4}$, $\frac{23}{4}$, $\frac{24}{4}$, $\frac{25}{4}$

23. B) $2\frac{1}{4}$, $2\frac{2}{4}$, $2\frac{3}{4}$, 3, $3\frac{1}{4}$, $3\frac{2}{4}$, $3\frac{3}{4}$, 4, $4\frac{1}{4}$, $4\frac{2}{4}$, $4\frac{3}{4}$, 5, $5\frac{1}{4}$, $5\frac{2}{4}$, $5\frac{3}{4}$, 6, $6\frac{1}{4}$

ANSWERS EXERCISES 3-C – Chapter 3 Custom Enhancement

1. A) $\frac{1}{2}$, $\frac{2}{2}$, $\frac{3}{2}$, $\frac{4}{2}$, $\frac{5}{2}$, $\frac{6}{2}$, $\frac{7}{2}$, $\frac{8}{2}$ **B)** $\frac{1}{2}$, 1, $1\frac{1}{2}$, 2, $2\frac{1}{2}$, 3, $3\frac{1}{2}$, 4

2. A) $\frac{1}{2}$, $\frac{2}{2}$, $\frac{3}{2}$, $\frac{4}{2}$, $\frac{5}{2}$, $\frac{6}{2}$, $\frac{7}{2}$, $\frac{8}{2}$, $\frac{9}{2}$, $\frac{10}{2}$, $\frac{11}{2}$ **B)** $\frac{1}{2}$, 1, $1\frac{1}{2}$, 2, $2\frac{1}{2}$, 3, $3\frac{1}{2}$, 4, $4\frac{1}{2}$, 5, $5\frac{1}{2}$

3. A) $\frac{1}{4}$, $\frac{2}{4}$, $\frac{3}{4}$, $\frac{4}{4}$, $\frac{5}{4}$, $\frac{6}{4}$, $\frac{7}{4}$, $\frac{8}{4}$, $\frac{9}{4}$ **B)** $\frac{1}{4}$, $\frac{2}{4}$, $\frac{3}{4}$, 1, $1\frac{1}{4}$, $1\frac{2}{4}$, $1\frac{3}{4}$, 2, $2\frac{1}{4}$

4. A) $\frac{1}{4}$, $\frac{2}{4}$, $\frac{3}{4}$, $\frac{4}{4}$, $\frac{5}{4}$, $\frac{6}{4}$, $\frac{7}{4}$, $\frac{8}{4}$, $\frac{9}{4}$, $\frac{10}{4}$, $\frac{11}{4}$, $\frac{12}{4}$, $\frac{13}{4}$, $\frac{14}{4}$

4. B) $\frac{1}{4}$, $\frac{2}{4}$, $\frac{3}{4}$, 1, $1\frac{1}{4}$, $1\frac{2}{4}$, $1\frac{3}{4}$, 2, $2\frac{1}{4}$, $2\frac{2}{4}$, $2\frac{3}{4}$, 3, $3\frac{1}{4}$, $3\frac{2}{4}$

5. A) $\frac{1}{3}$, $\frac{2}{3}$, $\frac{3}{3}$, $\frac{4}{3}$, $\frac{5}{3}$, $\frac{6}{3}$, $\frac{7}{3}$, $\frac{8}{3}$, $\frac{9}{3}$, $\frac{10}{3}$, $\frac{11}{3}$, $\frac{12}{3}$ **B)** $\frac{1}{3}$, $\frac{2}{3}$, 1, $1\frac{1}{3}$, $1\frac{2}{3}$, 2, $2\frac{1}{3}$, $2\frac{2}{3}$, 3, $3\frac{1}{3}$, $3\frac{2}{3}$, 4

6. A) $\frac{1}{3}$, $\frac{2}{3}$, $\frac{3}{3}$, $\frac{4}{3}$, $\frac{5}{3}$, $\frac{6}{3}$, $\frac{7}{3}$, $\frac{8}{3}$, $\frac{9}{3}$, $\frac{10}{3}$, $\frac{11}{3}$, $\frac{12}{3}$, $\frac{13}{3}$, $\frac{14}{3}$, $\frac{15}{3}$, $\frac{16}{3}$

6. B) $\frac{1}{3}$, $\frac{2}{3}$, 1, $1\frac{1}{3}$, $1\frac{2}{3}$, 2, $2\frac{1}{3}$, $2\frac{2}{3}$, 3, $3\frac{1}{3}$, $3\frac{2}{3}$, 4, $4\frac{1}{3}$, $4\frac{2}{3}$, 5, $5\frac{1}{3}$

7. A) $\frac{1}{5}$, $\frac{2}{5}$, $\frac{3}{5}$, $\frac{4}{5}$, $\frac{5}{5}$, $\frac{6}{5}$, $\frac{7}{5}$, $\frac{8}{5}$, $\frac{9}{5}$, $\frac{10}{5}$ **B)** $\frac{1}{5}$, $\frac{2}{5}$, $\frac{3}{5}$, $\frac{4}{5}$, 1, $1\frac{1}{5}$, $1\frac{2}{5}$, $1\frac{3}{5}$, $1\frac{4}{5}$, 2

8. A) $\frac{1}{5}$, $\frac{2}{5}$, $\frac{3}{5}$, $\frac{4}{5}$, $\frac{5}{5}$, $\frac{6}{5}$, $\frac{7}{5}$, $\frac{8}{5}$, $\frac{9}{5}$, $\frac{10}{5}$, $\frac{11}{5}$, $\frac{12}{5}$, $\frac{13}{5}$, $\frac{14}{5}$, $\frac{15}{5}$, $\frac{16}{5}$

8. B) $\frac{1}{5}$, $\frac{2}{5}$, $\frac{3}{5}$, $\frac{4}{5}$, 1, $1\frac{1}{5}$, $1\frac{2}{5}$, $1\frac{3}{5}$, $1\frac{4}{5}$, 2, $2\frac{1}{5}$, $2\frac{2}{5}$, $2\frac{3}{5}$, $2\frac{4}{5}$, 3, $3\frac{1}{5}$

9. A) $\frac{1}{6}$, $\frac{2}{6}$, $\frac{3}{6}$, $\frac{4}{6}$, $\frac{5}{6}$, $\frac{6}{6}$, $\frac{7}{6}$, $\frac{8}{6}$, $\frac{9}{6}$, $\frac{10}{6}$, $\frac{11}{6}$, $\frac{12}{6}$, $\frac{13}{6}$, $\frac{14}{6}$, $\frac{15}{6}$, $\frac{16}{6}$, $\frac{17}{6}$, $\frac{18}{6}$, $\frac{19}{6}$, $\frac{20}{6}$

9. B) $\frac{1}{6}$, $\frac{2}{6}$, $\frac{3}{6}$, $\frac{4}{6}$, $\frac{5}{6}$, 1, $1\frac{1}{6}$, $1\frac{2}{6}$, $1\frac{3}{6}$, $1\frac{4}{6}$, $1\frac{5}{6}$, 2, $2\frac{1}{6}$, $2\frac{2}{6}$, $2\frac{3}{6}$, $2\frac{4}{6}$, $2\frac{5}{6}$, 3, $3\frac{1}{6}$, $3\frac{2}{6}$

10. A) $\frac{1}{6}$, $\frac{2}{6}$, $\frac{3}{6}$, $\frac{4}{6}$, $\frac{5}{6}$, $\frac{6}{6}$, $\frac{7}{6}$, $\frac{8}{6}$, $\frac{9}{6}$, $\frac{10}{6}$, $\frac{11}{6}$, $\frac{12}{6}$ **B)** $\frac{1}{6}$, $\frac{2}{6}$, $\frac{3}{6}$, $\frac{4}{6}$, $\frac{5}{6}$, 1, $1\frac{1}{6}$, $1\frac{2}{6}$, $1\frac{3}{6}$, $1\frac{4}{6}$, $1\frac{5}{6}$, 2

11. A) $\frac{1}{7}$, $\frac{2}{7}$, $\frac{3}{7}$, $\frac{4}{7}$, $\frac{5}{7}$, $\frac{6}{7}$, $\frac{7}{7}$, $\frac{8}{7}$, $\frac{9}{7}$, $\frac{10}{7}$, $\frac{11}{7}$, $\frac{12}{7}$, $\frac{13}{7}$, $\frac{14}{7}$, $\frac{15}{7}$, $\frac{16}{7}$, $\frac{17}{7}$

11. B) $\frac{1}{7}$, $\frac{2}{7}$, $\frac{3}{7}$, $\frac{4}{7}$, $\frac{5}{7}$, $\frac{6}{7}$, 1, $1\frac{1}{7}$, $1\frac{2}{7}$, $1\frac{3}{7}$, $1\frac{4}{7}$, $1\frac{5}{7}$, $1\frac{6}{7}$, 2, $2\frac{1}{7}$, $2\frac{2}{7}$, $2\frac{3}{7}$

12. A) $\frac{1}{8}, \frac{2}{8}, \frac{3}{8}, \frac{4}{8}, \frac{5}{8}, \frac{6}{8}, \frac{7}{8}, \frac{8}{8}, \frac{9}{8}, \frac{10}{8}, \frac{11}{8}, \frac{12}{8}, \frac{13}{8}, \frac{14}{8}, \frac{15}{8}, \frac{16}{8}$

12. B) $\frac{1}{8}, \frac{2}{8}, \frac{3}{8}, \frac{4}{8}, \frac{5}{8}, \frac{6}{8}, \frac{7}{8}, 1, 1\frac{1}{8}, 1\frac{2}{8}, 1\frac{3}{8}, 1\frac{4}{8}, 1\frac{5}{8}, 1\frac{6}{8}, 1\frac{7}{8}, 2$

ANSWERS EXERCISES 3-D – Chapter 3 Custom Enhancement

1. $\frac{1}{2} + \frac{2}{2} = \frac{3}{2}$ **2.** $\frac{1}{4} + \frac{3}{4} = \frac{4}{4}$ or $\frac{1}{4} + \frac{3}{4} = 1$ **3.** $1 + \frac{3}{2} = 1\frac{3}{2}$ or $\frac{2}{2} + \frac{3}{2} = \frac{5}{2}$ or $1 + 1\frac{1}{2} = 2\frac{1}{2}$

4. $2 + \frac{2}{4} = 2\frac{2}{4}$ or $\frac{8}{4} + \frac{2}{4} = \frac{10}{4}$ or $2 + \frac{1}{2} = 2\frac{1}{2}$ **5.** $\frac{1}{2} + \frac{2}{4} = 1$ or $\frac{2}{4} + \frac{2}{4} = \frac{4}{4}$ or $\frac{1}{2} + \frac{1}{2} = 1$

6. $\frac{3}{4} + \frac{1}{4} = 1$ or $\frac{3}{4} + \frac{1}{4} = \frac{4}{4}$ **7.** $1\frac{1}{4} + 1\frac{1}{2} = 2\frac{3}{4}$ or $\frac{5}{4} + \frac{6}{4} = \frac{11}{4}$

ANSWERS EXERCISES 3-E – Chapter 3 Custom Enhancement

1. $\frac{3}{2} - \frac{1}{2} = \frac{2}{2}$ or $1\frac{1}{2} - \frac{1}{2} = 1$ **2.** $\frac{3}{4} - \frac{2}{4} = \frac{1}{4}$ or $\frac{3}{4} - \frac{1}{2} = \frac{1}{4}$ **3.** $1 - \frac{1}{2} = \frac{1}{2}$ or $\frac{2}{2} - \frac{1}{2} = \frac{1}{2}$

4. $2 - \frac{2}{4} = 1\frac{2}{4}$ or $\frac{8}{4} - \frac{2}{4} = \frac{6}{4}$ or $2 - \frac{1}{2} = 1\frac{1}{2}$ **5.** $\frac{1}{2} - \frac{1}{4} = \frac{1}{4}$ or $\frac{2}{4} - \frac{1}{4} = \frac{1}{4}$

6. $1\frac{1}{4} - \frac{2}{4} = \frac{3}{4}$ or $\frac{5}{4} - \frac{2}{4} = \frac{3}{4}$ **7.** $2\frac{1}{2} - 1\frac{3}{4} = \frac{3}{4}$ or $\frac{10}{4} - \frac{7}{4} = \frac{3}{4}$ or $1\frac{6}{4} - 1\frac{3}{4} = \frac{3}{4}$

ANSWERS EXERCISES 3-F – Chapter 3 Custom Enhancement

1. SA = $\frac{1}{2}$, UA = $\frac{1}{2}$, T = 1   **2.** SA = $\frac{3}{4}$, UA = $\frac{1}{4}$, T = 1   **3.** SA = $\frac{1}{3}$, UA = $\frac{2}{3}$, T = 1

4. SA = $\frac{4}{3}$ or $1\frac{1}{3}$, UA = $\frac{2}{3}$, T = 2 or $\frac{6}{3}$ **5.** SA = $\frac{7}{4}$ or $1\frac{3}{4}$, UA = $\frac{1}{4}$, T = 4 or $\frac{8}{2}$

6. SA = $\frac{1}{2}$, UA = $\frac{3}{2}$ or $1\frac{1}{2}$, T = 2 or $\frac{6}{3}$ **7.** SA = $\frac{5}{4}$ or $1\frac{1}{4}$, UA = $\frac{3}{4}$, T = 2 or $\frac{6}{3}$

8. SA = $\frac{3}{2}$ or $1\frac{1}{2}$, UA = $\frac{3}{2}$ or $1\frac{1}{2}$, T = 3   **9.** SA = $\frac{1}{6}$, UA = $\frac{5}{6}$, T = 1 or $\frac{6}{6}$

10. SA = $\frac{7}{3}$ or $2\frac{1}{3}$, UA = $\frac{2}{3}$, T = 3   **11.** SA = $\frac{6}{8}$ or $\frac{3}{4}$, UA = $\frac{2}{8}$ or $\frac{1}{4}$, T = 1 or $\frac{6}{6}$

12. SA = $\frac{7}{4}$ or $1\frac{3}{4}$, UA = $\frac{5}{4}$ or $1\frac{1}{4}$, T = 3   **13.** SA = $\frac{2}{5}$, UA = $\frac{3}{5}$, T = 1 or $\frac{5}{5}$

14. SA = $\frac{17}{6}$ or $2\frac{5}{6}$, UA = $\frac{7}{6}$ or $1\frac{1}{6}$, T = 4 or $\frac{24}{6}$

ANSWERS EXERCISES 3-G – Chapter 3 Custom Enhancement

1. $0, \frac{1}{2}, 1, 1\frac{1}{2}, 2$ **2.** $0, \frac{1}{2}, \frac{2}{2}, \frac{3}{2}, \frac{4}{2}$ **3.** $1, 1\frac{1}{2}, 2, 2\frac{1}{2}, 3$ **4.** $\frac{4}{2}, \frac{5}{2}, \frac{6}{2}, \frac{7}{2}, \frac{8}{2}$

5. $0, \frac{1}{3}, \frac{2}{3}, 1, 1\frac{1}{3}, 1\frac{2}{3}, 2, 2\frac{1}{3}$ **6.** $0, \frac{1}{3}, \frac{2}{3}, \frac{3}{3}, \frac{4}{3}, \frac{5}{3}, \frac{6}{3}, \frac{7}{3}$ **7.** $1, 1\frac{1}{3}, 1\frac{2}{3}, 2, 2\frac{1}{3}, 2\frac{2}{3}, 3, 3\frac{1}{3}$

8. $\frac{6}{3}, \frac{7}{3}, \frac{8}{3}, \frac{9}{3}, \frac{10}{3}, \frac{11}{3}, \frac{12}{3}, \frac{13}{3}$ **9.** $0, \frac{1}{4}, \frac{2}{4}, \frac{3}{4}, \frac{4}{4}, \frac{5}{4}$ **10.** $1, 1\frac{1}{4}, 1\frac{2}{4}, 1\frac{3}{4}, 2, 2\frac{1}{4}$

ANSWERS EXERCISES 3-H – Chapter 3 Custom Enhancement

1. $0, \frac{1}{2}, 1, 1\frac{1}{2}, 2$ **2.** $1, 1\frac{1}{2}, 2, 2\frac{1}{2}, 3$ **3.** $2, 2\frac{1}{2}, 3, 3\frac{1}{2}, 4$ **4.** $0, \frac{1}{3}, \frac{2}{3}, 1, 1\frac{1}{3}, 1\frac{2}{3}, 2, 2\frac{1}{3}$

5. $\frac{1}{3}, \frac{2}{3}, 1, 1\frac{1}{3}, 1\frac{2}{3}, 2, 2\frac{1}{3}, 2\frac{2}{3}$ **6.** $3, 3\frac{1}{3}, 3\frac{2}{3}, 4, 4\frac{1}{3}, 4\frac{2}{3}, 5, 5\frac{1}{3}$ **7.** $0, \frac{1}{4}, \frac{2}{4}, \frac{3}{4}, 1, 1\frac{1}{4}$

8. $1, 1\frac{1}{4}, 1\frac{2}{4}, 1\frac{3}{4}, 2, 2\frac{1}{4}$ **9.** $\frac{2}{4}, \frac{3}{4}, \frac{4}{4}, \frac{5}{4}, \frac{6}{4}, \frac{7}{4}$ **10.** $0, \frac{1}{4}, \frac{2}{4}, \frac{3}{4}, 1, 1\frac{1}{4}, 1\frac{2}{4}, 1\frac{3}{4}, 2, 2\frac{1}{4}, 2\frac{2}{4}$

11. $1, 1\frac{1}{5}, 1\frac{2}{5}, 1\frac{3}{5}, 1\frac{4}{5}, 2, 2\frac{1}{5}, 2\frac{2}{5}, 2\frac{3}{5}, 2\frac{4}{5}, 3$ **12.** $1, 1\frac{1}{3}, 1\frac{2}{3}, 2, 2\frac{1}{3}, 2\frac{2}{3}, 3, 3\frac{1}{3}, 3\frac{2}{3}, 4, 4\frac{1}{3}$

ANSWERS EXERCISES 3-I – Chapter 3 Custom Enhancement

1. $\frac{3}{2}$ or $1\frac{1}{2}$ **2.** $\frac{3}{1}$ or 3 **3.** $\frac{9}{2}$ or $4\frac{1}{2}$ **4.** $\frac{3}{4}$ **5.** $\frac{5}{4}$ or $1\frac{1}{4}$ **6.** $\frac{7}{4}$ or $1\frac{3}{4}$ **7.** $\frac{5}{3}$ or $1\frac{2}{3}$

8. $\frac{2}{1}$ or 2 **9.** $\frac{4}{1}$ or 4 **10.** $\frac{3}{5}$ **11.** $\frac{8}{5}$ or $1\frac{3}{5}$ **12.** $\frac{12}{5}$ or $2\frac{2}{5}$ **13.** $1\frac{1}{2}$ or $\frac{3}{2}$ **14.** 2

15. $4\frac{3}{4}$ or $\frac{19}{4}$ **16.** $1\frac{2}{3}$ or $\frac{5}{3}$ **17.** $3\frac{1}{4}$ or $\frac{13}{4}$ **18.** $5\frac{1}{5}$ or $\frac{26}{5}$ **19.** $2\frac{5}{6}$ or $\frac{17}{6}$

20. $3\frac{4}{5}$ or $\frac{19}{5}$ **21.** $7\frac{1}{8}$ or $\frac{57}{8}$

ANSWERS EXERCISES 3-J – Chapter 3 Custom Enhancement

1. $\frac{3}{8}$ **2.** $\frac{5}{6}$ **3.** 1 **4.** 1 **5.** 2 **6.** 3 **7.** $\frac{4}{3}$ or $1\frac{1}{3}$ **8.** $\frac{2}{3}$ **9.** $\frac{5}{4}$ or $1\frac{1}{4}$ **10.** $\frac{1}{5}$

11. $\frac{7}{5}$ or $1\frac{2}{5}$ **12.** 2 **13.** $\frac{1}{4}$ **14.** $\frac{1}{5}$ **15.** $\frac{1}{2}$ **16.** $\frac{2}{3}$ **17.** $7\frac{1}{2}$ or $\frac{15}{2}$ **18.** $2\frac{1}{5}$ or $\frac{11}{5}$

19. $8\frac{1}{3}$ or $\frac{25}{3}$ **20.** $2\frac{3}{5}$ or $\frac{13}{5}$ **21.** $9\frac{1}{8}$ or $\frac{73}{8}$ **22.** $2\frac{4}{9}$ or $\frac{22}{9}$ **23.** $5\frac{1}{4}$ or $\frac{21}{4}$

24. $7\frac{1}{3}$ or $\frac{22}{3}$ **25.** $7\frac{3}{4}$ or $\frac{31}{4}$ **26.** 6 **27.** 10

ANSWERS EXERCISES 3-K – Chapter 3 Custom Enhancement

1. $\frac{5}{8}$ **2.** $\frac{1}{6}$ **3.** $\frac{2}{3}$ **4.** $\frac{1}{4}$ **5.** $1\frac{1}{2}$ or $\frac{3}{2}$ **6.** $1\frac{2}{5}$ or $\frac{7}{5}$ **7.** $2\frac{1}{3}$ or $\frac{7}{3}$ **8.** $5\frac{3}{8}$ or $\frac{43}{8}$

9. $4\frac{5}{7}$ or $\frac{33}{7}$ **10.** $5\frac{4}{7}$ or $\frac{39}{7}$ **11.** $5\frac{3}{5}$ or $\frac{28}{5}$ **12.** $5\frac{2}{5}$ or $\frac{27}{5}$ **13.** $1\frac{7}{8}$ or $\frac{15}{8}$

14. $1\frac{1}{8}$ or $\frac{9}{8}$ **15.** $1\frac{1}{4}$ or $\frac{5}{4}$ **16.** $\frac{1}{3}$ **17.** $8\frac{3}{4}$ or $\frac{35}{4}$ **18.** $3\frac{5}{7}$ or $\frac{26}{7}$ **19.** $7\frac{1}{3}$ or $\frac{22}{3}$

20. $6\frac{3}{5}$ or $\frac{33}{5}$ **21.** $4\frac{1}{4}$ or $\frac{17}{4}$ **22.** $2\frac{1}{2}$ or $\frac{5}{2}$ **23.** $3\frac{4}{11}$ or $\frac{37}{11}$ **24.** $7\frac{2}{3}$ or $\frac{23}{3}$

25. $6\frac{1}{2}$ or $\frac{13}{2}$ **26.** $5\frac{2}{3}$ or $\frac{17}{3}$ **27.** $\frac{2}{3}$

ANSWERS EXERCISES 3-L – Chapter 3 Custom Enhancement

1. $\frac{2}{2}, \frac{5}{5}, \frac{1}{1}$ **2.** $\frac{5}{5}, \frac{7}{7}, \frac{9}{9}$ **3.** $\frac{8}{4}, 1\frac{2}{2}, \frac{2}{1}, \frac{14}{7}$ **4.** $1\frac{5}{5}, \frac{6}{3}$ **5.** $\frac{6}{1}, \frac{18}{3}, 5\frac{4}{4}$ **6.** $4\frac{12}{6}, \frac{30}{5}, \frac{12}{2}$

7. $\frac{3}{9}, \frac{2}{6}$ **8.** $\frac{5}{15}, \frac{8}{24}$ **9.** $4\frac{7}{4}, \frac{23}{4}, 5\frac{6}{8}$ **10.** $3\frac{11}{4}, \frac{69}{12}, \frac{46}{8}$ **11.** $6\frac{5}{5}$ **12.** $7\frac{4}{4}$

13. $3\frac{12}{6}$ **14.** $1\frac{4}{2}$ **15.** $4\frac{5}{3}$ **16.** $6\frac{9}{5}$ **17.** $2\frac{11}{4}$ **18.** $4\frac{23}{8}$ **19.** $\frac{3}{1} = \frac{15}{5} = 2\frac{7}{7}$

20. $\frac{7}{1} = \frac{14}{2} = 6\frac{3}{3}$ **21.** $\frac{6}{10} = \frac{21}{35} = \frac{27}{45}$ **22.** $\frac{12}{14} = \frac{18}{21} = \frac{24}{28}$ **23.** $\frac{8}{10} = \frac{4}{5} = \frac{32}{40}$

24. $\frac{8}{9} = \frac{16}{18} = \frac{24}{27}$ **25.** $\frac{54}{16} = 3\frac{3}{8} = 3\frac{9}{24}$ **26.** $4\frac{6}{13} = 3\frac{19}{13} = 4\frac{12}{26}$ **27.** $\frac{22}{7} = 2\frac{8}{7} = 3\frac{4}{28}$

28. $\frac{51}{8} = 5\frac{11}{8} = 6\frac{9}{24}$ **29.** $\frac{14}{3} = 4\frac{2}{3} = 3\frac{5}{3}$ **30.** $\frac{39}{6} = \frac{13}{2} = 6\frac{1}{2}$

ANSWERS TO TRY THESE PROBLEMS – Chapter 4 Custom Enhancement

1. rate   2. distance   3. volume   4. rate   5. area   6. time

7. rate   8. time   9. distance   10. distance   11. volume   12. area

13. 9 feet per second, $2\frac{2}{3}$ gallons per week   14. 85 square meters   15. 16 ounces

16. 12 days   17. 72 feet   18. 4¢   19. $\frac{3}{5}$ ounce   20. 40 cartons   21. $27\frac{1}{4}$ hours

22. $2\frac{1}{2}$ years   23. $\frac{1}{3}$ mile   24. $\frac{1}{2}$ pint   25. 450 years   26. 45 gallons

27. 15 miles   28. 72 square meters   29. 13 miles   30. 178 feet

31. 288 square feet   32. 21 meters   33. 10 yards   34. $1\frac{2}{3}$ square inches

35. $\frac{45}{2}$ or $22\frac{1}{2}$ square inches   36. $\frac{24}{5}$ or $4\frac{4}{5}$ square miles

37. $7\frac{3}{4}$ or $\frac{31}{4}$ square miles   38. $5\frac{1}{4}$ or $\frac{21}{4}$ inches   39. 6   40. $\frac{1}{3}$ 41. $\frac{5}{2}$ or $2\frac{1}{2}$

42. 8 tons per hour   43. $\frac{1}{2}$ foot per second   44. $\frac{21}{40}$ carton per day   45. 45 trees

46. 112 feet   47. 8 loads   48. 16   49. $\frac{2}{7}$ 50. $\frac{16}{27}$ minute per cent

51. $\$\frac{7}{2}$ or $\$3\frac{1}{2}$ or $3.50   52. 195 inches   53. 15 barrels per pound   54. meters

55. squares meters   56. miles   57. gallons   58. inches per second

59. $ per person   60. miles   61. square feet   62. pounds   63. $ 64. yards

65. feet   66. gallons   67. miles per gallon   68. $6 for 1 ticket

69. 24 items per 1 carton   70. 45 miles every 1 hour   71. $\frac{1}{2}$ inch per 1 mile

72. $12\frac{1}{2}$ miles every 1 day   73. $\frac{2}{3}$ gallons each 1 minute   74. 50¢ per hour

75. 4 bottles per carton   76. 60 feet per second   77. $\frac{1}{20}$ pound per nail

78. $\frac{1}{4}$ ounce per person   79. $2\frac{2}{3}$ pounds per foot   80. 72¢ for 8 minutes

81. $32 for every 8 hot dogs   82. 128 miles per 8 hours

83. $\frac{16}{3}$ or $5\frac{1}{3}$ ounces in 8 minutes   84. 18 inches every 800 miles

85. $120 every 6 yards   86. 4¢ for $\frac{1}{5}$ minute   87. $3 every $\frac{1}{5}$ pound

88. $\frac{5}{2}$ or $2\frac{1}{2}$ miles in $\frac{4}{5}$ hour   89. $\frac{2}{5}$ ounce in $\frac{3}{5}$ minute   90. $\frac{15}{8}$ or $1\frac{7}{8}$ inches in $\frac{3}{5}$ day

91. $6 every 1 yard   92. 12   93. 5   94. $2\frac{1}{3}$ 95. $\frac{5}{4}$ or $1\frac{1}{4}$ 96. 1   97. 1   98. 1

99. 1   100. $\frac{1}{4}$ 101. $\frac{5}{3}$ or $1\frac{2}{3}$ 102. $\frac{3}{4}$ 103. $\frac{4}{3}$ or $1\frac{1}{3}$ 104. 1 hour   105. $\frac{9}{10}$ mile

106. 7 gallons   107. $\frac{4}{3}$ or $1\frac{1}{3}$ square miles   108. $\frac{3}{4}$ pound   109. 1 day

110. $3\frac{1}{10}$ liters   111. $\frac{1}{8}$ foot   112. $120   113. 21 minute   114. 40 miles

115. 8 pounds   116. 27 miles   117. $\frac{3}{8}$ ounce   118. $\frac{5}{4}$ or $1\frac{1}{4}$ minutes

119. $\$\frac{99}{2}$ or $\$49\frac{1}{2}$ or $49.50   120. $\frac{1}{6}$ adult   121. $24   122. $\frac{12}{5}$ or $2\frac{2}{5}$ gallons

123. $\frac{9}{2}$ or $4\frac{1}{2}$ hours   **124.** $\frac{6}{5}$ or $1\frac{1}{5}$ pounds   **125.** 6 miles   **126.** $\frac{4}{9}$ ounce

127. 77¢   **128.** $609   **129.** $\frac{27}{4}$ or $6\frac{3}{4}$ minutes   **130.** $6   **131.** $\frac{1}{40}$ pound

132. $\frac{44}{3}$ or $14\frac{2}{3}$ ounces   **133.** $105   **134.** 32 items   **135.** 33 miles   **136.** 76 feet

137. $\frac{25}{6}$ or $4\frac{1}{6}$ pounds   **138.** 42 ounces   **139.** $\frac{7}{8}$ inch   **140.** $\frac{2}{3}$ gallon   **141.** persons

142. inches per day   **143.** seconds   **144.** square miles   **145.** pounds   **146.** bottles

147. inches per week   **148.** $ **149.** 4 calculators   **150.** 5 persons per day

151. 8 hours   **152.** $\frac{16}{3}$ or $5\frac{1}{3}$ ounces per minute   **153.** $\frac{10}{3}$ or $3\frac{1}{3}$ seconds

154. $\frac{3}{4}$ day   **155.** $\frac{26}{3}$ or $8\frac{2}{3}$ inches per week   **156.** $\frac{1}{2}$ gallon   **157.** $3300

158. 12 days   **159.** $\frac{2}{3}$ lap per minute   **160.** $\frac{62}{3}$ or $20\frac{2}{3}$ yards   **161.** $\frac{2}{3}$ pound per foot

162. 8 pounds   **163.** $\frac{1}{64}$ inch per mile   **164.** $\frac{27}{8}$ or $3\frac{3}{8}$ gallons   **165.** $\frac{86}{7}$ or $12\frac{2}{7}$ miles

166. $\frac{3}{4}$ hour each day

ANSWERS TRY THESE PROBLEMS – Chapter 7 Custom Enhancement

1. $6   **2.** 384 gallons   **3.** $1.30   **4.** 1.5 pounds   **5.** 25 minutes   **6.** $22.10

7. 514.25 pounds   **8.** 500 barrels   **9.** 0.75 second   **10.** 2.25 pounds

11. $955.80   **12.** $5.68   **13.** 0.625 minute   **14.** 29.24 ounces   **15.** 0.6 mile

16. 20.6 pounds   **17.** 4500 miles   **18.** 7.4 minutes   **19.** 40.5 miles

20. $40   **21.** 28.8 gallons   **22.** 5 pounds   **23.** 530 minutes   **24.** $15.50

25. 14 seconds   **26.** 2.25 weeks   **27.** 1 foot   **28.** $2.80   **29.** 30 ounces

30. $390   **31.** $92   **32.** 3 hours   **33.** 19.5 pounds   **34.** 125 seconds

35. 102.6 gallons   **36.** 48.5 minutes   **37.** $140.40   **38.** 297.6 pounds

39. 2.5 hours   **40.** 0.25 minute   **41.** 21 pounds   **42.** 41.6 inches

43. 700 calories per meal   **44.** 18 ounces   **45.** 17.1 miles   **46.** 55.8 seconds

47. 2.5 seconds   **48.** 12.8 hours   **49.** 1.28 pounds per foot   **50.** $3.69

51. 0.005 ton   **52.** 2.25 minutes

ANSWERS TO TRY THESE PROBLEMS – Chapter 8 Custom Enhancement

1. 17 pounds   **2.** 9 years   **3.** 56 miles   **4.** $\frac{2}{5}$ **5.** 5 ounces   **6.** 72 square miles

7. 5   **8.** 232 years   **9.** 35 miles per hour   **10.** 4 ounces per day

11. 348.5 meters   **12.** 1.85 hours   **13.** 12.55 minutes   **14.** 5 feet per second

15. 36   **16.** $2\frac{1}{12}$ or $\frac{25}{12}$ inches   **17.** $\frac{16}{25}$ **18.** 34 cartons   **19.** $\$\frac{14}{3}$ or $\$2\frac{2}{3}$

20. 38 inches   **21.** $\frac{3}{4}$ ton per barrel   **22.** $4\frac{3}{8}$ or $\frac{35}{8}$ yards   **23.** $\frac{9}{8}$ or $1\frac{1}{8}$ children

24. 250 square yards   **25.** minutes   **26.** square inches   **27.** square miles

28. pounds   **29.** feet per second   **30.** $ **31.** hours   **32.** feet   **33.** pounds

34. square feet   **35.** gallons per hour   **36.** meters   **37.** gallons

38. calories per meal   **39.** 50 miles per hour   **40.** $15 per shirt

41. $\frac{3}{4}$ or 0.75 pounds per week   **42.** $\frac{3}{5}$ or 0.6 foot per second

43. 18.75 ounces per hour   **44.** 5.3 ounces per dollar   **45.** $0.025 per cup

46. $2.16 per gallon   **47.** $\frac{3}{4}$ or 0.75 ounces per second   **48.** $63 per yard

49. $\frac{21}{25}$ or 0.84 tons per load   **50.** $\frac{7}{24}$ pound per week

51. $\frac{20 \text{ inches}}{6 \text{ days}} = \frac{10}{3}$ or $3\frac{1}{3}$ inches per day   **52.** $\frac{7\frac{1}{2} \text{ inches}}{12 \text{ days}} = \frac{5}{8}$ inch per day

53. $\frac{15 \text{ inches}}{4.5 \text{ days}} = \frac{10}{3}$ or $3\frac{1}{3}$ inches per day   **54.** $\frac{1\frac{1}{2} \text{ inches}}{\frac{3}{4} \text{ day}} = 2$ inches per day

55. $\frac{15 \text{ gallons}}{300 \text{ miles}} = \frac{1}{20}$ or 0.05 gallon per mile   **56.** $\frac{2.1 \text{ gallons}}{8.4 \text{ miles}} = 0.25$ or $\frac{1}{4}$ gallon per mile

57. $\frac{\frac{5}{8} \text{ gallon}}{6\frac{1}{4} \text{ miles}} = \frac{1}{10}$ or 0.1 gallon per mile   **58.** $\frac{30 \text{ gallon}}{4\frac{1}{2} \text{ miles}} = \frac{20}{3}$ or $6\frac{2}{3}$ gallons per mile

59. $1.19   **60.** 0.02 or $\frac{1}{50}$ centimeter   **61.** 6 minutes   **62.** 9 minutes per ounce

63. 0.04 pound   **64.** 4 feet per hour   **65.** $\frac{1}{6}$ mile per minute

66. $\frac{72}{25}$ or $2\frac{22}{25}$ or 2.88 hours   **67.** $14.75   **68.** $1.80 per pound

69. $\frac{20 \text{ gallons}}{1 \text{ mile}}$ **70.** $\frac{36 \text{ pounds}}{1 \text{ carton}}$ **71.** $\frac{\$14.20}{1 \text{ calculator}}$

72. $\frac{\$0.65}{1 \text{ minute}}$ **73.** $\frac{\frac{3}{4} \text{ ton}}{1 \text{ barrel}}$ **74.** $\frac{6\frac{2}{3} \text{ inches}}{1 \text{ day}}$ or $\frac{\frac{20}{3} \text{ inches}}{1 \text{ day}}$ or $\frac{20 \text{ inches}}{3 \text{ days}}$

75. $288   **76.** $46.28   **77.** 0.18 meter   **78.** 96 gallons   **79.** 48 feet

80. $\frac{7}{48}$ inch   **81.** miles   **82.** feet   **83.** cars   **84.** seconds   **85.** $ per hour

86. gallons per minute   **87.** days   **88.** minutes   **89.** liters per bottle

90. 73.8 miles   **91.** 40 days   **92.** $\frac{8}{3}$ or $2\frac{2}{3}$ ounces per second

93. $\frac{3}{32}$ or 0.09375 mile   **94.** 24 hours   **95.** $7.12 per hour   **96.** 30 ounces

97. $390   **98.** $92   **99.** 3 hours   **100.** 19.5 pounds   **101.** 125 seconds

102. 102.6 gallons   **103.** 48.5 minutes